RADIO OPERATOR'S LICENSE
Q & A MANUAL

Revised Eighth Edition

RADIO OPERATOR'S LICENSE Q & A MANUAL

Revised Eighth Edition

MILTON KAUFMAN

53931

HAYDEN BOOK COMPANY, INC.
Rochelle Park, New Jersey

To Hazel, Elissa, and Richard

FIRST PRINTING — 1975
All material in this printing reflects the latest FCC Study Guide
and Supplement for the Radiotelephone Operator's License.

Library of Congress Cataloging in Publication Data

Kaufman, Milton.
  Radio operator's license Q & A manual.

  Includes index.
    1. Radio—Examinations, questions, etc. 2. Radio-
telephone—Examinations, questions, etc. 3. Radio
operators—United States. I. Title.
TK6554.5.K38   1975   621.3841'076   75-14105
ISBN 0-8104-0399-4
ISBN 0-8104-0398-6 pbk.

First Edition: December 1949; Second Edition: September 1950; Third
Edition: June 1951; Fourth Edition: January 1953; Fifth Edition: January
1955; Sixth Edition: May 1957; Supplement No. 1: January 1963; Supplement No. 2: April 1965; Supplement No. 3: April 1966; Seventh Edition:
June 1967; Appendix to Element III: March 1968; Eighth Edition: June 1975.

Preface

This revised Eighth Edition is in complete accordance with the latest FCC Study Guides, the Supplements to the Study Guides, and an FCC Information Bulletin relating to Element IX. It is designed to be used in preparing for the radiotelephone license examination for Third-Class, Second-Class, and First-Class Licenses and for Broadcast and Radar Endorsements. An extensive section on troubleshooting, specially prepared by the author, provides practice in solving problems similar to those given on the FCC examination. This edition is completely self-contained, with all of the elements necessary to study for the examinations for *any* class of radiotelephone operator's license.* The requirements for each class of radiotelephone operator's license are as follows:

Radiotelephone First-Class Operator License: Elements I, II, III, IV
Radiotelephone Second-Class Operator License: Elements I, II, III.
Radiotelephone Third-Class Operator License: Elements I, II, and IX
   (Element IX is optional, if a Broadcast Endorsement is desired.)
Restricted Radiotelephone Permit: No written or oral examination
Ship Radar Endorsement on Radiotelephone First-Class or Second-Class Operator Licenses: Element VIII

The examinations for Elements I and II consist of 20 questions each; Element III, 100 questions; Elements IV and VIII, 50 questions each; and Element IX, 40 questions. The examinations are of the multiple-choice type, and the candidate is asked to choose the best answer of the five given for each question. A grade of 75% is required to pass each examination.

Radiotelegraph Operator's License Q and A Manual is published as a separate book.

With a Broadcast Endorsement, an operator may *routinely* operate all types of AM and FM broadcast stations. (Note that this is an expansion of the types of stations which such operators were previously permitted to operate *routinely*.) In all cases, it is required that a first-class operator be employed by the station on either a full- or a part-time basis. The student should refer to Q.4.100, Q.9.08, Addendum to Element IX, and R & R 73.93 in Appendix I for additional important information regarding Broadcast Endorsement operation. Students are urged to study carefully all appendix information, references to which appear after a number of questions in this book.

Most of the answers to each *Question* are presented in two separate sections: a short but complete *Answer,* and a *Discussion.* This enables the student to make reference only to the *Answer* at first, and then return to the *Discussion* for more detailed information at a later date. *Discussion* sections are included for most of the questions in order to present much needed background material that should add considerably to the student's knowledge of radiotelephony. It is hoped that the *Discussion* material will save the student time that might otherwise be spent in reading various reference books.

Some very important changes and additions have been made to this edition. Some of these changes and additions are in accordance with the FCC Study Guides (plus addenda), while others are not found in the FCC material but have been added for the student's benefit.

Typical FCC-type practice examinations have been added to this edition following each element. These examinations have been structured carefully to cover all the vital topics of each element. Answers for these tests appear in the back of the book, and a text question number directly relating to the particular test question appears next to each answer in order to assist the student in obtaining additional information, or to help the student to better understand a difficult test question. These exams should be of great assistance to the student in passing the actual FCC tests.

Many of the previously existing answers to questions (such as in Q.3.09 and Q.3.36) have been expanded or clarified. It is anticipated that some of the new material added may appear on some FCC examinations. Two additional questions and answers (not found in FCC documents) much simpler in nature than the original have been added to Q.3.09 because they are more representative of the questions that might appear on FCC examinations.

Because of the increasing use of solid-state equipment, it is anticipated that FCC examinations will contain more questions on transistors and transistor circuitry. Consequently, many solid-state schematics and discussions have been added to existing FCC questions. In addition, a completely new group of transistor questions (not in FCC documents) has been added (Q.3.192(A) through Q.3.192(U), immediately following original *Question* 3.192).

The student is referred to the unusually comprehensive Index, which includes a complete listing of the additional transistor circuits. The student is also urged to read the Introduction to the Index, in order to benefit fully from the extensive special entries.

New addenda have been included immediately following Elements I and IX. These addenda are based on FCC publications and contain important material for all students interested in obtaining a Third-Class Radiotelephone License with Broadcast Endorsement.

Another improvement made in this edition is the updating and expansion of selected FCC Rules and Regulations, as well as other related topics, which are found in Appendices I through IV. Also, many of the references appearing directly after the questions for Element IX have been updated in accordance with the newly revised FCC Rules and Regulations. (The complete text of these newly revised Rules and Regulations may be purchased from the United States Government Printing Office.)

As in previous editions, most of the *Questions* (with certain exceptions) and their order and grouping are precisely the same as in the latest issue of the FCC Study Guide and Supplements. As an example, Element III is divided into the following categories:

1. Alternating and direct current
2. Electron tubes
3. Indicating instruments
4. Oscillators
5. Audio amplifiers
6. Radio-frequency amplifiers
7. Transmitters
8. Amplitude modulation
9. Frequency modulation
10. Transistors
11. Antennas
12. Transmission lines
13. Frequency measurements
14. Batteries
15. Motors and generators
16. Microwave equipment
17. Troubleshooting

One can see from this listing that the book contains considerable information about electricity and electronics. As such, it may serve as a valuable review and reference book.

Examinations on the various elements required for a particular class of license are given only in ascending order. The student must demonstrate that he has passed the elements required for the lowest class of license before being permitted to take the examinations for higher numbered elements. For example, if a student should desire to acquire a Radiotelephone Second-Class Operator License, he must first demonstrate that he has passed Elements I and II before he will be permitted to take Element III. Then, if he passes Element III, he will be eligible for the Second-Class License; if he fails Element III at this time, he will be eligible for the Radiotelephone Third-Class Operator License and must make an appointment to retake the examination for Element III at a later date.

Similarly, if a student desires a Radiotelephone First-Class Operator License and passes Elements I, II, and III but fails Element IV, he will be eligible for a Radiotelephone Second-Class License and must return at a later date for reexamination in Element IV to qualify for the Radiotelephone First-Class License. A Ship Radar Endorsement may be added to a First- or Second-Class Radiotelephone (or Radiotelegraph) License if the the operator passes Element VIII, *Ship Radar Techniques.*

The following fees are in effect in connection with applications for the various classes of licenses, renewals, duplicates, or endorsements:

Radiotelephone First-Class Operator License: $4.
Radiotelephone Second-Class Operator License: $4.
Radiotelephone Third-Class Operator License: $4.
Application for renewal of an operator license: $2.
Application for endorsement of an operator license: $2.
Application for a duplicate or replacement license: $2.

A useful supplement to this book in preparing for the Radiotelephone Second-Class Operator License and the Ship Radar Endorsement is *Practice FCC-Type Exams for Radiotelephone Operator's License— 2nd Class* by Richard J. Smith and Victor F. C. Veely, also published by the Hayden Book Company, which contains a number of typical FCC-type license examinations with answers and discussions.

The author is deeply grateful to Mr. Ed Williamson and Mr. Bernard Grob of RCA Institutes and Rossiter Marvier Schoenkfield and Patrick A. Scifo of the Sperry Gyroscope Company for invaluable assistance and criticism given during the preparation of the manuscript. In addition, the author wishes to express his appreciation to his wife, Hazel, for typing the manuscript.

MILTON KAUFMAN

New Hyde Park, N. Y.

Contents

ELEMENT I

BASIC LAW

(Note: References which appear after questions in all Elements give the law or regulation involved in answering the questions. Abbreviations used are as follows: Sec. refers to a section of the Communications Act of 1934; Art. refers to an article of the International Radio Regulations (Atlantic City, 1947); R & R refers to a provision of the Rules and Regulations of the Federal Communications Commission; and GLR refers to regulations annexed to the Agreement Between the United States and Canada for Promotion of Safety on the Great Lakes by Means of Radio.)

Question 1.01. Where and how are FCC licenses and permits obtained? (R & R 13.11(a))

Answer. In general, an operator license or permit is obtained by making application to the regional FCC office and by passing such examination elements as are required for the particular class of license desired. In the case of a restricted radiotelephone permit, no written or oral examination is required, but proper application must be made.

Discussion. See the Preface for a list of requirements regarding the various classes of licenses and endorsements.

Q. 1.02. When a licensee qualifies for a higher grade of FCC license or permit, what happens to the lesser grade license? (R & R 13.26)

A. If the higher grade of license is in the same group, the lesser grade will be cancelled upon the issuance of a new license.

Q. 1.03. Who may apply for an FCC license? (R & R 13.5(a))

A. Normally, commercial licenses are issued only to citizens and other nationals of the United States of America.

D. As an exception, in the case of an alien who holds an Aircraft Pilot certificate issued by the FAA and is lawfully in the United States, the Commission may waive the requirements of U.S. nationality.

Q. 1.04.   If a license or permit is lost, what action must be taken by the operator? (R & R 13.71, 13.72)

A.   An operator whose license or permit has been lost, mutilated or destroyed shall immediately notify the Commission.

D.   An application for a duplicate should be submitted to the office of issue embodying a statement attesting to the facts thereof. If a license has been lost, the applicant must state that reasonable search has been made for it, and further, that in the event it be found either the original or the duplicate will be returned for cancellation. The applicant must also give a statement of the service that has been obtained under the lost license.

Q. 1.05.   What is the usual license term for radio operators? (R & R 13.4(a))

A.   Five (5) years.

Q. 1.06.   What government agency inspects radio stations in the U.S.? (Sec. 303(n))

A.   The Federal Communications Commission.

D.   The licensee of any radio station shall make the station available for inspection by representatives of the Commission at any reasonable hour and under the regulations governing the class of station concerned.

Q. 1.07.   When may a license be renewed? (R & R 13.11)

A.   Within one year before expiration.

D.   However, a grace period exists which extends the renewal time to one year after the expiration of the license. Of course, the licensee may *not* operate with an expired license.

Q. 1.08.   Who keeps the station logs? (R & R 73.111)

A.   The licensee or permittee of each broadcast station.

D.   Each log shall be kept by the person or persons competent to do so, having actual knowledge of the facts required. Such person(s) shall sign the appropriate log when starting duty and again when going off duty.

Q. 1.09.   Who corrects errors in the station logs? (R & R 73.111)

A.   Any necessary correction may be made only by the person originating the entry who shall strike out the erroneous portion, initial the correction made, and indicate the date of correction.

Q. 1.10.   How may errors in the station logs be corrected? (R & R 73.111)

A. See Question 1.09.

Q. 1.11. Under what conditions may messages be rebroadcast? (Sec. 325(a))

A. No broadcasting station shall rebroadcast the program or any part thereof of another broadcasting station without the express authority of the originating station.

Q. 1.12. What messages and signals may not be transmitted? (R & R 13.66, 13.67, 13.68)

A. The following may not be transmitted:

1. Unnecessary, unidentified, or superfluous radio communications or signals.

2. Obscene, indecent, or profane language or meaning.

3. False or deceptive signals or communications by radio, or any call letter or signal which has not been assigned by proper authority to the radio station being operated.

Q. 1.13. May an operator deliberately interfere with any radio communication or signal? (R & R 13.69)

A. No.

D. No operator shall willfully or maliciously interfere with or cause interference to any radio communication or signal.

Q. 1.14. What type of communication has top priority in the mobile service? (Art. 37)

A. Top priority is given to distress calls, distress messages, and distress traffic.

D. The order of priority for other communications is as follows:

1. Communications preceded by the urgency signal.

2. Communications preceded by the safety signal.

3. Communications relating to radio-direction finding.

4. Communications relating to the navigation and safe movement of aircraft.

5. Communications relating to the navigation, movements, and needs of ships and weather observation messages destined for an official, meteorological service.

6. Government radio telegrams: Priorité Nations.

7. Government communications for which priority has been requested.

8. Service communications relating to the working of the radio communications previously exchanged.

9. Government communications other than those shown in 6 and 7 above and all other communications.

Q. 1.15. What are the grounds for suspension of operator licenses? (Sec. 303(m) (1))

A. The FCC has authority to suspend the license of any operator upon proof sufficient to satisfy the Commission that the licensee—

1. Has violated any provision of any act, treaty, or convention binding on the United States, which the Commission is authorized to administer, or any regulation made by the Commission under any such act, treaty, or convention; or

2. Has failed to carry out a lawful order of the master or person lawfully in charge of the ship or aircraft on which he is employed; or

3. Has willfully damaged or permitted radio apparatus or installations to be damaged; or

4. Has transmitted superfluous radio communications or signals or communications containing profane or obscene words, language, or meaning, or has knowingly transmitted false or deceptive signals or communications, or a call signal or letter which has not been assigned by proper authority to the station he is operating; or

5. Has willfully or maliciously interfered with any other radio communications or signals; or

6. Has obtained or attempted to obtain, or has assisted another to obtain or attempt to obtain, an operator's license by fraudulent means.

Q. 1.16. When may an operator divulge the contents of an intercepted message? (Sec. 605)

A. Only in the case of a radio communication broadcast transmitted by amateurs or others for the use of the general public; or in the case of messages relating to ships (or aircraft) in distress.

Q. 1.17. If a licensee is notified that he has violated an FCC rule or provision of the Communications Act of 1934, what must he do? (R & R 1.89)

A. Within 10 days from receipt of notice or such other period as may be specified, the licensee shall send a written answer, in duplicate, direct to the office of the Commission originating the official notice. If an answer cannot be sent nor an acknowledgment made within such 10-day period by reason of illness or other unavoidable circumstances, acknowledgment and answer shall be made at the earliest practicable date with a satisfactory explanation of the delay.

D. The answer to each notice shall be complete in itself and shall not be abbreviated by reference to other communications or answers to other notices. In every instance the answer shall contain a statement of action taken to correct the condition or omission complained of and to preclude its recurrence. In addition: If the notice relates to violations that may be due to the physical or electrical characteristics of transmitting apparatus and any new apparatus is to be installed, the answer shall state the date such apparatus was ordered, the name of the manufacturer, and the promised date of delivery. If the installation of such apparatus requires a construction permit, the file number of the application shall be given, or if a file number has not been assigned by the Commission, such identification shall be given as will permit ready identification of the application. If the notice of violation relates to lack of attention to or improper operation of the transmitter, the name and license number of the operator in charge shall be given.

Q. 1.18. If a licensee receives a notice of suspension of his license, what must he do? (R & R 1.85)

A. He may make written application for a hearing to the Commission (FCC) within 15 days of receipt of notice.

D. Whenever grounds exist for suspension of an operator license, as provided in section 303(m) of the Communications Act, the Chief of the Safety and Special Radio Services Bureau, with respect to amateur operator licenses, or the Chief of the Field Engineering Bureau, with respect to commercial operator licenses, may issue an order suspending the operator license. No order of suspension of any operator's license shall take effect until 15 days' notice in writing of the cause for the proposed suspension has been given to the operator licensee, who may make written application to the Commission at any time within said 15 days for a hearing upon such order. The notice to the operator licensee shall not be effective until actually received by him, and from that time he shall have 15 days in which to mail the said application. In the event that physical conditions prevent mailing of the application before the expiration of the 15-day period, the application shall then be mailed as soon as possible thereafter, accompanied by a satisfactory explanation of the delay.

Q. 1.19. What are the penalties provided for violating a provision of the Communications Act of 1934 or a Rule of the FCC? (Sec. 501, 502)

A. (a) Any person who willfully and knowingly does or causes or suffers to be done any act, matter, or thing, in the Communications Act, prohibited or declared to be unlawful, or who willfully and knowingly omits or fails to do any act, matter, or thing in this Act required to be done, or upon conviction thereof, shall be punished by such offense, for which no penalty (other than forfeiture) is provided therein, by a fine of not more than $10,000 or by imprisonment for a term of not more than one year, or both. For each subsequent offense the punishment shall be a fine of not more than $10,000, or imprisonment for a term not to exceed two years, or both.

(b) For violation of a Rule of the FCC, a fine of not more than $500 per day for each and every day of the offense is stipulated.

Q. 1.20. What acts, when performed by an operator on board a voluntarily equipped ship, may make him liable to a monetary forfeiture? (Sec. 510)

A. The acts are as specified below. If any radio station:

(1) is operated by any person not holding a valid radio operator license or permit of the class prescribed in the rules and regulations of the Commission for the operation of such station;

(2) fails to identify itself at the times and in the manner prescribed in the rules and regulations of the Commission;

(3) transmits any false call contrary to regulations of the Commission;

(4) is operated on a frequency not authorized by the Commission for use by such station;

(5) transmits unauthorized communications on any frequency designated as a distress or calling frequency in the rules and regulations of the Commission;

(6) interferes with any distress call or distress communication contrary to the regulations of the Commission;

(7) fails to attenuate spurious emissions to the extent required by the rules and regulations of the Commission;

(8) is operated with power in excess of that authorized by the Commission;

(9) renders a communication service not authorized by the Commission for the particular station;

(10) is operated with a type of emission not authorized by the Commission;

(11) is operated with transmitting equipment other than that authorized by the Commission; or

(12) fails to respond to official communications from the Commission.

D. The maximum amount of liability for violating any one of the above numbered clauses is $100. The maximum amount of liability for violating five or more of the above provisions is $500, regardless of how many provisions greater than five are violated.

The forfeiture liability described above shall apply only for a willful or a repeated violation.

Q. 1.21. Define "harmful interference." (Section III, Geneva, 1959, Treaty)

A. "Harmful interference" encompasses the following: any emission, radiation, or induction which endangers the functioning of a radionavigation service or of other safety services, or which seriously degrades, obstructs, or repeatedly interrupts a radiocommunication service operating in accordance with these Regulations.

ADDENDUM TO ELEMENT I

The following information, pertaining to Element I, does not appear as part of the preceding questions and answers for Element I. However, such information is given in an FCC Study Guide, where it is described as material which may appear in FCC Element I examinations. The following additional information is therefore presented here for the benefit of the students, to ensure that they will be aware of all of the required information for the examination.

BACKGROUND

The Federal Communications Commission was created by the Communications Act of 1934 for the purpose of regulating interstate and foreign commerce in communication by wire and radio. One of the general powers given to the Commission is the authority to prescribe the qualifications of station operators, to classify them according to the duties to be performed, and, except for alien aircraft pilots, to issue commercial operator licenses only to United States citizens and nationals. (Section 1 and 303(1)(1))

POSTING OPERATOR LICENSES

Most third-class operator permits are required to be posted at the operator's place of duty. When an application for a duplicate, replacement, or renewal of a commercial operator license is submitted, the license then held, if available, must accompany the application. In this case the operator may post a signed copy of the application submitted by him in lieu of the license document. (R&R 13.72)

FAILING AN EXAMINATION ELEMENT

An applicant who fails a commercial operator examination element will be ineligible to retake that same element for a two-month period. (R&R 13.27)

SUSPENSION OF OPERATOR LICENSES

Upon receipt by the Commission of application for hearing, the order of suspension shall be held in abeyance until the conclusion of the hearing which shall be conducted under such rules as the Commission may prescribe. Upon the conclusion of the hearing the Commission may affirm, modify, or revoke its order of suspension. (Section 303(m) (2) and R&R 1.85)

FALSE DISTRESS SIGNALS

No person within the jurisdiction of the United States shall knowingly utter or transmit, or cause to be uttered or transmitted, any false or fraudulent signal of distress, or communication relating thereto. (Section 325(a))

DISTRESS TRAFFIC

Each station licensee shall give absolute priority to radiocommunications or signals relating to ships or aircraft in distress. The control of distress traffic is the responsibility of the mobile station in distress. Any station which becomes aware that a mobile station is in distress may retransmit the distress message when there is reason to believe that the distress call it has intercepted has not been received by any station in a position to render aid. (R&R 2.401, 2.402, and 2.403)

OPERATION DURING EMERGENCY

The licensee of any station (except amateur, standard broadcast, FM broadcast, noncommercial educational FM broadcast, or television broadcast) may, during a period of emergency in which normal communication facilities are disrupted as a result of hurricane, flood, earthquake, or similar disaster, utilize such station for emergency communication service in communicating in a manner other than that specified in the instrument of authorization. (R&R 2.405)

FCC-TYPE SAMPLE TEST FOR ELEMENT I

I-1. When may an operator deliberately interfere with radio communications? (Q. 1.13)
   (a) Between 12 midnight and 6 A.M.
   (b) At no time.
   (c) When sending government radio telegrams.
   (d) When rebroadcasting the program of another station.
   (e) None of the above.

I-2. The penalty for violating a rule of the FCC is: (Q. 1.19)
   (a) A $10,000 fine.
   (b) Revocation of the operator's license.
   (c) Suspension of the operator's license.
   (d) $500 per day maximum for each day of the offense.
   (e) $50 per day for each day of the offense.

I-3. The penalty for violating a provision of the Communications Act of 1934 (first offense) is: (Q. 1.19)
   (a) An official warning.
   (b) Suspension of the operator's license for 90 days.
   (c) A fine of not more than $10,000, or imprisonment for not more than one year, or both.
   (d) A fine of not more than $1,000, or imprisonment for not more than one year, or both.
   (e) A fine of not more than $10,000, or imprisonment for not more than two years, or both.

I-4. One of the grounds for suspension of an operator's license is: (Q. 1.15)
   (a) Has failed to carry out a lawful order of the master in charge of the ship on which he is employed.
   (b) Has failed to keep correct station logs.
   (c) Has failed to put in the correct number of working hours at his station.
   (d) Has permitted his station to operate off frequency.
   (e) None of the above.

I-5. The following messages or signals may not be transmitted: (Q. 1.12)
   (a) Government communications relating to aircraft schedules.
   (b) Unidentified radio signals.
   (c) Communications relative to station log entries.
   (d) Private messages.
   (e) Communications relative to ship schedules.

I-6. Messages may be rebroadcast under the following condition: (Q. 1.11)
   (a) If a proper entry is made in the station log.

(b) If requested by the master of the ship.

(c) Only by an operator having a first-class radiotelephone or radiotelegraph license.

(d) By permission of the originating station.

(e) Between 12 midnight and 6 AM.

I-7.   The usual license term for radio operators is: (Q. 1.05)

(a) One year.

(b) Three years.

(c) Two years.

(d) Four years.

(e) None of the above.

I-8.   Where may FCC licenses be obtained? (Q. 1.01)

(a) At the regional FAA office.

(b) At any state licensing agency.

(c) At any Federal licensing agency.

(d) At any regional FCC office.

(e) Only at the Washington, D.C., FCC office.

I-9.   The following persons may apply for an FCC license: (Q. 1.03)

(a) Holders of any foreign radio operator's license.

(b) Only holders of a restricted radio license.

(c) Citizens or other nationals of the United States.

(d) Aliens who have applied for citizenship.

(e) Persons who have graduated from an approved radio school.

I-10.   The three top priority types of communications, in their correct
order, are: (Q. 1.14)

(a) Distress, urgency, and safety.

(b) Urgency, distress, and safety.

(c) Distress, safety, and navigation.

(d) Distress, urgency, and navigation.

(e) Distress, urgency, and government.

I-11.   An operator may divulge the contents of an intercepted message
only: (Q. 1.16)

(a) When authorized by a first-class license holder.

(b) When authorized by the master of a ship or aircraft.

(c) If it relates to distress, or is for the use of the general public.

(d) If it relates to government communications.

(e) If it is an internal company message.

I-12.   The agency which is authorized to inspect radio stations in the
United States is: (Q. 1.06)

(a) The Federal Aviation Administration.

(b) Any authorized Federal agency.

(c) The local State Communications Administration.

(d) The Federal Communications Commission.

(e) None of the above.

I-13.   An operator's license may be renewed: (Q. 1.07)
   (a) Every three years.
   (b) Only after it has expired.
   (c) Only if proof of operation is given.
   (d) Automatically.
   (e) Within one year before expiration.

I-14.   Station logs are kept by: (Q. 1.08)
   (a) The owner of the station.
   (b) The licensee or permittee of each station.
   (c) Only the individual in charge of maintenance of the station equipment.
   (d) Any individual having a proper operator's license.
   (e) Only by an operator who has never been convicted of violating a provision of a rule of the FCC.

I-15.   If a licensee receives a notice of suspension of his license, he must: (Q. 1.18)
   (a) Immediately cease to operate any station.
   (b) Make written application for a hearing within 15 days.
   (c) Make written application for a hearing within 30 days.
   (d) Immediately mail his license to the FCC, pending a hearing.
   (e) Wait for additional instructions from the FCC.

I-16.   If a licensee has been notified that he has violated an FCC rule, he must send a written answer: (Q. 1.17)
   (a) To the Washington, D.C., office, within 15 days.
   (b) To the originating FCC office, within 10 days.
   (c) To the originating FCC office, within 15 days.
   (d) To the Washington, D.C., FCC office, within 10 days.
   (e) To the originating FAA office, within 10 days.

I-17.   Errors in the station log may be corrected by: (Q. 1.09)
   (a) Erasing the erroneous material and writing over it in a neat manner.
   (b) Anyone working in the station.
   (c) Anyone possessing a first- or second-class operator's license.
   (d) Only the person originating the entry.
   (e) Only a person designated by the manager of the station or the master of a ship.

I-18.   If an operator loses his license, he must: (Q. 1.04)
   (a) Notify the FCC within 15 days.
   (b) Notify the FAA within 15 days.
   (c) Notify the FCC immediately.
   (d) Not operate any station.
   (e) None of the above.

I-19.   Unidentified radio communications may be transmitted under the following condition: (Q. 1.12)

(a) For distress messages.
(b) Under no condition.
(c) For urgency calls.
(d) For government communications.
(e) For weather messages.

I-20.   If a licensee has a second-class radiotelephone license and then qualifies for a first-class radiotelephone license, the lesser grade of license: (Q. 1.02)

(a) Remains in force.
(b) Is needed to perform maintenance on the station.
(c) Will be cancelled.
(d) Must be immediately mailed back to the FCC.
(e) Is still effective for routine communications.

ELEMENT II

BASIC OPERATING PRACTICE

(Note: The questions of Element II have been subdivided into two categories. The candidate for a license may elect to answer questions in the general category (O), or to answer questions in marine category (M)).

CATEGORY "O" — GENERAL

Question 2.01. What should an operator do when he leaves a transmitter unattended?

Answer. If an operator leaves a transmitter unattended, the transmitter must be made inaccessible or inoperable with respect to all unauthorized persons.

Q. 2.02. What are the meanings of clear, out, over, roger, words twice, say again, and break?

A. 1. The word "clear" signifies that the transmission is ended and that no response is expected.

2. The word "out" signifies that the conversation is ended and that no response is expected.

3. The word "over" signifies "My transmission is ended and I expect a response from you."

4. The word "roger" signifies "I have received all of your last transmission."

5. The words "words twice" means:

   (a) As a request: "Communication is difficult. Please send every phrase twice."

   (b) As information: "Since communication is difficult every phrase in this message will be sent twice."

6. The words "say again" signifies repeat.

7. The word "break" signifies a separation between portions of a message.

Q. 2.03.   How should a microphone be treated when used in noisy locations?

A.   The microphone should be shielded with the hands in order to reduce outside noises thus making communications more intelligible.

D.   In severe cases, special noise-cancelling microphones may be used.

Q. 2.04.   What may happen to the received signal when an operator has shouted into a microphone?

A.   Shouting into the microphone is poor practice, because while it probably will not injure the microphone, it may very well overdrive some speech amplifier or cause overmodulation. Either of these effects may cause severe distortion of the speech and possible interference with adjacent channels.

Q. 2.05.   Why should radio transmitters be "off" when signals are not being transmitted?

A.   To prevent interference with other stations using the channel.

D. Even if an unmodulated carrier is transmitted, it may cause heterodyning interference with other station carriers, making communication very difficult.

Q. 2.06.   Why should an operator use well-known words and phrases?

A.   The operator should use simple language and well-known words and phrases to ensure accurate, efficient communications and to eliminate repetition as much as possible.

Q. 2.07.   Why is the station's call sign transmitted?

A.   The station's call sign should be transmitted in order to clearly identify the originator of messages being transmitted.

Q. 2.08.   Where does an operator find specifications for obstruction marking and lighting (where required) for the antenna towers of a particular radio station?

A.   Specifications are found in Part 17 of the Rules and Regulations of the FCC (R & R 17.23, 17.25, 17.27, and 17.42).

Q. 2.09.   What should an operator do if he hears profanity being used at his station?

A.   He should take steps to conclude the transmission and enter the details in the station log. The incident should be reported to the FCC.

Q. 2.10.   When may an operator use his station without regard to certain provisions of his station license? (R & R 2.405)

A.   The licensee of any station, except amateur, may, during a period of emergency in which normal communication facilities are disrupted as a result of hurricane, flood, earthquake or similar disaster, utilize such station for emergency communication service in communicating in a manner other than that specified in the instrument of authorization.

Q. 2.11.   Who bears the responsibility if an operator permits an unlicensed person to speak over his station?

A.   The licensed operator in charge of the station always bears the responsibility for its operation, regardless of who is speaking over it.

Q. 2.12.   What is meant by a "phonetic alphabet" in radiotelephone communications?

A.   A phonetic alphabet is one in which each letter is associated with a particular word. For example: A—Alpha, B—Bravo, C—Coca, etc.

D.   A phonetic alphabet is used in radiotelephone communication to ensure that certain letters or words are clearly understandable to the receiving station.

Q. 2.13.   How does the licensed operator of a station normally exhibit his authority to operate the station?

A.   The original license of each station operator shall be posted at the place where he is on duty or kept in his possession in the manner specified in the regulations governing the class of station concerned.

Q. 2.14.   What precautions should be observed in testing a station on the air?

A.   The operator should listen on the transmission frequency to ensure that interference will not be caused to a communication in progress.

FCC-TYPE SAMPLE TEST FOR ELEMENT II
(CATEGORY "O"—GENERAL)

II-1 (O).   A station's call sign is transmitted: (Q. 2.207)
  (a) For the purpose of testing the transmitter.
  (b) To allow the receiving station to tune his receiver properly.
  (c) To identify clearly the originator of the messages.
  (d) To identify clearly the receiver of the messages.
  (e) To fill in "dead" air time.

II-2 (O).   When an operator leaves his transmitter unattended, he must: (Q. 2.01)
  (a) Place it on automatic operation.
  (b) Make it inaccessible or inoperable to all unauthorized persons.

(c) Post a notice on the station door, stating when he intends to return.

(d) Be certain it is operating properly and on the correct frequency.

(e) Make prior notification to the regional FCC office.

II-3(O).   An operator should check for possible communications in progress on his assigned frequency prior to: (Q. 2.14)

(a) Increasing the power of his transmitter.

(b) Changing the frequency of his transmitter.

(c) Testing his station on the air.

(d) Transmitting station identification.

(e) None of the above.

II-4(O).   Accurate and efficient communications are helped by: (Q. 2.06)

(a) The use of simple phrases and well-known words.

(b) The use of the lowest possible transmitting power.

(c) Using low levels of amplitude modulation.

(d) Maximum repetition of phrases.

(e) Selective overmodulation of the transmitter.

II-5(O).   If a transmission is ended and no response is expected, the transmission is ended with the word: (Q. 2.02)

(a) Out.

(b) Over.

(c) Roger.

(d) Break.

(e) None of the above.

II-6(O).   A phonetic alphabet (ex.: A—Alpha) is sometimes made use of in radio communications to: (Q. 2.12)

(a) Extend the range of transmission.

(b) Reduce the average modulation percentage.

(c) Ensure that certain words or letters are clearly understandable.

(d) Reduce charges for some types of radiotelegrams.

(e) Transmit weather information by radio.

II-7(O).   To prevent interference from other transmitters using a common channel: (Q. 2.05)

(a) A low level of modulation should be used.

(b) Only frequency modulation should be employed.

(c) Phase modulation is preferred.

(d) All transmitters not involved in the particular transmission should be off.

(e) The microphone should be held several inches away from the operator's lips.

II-8(O).   The word "clear" signifies that the transmission: (Q. 2.02)

(a) Is ended and that a response is expected.

(b) Is ended and that no response is expected.

(c) Cannot be continued because of transmitter problems.
(d) Has been received and completely understood.
(e) Should be repeated.

II-9(O).   The original license of each station operator shall be: (Q. 2.13)

(a) Kept in a safe place, such as a safety deposit box.
(b) Duplicated and the duplicate posted at the station.
(c) Posted at his station, or kept in his possession.
(d) Given into the safekeeping of the station manager or the master of his ship.
(e) Displayed only when he is testing the station.

II-10(O).   If an operator shouts into a microphone, this may: (Q. 2.04)

(a) Cause voice strain.
(b) Damage the microphone.
(c) Cause interference with adjacent channels.
(d) Reduce the effective distance of transmission.
(e) None of the above.

II-11(O).   If communication is difficult, the receiver may send the following request: (Q. 2.02)

(a) Speak louder.
(b) Speak closer to the microphone.
(c) Speak farther from the microphone.
(d) Increase your transmitter power.
(e) Words twice.

II-12(O).   If an unlicensed person speaks over a station, this is the responsibility of: (Q. 2.11)

(a) The licensed operator in charge of the station.
(b) The Federal Communications Commission.
(c) The manager of the station.
(d) Any license holder at the station.
(e) The Federal Bureau of Investigation.

II-13(O).   If an operator hears profanity being broadcast over his station, he should: (Q. 2.09)

(a) Ignore it, as no censorship is permitted.
(b) Report it to the station manager.
(c) Caution the operator, but take no further steps.
(d) Have the transmission concluded and report it to the Federal Communications Commission.
(e) Immediately shut down the transmitter.

II-14(O).   When an operator wishes a repeat of a transmission or a portion thereof, he will say: (Q. 202)

(a) Say again.
(b) Please repeat.

(c) I did not understand the last transmission.

(d) Your last transmission was not clear.

(e) Your transmission is breaking up.

II-15(O). A separation between portions of a message is signified by the word: (Q. 2.02)

(a) Separate.

(b) Space.

(c) Break.

(d) Hyphen.

(e) Colon.

II-16(O). A microphone should be shielded with the hands: (Q. 2.03)

(a) To protect it from the wind.

(b) To reduce outside noises.

(c) In cold weather.

(d) To improve the high-frequency response.

(e) To increase its output.

II-17(O). Specifications for obstruction marking and lighting for antenna towers are found: (Q. 2.08)

(a) On a plate fastened to the antenna.

(b) In the regulations of the Federal Aviation Administration.

(c) In the regulations of the State Aviation Authority.

(d) In Part 17 of the Rules and Regulations of the FCC.

(e) In Part 57 of the Rules and Regulations of the FCC.

II-18(O). When communications are disrupted as a result of a disaster, the licensee of a station may: (Q. 2.10)

(a) Shut down his station.

(b) Decrease the power of his station.

(c) Utilize the station for emergency communications.

(d) Operate his station with unlicensed personnel.

(e) None of the above.

II-19(O). When an operator has ended a transmission and expects a response, he uses the word: (Q. 2.02)

(a) Respond.

(b) Reply.

(c) Roger.

(d) Over.

(e) Break.

II-20(O). When an operator wishes to indicate that he has received all of the last transmission, he uses the word: (Q. 2.02)

(a) Received.

(b) Roger.

(c) Over.

(d) OK.

(e) Clear.

CATEGORY "M"—MARITIME

Q. 2.01.   What is the importance of the frequency 2182 kc? (R & R 83.352, 83.353(a))

A.   This frequency may be used in two ways:

1. It is the international distress frequency for radiotelephony, ships, aircraft and survival-craft stations.

2. It is the international general radiotelephone calling frequency for the maritime mobile service.

Q. 2.02.   Describe completely what actions should be taken by a radio operator who hears a distress message; a safety message. (R & R 83.239, 83.240, 83.241, 83.242)

A.   1. How to acknowledge a distress message:

(a) Stations of the maritime mobile service which receive a distress message from a mobile station which is, beyond any possible doubt, in their vicinity, shall immediately acknowledge receipt. However, in areas where reliable communication with one or more coast stations are practicable, ship stations may defer this acknowledgment for a short interval so that a coast station may acknowledge receipt.

(b) Stations of the maritime mobile service which receive a distress message from a mobile station which, beyond any possible doubt, is not in their vicinity, shall allow a short interval of time to elapse before acknowledging receipt of the message, in order to permit stations nearer to the mobile station in distress to acknowledge receipt without interference.

2. Form of acknowledgment:

(a) The acknowledgment of receipt of a distress message is transmitted, when radiotelegraphy is used, in the following form:

(1) The call sign of the station sending the distress message, sent three times;

(2) The word DE;

(3) The call sign of the station acknowledging receipt, sent three times;

(4) The group RRR;

(5) The distress signal SOS.

(b) The acknowledgment of receipt of a distress message is transmitted, when radiotelephony is used, in the following form:

(1) The call sign or other identification of the station sending the distress message, spoken three times;

(2) The words THIS IS;

(3) The call sign or other identification of the station acknowledging receipt, spoken three times;

(4) The word RECEIVED;

(5) The distress signal MAYDAY.

3. Information furnished by acknowledging station:

(a) Every mobile station which acknowledges receipt of a distress message shall, on the order of the master or person responsible for the ship, aircraft, or other vehicle carrying such mobile station, transmit as soon as possible the following information in the order shown:

(1) Its name;

(2) Its position, in the form prescribed in R & R 83.236(c);

(3) The speed at which it is proceeding towards, and the approximate time it will take to reach, the mobile station in distress.

(b) Before sending this message, the station shall ensure that it will, not interfere with the emissions of other stations better situated to render immediate assistance to the station in distress.

4. Transmission of distress message by a station not itself in distress:

(a) A mobile station or a land station which learns that a mobile station is in distress shall transmit a distress message in any of the following cases:

(1) When the station in distress is not itself in a position to transmit the distress message;

(2) When the master or person responsible for the ship, aircraft, or other vehicle not in distress, or the person responsible for the land station, considers that further help is necessary;

(3) When, although not in a position to render assistance, it has heard a distress message which has not been acknowledged. When a mobile station transmits a distress message under these conditions, it shall take all necessary steps to notify the authorities who may be able to render assistance.

(b) The transmission of a distress message under the conditions prescribed in paragraph (a) of this section shall be made on either or both of the international distress frequencies (500 kc/s radiotelegraph; 2182 kc/s radiotelephone) or on any other available frequency on which attention might be attracted.

(c) The transmission of the distress message shall always be preceded by the call indicated below, which shall itself be preceded whenever possible by the radiotelegraph or radiotelephone alarm signal. This call consists of:

(1) When radiotelegraphy is used:

(i) The signal DDD SOS SOS SOS DDD;

(ii) The word DE.

(iii) The call sign of the transmitting station, sent three times;

(2) When radiotelephony is used:

(i) The signal MAYDAY RELAY, spoken three times;

(ii) The words THIS IS;

(iii) The call sign or other identification of the transmitting station, spoken three times.

(d) When the radiotelegraph alarm signal is used, an interval of two minutes shall be allowed, whenever this is considered necessary, before the transmission of the call mentioned.

5. Safety Message: A safety message is one which provides information concerning the safety of navigation, or important meteorological warnings. A radio operator receiving such a message should immediately forward the message to the ship's master.

Q. 2.03. What information must be contained in distress messages? What procedure should be followed by a radio operator in sending a distress message? What is a good choice of words to be used in sending a distress message? (R & R 83.234 through 83.238)

A. 1. The following information must be contained in distress messages:

The message shall include the distress call followed by the name of the ship, aircraft, or the vehicle in distress, information regarding the position of the latter, the nature of the distress and the nature of the help requested, and any other further information which might facilitate this assistance.

2. The following procedure should be followed:

(a) Distress signals:

(1) The international radiotelegraph distress signal consists of the group "three dots, three dashes, three dots" (··· — — — ···), symbolized herein by SOS, transmitted as a single signal in which the dashes are slightly prolonged so as to be distinguished clearly from the dots.

(2) The international radiotelephone distress signal consists of the word MAYDAY, pronounced as the French expression "m'aider."

(3) These distress signals indicate that a mobile station is threatened by grave and imminent danger and requests immediate assistance.

(b) Radiotelephone distress call and message transmission procedure:

(1) The radiotelephone distress procedure shall consist of:

(i) The radiotelephone alarm signal (whenever possible);

(ii) The distress call;

(iii) The distress message.

(2) The radiotelephone distress transmissions shall be made slowly and distinctly, each word being clearly pronounced to facilitate transcription.

(3) After the transmission by radiotelephony of its distress message, the mobile station may be requested to transmit suitable signals followed by its call sign or name, to permit direction-finding stations to determine its position. This request may be repeated at frequent intervals if necessary.

(4) The distress message, preceded by the distress call, shall be repeated at intervals until an answer is received. This repetition shall be preceded by the radiotelephone alarm signal whenever possible.

(5) When the mobile station in distress receives no answer to a distress message transmitted on the distress frequency, the message may be repeated on any other available frequency on which attention might be attracted.

3. A suitable choice of words would be "Mayday, Mayday, Mayday, this is Trans Ocean Airlines Flight 907, 14 miles due East of Cape Hatteras, three engines out, require immediate assistance to pick up all on board after ditching. Estimate ditching to occur in 30 seconds; number 3 engine on fire, Over."

Q. 2.04.   What are the requirements for keeping watch on 2182 kc? If a radio operator is required to "stand watch" on an international distress frequency, when may he stop listening? (R & R 83.223)

A.   1. The requirements are as follows:

(a) Each ship station on board a ship navigating the Great Lakes and licensed to transmit by telephony on one or more frequencies within the band 1600 to 3500 kc/s shall, during its hours of service for telephony, maintain an efficient watch for the reception of class A3 emission on the radio-channel of which 2182 kc/s is the assigned frequency, whenever the station is not being used for transmission on that channel or for communication on other radio-channels.

(b) Except for stations on board vessels required by law to be fitted with radiotelegraph equipment, each ship station (in addition to those ship stations specified in paragraph (a) of this section) licensed to transmit by telephony on one or more frequencies within the band 1600 to 3500 kc/s shall, during its hours of service for telephony, maintain an efficient watch for the reception of class A3 emission on the radio-channel of which 2182 kc/s is the assigned frequency, whenever such station is not being used for transmission on that channel or for communication on other radio-channels. When the ship station is in Region 1 or 3, such watch shall, insofar as is possible, be maintained at least twice each hour for three minutes commencing at x h. 00 and x h. 30, Greenwich Mean Time (G. M. T.).

2. He may stop listening whenever the station is being used for transmission on that channel or for communication on other radio-channels.

Q. 2.05.   Under what circumstances may a coast station contact a land station by radio? (R & R 81.302(a) (2))

A.   For the purpose of facilitating the transmission or reception of safety communication to or from a ship or aircraft station.

Q. 2.06.   What do distress, safety, and urgency signals indicate? What are the international urgency, safety, and distress signals? In the case of a mobile radio station in distress what station is responsible for the control of distress message traffic? (R & R 83.234 through 83.249)

A. 1. (a) The distress signal (MAYDAY) indicates that the ship, aircraft or any other vehicle which sends the distress signal is threatened by serious and imminent danger and requests immediate assistance.

(b) The safety signal (SECURITY) announces that the station is about to transmit a message concerning the safety of navigation or giving important meteorological warnings. Hence, it should precede such a transmission.

(c) The urgent signal (PAN) shall indicate that the calling station has a very urgent message to transmit concerning the safety of a ship, an aircraft, or another vehicle, or concerning the safety of some person on board or sighted from on board.

2. The control of distress traffic shall be the responsibility of the mobile station in distress or upon the station which, by application of the provisions of the Commission's rules and regulations has sent the distress call. These stations may delegate the control of the distress traffic to another station.

Q. 2.07. In regions of heavy traffic why should an interval be left between radiotelephone calls? Why should a radio operator listen before transmitting on a shared channel? How long may a radio operator in the mobile service continue attempting to contact a station which does not answer? (R & R 83.366)

A. 1. An interval should be left (and is required by law) to permit other stations to share the radio channel. (See R & R 83.366 for details.)

2. He should listen on the shared channel first to avoid disrupting communication which may already be in progress.

3. Calling a particular station shall not continue for more than 30 seconds in each instance. If the called station is not heard to reply, that station shall not again be called until after an interval of 2 minutes. When a station called does not reply to a call sent three times at intervals of 2 minutes, the calling shall cease and shall not be renewed until after an interval of 15 minutes; however, if there is no reason to believe that harmful interference will be caused to other communications in progress, the call sent three times at intervals of 2 minutes may be repeated after a pause of not less than 3 minutes. In event of an emergency involving safety, the provisions of this paragraph shall not apply.

Q. 2.08. Why are test transmissions sent? How often should they be sent? What is the proper way to send a test message? How often should the station's call sign be sent? (R & R 83.365)

A. 1. Test transmissions are sent to ensure that the radio equipment is functioning normally.

2. They should be sent each day unless normal use of the radiotelephone installation demonstrates that the equipment is in proper operating condition.

3. The official call sign of the testing station, followed by the word "test," shall be announced on the radio-channel being used for the test, as a warning that test emissions are about to be made on that frequency.

4. The station's call sign shall be sent at the conclusion of each test message, which should not exceed 10 seconds.

D. If, as a result of the announcement prescribed in subparagraph 3 above, any station transmits by voice the word "wait," testing shall be suspended. When, after an appropriate interval of time, such announcement is repeated and no response is observed, and careful listening indicates that harmful interference should not be caused, the operator shall proceed as follows:

The operator shall announce the word "testing" followed in the case of a voice transmission test by the count "1, 2, 3, 4 * * * etc." or by test phrases or sentences not in conflict with normal operating signals; or followed, in the case of other emission, by appropriate test signals not in conflict with normal operating signals. The test signals in either case shall have a duration not exceeding ten seconds. At the conclusion of the test, there shall be voice announcement of the official call sign of the testing station, the name of the ship on which the station is located, and the general location of the ship at the time the test is being made. This test transmission shall not be repeated until a period of at least one minute has elapsed; on the frequency 2182 kc/s or 156.8 mc/s in a region of heavy traffic, a period of at least five minutes shall elapse before the test transmission is repeated.

When testing is conducted on any frequency assignment within the band 2170 kc/s to 2194 kc/s, within the band 156.75 mc/s to 156.85 mc/s, within the band 480 kc/s to 510 kc/s (lifeboat transmitters only), or within the band 8362 kc/s to 8366 kc/s (lifeboat transmitters only), no test transmissions shall occur which are likely to actuate any automatic alarm receiver within range. Lifeboat stations using telephony shall not be tested on the assigned frequency 500 kc/s during the 500 kc/s silence periods.

If a radio station is used only for occasional calls, it is a good practice to test the station regularly. Regular tests may reveal defects or faults which, if corrected immediately may prevent delays when communications are necessary. Caution should be observed by persons testing a station to make certain their test message will not interfere with other communications in progress in the same channel. Technical repairs or adjustments to radio telephone communication stations are made only by or under the immediate supervision and responsibility of operators holding first- or second-class licenses.

Q. 2.09. In the mobile service, why should radiotelephone messages be as brief as possible?

A. It is a good policy to be brief to permit other stations to operate without interference and also from the standpoint of efficient station operation.

Q. 2.10.   **What are the meanings of: Clear, Out, Over, Roger, Words Twice, Repeat, and Break?**

A. See Q. 2.02, Category "O" — General.

Q. 2.11   **Does the Geneva, 1959 treaty give other countries the authority to inspect U. S. vessels? (Art. 21)**

A. Yes.

D. The governments or appropriate administrations of countries which a mobile station visits, may require the production of the license for examination. The operator of the mobile station, or the person responsible for the station, shall facilitate this examination. The license shall be kept in such a way that it can be produced upon request. As far as possible, the license, or a copy certified by the authority which has issued it, should be permanently exhibited in the station.

Q. 2.12.   **Why are call signs sent? Why should they be sent clearly and distinctly?**

A. 1. Call signs are sent to enable monitoring stations to identify the station of origin.

2. They should be sent clearly and distinctly to avoid unneccessary repetition and to assist monitoring stations in identifying calls.

Q. 2.13.   **How does the licensed operator of a ship station exhibit his authority to operate a station? (R & R 83.156)**

A. When a licensed operator is required for the operation of a station, the original license of each such operator while he is employed or designated as radio operator of the station shall be posted in a conspicuous place at the principal location on board ship at which the station is operated: Provided, that in the case of stations of a portable nature, including marine-utility stations, or in the case where the operator holds a restricted radiotelephone operator permit, the operator may in lieu of posting have on his person either his required operator license or a duly issued verification card (FCC form 758-F) attesting to the existence of that license.

Q. 2.14.   **When may a coast station NOT charge for messages it is requested to handle? (R & R 81.179)**

A. 1. No charge shall be made by any station in the maritime mobile service of the United States for the transmission of distress messages and replies thereto in connection with situations involving the safety of life and property at sea.

2. No charge shall be made by any station in the maritime mobile service of the United States for the transmission receipt, or relay of the information concerning dangers to navigation, originating on a ship of the United States or of a foreign country.

Q. 2.15. What is the difference between calling and working frequencies? (R & R 83.6)

A. A calling frequency is one to which all stations generally listen, for example 500 kilocycles. A working frequency is an assigned frequency other than a calling frequency on which the main body of the communication would take place after the initial calling.

FCC-TYPE SAMPLE TEST FOR ELEMENT II
(CATEGORY "M"—MARITIME)

II-1 (M). A coast station may contact a land station by radio: (Q. 2.05)
    (a) To facilitate the transmission or reception of a safety communication.
    (b) To facilitate the transmission or reception of an alarm communication.
    (c) For the transmission of a government communication.
    (d) If so directed by the station manager.
    (e) If it is having difficulties with its transmitter.

II-2 (M). To permit other stations to operate without interference, radiotelephone messages should be: (Q. 2.09)
    (a) Sent by frequency modulation.
    (b) Sent with reduced amplitude modulation.
    (c) As brief as possible.
    (d) Sent with reduced transmitter output power.
    (e) None of the above.

II-3 (M). A calling frequency is one on which: (Q. 2.15)
    (a) The main body of communications take place.
    (b) Calls are always made to land stations.
    (c) Communications are always made to aircraft stations.
    (d) Calls are made from land stations to marine stations.
    (e) All stations generally listen.

II-4 (M). The licensed operator of a ship station is required to show his authority to operate the station by: (Q. 2.13)
    (a) An FCC registration attached to his outer clothing.
    (b) Posting his license at the main station location.
    (c) Posting a duplicate of his license at the main station location.

(d) A letter of approval from the FCC.

(e) A license from the Federal Maritime Authority.

II-5 (M).   If a ship or other vehicle is in imminent danger, it should transmit the: (Q. 2.03)

(a) Distress signal (PAN).

(b) Urgency signal (MAYDAY).

(c) Distress signal (IMI).

(d) Distress signal (MAYDAY).

(e) Urgency signal (PAN).

II-6 (M).   The frequency 2182 kc may be used in the following way: (Q. 2.01)

(a) To communicate with commercial broadcast stations.

(b) To communicate with the Federal Communications Commission.

(c) To send telegrams between ship stations and land stations.

(d) For distress calls.

(e) To report on the passing of other ships.

II-7 (M).   Maritime stations receiving a distress call from a station in their vicinity shall (Q. 2.02)

(a) Immediately relay the information to a coast station.

(b) Keep radio silence.

(c) Immediately acknowledge receipt.

(d) Immediately notify the Federal Communications Commission.

(e) Send out a series of SOS signals.

II-8 (M).   Test transmissions should be sent each day unless: (Q. 2.08)

(a) The operator is prevented from doing so by official duties.

(b) The operator is ordered not to do so by the master of the ship.

(c) The power output exceeds the permissible value.

(d) Normal use shows the equipment to be working properly.

(e) Normal use shows that the equipment is in need of maintenance.

II-9 (M).   A working frequency is one that is: (Q. 2.15)

(a) Used during normal working hours of the operator.

(b) Used for the main body of the communication.

(c) Generally listened to by all stations.

(d) Used only for test purposes during daylight hours.

(e) Known to be transmitting at the FCC required power.

II-10 (M).   Call signs should be sent clearly and distinctly in order to: (Q. 2.12)

(a) Alert the auto alarm system.

(b) Make possible accurate radio-direction finding.

(c) Conserve transmission power.

(d) Avoid unnecessary repetition.

(e) Avoid excessive amplitude modulation.

II-11 (M).   Under the Geneva, 1959 treaty, other countries may: (Q. 2.11)

(a) Check the type of radio equipment being used on board a U.S. vessel.

(b) Require the production of a marine operator's license.

(c) Require that a U.S. vessel's transmitter be shut down.

(d) Require that a U.S. vessel does not transmit within the 12-mile limit.

(e) None of the above.

II-12(M). A radio operator in the mobile service may continue attempting to contact a station which does not answer: (Q. 2.07)

(a) For a total of three times, at intervals of two minutes each.

(b) For a total of 30 seconds.

(c) Once every 15 minutes.

(d) On a continuous basis.

(e) At the discretion of the master of the ship.

II-13(M). A mobile station which acknowledges receipt of a distress message shall transmit: (Q. 2.02)

(a) Its name, its position, and the master's name.

(b) Its name, its transmitting frequency, and its position.

(c) Its name, its position, and the approximate time needed to reach the distressed vessel.

(d) Its name, its position, and its tonnage.

(e) Its name, its position, and the call signs of other vessels it is in communication with.

II-14(M). Ship stations navigating the Great Lakes and during their hours of service for telephony are required to keep watch on: (Q. 2.04)

(a) 2182 kc.

(b) 2812 kc.

(c) 2112 kc.

(d) 8212 kc.

(e) 1282 kc.

II-15(M). The urgent signal PAN indicates: (Q. 2.06)

(a) A communication for Pan American Airways.

(b) The calling station has a message relating to the safety of a ship.

(c) The calling station has a message relating to a storm.

(d) The calling station is in distress.

(e) A low priority ship-to-ship communication.

II-16(M). The safety signal SECURITY takes priority over: (Q. 2.06)

(a) All other communications.

(b) The urgent signal PAN.

(c) The distress signal MAYDAY.

(d) No other communications.

(e) None of the above.

II-17 (M).   A coast station may not charge for the following type of message: (Q. 2.14)

(a) Any U.S. government communication.

(b) Distress messages.

(c) Ship-to-aircraft messages.

(d) Ship-to-shore messages.

(e) Messages to a foreign government official.

II-18 (M). When a distress message is being sent, the following information must be included: (Q. 2.03)

(a) Name of the ship; position; nature of distress; and nature of help requested.

(b) Name of the master; country of registry; and nature of help requested.

(c) Country of registry; frequency of the distress transmission; and frequency of the reply transmission.

(d) Magnetic course of the ship; speed of the ship; ship tonnage; and name of the master.

(e) Position of the ship; name of the master; and frequency of the distress transmission.

II-19 (M).   When may a radio operator stop listening on an international distress frequency? (Q. 2.04)

(a) Whenever directed to do so by the chief radio operator.

(b) Whenever the station is being used for transmission on that channel.

(c) During periods of transmitter maintenance.

(d) When the ship is within the 12-mile limit.

(e) Whenever the ship is not under way.

II-20 (M).   Test transmissions are sent: (Q. 2.08)

(a) To facilitate direction finding.

(b) To actuate the auto alarms of neighboring ships.

(c) If the called station does not answer immediately.

(d) To check for radar interference.

(e) None of the above.

ELEMENT III

BASIC RADIOTELEPHONE

ALTERNATING AND DIRECT CURRENT

Question 3.01. By what other expression may a "difference of potential" be described?

Answer. Common expressions are: voltage, electromotive force, IR drop, voltage drop.

Discussion. Terms such as "voltage," and "electromotive force" usually apply to a source of electrical energy. For example, the terms "generator voltage or emf," and "battery voltage or emf," are in common use. On the other hand, the terms, "IR drop," and "voltage drop" usually apply to a circuit or portion of a circuit, to which the voltage is applied. The distinction is not strict, however.

Q. 3.02. By what other expression may an "electric current flow" be described?

A. Electron flow or electron drift may be used, or the term *amperage* is sometimes used.

D. The term "current flow" is not particularly definite as to the direction of the flow or to the polarity of the charges in motion. So called "conventional current" assumes positive charges to be in motion and the direction externally of the generator is from + to —. On the other hand, the terms "electron flow" or "electron drift" are quite definite. In this case the moving particles are negative charges and the direction external of the generator is from — to +. "Electron flow" is applied most correctly in such cases as vacuum tubes, while the term "electron drift" would more aptly describe the motion of electrons in a solid conductor.

Q. 3.03. Explain the relationship between the physical structure of the atom and electrical current flow.

A. See discussion of Q. 3.04.

Q. 3.04. With respect to electrons, what is the difference between conductors and non-conductors?

A. A good conductor has a large number of "free" electrons, while an insulator or non-conductor has very few free electrons.

D. In any substance, the outer ring of electrons of an atom of that substance determines its electrical characteristics. If the outer ring is lightly bound to the atom, it is possible that one or more electrons in the outer ring will leave the atom without much urging from an external source. Such an electron is called a "free" or conduction electron. If many of these electrons are present within a substance, their movement under an applied emf constitutes an electric current, and the substance is then a good conductor. On the other hand, if there are very few of these "free" electrons, the current will be extremely small; in such a case, the substance is called an insulator or non-conductor.

Q. 3.05. What is the difference between electrical power and electrical energy? In what units is each expressed?

A. Electrical power is the *rate* of doing work (the rate of expending energy) by electricity. Electrical energy is the *capacity* or *ability* to accomplish work by electricity. ("Work" in this sense includes production of heat, or conversion into any other form of energy.)

D. Electrical power is measured by a unit called the *watt*. One watt is the power expended in heat in a circuit when a current of one ampere $(6.28 \times 10^{18}$ electrons per second) flows through a resistance of one ohm. One watt is one joule per second.

Electrical energy is measured by a unit called the *joule*. Energy in electrical circuits is transferred into the form of heat. A joule is the *amount* of energy expended in moving one coulomb (6.28×10^{18}) of electricity through a resistance of one ohm. One joule = .7376 ft. pound; 3600 joules = 1 watt-hour.

Q. 3.06. What is the relationship between impedance and admittance? Between resistance and conductance?

A. Admittance (Y) is the reciprocal of impedance (Z). Conductance (G) is the reciprocal of resistance (R).

D. Impedance may be defined as, "the total opposition to current flow in alternating current circuits," and is expressed by the symbol "Z." The impedance of a circuit may contain, resistance, inductive reactance and capacitive reactance. For a series circuit, impedance may be found from the equation:

$$Z = \sqrt{R^2 + (X_L - X_C)^2}$$

and is expressed in ohms.

Admittance is $\frac{1}{Z}$ or Y. Admittance is used as a convenience in analyzing parallel a–c circuits and is expressed in mhos. For a parallel a–c circuit the admittance may be found from the equation:

$$Y = \sqrt{G^2 + B^2}$$

where, Y = Admittance in mhos
        G = Conductance in mhos
        B = Susceptance (reciprocal of reactance) in mhos

Note that the susceptance of an inductance is negative and that of a capacitance is positive. These signs are opposite to the situation when handled as reactances.

Resistance is the factor of proportionality between voltage and current, in a d-c circuit, giving Ohm's Law: $E = IR$. In an a-c circuit, the "in-phase" component of current must be used, and the resistance is the quantity which determines the power lost or dissipated.

Conductance is the ratio of current through a conductor to the voltage which produces it. (In a reactive a-c circuit, it is the ratio of "in-phase" current to the applied voltage.) Conductance of a circuit or component is numerically equal to $1/R$, where R is its resistance in ohms. The unit of conductance is the "mho," and the usual symbol is G. Conductance is a measure of the ease with which a circuit is able to pass current. Conductance is a property of a given circuit and must be distinguished from conductivity, which is a property of material.

Q. 3.07.   A relay with a coil resistance of 500 ohms is designed to operate when a current of 0.2 ampere flows through the coil. What value of resistance must be connected in series with the coil if it is to be energized by a 110 volt dc source?

A.   A series resistance of 50 ohms is needed.

D.   The normal working voltage of the relay coil equals .2×500 = 100 volts. Ten volts at .2 ampere must be dropped in the series resistor, $R = \frac{10}{.2} = 50$ ohms.

Q. 3.08.   Draw a circuit composed of a 12 volt battery with 3 resistors (10, 120, and 300 ohms, respectively) arranged in a "pi" network.

(a) What is the total current; the current through each resistor?
(b) What is the voltage across each resistor?

(c) **What power is dissipated in each resistor; the total power dissipated by the circuit?**

A. See Fig. 3.08.

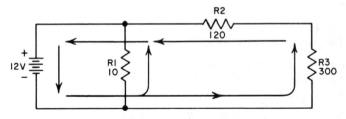

Fig. 3.08. A "pi"-network battery circuit.

(a) (1) Total current (I_T) = 1.23 amperes.
     (2) Current through R1 (I_{R1}) = 1.2 amperes.
     (3) Current through R2 (I_{R2}) = .0286 ampere.
     (4) Current through R3 (I_{R3}) = .0286 ampere.
(b) (1) Voltage across R1 (E_{R1}) = 12 volts.
     (2) Voltage across R2 (E_{R2}) = 3.43 volts.
     (3) Voltage across R3 (E_{R3}) = 8.58 volts.
(c) (1) Power dissipated in R1 (P_{R1}) = 14.4 watts.
     (2) Power dissipated in R2 (P_{R2}) = 0.0978 watt.
     (3) Power dissipated in R3 (P_{R3}) = 0.245 watt.
     (4) Total power dissipated (P_T) = 14.743 watts.

D. Part (a)(1) of the question.

Step 1: Find the total resistance (R_T) across the battery.

$$R_T = \frac{R1 \times (R2 + R3)}{R1 + (R2 + R3)} = \frac{10 \times (120 + 300)}{10 + (120 + 300)} = \frac{4200}{430} = 9.76 \text{ ohms}$$

Step 2: Find the total current (I_T).

$$I_T = \frac{E}{R_T} = \frac{12}{9.76} = 1.23 \text{ amperes}$$

Part (a)(2) of the question.

$$I_{R1} = \frac{E}{R1} = \frac{12}{10} = 1.2 \text{ amperes}$$

Part (a)(3) of the question.

Step 1: Find the series current through R2 and R3.

$$I_{R2, R3} = \frac{E}{R2 + R3} = \frac{12}{420} = .0286 \text{ ampere}$$

Step 2: Find the current through R2 (I_{R2}) which is the series current, or .0286 ampere.

Part (a)(4) of the question.
The current through R3 (I_{R3}) is also the series current, or .0286 ampere.

Part (b)(1) of the question.
The voltage across R1 (E_{R1}) is the battery voltage = 12 volts.

Part (b)(2) of the question.
$E_{R2} = I_{R2} \times R_2 = .0286 \times 120 = 3.43$ volts.

Part (b)(3) of the question.
$E_{R3} = I_{R3} \times R_3 = .0286 \times 300 = 8.58$ volts.

Part (c)(1) of the question.
The power dissipated in R1(P_{R1}) is
$P_{R1} = E \times I_{R1} = 12 \times 1.2 = 14.4$ watts.

Part (c)(2) of the question.
The power dissipated in R2(P_{R2}) is
$P_{R2} = E_{R2} \times I_{R2} = 3.42 \times .0286 = .0978$ watts or 97.8 milliwatts.

Part (c)(3) of the question.
The power dissipated in R3(P_{R3}) is
$P_{R3} = E_{R3} \times I_{R3} = 8.58 \times .0286 = 0.245$ watt.

Part (c)(4) of the question.
The total power (P_T) dissipated by the circuit is the sum of the power dissipated in each resistor, or
$$P_T = P_{R1} + P_{R2} + P_{R3} = 14.4 + 0.0978 + 0.245 = 14.743 \text{ watts.}$$

Q. 3.09. To provide additional useful information to the student regarding the solution of typical ac impedance problems, two additional problems have been added to this Question. The original FCC question now appears as Q. 3.09(A) and requires the use of j factors for its solution. A series-ac impedance problem (not in FCC Study Guide) is given as Q. 3.09(B), while a series-parallel-ac impedance problem (not in FCC Study Guide) is given as Q. 3.09 (C). Neither of the latter two additional problems requires the use of j factors for its solution. In the event that the student is not too well versed in the use of j factors, he should concentrate on the latter two problems only and these will enable him to answer the ac impedance problems given in the FCC examinations.

Q. 3.09(A). Draw a circuit composed of a voltage source of 100 volts—1000 cps, a 1-microfarad capacitor in series with the source, followed by a "T" network composed of a 2-millihenry inductor, a 100-ohm resistor and a 4-millihenry inductor. The load resistor is 200 ohms.

   (a) What is the total current; the current through each circuit element?

   (b) What is the voltage across each circuit element?

   (c) What "apparent" power is being consumed by the circuit?

   (d) What real or actual power is being consumed by the circuit; by the 200-ohm resistor?

A.   See Fig. 3.09(a1).

    1. The total current $(I_T) = 0.63$ ampere.
    2. The current through C1 and L1 $(I_T) = 0.63$ ampere.
    3. The current through R1 $(I1) = 0.43$ ampere.
    4. The current through L2 and R2 $(I2) = 0.21$ ampere.

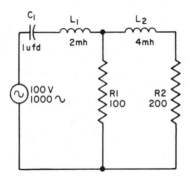

Fig. 3.09(a1).   *"T" network and load connected to an ac generator.*

    5. The voltage across C1 $(E_{C1}) = 100.17$ volts.
    6. The voltage across L1 $(E_{L1}) = 7.91$ volts.
    7. The voltage across R1 $(E_{R1}) = 42.65$ volts.
    8. The voltage across L2 $(E_{L2}) = 5.27$ volts.
    9. The voltage across R2 $(E_{R2}) = 42$ volts.
   10. The apparent power $= 63$ watts.
   11. The real power $= 27.03$ watts.
   12. The power consumed by the 200-ohm resistor $= 8.8$ watts.

D. The solution of this problem requires the use of complex numbers. While there are a fairly large number of steps in its solution, these proceed in logical sequence and are not difficult to follow.

(A). The first answer required is to find the total current (I_T). However, in order to accomplish this, the total equivalent impedance (Z_T)

must first be computed. This is the equivalent series impedance of all the circuit elements shown in Figure 3.09(a1). Thus, the series equivalent impedance of C1 and L1 is added vectorially to the series equivalent impedance of R1, R2 and L2 to provide Z_T.

Step 1: Find the equivalent series impedance (Z_p) of R1, R2 and L2.

$$Z_p = \frac{Z1 \; Z2}{Z1 + Z2}$$

Expressed as complex numbers; first in rectangular form, we have

$$Z_p = \frac{(100 + j\theta) \times (200 + jX_{L2})}{(100 + j\theta) + (200 + jX_{L2})}$$

We must find X_{L2}

$$X_{L2} = 2\pi fL2 = 6.28 \times 1000 \times 4 \times 10^{-3} = 25.12 \;\; \text{ohms}$$

$$Z_p = \frac{(100 + j\theta) \times (200 + j25.12)}{(100 + j\theta) + (200 + j25.12)} = \frac{20,000 + j2,512}{300 + j25.12}$$

In order to reduce this fraction, both numerator and denominator must be expressed in the polar form.

Step 2: Change the numerator to polar form.

$$\tan \theta = \frac{X}{R} = \frac{2512}{20,000} = .125$$

$$\theta = 7.1°$$

$$Z \text{ (numerator)} = \frac{X}{\text{Sin } \theta} = \frac{2512}{0.1236} = 20,323 \;\underline{/7.1°}$$

Step 3: Change the denominator to polar form.

$$\tan \theta = \frac{X}{R} = \frac{25.12}{300} = .084$$

$$\theta = 4.8°$$

$$Z \text{ (denominator)} = \frac{X}{\text{Sin } \theta} = \frac{25.12}{.0837} = 300.12 \text{ ohms}$$

Therefore, in polar form

$$Z_p = \frac{20,323 \;\underline{/7.1°}}{300.12 \;\underline{/4.8°}} = 67.7 \;\;\underline{/2.3°}$$

(B). It is now necessary to determine the equivalent impedance (Z_s) of C1 and L1.

Step 1: Find the reactance of C1.

$$X_{C1} = \frac{1}{2\pi fC1} = \frac{0.159}{1000 \times 1 \times 10^{-6}} = 159 \text{ ohms}$$

Step 2: Find the reactance of L1.

$$X_{L1} = 2\pi fL1 = 6.28 \times 1000 \times 2 \times 10^{-3} = 12.56 \text{ ohms}$$

Step 3: Find the combined impedance (Z_s) of C1 and L1.

$$Z_s = 12.56 - 159 = -146.44 \text{ ohms (capacitive)}$$

(C). The next step is to combine Z_p and Z_s vectorially to find Z_T, which is the actual load on the generator. With the aid of Z_T, we may determine the generator current (I_T) and then the remainder of the answers to this problem.

Step 1: $Z_T = Z_p + Z_s$
$Z_T = 67.7 \text{ } \underline{/2.3^\circ} + (0 - j146.44)$

To perform this addition, Z_p must first be converted to rectangular form.

$$Z_p = 67.7 \text{ (cos } 2.3^\circ + j \sin 2.3^\circ)$$
$$Z_p = 67.7 \text{ } (0.9990 + j0.0454) = 67.63 + j3.07, \text{ and}$$
$$Z_T = (67.63 + j3.07) + (0 - j146.44) = 67.63 - j143.37$$

Step 2: It is now necessary to convert the rectangular form of Z_T (above) to its polar form.

$$\tan \theta = \frac{X_c}{R} = \frac{143.37}{67.63}$$

$$\tan \theta = 2.1$$

$$\theta = -64.6^\circ$$

$$Z_T = \frac{X}{\sin \theta} = \frac{143.37}{\sin 64.6^\circ} = \frac{143.37}{0.9033} = 158.7 \text{ ohms}$$

Z_T in polar form $= 158.7 \text{ } \underline{/-64.6^\circ}$

(D). Find the total current (I_T).

$$I_T = \frac{E}{Z_T} = \frac{100}{158.7} = 0.63 \text{ ampere}$$

(E). Find the current through C1 and L1. This is the same as I_T, or 0.63 ampere.

(F). Find the currents 11 and 12 (see Fig. 3.09(a2)).

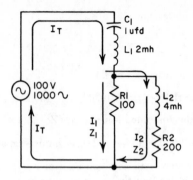

Fig. 3.09 (a2). The diagram is redrawn here for clarity in solving the problem.

Step 1: Find the voltage (E_p) across the parallel branch (Z_p) composed of R1 and R2, L2.

$$E_p = I_T \times Z_p = 0.63 \times 67.7 = 42.65 \text{ volts.}$$

Step 2: $I1 = \dfrac{E_p}{Z1} = \dfrac{42.65}{100} = 0.43 \text{ ampere}$

Step 3: $I2 = \dfrac{E_p}{Z2}$

We must find the value of Z2, which is the vector sum of X_{L2} and R2 in series.

$$Z2 = \sqrt{(R2)^2 + (X_{L2})^2} = \sqrt{(200)^2 + (25.12)^2} = 201.5 \text{ ohms}$$

$$I2 = \frac{42.65}{201.5} = 0.21 \text{ ampere}$$

This is the current in L2 and R2

(G). We are now ready to find the voltages across each circuit element. (The voltage across R1 is the same as E_p, or 42.65 volts.)

Step 1: Find the voltage across L2

$$E_{L2} = I2 \times X_{L2} = 0.21 \times 25.12 = 5.27 \text{ volts.}$$

Step 2: Find the voltage across R2
$$E_{R2} = I2 \times R2 = 0.21 \times 200 = 42 \text{ volts.}$$

Step 3: Find the voltage across C1

$$E_{C1} = I_T \times X_{C1} = 0.63 \times 159 = 100.17 \text{ volts.}$$

Step 4: Find the voltage across L1.

$$E_{L1} = I_T \times X_{L1} = 0.63 \times 12.56 = 7.91 \text{ volts.}$$

Note: It may appear that the individual voltages add up to more than the generator voltage. However, these are out of phase and must be added vectorially.

(H). Find the apparent power (P_a) consumed by the circuit.

$$P_a = E \times I_T = 100 \times 0.63 = 63 \text{ volt-amperes.}$$

(I). Find the real power consumed by the circuit (P_R)

$$P_R = E \times I_T \times \cos \theta \ (64.6°) = 100 \times 0.63 \times 0.4289 = 27.03 \text{ watts}$$

(J). Find the power consumed by the 200 ohm resistor, R2

$$P_{R2} = I2^2 \times R2 = (0.21)^2 \times 200 = .044 \times 200 = 8.8 \text{ watts.}$$

Q. 3.09(B). In a series circuit composed of a series resistance of 40 ohms, an inductive reactance of 80 ohms, and a capacitive reactance of 30 ohms, a current of 0.5A is flowing. What is the applied voltage?

A. The applied voltage = 32 volts.

D. To solve this problem [see Fig. 3.09(b)], it is first necessary to determine the total series ac impedance (Z_T). Once Z_T is known and since the total current (I_T) is given (0.5A), the applied voltage (E_A) may be easily found from the equation, $E_A = I_T \times Z_T$.

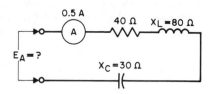

Fig. 3.09(b). An a-c series circuit, where the applied voltage (E_A) must be found.

Step 1: Determine the total ac series impedance (Z_T) of R, X_L, and X_C, in Fig. 3.09(b) :

$$Z_T = \sqrt{R^2 + (X_L - X_C)^2} = \sqrt{40^2 + (80 - 30)^2} = \sqrt{40^2 + 50^2} = \sqrt{1600 + 2500} = \sqrt{4100} = 64 \text{ ohms}$$

Step 2: Find the applied voltage (E_A): $E_A = I \times Z_T = 0.5 \times 64 = 32$ volts.

Q. 3.09(C). What is the total impedance of a resistance of 75 ohms in series with the parallel combination of an inductive reactance of 20 ohms and a capacitive reactance of 25 ohms, across a supply voltage of 1000 volts? What is the line current?

A.   [See Fig. 3.09(c1)]
1. The total (ac) impedance (Z_T) is 125 ohms.
2. The line current (I_L) is 8A.

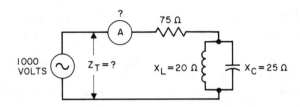

Fig. 3.09(c1).   An a-c, series-parallel circuit,
where the line current (I_L) must be found.

D.   To solve this problem, it is first necessary to separate the series resistor from the parallel circuit. Next, by assuming a voltage (100V) across the parallel circuit [see Fig. 3.09(c2)], its resultant impedance is found. Then, the impedance of the parallel circuit is combined (vectorially) with the resistance to determine the total impedance (Z_T). Finally, the line current (I_L) is determined from the equation, $I_L = \dfrac{E_T}{Z_T}$ where E_T is the applied voltage in Fig. 3.09(c1), or 1000 volts.

Note: This problem could have been presented so that only the total impedance (Z_T) was required to be found. In this case, the item of 1000V given in the question must be ignored. In some FCC questions, added information is sometimes given that is not required for the solution of a problem. It is up to the student to determine if this is the case and to eliminate unnecessary information if required.

Step 1: Assume a voltage of 100V across the parallel branch only and solve for the branch currents [see simplified diagram of Fig. 3.09(c2)]:

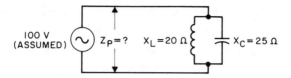

Fig. 3.09(c2). Simplified diagram of Fig. 3.09(c1) to help determine the impedance (Z_P) of the parallel circuit alone.

$$I_1 = \frac{E}{X_L} = \frac{100}{20} = 5A$$

$$I_2 = \frac{E}{X_C} = \frac{100}{25} = 4A$$

Step 2: Find the total current (I_T) flowing through the parallel branch: $I_T = I_1 - I_2 = 5 - 4 = 1A$ (inductive).

Step. 3: Find the impedance (Z_p) of the parallel branch (only) by the equation:

$$Z_p = \frac{E \ (\text{assumed})}{I_T}$$

$$Z_p = \frac{100}{1} = 100 \text{ ohms (inductive)}$$

Step 4: Find the total impedance (Z_p) of the entire circuit of Fig. 3.09(c1):

$$Z_T = \sqrt{R^2 + X_L{}^2} =$$
$$\sqrt{75^2 + 100^2} = \sqrt{5625 + 10,000} =$$
$$\sqrt{15,625} = 125 \text{ ohms}$$

Step 5: Find the line current (I_L):

$$I_L = \frac{E \ (\text{given})}{Z_T} = \frac{1000}{125} = 8A$$

Note: In some examples it may be required to find the phase angle (θ) of the line current. This is easily done by first finding the cosine of the angle (θ) and then determining the angle from the cosine tables:

$$\cos \theta = \frac{R}{Z_T} = \frac{75}{125} = 0.6$$

$$\theta = 53°$$

[See also Q. 3.235(a).]

Q. 3.10. What is the relationship between wire size and resistance of the wire?

A. The resistance of a wire varies inversely with the cross-sectional area of the wire and directly with its length.

D. The resistance of a conductor varies inversely with the cross-sectional area of the conductor. Thus any increase in the area will decrease the resistance. However, the area varies as the square of the diameter. If the diameter is doubled the area will be increased by four times. Since the area is four times greater, then the resistance is now four times less, or equal to one-quarter of the original value.

Resistance of a conductor varies in direct proportion to the length of the conductor. For example, doubling the length also doubles the resistance. The resistivity of a material is determined by its atomic structure; some materials have more free electrons than others. The ones with the greater number of free electrons will have less resistance. The resistance of most substances is affected by temperature. Most metals have a positive temperature coefficient: that is, an increase in temperature will cause an increased resistance. Most non-metals, carbon, for example, have lower resistance at higher temperatures; some ceramic substances which are good insulators at ordinary temperatures become fairly good conductors at a red-heat.

Q. 3.11. What is "skin effect"? How does it affect the resistance of conductors at the higher radio frequencies?

A. (a) "Skin effect" is the tendency of alternating currents to exist in the area of a conductor approaching the surface, rather than in the entire cross-sectional area of the conductor.

(b) It causes the effective resistance of conductors to increase with the frequency of the applied wave.

D. The term "skin effect" is most generally used in connection with radio frequencies. However, "skin effect" is present at all frequencies, the magnitude of the effect decreasing as the frequency decreases. At extremely high frequencies, the depth of current penetration is very small, most of the current existing practically on the surface of the conductor. It is for this reason that tubular conductors with large surface areas are used at ultra high frequencies. "Skin effect" exists due to the fact that more magnetic lines of force cut the center of the conductor than cut the outer sections. Thus the self inductance of the conductor is greatest at the center and decreases toward the outer edges. There is more counter-emf developed at the center of the conductor and, therefore, the least amount of current exists at this point. As the frequency increases, the cemf at the center approaches the magnitude of the applied voltage and current practically does not exist at the center. Where the conductor is a round wire or tube, the high frequency resistance at high frequencies in ohms per centimeter $= \dfrac{83.2\sqrt{f} \times 10^{-9}}{d}$, where d is the outside diameter in centimeters, and f is the frequency in cycles.

Q. 3.12.   Why is impedance matching between electrical devices an important factor? Is it always to be desired? Can it always be attained in practice?

A.   (a) Impedance matching is important in certain cases in order to effect maximum transfer of power, minimum VSWR (on transmission lines) and consequently a reasonably flat frequency response of a line (within the practical design limits).

(b) Impedance matching is not always desirable, as is the case in some amplifiers.

(c) Perfect impedance matching is not always attained in practice since the magnitude and phase angle of the impedances must be matched. However, from a practical standpoint and utilizing a given frequency band of operation, satisfactory impedance matching may be achieved.

D.   Impedances should be matched in speech-input equipment in order that maximum transfer of power may take place and to preserve the proper frequency response of the equipment. In short transmission lines, impedance matching is not too important. However, if the line is long and standing waves are present (due to mismatch), the input impedance of the line may change radically and this change will be reflected into the circuit through the matching transformer. This in turn may cause distortion and incorrect frequency response characteristic.

In amplifiers, an impedance match is usually not desirable. For minimum distortion, triode amplifiers require a load impedance several times greater than the plate resistance; while screen-grid amplifiers require a load only a small fraction of the plate resistance. For example, a power amplifier tube, with a plate impedance of 52,000 ohms, requires a load resistance of only 5000 ohms or less than 1/10 of the plate impedance.

Where distortion is not a factor, a 1-to-1 impedance match is desirable for maximum power transfer between circuits.

Q. 3.13.   A loudspeaker with an impedance of 4 ohms is working in a plate circuit which has an impedance of 4000 ohms. What is the impedance ratio of an output transformer used to match the plate circuit to the speaker? What is the turns ratio?

A.   (a) The impedance ratio is 1000 to 1.
(b) The turns ratio is 31.6 to 1.

D. Let the plate circuit impedance equal Z_p (primary impedance). Let the loudspeaker impedance equal Z_s (secondary impedance). The impedance ratio is

$$\frac{Z_p}{Z_s} = \frac{4000}{4} = 1000 \text{ to } 1$$

A basic (approximate) formula relating impedance ratio and turns ratio is:

$$\frac{N_p}{N_s} = \sqrt{\frac{Z_p}{Z_s}}, \text{ or } \left(\frac{N_p}{N_s}\right)^2 = \frac{Z_p}{Z_s}$$

where N_p is the number of turns in the primary.
N_s is the number of turns in the secondary.
Z_p is the primary impedance.
Z_s is the secondary impedance.

From the above, the turns ratio is found by,

$$\frac{N_p}{N_s} = \sqrt{\frac{Z_p}{Z_s}} = \sqrt{\frac{4000}{4}} = 31.6$$

Q. 3.14. Compare some properties of electrostatic and electromagnetic fields.

A. (1) If two conductors are separated by an insulator and a difference of potential applied between the two conductors, it can be shown that electric energy is stored between the two conductors. This energy is said to exist in an electrostatic field between (mainly) the conductors. If the charging source is removed, the charge (or energy) remains as before and we have a charged capacitor, which stores potential energy in its field. The amount of energy stored is expressed by the equation

$$W = \frac{1}{2}CE^2 \text{ joules}$$

where C = capacitance in farads
E = charging potential in volts
W = energy of the electrostatic field in joules (watt-seconds)

The lines of electrostatic force between two unlike charges (corresponding to magnetic lines of force) are depicted in Fig. 3.14.

The directional arrows on the lines show the direction of force on an electron placed in the field. The electron would be attracted by the positive charge and repelled by the negative charge. Coulomb's law is useful in describing the electrostatic field. This law states that the force between two charges is proportional to the product of the charges and inversely proportional to the square of the distance between them. In Fig. 3.14, if a dielectric material was placed between the unlike charges, some of the electrons in the dielectric would be attracted toward the positive charge and potential energy would now be stored in the dielectric. This process is called "electrostatic induction" and corresponds to the induction caused by an electromagnetic field.

(2) If a current of electricity is passed through a wire (or coil), it will be found that an electromagnetic field will build up to a maximum

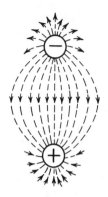

Fig. 3.14. Electrostatic field between unlike charges.

value in the space surrounding the wire. A certain amount of electrical energy will exist in this electromagnetic field and may be expressed by the equation

$$W = \tfrac{1}{2}LI^2$$

where   L = inductance in henries
        I = current in amperes
       W = energy of the electromagnetic field in joules
             (watt-seconds)

Unlike the electrostatic field, if the current is cut off, the electromagnetic field shortly ceases to exist, the energy being returned to the wire (or coil). (In actuality, there is always stray capacity across the inductance. Thus, when the excitation is cut off, the energy creates damped oscillations of this tuned circuit.) Since the electromagnetic field requires a current flow to exist, the energy involved is kinetic energy.

If a conductor is moved through the magnetic field (but not parallel to it) magnetic induction will take place and a current will be caused to flow in the conductor. Similarly, if the excitation of the original wire (or coil) is varied, a current will be induced into a stationary wire or coil. In this case, the electromagnetic field is caused to move past the wire and the moving field induces a secondary current. Note an important distinction between electrostatic and electromagnetic fields. An electrostatic field (kinetic energy) may cause induction while stationary. Conversely, an electromagnetic field (or the secondary conductor) must be in motion to produce induction.

D. It is important to note that a radiated wave from a transmitting antenna (or other radiator) is composed of both electrostatic and electromagnetic fields. The total energy content of the wave is constant over one cycle. However, the two fields are 90° apart in phase (as well as in space) and the energy is continuously interchanged between the electrostatic and electromagnetic fields. In the case of a vertical radiator (vertically polarized) the electrostatic lines of force are situated mainly in the vertical plane and the electromagnetic lines of force are mainly in the horizontal plane. For maximum efficiency of a receiving antenna for this wave, the receiving antenna should also be vertical. In this case the maximum induced electrostatic and electromagnetic field energy will occur in the receiving antenna.

Q. 3.15.   In what way are electrical properties of common circuit elements affected by electromagnetic fields? Are interstage connecting leads susceptible to these fields?

A.   1. The independent electrical properties of circuit elements are not affected by electromagnetic fields. However, the performance of electrical circuits is sometimes affected by the coupling of electromagnetic fields into common circuit elements, such as coils, capacitors and vacuum tubes. Such coupling may (depending on phase relationships) cause oscillation and/or bandwidth problems. It may also result in such conditions as hum pickup.

2. Interstage connecting leads may pick up electromagnetic fields and cause problems similar to those mentioned above.

D.   In the design of electronic circuits, particularly where high-gain stages are involved, one of the most important considerations is the prevention of undesired coupling between stages of the circuitry. As mentioned above, such coupling (or undesired feedback) may be of such phase as to reinforce the signal appearing at an earlier stage. This can cause instability, regeneration, oscillation and/or a reduction of bandwidth of the circuit. Such undesired coupling can be simple induced currents into common circuit elements, or into inter- or intra-stage wiring. In some situations, the coupling may be through the route of the metal chassis itself. It it not possible in this book to present detailed design information for the avoidance of this condition. However, some of the more common design precautions are:

(1) Shielding of glass vacuum tubes in critical circuits.

(2) Shielding of selected input or output leads wherever possible and desirable.

(3) Shielding of coils and/or of entire stages which may be susceptible to feedback problems.

(4) Restriction of the gain of each critical stage to reduce the magnitude of feedback.

(5) Shielding the entire bottom of the chassis to eliminate pick up of stray adjacent fields.

(6) Use of special circuit grounding procedures, such as all grid-circuit returns to one ground and all plate-circuit returns to another ground, or at least to another portion of the metal chassis.

(7) Use of adequate decoupling circuits between stages, including such items as filament-circuit chokes and plate and grid-decoupling RC circuits.

Q. 3.16.   Which factors determine the amplitude of the emf induced in a conductor which is cutting magnetic lines of force?

A.   There are four basic factors as follows:

1.   The flux density, or magnetic strength.

2.   The rate or velocity at which the conductor cuts through the magnetic lines of force.

3.   The length of the conductor, or if a coil is used, both the number of turns and the length of the coil are important.

4.   The angle at which the conductor or coil is cutting through the magnetic lines of force. Maximum emf is induced if the conductor is moving in a direction perpendicular to the lines of force.

D.   The formula to determine the emf induced in a conductor is

$$E = \frac{NBlv}{10^8} \text{ volts}$$

where E equals the induced voltage
N equals the number of turns
B equals the flux density
l equals the length of conductor
v equal the velocity of cutting.

It is seen that E is *directly proportional* to all above factors.

Q. 3.17.   Define the term "reluctance."

A.   Reluctance is the opposition to the creation of magnetic lines of force in a magnetic circuit.

D.   Reluctance is the same in its relation to magnetic circuits as resistance is to electric circuits. Magnetic flux is analogous to current, and mmf is analogous to emf. Thus the greater the reluctance of a magnetic circuit, the weaker will be the magnetic flux. The total reluctance of a magnetic circuit is the sum of all the reluctances which are in series.

Thus for an iron core with air gap the reluctance is, $R = \dfrac{l}{\mu A} + \dfrac{l_1}{A_1}$ units where

R = the reluctance
l = the length of iron in cm
μ = permeability of iron
A = cross-sectional area of iron in cm squared
A_1 = cross-sectional area of the air gap in cm squared
l_1 = length of air gap in cm.

Reluctance is the ratio of magnetomotive force to magnetic flux, as

$$R = \frac{\text{gilberts}}{\text{lines per sq. cm.}}$$. It is the number by which the desired flux is multiplied in order to compute the necessary mmf.

Q. 3.18. In what way does an inductance affect the voltage-current phase relationship of a circuit? Why is the phase of a circuit important?

A. (a) A series inductance acting alone in an alternating current circuit has the property of causing the circuit current to lag the applied voltage by 90 degrees, and limits the value of current, which is proportional to the voltage and inversely proportional to the frequency and inductance.

(b) Phase may be important for various reasons depending upon the application of the circuit. For example, in power circuits, phase angle determines the power factor. In color TV receivers, the correct phase of the demodulation signals is vital to insure proper color reproduction. For other examples, see the discussion.

D. Several other cases where phase is important to the circuitry involved are:

(1) Operation of two or three phase motors.

(2) Operation of servo systems.

(3) Correct speaker and circuit phasing in stereophonic audio systems.

(4) Synchronization of TV and FM multiplex signals at both transmitter and receiver.

(5) Aircraft navigational receivers.

There are numerous other examples where phasing is important. However, there are also many circuits where phasing is not important. For example:

(1) Broadcast receivers and transmitters.

(2) Ordinary FM receivers.

(3) Single-channel amplifiers.

(4) Power supplies.

(5) Many types of test equipment.

Q. 3.19. Draw two cycles of a sine wave on a graph of amplitude versus time. Assume a frequency of 5 mc/s.

(a) What would be the wavelength of one cycle in meters; in centimeters?

(b) How many degrees does one cycle represent?

(c) How much time would it take for the wave to "rotate" 45°; 90°; 280°?

(d) If there were a second harmonic of this frequency, how many cycles thereof would be represented on this graph?

(e) On the same graph draw two cycles of another sine wave leading the first by 45°.

(f) What would be the velocity of this wave or any other electromagnetic wave in free space?

A. See Fig. 3.19.

(a)(1) Wavelength in meters = 60 meters.

(2) Wavelength in centimeters = 6000 centimeters.

(b) One cycle represents 360 degrees.

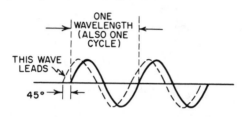

Fig. 3.19. Two cycles of two sine waves, one leading the other by 45 degrees.

(c)(1) The wave will rotate 45 degrees in .025 microsecond.

(2) The wave will rotate 90 degrees in .05 microsecond.

(3) The wave will rotate 280 degrees in 0.155 microsecond.

(d) The second harmonic would be represented by 4 cycles.

(e) See Fig. 3.19.

(f) The velocity would be 300,000,000 meters per second.

D. (a) The wavelength of one cycle in meters is,

$$\lambda = \frac{300}{f(mc)} = \frac{300}{5} = 60 \text{ meters}$$

The wavelength in centimeters is,

$$\lambda \text{ (cm)} = \frac{300}{f(mc)} \times 100 = \frac{30,000}{5} = 6,000 \text{ cm.}$$

Note: In common usage, centimeters are used to describe wavelengths at much higher frequencies. For example at 10,000 mc, the wavelength is 3 cm. This is a matter of convenient notation.

(b) One cycle represents 360°, since it may be considered to be derived from a vector rotating inside of a 360 degree circle.

(c)(1) The wave will rotate 45° in $\frac{1}{8}\left(\frac{45}{360}\right)$ of the time required for one complete cycle, which is,

$$T \text{ (sec)} = \frac{1}{f \text{ (cycles)}}$$

$$T \text{ (microsec)} = \frac{1}{f \text{ (megacycles)}}$$

$$= \frac{1}{5} \text{ or } 0.2 \text{ microsec for one complete cycle.}$$

For $45°$, $T = \dfrac{0.2}{8} = .025$ microsec.

(2) The wave will rotate $90°$ ($\frac{1}{4}$ cycle) in

$$T = \frac{0.2}{4} = .05 \text{ microsecond.}$$

(3) The wave will rotate $280°$ in

$$T = 0.2 \times \frac{280}{360} = 0.155 \text{ microsecond}$$

(d) The second harmonic would be 10 megacycles, each cycle occupying $\frac{1}{2}$ the time of a 5 megacycle wave. Therefore, 4 cycles of the second harmonic would be shown on the graph.

(e) See Fig. 3.19.

(f) The velocity of any electromagnetic wave in free space is 300,-000,000 meters per second.

Q. 3.20. Explain how to determine the sum of two equal vector quantities having the same reference point but whose directions are $90°$ apart; $0°$ apart; $180°$ apart? How does this pertain to electrical currents or voltages?

A. (1) This may be accomplished by graphical means or by trigonometry. (See Discussion.)

(2) Electrical currents or voltages are frequently represented by vector quantities in the solution of electrical problems.

D. (1) Two forces (or quantities) acting simultaneously on the same reference point may be summed and replaced by a single quantity. This single quantity will produce the same effect on the reference point, as the two individual quantities. The two initial quantities being added are vectors. That is, they have both magnitude and direction. The resultant of the two vectors will also be a vector and must be expressed in magnitude and direction. Two vectors $90°$ apart are illustrated in Fig. 3.20.

In order for this example to have the greatest meaning, quantities involving actual electrical elements are used. Thus the figure shows a resistance of 100 ohms and an inductive reactance of 100 ohms at right angles and as they are normally depicted in graphical form. The resultant quantity (Z) will be the impedance of a series circuit of the two elements. The determination of the sum of R and X_L may be done graphically, that is, by drawing Fig. 3.20 to any convenient scale and measuring the magnitude and direction (phase angle) of Z. The more usual method is by means of a common trigonometric theorum which yields the equation

$$Z = \sqrt{R^2 + X_L^2} = \sqrt{100^2 + 100^2} = 141.4 \text{ ohms}$$

The direction (phase angle) is

$$\theta = \tan^{-1} \frac{X_L}{R} = \tan^{-1} 1$$

$$\theta = 45 \text{ degrees}$$

(2) Two vector quantities which are 0 degrees apart (in phase) are simply added arithmetically. The direction remains unchanged.

(3) Two vectors which are 180 degrees apart (180 degrees out of phase) are added algebraically. For example, if vector 1 equals $+100$ and vector 2 equals -150 the resultant is $100 -150 = -50$.

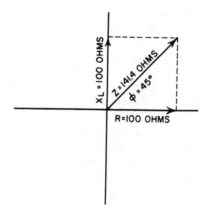

Fig. 3.20. Illustrating the solution of two vectors which are 90 degrees apart.

(4) A vector may represent any type of quantity having both magnitude and direction. In electrical circuits, there is no physical direction involved. However, there is frequently the problem of phase angle. A typical example of a phase angle has been given in this discussion. (See also Q. 3.09, 3.18 and 3.19, above.) Generally, the problem of most frequent interest is the phase angle between the voltage and current in a circuit. In the solution of electrical problems, vectors are commonly employed and the student should acquire a working knowledge of vectors and complex numbers.

Q. 3.21. Explain how the values of resistance and capacitance in an RC network affect its time constant. How would the output waveform be affected by the frequency of the input in an RC network?

A. (1) The charging time is determined by the value of the capacitor and resistor in the circuit and both of these elements directly affect the time constant. Assuming R and C to be in series with the d–c supply voltage; if the resistor is increased in value, the charging current is reduced. This increases the time required to charge the capacitor to any given voltage level. On the other hand, increasing the value of capacitance (storage tank) with a fixed resistor, requires the current (which is limited by the resistor) to flow for a greater period of time.

(2) If the waveform is a sine wave, the shape of the wave is unaffected by the RC network, regardless of its frequency. However, the amplitude of the output waveform may be reduced as the frequency is reduced below certain limits.

D. (1) The "time constant" of an *RC* circuit is defined as the length of time (in seconds) which is required for a capacitor to attain a voltage across its terminals which is equal to 63.2% of the applied voltage. The "time constant" may also be defined as the time required for a capacitor to discharge 63.2% of the original charge in the capacitor. (The remaining charge at the end of one "time constant" is therefore 36.8%.) In each succeeding time constant, the charge in the capacitor will again change (charge or discharge) by 63.2%. For all practical purposes a capacitor may be considered to be fully charged or discharged in 5 "time constants." The "time constant" is $T = RC$ seconds, where R is the resistance in ohms and C is the capacitance in farads. If R is in ohms and C is in microfarads, then T is in microseconds. The voltage across a capacitor under charge, at any instant may be found from the formula, $E_c = E_A (1 - \varepsilon^{-t/RC})$, where E_c is the voltage across the capacitor, E_A is the applied voltage, $\varepsilon = 2.718$, t is the elapsed time, RC equals one time constant.

(2) As a rule of thumb, if the waveform period of one cycle is equal to or less than $\frac{1}{5}$ of the time constant, the waveform will be passed by the RC network undistorted and without loss of amplitude. As the length of a cycle increases (frequency decreases), the period becomes less than $\frac{1}{5}$ of the given time constant. The result in the case of a sine wave was given above. For other waveforms, the waveform will be differentiated as the frequency decreases. The possibilities and theoretical concepts are too lengthy to be completely enumerated here. However, a familiar case of extreme differentiation occurs when a square wave is fed into an RC network and the output consists of sharply peaked positive and negative "pips." In such a case, the time constant may be only a fraction of the period of one cycle of the square wave.

Q. 3.22. Explain how the values of resistance and inductance in an RL network affect its time constant.

A. The time constant of an RL network is defined as the time (in seconds) required for the current to reach 63.2% of its maximum possible value. An increase in the value of inductance will directly increase the time constant. This is true because an inductance tends to resist any change of current and this property is directly proportional to the value of inductance. However, unlike the RC case, an increase of resistance will actually decrease the time constant. The reason an increase of resistance causes a decrease of the RL time constant is that the magnitude of the current at any given time is reduced. A reduced current results in a lesser rate of change of current at any given time. Since the rate of change of current determines the counter emf and therefore the opposition to current flow, a lesser rate permits the current to rise faster; hence a shorter time constant is attained. Of course, the converse is also true and a smaller resistance will result in a longer time constant for an RL circuit.

D. The time constant of an RL circuit may be found by the equation

$$T = \frac{L}{R} \text{ seconds,}$$

where L = inductance in henries
         R = total series resistance in ohms (including the resistance of the inductance).

When the charging circuit is opened, the time constant of an RL circuit is changed. Assuming current had been at a maximum in the coil when the source was instantaneously disconnected, the energy in the coil is dissipated in the resistance of an oscillating circuit consisting of the coil (with its inherent resistance), the stray capacity of the circuit and the coil itself.

Q. 3.23. Explain the theory of molecular alignment as it affects magnetic properties of materials.

A. The theory of molecular alignment is based on the assumption that magnetic materials contain tiny molecular magnets called "magnetic dipoles." If the dipoles are caused to be in alignment, with like poles all pointing the same way, the material is said to be magnetized. In this case magnetic North and South poles appear at opposite ends of the magnetic material.

D. In soft magnetic metals, the molecular alignment must be maintained by an electric current (electromagnet). When the current is removed the alignment becomes largely random and only a small "residual" magnetism remains. Iron is a soft magnetic material. However, there are certain hard magnetic materials, such as Cobalt or Alnico. When these are magnetized, they retain their magnetism indefinitely, if given proper care. It is assumed that in this case the molecular structure of the material is such that it is difficult for the magnetic dipoles to be moved from their aligned position. Such "permanent" magnets can be weakened or demagnetized by being subjected to mechanical shock, excessive heat, or an electromagnetic field which opposes the magnetization of the permanent magnet.

Q. 3.24. **What is the relationship between the inductance of a coil and the number of turns of wire in the coil; the permeability of the core material used?**

A. (a) The inductance of a coil varies approximately as the square of the number of turns.

(b) The inductance of a coil varies directly with the permeability of the core.

D. (a) If the coil consists of only one turn, then its magnetic field will cut this turn, producing a certain counter-emf. However, if the coil consists of 2 turns the flux about *each* turn cuts 2 turns, and the resultant counter-emf is 4 times greater. Therefore, the inductance must also be 4 times greater or vary as the *square* of the number of turns.

Actually, the inductance increases slightly less than proportionally to the number of turns, as in a large many-turn coil, some lines "leak" out and do not cut all the other turns.

(b) The permeability of a substance is the ratio of magnetic flux density in that substance to the field strength which produces it. Permeability is a property of a material which is somewhat analogous magnetically to conductivity in an electric circuit. If a magnetic field of strength H exists in a certain space, and the space is then filled with a permeable material, the new field intensity will be $B = \mu H$, where μ is the permeability of the material.

Q. 3.25. **What factors influence the direction of magnetic lines of force produced by an electromagnet?**

A. There are two main factors involved:
1. The direction of electron flow through the coil.
2. The manner of winding the turns.

D. A simple rule for determining the direction of lines of force of a coil is as follows. With the left hand, grasp the coil so that the fingers curl around the turns in the same direction as electrons are moving through these turns. The thumb of the left hand will then point to the north pole of the magnetic field, or the direction of lines of force *within* the coil. Outside the coil, the lines return to the south pole to form a closed loop.

Q. 3.26. Explain how self and mutual inductance produce trans-former action.

A.   When current flows through the primary winding of a trans-former, the self inductance of the primary causes a counter emf to appear across it because of the expanding magnetic field around the primary. (With a sine wave input into the primary, the primary magnetic field is continuously expanding and contracting at the frequency of the sine wave.) The expanding (or contracting) magnetic field not only affects the primary, but also cuts across the secondary winding of the transformer. This causes a voltage to be induced into the secondary winding by mutual inductance and a current to flow in the secondary winding, if a load is connected across it.

D.   The mutual inductance of a transformer may be calculated from the equation

$$M = K \sqrt{L1L2} \text{ henries,}$$

where   M = mutual inductance in henries
K = coefficient of coupling (see Q. 3.27 below) between the coils.
L1 and L2 = values of self inductance of the two coils.

In practice, the mutual inductance may be greatly increased by winding the inductances on some form of iron core. This has the effect of increasing the coefficient of coupling greatly, since the magnetic flux generated by the primary will be confined to a large extent by the iron core and will therefore link the secondary winding more completely.

Q. 3.27. What does coefficient of coupling mean?

A.   The coefficient of coupling is a number (usually a decimal) which defines the ratio of the amount of magnetic flux linking a secondary coil, as compared to the original magnetic flux generated in the primary coil.

D.   Coefficient of coupling is expressed by the equation

$$K = \frac{M}{\sqrt{L1L2}}$$

where   K = coefficient of coupling (a decimal)
M = mutual inductance of the two coils
L1 and L2 = self inductances of the two coils.

The coefficient of coupling may be increased by one or more of several possible expedients:

1. Placing the windings closer together.
2. Winding the primary and secondary wires adjacent to one another (bi-filar winding).
3. Winding the coils on a common iron core.

Where all the flux generated by one coil links the second coil, the value of K = 1. However, typical values of K are 0.05 to 0.3 for air-core coils and K may approach unity for common wound iron-core coils.

Q. 3.28. How does the capacitance of a capacitor vary with area of plates; spacing between plates; dielectric material between plates?

A. (a) The capacitance varies directly in proportion to the area of the plates.

(b) The capacitance varies inversely with the spacing between the plates (thickness of the dielectric).

(c) The capacitance varies directly in proportion to the dielectric constant of the dielectric material.

D. To determine the capacitance of a two-plate capacitor, the following formula applies

$$C (\mu\mu f) = \frac{0.225KA}{S}$$

where   C = capacitance in micromicrofarads
K = dielectric constant of insulating material
A = area of one plate in square inches
S = spacing between plates in inches

For a multi-plate capacitor, the formula is

$$C (\mu\mu f) = \frac{0.225KA (N-1)}{S}$$

where N = number of plates

All dielectric materials are compared to a vacuum, which has a dielectric constant of 1. For practical purposes, the dielectric constant of air is also 1, the actual value being less than 0.06% greater. Therefore, if a certain capacitor has a capacity of .001 μf with air dielectric, and mica, with a dielectric constant of 7, is placed in the capacitor so as to replace the air completely, its capacity will increase by 7 times and become .007 μf. Any increase in the dielectric constant will increase the capacity in direct proportion.

Q. 3.29. Assuming the voltage on a capacitor is at or below the maximum allowable value, does the value of the capacitor have any relationship to the amount of charge it can store? What relationship does this storage of charge have to the total capacitance of two or more capacitors in series; in parallel?

A. (a) The amount of charge which can be stored in a capacitor is directly proportional to it capacitance.

(b) The amount of charge which can be stored in two or more capacitors in series is *less* than can be stored in any individual capacitor of the combination, because the *total* capacitance is *reduced*.

(c) The amount of charge which can be stored in two or more capacitors in parallel is *greater* than can be stored in any individual capacitor of the combination, because the *total* capacitance is *increased*.

D. (a) The amount of charge stored in a capacitor (or equivalent combination) is expressed by the equation:

$$Q = CE$$

where Q = charge in coulombs
C = capacitance in farads
E = voltage across the capacitor

The coulomb, not often seen in practice, is a measure of quantity, or charge of electricity. One ampere is a current of one coulomb per second. A coulomb is the electric charge of 6.28×10^{18} electrons.

C denotes capacity in farads. This quantity, equal to 1,000,000 microfarads, is defined as that capacity which will have a potential of one volt, for one coulomb stored in it. The formula above, is actually a working definition of capacity, where E is the applied voltage.

(b) Capacitors in series are figured the same as resistors in parallel. Capacitors in parallel are simply additive, as are resistors in series.

In a series circuit, the same current flows for the same time in all parts. Therefore, each capacitor has the same charge, and this value is also the charge in the combination. The voltages are:

$E_1 = \dfrac{Q}{C_1}$, $E_2 = \dfrac{Q}{C_2}$, $E_3 = \dfrac{C_3}{C_3}$, etc. The voltage on the combination, since it is in series connection, is $E_1 + E_2 + E_3$ . . . . . . or

$$E_T = \frac{Q}{C_1} + \frac{Q}{C_2} + \frac{Q}{C_3} \ldots = Q\left(\frac{1}{C_1} + \frac{1}{C_2} + \frac{1}{C_3} \ldots\right)$$

but $E_T = \dfrac{Q}{C_T}$, therefore $\dfrac{1}{C_T} = \dfrac{1}{C_1} + \dfrac{1}{C_2} + \dfrac{1}{C_3}$ . . . . . . , and

$$C_T = \frac{1}{\dfrac{1}{C_1} + \dfrac{1}{C_2} + \dfrac{1}{C_3} \ldots}$$

(c) When capacitors are in parallel, each capacitor has the same applied voltage as the combination. The charge in the combination is equal to the sum of the charges on the capacitors. The combination is equivalent to one capacitor which would hold the total of the charges at the applied voltage; such a capacitor would have a capacity equal to $C_T = C_1 + C_2 = C_3 +$ etc.

Q. 3.30. How should electrolytic capacitors be connected in a circuit in relation to polarity? Which type of low leakage capacitor is used most often in transmitters?

A. (a) Electrolytic capacitors must be connected so that the positive terminal is connected to a voltage point which is more positive than the voltage fed to the negative terminal.

(b) Where large values are required, oil-filled paper dielectric capacitors are frequently used. For smaller values of capacitance, mica and ceramic dielectric capacitors are frequently used.

D. The properties of the electrolytic capacitor are due to a dielectric film of an oxide which is formed on the positive plate of the capacitor. When connecting electrolytic capacitors the polarity marked on the body of the component must be observed. If this precaution is not observed the capacitor will be ruined. An electrolytic capacitor consists of four basic parts: the anode (positive plate), the cathode (negative plate), the electrolyte, and the dielectric film which is formed electrochemically on the surface of the anode. The dielectric material of an electrolytic capacitor consists of an extremely thin oxide film which is formed upon the surface of the anode. Certain metals, including aluminum, when immersed in special electrolytic solutions, will form a non-conducting film upon the surface when a current is passed through the metal and electrolyte to another metal plate. This film will be of such a nature as to oppose the flow of current, and will act as an insulator only as long as the same "forming" polarity is maintained. Thus an electrolytic capacitor is formed, utilizing aluminum as the plates and the oxide film as the dielectric. Because the film is very thin, the capacity is very high for a given physical size.

A filter capacitor should be checked for leakage current with its normal operating voltage applied, by means of a milliammeter. While some indication of the condition of a capacitor may be found from a simple ohmmeter check, the proper method involves the application of normal operating potentials. The method of testing a standard 8-microfarad, 450-volt electrolytic capacitor is as follows: The capacitor is connected in series with a 450-volt d-c source, a milliammeter (about 10 ma full scale) and a resistance of about 50,000 ohms shunted by a switch. The capacitor is permitted to charge for 5 minutes after which the shunting switch is closed. The milliammeter is then read. A well made electrolytic capacitor will have a very small leakage current when in continuous use. On intermittent operation the normal value of leakage current of an electrolytic capacitor is in the order of 50 to 100 microamperes per microfarad. For example, an 8-microfarad 450-volt electrolytic capacitor in good condition will have a leakage current of about .5 milliamperes. The maximum leakage current should not exceed about 5 milliamperes.

Q. 3.31. A certain power company charges 7¢ per kilowatt-hour. How much would it cost to operate three 120 volt lamp bulbs, connected in parallel, each having an internal resistance of 100 ohms, for 24 hours?

A. The cost would be 73 cents.

D. Step 1: Find the power used by each bulb.

$$P = \frac{E^2}{R} = \frac{14,400}{100} = 144 \text{ watts}$$

Step 2: The power used by three bulbs is $144 \times 3 = 432$ watts.

Step 3: Find the watt-hours for the three bulbs. This is $432 \times 24 = 10,368$ watt-hours.

Step 4: To find the kilowatt hours, divide the watt-hours by 1000, or $\frac{10,368}{1000} = 10.368$ kilowatt hours (kwh).

Step 5: To find the cost, multiply the total kwh by the unit cost per kwh, or $10.368 \times .07 = 73$ cents.

Q. 3.32. The output of an amplifier stage having a voltage gain of 30 db is 25 volts. What is the input voltage level?

A. The input-voltage level $= 0.791$ volt.

D. Step 1: The input voltage level of an amplifier is equal to the output voltage divided by the gain of the amplifier, or

$$E_{in} = \frac{E_{out}}{Gain}$$

Step 2: Since the voltage gain is given in db (30 db), it is necessary to change the db ratio to a voltage ratio. We have,

$$db = 20 \log_{10} \left(\frac{E_{out}}{E_{in}} \right); \text{ transposing and substituting:}$$

$$\log \left(\frac{E_{out}}{E_{in}} \right) = \frac{30}{20} = 1.5$$

$$\log^{-1} 1.5 = 31.6 \text{ (the voltage gain)}$$

Step 3: Substituting in the original formula.

$$E_{in} = \frac{E_{out}}{Gain} = \frac{25}{31.6} = 0.791 \text{ volt.}$$

Q. 3.33. What is the impedance of a parallel circuit which is composed of a pure inductance and a pure capacitance at resonance; of a series circuit at resonance?

A. (a) The impedance of the parallel circuit at resonance is infinite.
(b) The impedance of the series circuit at resonance is zero.

D. (a) The assumption is made in the question that zero resistance appears in both legs of the circuit. Under this condition parallel resonance occurs when $X_L = X_C$. These are equal and opposite reactances and the total reactance will then be zero. The impedance measured across the combination will be infinite. Actually this is a theoretical condition since there is always appreciable resistance in the inductance leg of the parallel resonant circuit. In this case the net reactance will be capacitive. In order to have the line current in phase with the applied voltage, X_C must equal $X_L + \dfrac{R}{Q}$.

(b) The definition of series resonance specifies that the inductive reactance and the capacitive reactance are equal. Since the inductance tends to cause a 90° lag of current and the capacitance a 90° lead of current, the effect of the two reactances cancel, being equal and opposite, and the net impedance is zero.

Q. 3.34. What is the "Q" of a circuit? How is it affected by the circuit resistance? How does the "Q" of a circuit affect bandwidth?

A. (a) The Q of a circuit is the ratio of the energy stored to the energy dissipated in the circuit over a period of one cycle. In practice, most of the energy is dissipated by coil losses and the coil Q determines the circuit Q.

(b) The greater the internal (series) circuit resistance, the lower the Q. The lower the external-shunt circuit resistance, the lower the Q.

(c) The bandwidth of a circuit is inversely proportional to its Q.

D. (a) The term "circuit" as used in the question relates most commonly to a parallel resonant circuit and is treated here as such. The "Q" of a parallel resonant circuit is determined mainly by the "Q" of the inductance.

The energy storage is within the field of the pure inductance (no resistance) of the coil while the energy losses are due to a so-called "resistance," made up of several parts. This resistance is designated *effective resistance* and consists of:

1. The d-c resistance of the coil.
2. The a-c resistance of the coil (skin effect).
3. Dielectric losses in the wire insulation and coil form.
4. Core losses.
5. Radiation from the coil (if an appreciable part of a wavelength long).

From the above, we see that Q may be described by the formula

$$Q = \frac{X_L}{R_{\text{effective}}}$$

Sometimes eddy current losses in nearby bodies (such as a coil shield) are included, since the effect on circuit performance is the same as any other loss.

(b) The bandwidth of a tuned circuit may be defined as the band of frequencies between the two points on the resonance curve which are three db down from maximum (or 0.707 of the maximum amplitude of the resonance curve). If we express the two points (frequencies) as f_1 and f_2, then the bandwidth is $(f_2 - f_1)$ and may be expressed by the equation

$$(f_2 - f_1) = \frac{f_r}{Q}$$

where f_1 and f_2 are frequencies at the three db points and f_r is the resonant frequency of the tuned circuit.

From this equation, it is apparent that the higher the value of Q, the narrower the circuit bandwidth will become (more sharply tuned).

(c) In some cases a loading resistor is deliberately placed across a tuned circuit with the intention of increasing its bandwidth response by lowering the Q (increasing dissipated energy). Since this reduces the parallel impedance of the tuned circuit, a proportional reduction in gain takes place. This device is often used in television i-f amplifiers to obtain the necessary band-pass. A simple formula to determine the value of loading resistance is $R = X_r \dfrac{(2\,\Delta\,f)}{f_r}$, where $2\,\Delta\,f$ is the desired bandwidth, f_r is the resonant frequency, X_r is the reactance of L at the resonant frequency.

Q. 3.35. Draw a circuit diagram of a low-pass filter composed of a "constant-k" and an "m-derived" section.

A.   See Fig. 3.35.

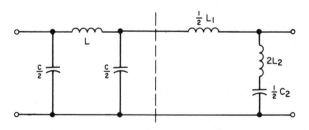

Fig. 3.35. Low-pass filter, composed of a "constant-k" section (left of dotted line) and an "m-derived" section (right of dotted line).

D.   Both the "constant-k" and "m-derived" filters are special cases
of basic filters (see also Q. 3.36). Basically, such filters are used
to achieve sharper attenuation characteristics. The "m-derived" section
is known as the "series-derived" type. There is also a "shunt-derived"
type (not shown) where C_2 would be eliminated from the shunt arm
and placed across L_1. The "constant-k" section shown is a pi section.
Design data for such filters may be found in electrical engineering
text books.

Filters are designed to operate into a resistive terminating impedance.
When this is true, the impedance looking into the input of the filter has
the same impedance value throughout most of the filter pass-band. This
constant impedance property (over the pass-band) is more readily
achieved by using "m-derived" and "constant-k" filters than with simple filters.

**Q. 3.36.   In general, why are filters used? Why are "band-stop,"
"high-pass," and "low-pass" filters used? Draw schematic diagrams of the
most commonly used filters.**

A.   (1) In general, the purpose of a filter is to select the desired
frequency component(s) (from a complex input wave); to reject the
undesired frequency component(s) and to apply only the desired com-
ponent(s) to the circuit(s) where they are required. (This is an idealistic
definition, since in practice, some portion of the undesired frequency
components will also be present at the output of the filter.)

(2) A "band-stop" (also called "band suppression," or "band exclu-
sion") filter is one which discriminates against a band of frequencies
within a spectrum and which passess frequencies above and below this
band.

(3) A "high-pass" filter is one which permits all frequencies above a
selected cut-off frequency to be passed without attenuation and rejects
frequencies below the cut-off frequency.

(4) A "low-pass" filter is one which permits all frequencies below a
selected cut-off frequency to be passed without attenuation and rejects
frequencies above the cut-off frequency.

(5) Schematic diagrams of commonly used filters are given in Fig.
3.36. The most commonly used types are known as, "L," "T," and "Pi"
filters. These may be used in single sections or in multiple sections to
provide the desired filtering action. In addition to these, there are various
other types of filters which provide special filter-response characteristics
when needed.

D.   Two of the most commonly used filters are known as the "constant-k" and the "m-derived" filters. Various common configurations
of these filters as well as three common types of RC filters are shown
in Fig. 3.36. In the case of the m-derived filters, note that there are

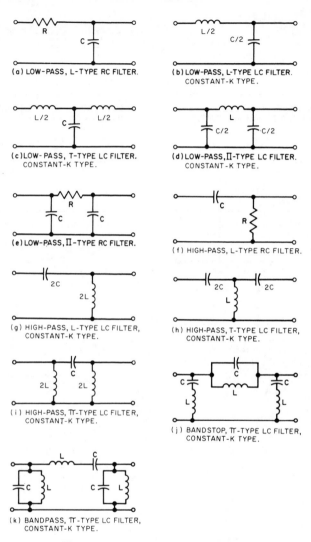

(a) LOW-PASS, L-TYPE RC FILTER.

(b) LOW-PASS, L-TYPE LC FILTER. CONSTANT-K TYPE.

(c) LOW-PASS, T-TYPE LC FILTER. CONSTANT-K TYPE.

(d) LOW-PASS, Π-TYPE LC FILTER. CONSTANT-K TYPE.

(e) LOW-PASS, Π-TYPE RC FILTER.

(f) HIGH-PASS, L-TYPE RC FILTER.

(g) HIGH-PASS, L-TYPE LC FILTER, CONSTANT-K TYPE.

(h) HIGH-PASS, T-TYPE LC FILTER, CONSTANT-K TYPE.

(i) HIGH-PASS, π-TYPE LC FILTER, CONSTANT-K TYPE.

(j) BANDSTOP, π-TYPE LC FILTER, CONSTANT-K TYPE.

(k) BANDPASS, π-TYPE LC FILTER, CONSTANT-K TYPE.

Fig. 3.36. Common types of filters.

both series and shunt types and examples are given of each, although space does not permit showing each possible variation. In addition, typical response curves for the four basic variations of constant-k filters are also shown in Fig. 3.36. (See also Q. 3.35 for additional information.)

The constant-k filter (actually a form of artificial transmission line) is designed by the so-called "image-parameter" method (as is the m-derived type). This simply means that the generator (input) looks

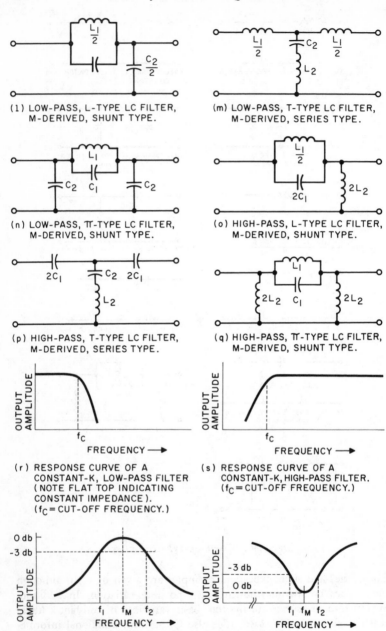

(1) LOW-PASS, L-TYPE LC FILTER, M-DERIVED, SHUNT TYPE.

(m) LOW-PASS, T-TYPE LC FILTER, M-DERIVED, SERIES TYPE.

(n) LOW-PASS, π-TYPE LC FILTER, M-DERIVED, SHUNT TYPE.

(o) HIGH-PASS, L-TYPE LC FILTER, M-DERIVED, SHUNT TYPE.

(p) HIGH-PASS, T-TYPE LC FILTER, M-DERIVED, SERIES TYPE.

(q) HIGH-PASS, π-TYPE LC FILTER, M-DERIVED, SHUNT TYPE.

(r) RESPONSE CURVE OF A CONSTANT-K, LOW-PASS FILTER (NOTE FLAT TOP INDICATING CONSTANT IMPEDANCE). (f_C = CUT-OFF FREQUENCY.)

(s) RESPONSE CURVE OF A CONSTANT-K, HIGH-PASS FILTER. (f_C = CUT-OFF FREQUENCY.)

(t) RESPONSE CURVE OF A CONSTANT-K, BANDPASS FILTER.

(u) RESPONSE CURVE OF A CONSTANT-K, BAND-STOP FILTER.

Fig. 3.36. Common types of filters.

into its own impedance, while the load (output) also looks into its impedance even though the two impedances may be different. Thus, such filters serve two functions: the elimination of undesired frequencies and the matching of two different impedances. The flat tops on the response curves for the low- and high-pass filters, shown in Fig. 3.36, indicate that the impedance of a properly designed constant-k (or m-derived) filter of these types remains substantially constant throughout the design pass band. The design of the constant-k (and other LC filters) is practical over a range of frequencies from about 1kc to 100 Mc/s. It is important to note that in the case of the filters herein discussed the cut-off characteristics can be made sharper by the use of additional filter sections in cascade. Thus, a three-section filter will have a much sharper cut-off than a single section filter.

M-derived filters (shown in Fig. 3.36) have an advantage over the constant-k types in that they exhibit a considerable improvement in the sharpness of the filter response. [M-derived and constant-k types may be combined (see Fig. 3.35) to achieve characteristics not achievable with constant-k types alone.] In addition, the frequencies of infinite attenuation are readily selected with the m-derived filters, but not for the constant-k types.

The meaning of the term "constant-k" can be seen readily with the aid of Fig. 3.36(b). If the values of the inductance and capacitance are chosen correctly, any change of reactance of either one (due to change in frequency) will be exactly offset by an equal and opposite change in the other. Therefore, their product will always be a constant, which is here called the "constant-k."

The term "m," from "m-derived," is not as easily explained, but it is a term which is used in the calculation of the value of the reactances used in m-derived filters and is related to the ratio of the filter cut-off frequency to its frequency of infinite attenuation. It is interesting to note that when the value of m becomes one, the filter becomes a constant-k filter.

The uses of filters may be generally listed as follows:

1. Power supply ripple smoothing.
2. Decoupling amplifier stages.
3. Tuned circuits, as in RF or IF stages.
4. Selection of desired products of heterodyning, as in the case of selecting particular sidebands in single sideband transmitters.
5. Harmonic frequency suppression in transmitters.
6. Coupling circuits between amplifier stages.
7. Elimination of undesired frequencies in receivers, as in the case of a 4.5 Mc/s trap in a TV receiver.
8. Elimination of IF frequencies in a receiver, following detection.

9. Improvement of the high- and low-frequency responses in video amplifiers.

10. Restricting the audio frequency band-pass to be used; such as limiting it to 300 to 3000 cycles for use in a single-sideband transmitter.

11. Cross-over networks used with loudspeaker arrangements, where lower audio frequencies are fed to a "woofer" and the higher audio frequencies are fed to a "tweeter."

12. Elimination of undesired interference frequencies from motors, generators and other electrical or electronic equipment.

13. A virtually infinite application for other special uses.

Q. 3.37. Name four materials that make good insulators at low frequencies, but not at UHF, or above.

A. The following materials are adequate for low radio frequencies, but not at UHF and above.

1. Rubber
2. Fiber
3. Paper
4. Glass
5. Bakelite
6. Cambric
7. Cotton

D. Insulators which are more suitable at the higher radio frequencies, include:

1. Ceramics
2. Mica
3. Polystyrene
4. Polyethlyene
5. Special plastics

Q. 3.38. In an iron-core transformer, what is the relationship between the transformer turns ratio and primary to secondary current ratio; between turns ratio and primary to seconday voltage ratio? (Assume no losses.)

A. (1) The ratio of primary to secondary currents is approximately in inverse ratio to the turns ratio.

(2) The primary to secondary voltage ratio is in proportion to the turns ratio. (In the ideal case, this is true if the secondary is unloaded.)

D. If the losses in the transformer are neglected, it can be assumed that the power which the primary draws from the line is all transformed to the secondary. If the power ratio is the same and the voltage ratio is 1 to 5, then the current ratio must be in inverse proportion to the voltage ratio, or 5 to 1. The voltage ratio is proportional to the turns ratio or, $\dfrac{N_p}{N_s} = \dfrac{E_p}{E_s}$. The current ratio is inversely proportional to the turns ratio, $\dfrac{N_p}{N_s} = \dfrac{I_s}{I_p}$.

Q. 3.39. What prevents high currents from flowing in the primary of an unloaded power transformer?

A.   The relatively high value of inductive reactance of the primary winding.

D.   When power is taken from the secondary, the secondary current sets up a magnetic field from this winding. Since the windings have mutual inductance, the secondary field cuts the primary winding and induces a voltage into the primary which causes additional primary current to flow. The additional current is taken from the line to supply the power requirements of the secondary. In effect, the secondary field causes a reduction of primary inductance and the smaller reactance permits additional primary current to be taken from the line.

Q. 3.40. An audio transformer has a resistive load connected across its secondary terminals. What is the relationship between this resistance, the turns ratio and the input impedance at the primary terminals? How is this principle useful in matching impedances?

A.   (1) The input impedance is equal to the value of the resistance multiplied by the square of the turns ratio.
(2) Any two impedances may be matched (within practical limits) by using the proper turns ratio of a transformer.

D.   The impedance ratio which a transformer can match is a function of the transformer turns ratio. A basic formula relating impedance ratio and turns ratio is:

$$\frac{N_p}{N_s} = \sqrt{\frac{Z_p}{Z_s}}, \qquad \text{or} \quad \left(\frac{N_p}{N_s}\right)^2 = \frac{Z_p}{Z_s}, \text{ where}$$

N_p is the number of turns in the primary
N_s is the number of turns in the secondary
Z_p is the primary impedance
Z_s is the secondary impedance
This means, for example, that if 5400 ohms were connected to the secondary of a 1:3 step-up transformer, the apparent impedance, measured at the primary, would be $5400 \times \left(\dfrac{1}{3}\right)^2$ ohms, or 600 ohms.

Q. 3.41.   How is power lost in an iron-core transformer? In an air-core transformer?

A. (1) Power is dissipated through the following losses (iron core):

(a) Eddy current losses.
(b) Hysteresis losses.
(c) Copper losses.

(2) Power is dissipated through the following losses (air core):

(a) Radiation.
(b) Skin effect.
(c) Absorption through mutual coupling and/or shield losses.
(d) Bandwidth loading resistor, where used in shunt with the coil.

D.   Eddy current losses are due to presence of circulating currents throughout the core material. The current in any path is directly proportional to the emf induced in it, and inversely proportional to the resistance of the path. The heat produced is proportional to the square of the induced current. Eddy current losses can be reduced by building the core out of thin laminations individually insulated, and by using material having high specific resistivity. Eddy current losses are proportional to the square of the maximum flux density, the square of the thickness of laminations, and the square of the frequency. This loss is unaffected by d-c core saturation.

Magnetic hysteresis is a property of magnetic material by virtue of which the magnetic flux density corresponding to a given magnetizing force (gilberts, ampere-turns) depends on the previous conditions of magnetization of the material. The effect of hysteresis, when the field is alternating, is an energy loss appearing as heat in the material. If a magnetic field is established in air, it will be found that under normal conditions all of the energy stored in the magnetic field will be returned to the circuit upon the collapse of the field. If the field is established in iron or steel, however, only a part of the energy will be returned to the circuit, the remainder appearing as heat in the iron or steel. This heat loss is partly due to the effect of hysteresis. According to the molecular theory of magnetism, the molecules in a magnetic material are haphazardly arranged when the material is unmagnetized. When a magnetizing force is applied, these tiny magnets turn and become aligned with the magnetic field. Their motion is resisted by a force which is called molecular friction. The work done in overcoming this friction is the hysteresis energy loss, which appears as heat. This loss is given by the equation: $P = Kf(B_{max})^{1.6}$ watts, where K is a constant of the magnetic material, f is the frequency in cycles per second, and B_{max} is the maximum flux density in the material.

The "copper losses" of a transformer are determined by the effective resistance of the primary and secondary windings and the current through each winding. At power frequencies the copper losses may be found by determining the d-c resistance of each winding and multiplying this value by the square of the current in the winding.

At radio frequencies, "skin effect" must be taken into account, as the effective resistance may be much greater than the d-c resistance alone. At radio frequencies, therefore, the copper loss is found by, $P = I^2 \times R_{eff}$ watts. See also Q. 3.11 for "skin effect."

Q. 3.42.   Explain the operation of a "break-contact" relay; a "make-contact" relay.

A.   (1) A *"break-contact"* relay is also known as a "normally-closed" relay. In this type of relay, when the coil is de-energized, one or more sets of contacts are closed and will open only when the relay coil is energized.

(2) A *"make-contact"* relay is also known as a "normally-open" relay. In this case, one or more sets of contacts remain open in the de-energized condition and close only when the relay coil is energized.

Q. 3.43.   What is the value and tolerance of a resistor which is color-coded (left-to-right): RED, BLACK, ORANGE, GOLD?

A.   The value of the resistor is 20,000 ohms. Gold signifies a $\pm$ 5 percent tolerance.

Q. 3.44.   What would be the value, tolerance and voltage rating of an EIA mica capacitor whose first row colors were (from left-to-right): BLUE, RED, GREEN: second row: GREEN, SILVER, RED?

A.   In the EIA system, six dots are used to identify the capacitor The top three dots are read from left-to-right, but the bottom three are read from right-to-left (continuing around the loop). Thus, in the question, the colors should be read in sequence as, (1) BLUE, (2) RED, (3) GREEN, (4) RED, (5) SILVER, (6) GREEN. However, in the EIA system the first dot (1) would be white, identifying the code as that of EIA and not MIL (which would have a black first dot). Therefore, the color sequence should read instead, (1) WHITE, (2) RED, (3) GREEN, (4) RED, (5) SILVER, (6) GREEN.

The value of capacitance (in $\mu\mu$fds) is taken from dots 2, 3 and 4 and is 2500 $\mu\mu$fds.

The tolerance is taken from dot 5 (Silver) and is $\pm$ 10 percent.

Dot 6 gives the EIA class (A through G) which specifies temperature coefficient, leakage resistance and other variable factors. The voltage rating is not given by any color dot directly but is generally 500 volts (Voltage ratings may be found in the manufacturer's data sheets or in supply catalogues, when in doubt.)

EIA are the initials for the Electronic Industries Association, formerl known as the RETMA; which stood for the Radio-Electronics-Television Manufacturers Association.

Q. 3.45. **List three precautions which should be taken in soldering electrical connections to assure a permanent junction.**

A.   Some precautions in soldering are:

1. Clean parts thoroughly, if they are not already tinned. If the parts are not tinned, it is helpful to tin then before soldering.

2. Make a good mechanical connection between the parts.

3. If the solder does not have an inner rosin core, it will be helpful to apply a small quantity of rosin to the joint. (Most electronic-type solders have an inner core of rosin or other non-corrosive flux.)

4. Use a soldering iron or soldering gun of high enough wattage rating so the joint will be adequately heated.

5. Heat the joint so it is hot enough to melt the solder. Don't "paste" molten solder on a cold joint.

6. Maintain the heat for a sufficient time to permit the solder to flow freely over the entire joint.

7. Use just enough solder to cover the entire joint evenly.

8. Never use acid flux in electrical work, as it is highly corrosive.

9. Be certain the parts of the joint do not move while the solder is cooling.

ELECTRON TUBES

Q. 3.46. **Discuss the physical characteristics and a common usage of each of the following electron tube types:**
a. diode
b. triode
c. tetrode
d. pentode
e. beam power
f. remote cut-off
g. duo-triode
h. cold-cathode
i. thyratron

A.   (a) Diode: A two-electrode vacuum tube (Fig. 3.46(a)) containing a cathode and a plate housed in a glass or metal-evacuated envelope. Connections from the elements are brought out to a plug-in base, or to wires in the case of sub-miniature tubes. The cathode may be a directly-heated wire or an indirectly-heated metal sleeve. In the case of the sleeve, this is given an oxide coating which is an efficient electron emitter. (Directly-heated cathodes are also oxide coated to improve their emission characteristics.) Indirectly-heated cathode sleeves are brought up to operating temperature by a heated filament wire inside of, but insulated from, the emitter sleeve. Diodes are rectifiers and are used as r–f detectors, peak detectors and power-supply rectifiers. They are also commonly used as d–c restorers (clampers), limiters and clippers.

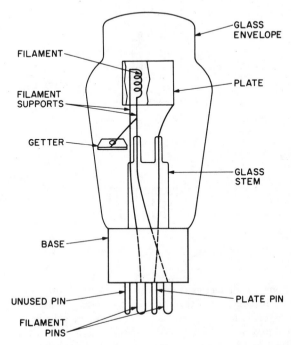

GLASS
ENVELOPE

FILAMENT

PLATE

FILAMENT
SUPPORTS

GETTER

GLASS
STEM

BASE

UNUSED PIN

PLATE PIN

FILAMENT
PINS

Fig. 3.46(a). Cross-section of a diode.

(b) Triode: A triode is a three-element tube. It contains either a filament or cathode structure, a grid, and a plate (Fig. 3.46(b)). If the emitter is of the filament type, it is usually made of thoriated tungsten. This is formed by dissolving a small amount of thorium oxide and carbon in a tungsten filament. The conventional cathode is formed in two sections. The outer section consists of a hollow nickel cylinder which is coated with thorium oxide. Within the cylinder is a tungsten wire suitably insulated from the cylinder. This wire may be heated by either a.c. or d.c. and in turn causes the cylinder to become properly heated. The usable emission comes from the outer surface of the cylinder. The grid which surrounds the cathode is usually made of molybdenum wire which is spirally wound upon two vertical supporting wires. The plate is usually made of nickel or iron pressed out of sheet material and crimped or flanged to increase rigidity. It is usually blackened to increase the heat radiation. Some large power tubes have graphite plates which are superior under high temperature conditions.

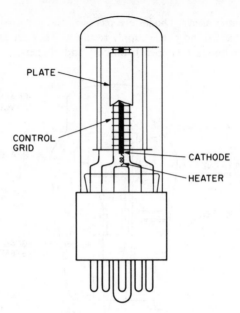

PLATE

CONTROL
GRID

CATHODE

HEATER

Fig. 3.46(b)   Cross-section of a triode.

Connections to all elements are usually made through a base at the bottom of the tube. Triodes are used for a variety of functions. Some of these are: oscillator, r-f or a-f amplifier, clamper, voltage regulator and cathode follower.

(c) Tetrode: A tetrode is similar in physical construction to a triode, but with the addition of a spirally wound screen grid placed between the plate and control grid. Connections to elements are usually made to a base at the bottom, although in some high frequency tubes connections to grid and plate are brought out through the side and top. Tetrodes are seldom if ever used in receiving circuits. They are sometimes used in transmitters as power r-f amplifiers or modulators.

(d) Pentode: The pentode has 5 elements. (See Fig. 3.46(d).) These are four elements identical to tetrode arrangements plus another spirally wound wire grid which is located between the screen grid and the plate. This addition is called the suppressor grid. Pentodes have a very wide variety of uses. Some of these are: r-f amplifier, video amplifier, cathode follower, audio amplifier (usually pre-amplifier or speech amplifier), i-f amplifier, oscillator (generally crystal), mixer and control tube for voltage regulator.

(e) Beam Power: A tube usually consisting of a cathode, control grid, screen grid, plate, and two "beam forming" plates on either side of the cathode (Fig. 3.46(e)). These plates are operated at cathode potential. The control grid and screen grid wires are aligned with each other so that the electron stream flows through them in "sheets." This reduces the screen grid current and thus increases the tube efficiency. These "sheets" diverge beyond the screen grid and cross the paths of other sheets thus forming an area of high

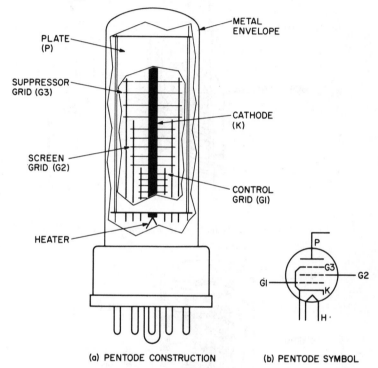

(a) PENTODE CONSTRUCTION   (b) PENTODE SYMBOL

Fig. 3.46(d). Cross-section of a pentode.

electron density just short of the plate. This dense negatively charged area serves the same purpose as a suppressor grid, but permits more linear tube operation, with a reduction of third harmonic distortion. The "beam forming" plates confine the electrons to beams and also serve to prevent any stray secondary-emission electrons from approaching the screen grid from the sides of the tube.

(f) Remote Cut-Off: Generally refers to pentodes with special control-grid spacing (Fig. 3.46(f)). The grid turns are closer together at both ends, but have a wider spacing in the center. A common application for these tubes is in AGC (or AVC) controlled i–f amplifiers. Another use would be in audio volume expander or compresser circuits. In general, they are used in circuits where an automatic (or manual) control of circuit gain is desired, by changing the control-grid voltage(s) of the stage(s).

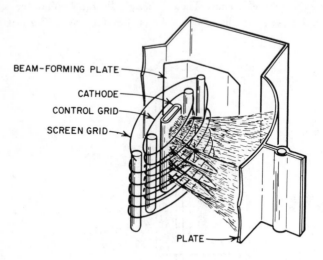

Fig. 3.46(e). Cross-section of a beam power tube.

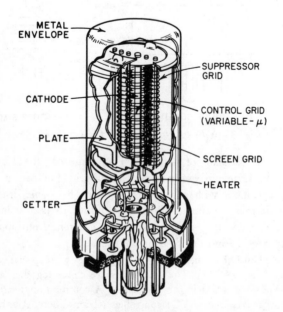

Fig. 3.46(f). Cross-section of a remote cut-off tube.

(g) Duo-Triode: This merely indicates that two triodes are in one tube envelope. The primary advantages are the savings in space, parts and cost. The uses are the same as given in part (b).

(h) Cold Cathode: A typical cold-cathode gassy-diode rectifier tube consists of a large area cathode (which is coated with suitable emitting material such as barium or strontium), a small diameter rod-shaped pointed anode, and a starter anode. (See Figure 3.46(h).) These elements are enclosed in an envelope containing a gas such as helium, acetylene, argon, or neon. The gas pressure is critical for correct operation. Common uses for these tubes are as voltage regulators and rectifiers.

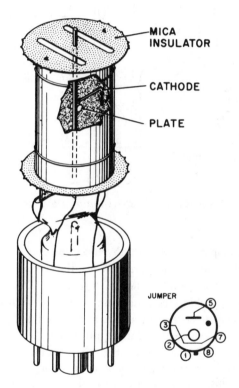

Fig. 3.46(h). Cross-section of a cold cathode tube.

(i) Thyratron: A mercury vapor or gas filled tube (Fig. 3.46(i)) having special characteristics which make it adaptable for power or voltage control in electronic devices. The thyratron may be found in either triode or tetrode form. However, the nature of the grid control is considerably different from the normal control as found in

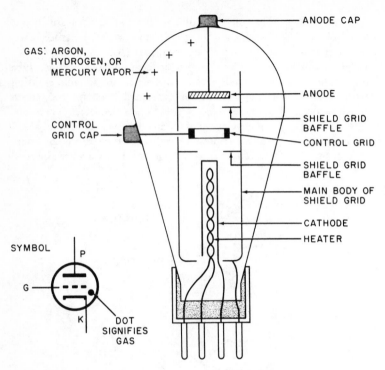

GAS: ARGON,
HYDROGEN, OR
MERCURY VAPOR

ANODE CAP

ANODE

SHIELD GRID
BAFFLE

CONTROL
GRID CAP

CONTROL GRID

SHIELD GRID
BAFFLE

MAIN BODY OF
SHIELD GRID

CATHODE

HEATER

SYMBOL

P

G

K

DOT
SIGNIFIES
GAS

Fig. 3.46(i). Cross-section of a thyratron.

conventional amplifier tubes. In a thyratron, the grid is capable only of
controlling the start of plate current. Once the current has started, the
grid can neither stop it, nor alter its magnitude. The current can be
stopped only by making the plate potential zero or negative for a short
period of time. In the case of a tetrode thyratron the purpose of the
screen grid is to reduce the control grid current which flows during
periods of non-conduction. In another type of tetrode thyratron, both
grids must receive positive triggering voltages simultaneously for the
tube to fire. This type is sometimes called a "coincidence tube." One
use of a small thyratron is as a sawtooth generator in an oscilloscope.
In this case, the control grid serves as a synchronizing device. The larger
thyratrons are used as inverters, as d-c motor control devices, and to
fire ignitrons. The "coincidence tube" is used wherever it is desired to
initiate an operation when two signals are in the correct phase and amplitude. It is used in radar, beacon-AFC circuits and in industrial electronics circuits.

D. (a)(b) Diode, Triode: Take first the diode conditions. Assume the plate voltage is zero and that the cathode is properly heated. Electrons will be emitted by the cathode, and attracted back to the cathode in such a way that an electron "cloud" of constant density will form around the immediate vicinity of the cathode. This "cloud" is called the space charge. If a relatively low positive potential is applied to the plate (with respect to the cathode), the plate assumes a positive charge, as in any capacitor, and an electrostatic field will exist between the plate and cathode. The forces acting in this field will be in such a direction as to urge electrons to move toward the plate and away from the space charge. With a low value of plate voltage applied, the forces will be relatively weak and a comparatively small number of electrons will move into the plate and produce a small value of plate current in the external circuit. If the plate voltage is increased, the positive charge of the plate will also be increased and this in turn will increase the forces acting in the electrostatic field. More electrons will be removed from the space charge during any given period of time (and replenished from the cathode emission) and thus cause an increased plate current. On the other hand if the original plate voltage were maintained, but the spacing between the plate and cathode were reduced, the plate current would again be increased in inverse proportion to the spacing. (This would be similar to decreasing the spacing between the plates of a capacitor and thereby increasing its charging capabilities by increasing its capacitance.) A simple expression which describes the electrostatic forces acting upon the space charge is $F = \dfrac{E}{300d}$, where F is the force acting upon the space charge and is measured in dynes (one dyne $= 1/28,000$ ounce), E is the potential difference between cathode and plate, and d is the plate-to-cathode spacing in centimeters. The formula shows that the electrostatic forces acting upon the space charge (and producing plate current) vary directly as the applied plate potential, and inversely as the plate-to-cathode spacing. For example, if the plate potential and the plate-to-cathode spacing were simultaneously cut in half, the plate current would remain unchanged. If the plate-to-cathode spacing were reduced to $1/10$ of its original distance, the original plate current magnitude could be maintained with only $1/10$ of the original plate potential. In other words, for any given applied potential, the degree of control which an electrode possesses with regard to the space charge increases as the electrode is brought closer to the space charge.

The triode has three elements: a cathode; a plate, which is relatively distant from the cathode; and a grid located quite close to the cathode. The grid might be considered to be another plate, but so constructed as to permit the passage of electrons through its wires. The fact that the grid is located so much closer to the cathode than the plate means that, for a given applied potential, the grid will exert a much greater influence upon the space charge and plate current than the plate. Thus a relatively small change of grid voltage is capable of producing a large change in plate current. If an impedance is placed in series with the plate current flow, a relatively large voltage drop will appear across its terminals for each small change of grid potential. Thus, the tube is able to amplify because the control electrode (grid) is placed relatively close to the cathode, in comparison to the plate.

(c) Tetrode: The tetrode has an additional screen grid usually operated at about 1/3 of plate supply voltage for voltage amplifiers, and approximately equal to plate supply voltage for power amplifiers. The screen grid has two important functions: first, it greatly reduces the grid to plate capacitance, thus making it unnecessary to neutralize r-f amplifiers except at very high frequencies, and second, it makes the plate current substantially independent of plate voltage. This factor makes it possible to obtain much higher values of amplification than with triodes. The plate efficiency is about 10% greater than with triodes.

(d) Pentode: This is a 5-element tube, the added element being a suppressor grid. The suppressor grid is usually at cathode potential making it extremely negative relative to the plate. The suppressor grid further reduces interelectrode capacitance between control grid and plate, and also makes possible greater power output and higher gain than a tetrode tube. Primarily the suppressor grid acts to return secondary electrons to the plate rather than to permit them to be picked up by the screen grid. Pentodes can be operated at higher r-f frequencies without neutralization than tetrodes.

(e) Beam Power: The variations of plate current with changes in plate voltage in a beam power tube are similar to those of a normal pentode, the main difference being that in circuits where there is considerable plate current flow, the plate current in a beam power tube will be relatively independent of plate voltage down to a lower value of plate voltage than the plate current in a pentode. Thus, the effective operating range of a beam power tube is somewhat greater than that of an equivalent or similar pentode. By concentrating the electrons in smooth beams or sheets (as contrasted with the uneven structure of a suppressor grid), the suppressor action of the space charge formed in a beam power tube provides superior action to that offered by a suppressor grid of the conventional type.

The beam power tube is commonly used as an audio amplifier in the output and power stages of circuits having low- to moderately high-output ratings. The beam power tube is less frequently used as a radio-frequency power amplifier.

(h) Cold Cathode: Electron emission from the cathode is due to two major factors:

1. If the electrostatic field produced by the starter anode is sufficiently great, electrons will be pulled from the cathode coating by force of attraction.

2. Any gas is always in a state of partial ionization. The existing positive ions are accelerated by the cathode to starter-anode voltage so

that they strike the cathode with sufficient force to aid in the emission of electrons. The rectifying action of such a tube makes use of the fact that the current which ionization causes to exist between two electrodes in a low-pressure gas is approximately proportional to the area of the cathode. If one electrode has a very large area (cathode) and the other electrode a very small area (anode), electrons will flow in the direction from cathode to anode. Conduction occurs on that half cycle which makes the anode positive with respect to the cathode.

Q. 3.47. What is the principal advantage of a tetrode tube over a triode tube as a radio-frequency amplifier?

A.   The lack of necessity for neutralizing, except possibly at ultra high frequencies.

D.   If an r-f amplifier is operated with its plate and grid circuits tuned to approximately the same frequency, there is a strong likelihood that the amplifier will act as a tuned-grid tuned-plate oscillator. This is particularly true of triode amplifiers, where the value of grid-to-plate capacitance is relatively large; this would cause large energy feedback from the plate to the grid circuit, and thus permit sustained oscillations to occur. The problem is less serious in tetrodes or pentodes, where the grid-to-plate capacitance is much smaller.

Q. 3.48.   Compare tetrode tubes to triode tubes in reference to high plate current and interelectrode capacitance.

A.   (1) Tetrode tubes of similar construction to triodes, are capable of higher plate currents, because the plate current is largely dependent upon a constant value of screen-grid voltage. (See Discussion.)

(2) Tetrodes have greatly reduced values of control grid-to-plate capacitance compared to triodes. (See Discussion.)

D.   (1) Maximum plate current characteristics of tetrodes versus triodes cannot be directly compared, since this is largely a function of the permissible plate dissipation of a particular tube. However, all other conditions being equal, the affect of the screen grid operation is to make the plate current relatively independent of the plate voltage and to reduce the space charge in the vicinity of the plate. When the actual plate voltage of a triode is reduced because of high current through the plate load, this in turn tends to limit the maximum possible plate current. However, in the tetrode (or pentode), the plate current is more dependent upon screen-grid (than plate) voltage and may therefore be driven to a higher value, since the screen-grid voltage remains at a relatively fixed value, regardless of the plate current.

(2) In the tetrode, the screen grid is interposed between the control grid and the plate. The a–c ground of the screen grid is returned to ground or to the cathode and has the effect of an electrostatic shield

between the plate and control grid. The effective grid-to-plate capacitance now consists of two small capacitances in series, the control grid-to-screen grid capacitance and the screen grid-to-plate capacitance. The resultant capacitance (control grid-to-plate) is smaller than either capacitance and may be in the order of .01 $\mu\mu$fd. In comparison, a triode of similar dimensions and ratings may have a grid-to-plate capacitance of 2.0 $\mu\mu$fd. The lower capacitance of the tetrode greatly reduces plate to control grid feedback and consequently the possibility of sustaining oscillations or regeneration in the stage. See also Questions 3.46 and 3.47, above.

Q. 3.49. Are there any advantages or disadvantages of filament type vacuum tubes when compared with the indirectly-heated types?

A.   (1) Filament-type tubes: — Advantages.
(a) Quick heating.
(b) More efficient in converting heating power into thermal emission.
(c) Used to provide high values of current (i.e., in rectifiers, or high power tubes).
(2) Filament-type tubes: — Disadvantages.
(a) Prone to hum problems.
(b) Lower gain.
(c) Prone to filament breakage.
(d) Require higher operating temperatures for efficient emission.
(3) Indirectly-heated tubes: — Advantages.
(a) Elimination of heater hum problems.
(b) Operates at relatively low temperatures.
(c) Can be made with much higher gains, since grid can be wound closer to the cylindrical cathode.
(d) Cathode can be coated with a material which is an efficient electron emitter; such as barium, calcium and strontium oxides.
(4) Indirectly-heated tubes: — Disadvantages.
(a) Longer warm-up time.
(b) Cathode surface is not as rugged as a directly-heated filament.
(c) Cannot be used to supply very high values of current.

Q. 3.50. Draw a simple circuit diagram consisting of each of the following and describe its operation. Show a signal source and include coupling and by-pass capacitors, power supply connections and plate load.

(a) AF "grounded-cathode" triode amplifier with cathode resistor biasing, as for "Class A" operation.
(b) AF "grounded-cathode" pentode amplifier with battery biasing, for "Class A" operation.
(c) RF "grounded-grid" triode amplifier with LC tank plate-load for "Class B" operation.
(d) AF "cathode-follower" triode amplifier.

(e) AF "push-pull" pentode amplifier operated "Class B" with transformer coupling to a speaker.

A. (a) See Figure 3.50(a) for diagram of the triode amplifier. The incoming audio frequency signal is applied to the grid through coupling capacitor, C_c, and the grid resistor, R_g. The actual tube-grid signal is developed across R_g which also provides the necessary d–c ground for the grid. The time constant of $R_g \times C_c$ is chosen to pass the lowest desired audio frequency with minimum attenuation. The correct bias for Class A operation is provided by the voltage drop across R_K which occurs because of plate current passing through it. The cathode

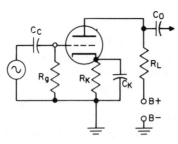

Fig. 3.50(a).   Triode-audio amplifier, with cathode bias.

is thus caused to become positive with respect to the grid (grid is negative with respect to cathode). To prevent degeneration (loss of gain) in the amplifier, R_K is bypassed by a suitable value of capacitor, C_K. The time constant $R_K \times C_K$ is chosen to be at least five times as long as the period of the lowest frequency involved. (The same is true for the time constant of $C_c \times R_g$.) The input signal is amplified and inverted in polarity in the plate circuit and appears across the plate load resistor, R_L. The output signal is coupled from the amplifier via coupling capacitor, C_o. (See also Q. 3.46b, above.)

(b) See Figure 3.50(b) for diagram of the pentode amplifier. The basic operation of the pentode is the same as the triode (above). However, fixed battery-grid biasing is used. This scheme for biasing is not commonly used in Class A audio amplifiers, but has the advantage of being independent of plate and screen grid currents. Fixed bias schemes are seen more frequently in transmitters and for Class AB and Class B audio amplifiers. The correct screen-grid voltage is obtained by the correct value of screen-grid dropping resistor (R_{sg}). Capacitor C_{sg} prevents screen grid degeneration and provides an a–c ground for the shielding effect of the screen. (See also Q. 3.46 (d), above.)

(c) In the grounded-grid amplifier, the grid is at signal ground and the signal is fed into the cathode circuit. In the schematic, Fig. 3.50(c), fixed bias is employed to achieve Class B operation.

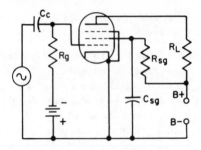

Fig. 3.50(b). Pentode-audio amplifier, with battery bias.

In the grounded-grid amplifier the input voltage is actually in series with the external load impedance connecting the plate and cathode (plate load, power supply, and cathode load) and the tube acts as though it were excited at the grid, but had an amplification factor of $(\mu + 1)$ instead of μ. The input (cathode impedance) of the grounded-grid amplifier is low, being approximately the reciprocal of the g_m of the tube. For a g_m of 6000 micromhos, the input impedance is 166 ohms. Thus it may be seen that the input may exert a considerable loading effect upon the driving source. The formula for computing the gain of a grounded-grid amplifier is:

$$G = \frac{R_L (\mu + 1)}{R_L + r_p}$$

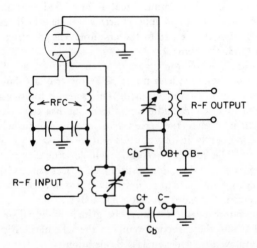

Fig. 3.50(c). A grounded-grid amplifier.

Note the similarity to the equation for the gain of a grounded-cathode amplifier.

Grounded grid amplifiers are sometimes used at very high frequencies because it is often possible to utilize triode tubes without the necessity for neutralization. In the grounded-grid amplifier the feedback capacitance is not the plate-grid capacitance, but is the much smaller plate-cathode capacitance. This smaller capacitance is less likely to cause oscillations, even at extremely high frequencies when special triodes (Lighthouse type) are used.

(d) The triode cathode-follower diagram is given in Fig. 3.50(d). The gain of a cathode-follower is always less than unity.

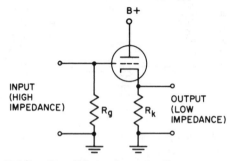

Fig. 3.50(d). Simplified schematic diagram of cathode-follower.

As shown in the figure, the output of a cathode-follower is taken across the cathode resistor (R_K). The output voltage is in phase with the input and is degenerative. Thus, the output voltage is always less than the input voltage. The gain is largely dependent upon the value of R_k and is given by the equation:

$$G = \frac{\mu R_K}{r_p + R_K (\mu + 1)}$$

An important characteristic of a cathode-follower is its very low output impedance which is approximately equal to R_K in parallel with the reciprocal of the tube's transconductance. Typical values for triodes are 200 to 400 ohms and for pentodes may be as low as 50 to 100 ohms. The low-output impedance coupled with the high-input (grid) impedance, makes the cathode-follower useful as an impedance-matching device when driving transmission lines or other low-impedance devices.

(e) In a Class B push-pull audio amplifier, both tubes are biased close to cut-off (this is known as extended cut-off). Bias is generally supplied by an external bias supply to provide a stable operating point. The grid-excitation voltages are higher than those used for Class A operation since they must cause grid current to flow in each tube. Because of the bias, each tube will draw plate current for slightly more than 180 degrees and will be cut off for the remainder of the input cycle. Grid current may flow in each tube for as much as 30 degrees of the input cycle. Although each tube conducts for only about one-half cycle, they conduct alternately and produce a full cycle of the input wave when combined in the output transformer. For diagram, see Fig. 3.50(e).

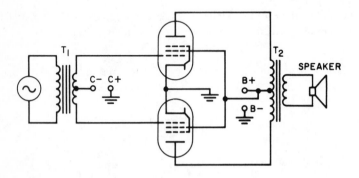

Fig. 3.50(e). Audio-frequency, push-pull pentode, Class B amplifier.

Class B operation for an audio amplifier provides maximum efficiency and power output, but this is coupled with higher audio distortion than Class AB or Class A operation in push-pull. Class B single-ended operation cannot ordinarily be used for audio frequencies because of extreme distortion. (The plate efficiency of a Class B amplifier may be in the order of 50 to 60 percent, compared to about 25 percent efficiency for a Class A amplifier.)

In the usual Class B operation, grid current flows for an appreciable portion of each cycle, thus presenting a low input impedance to the driving source. This requires that the driver be capable of delivering power to the grid circuits without being overloaded, to maintain low distortion at the input circuits. To provide a match from the relatively high output driver impedance to the lower grid input impedance of the Class B stages, a step-down transformer is generally employed. A well-regulated power supply is needed to supply Class B tubes because the average plate current varies in proportion to the grid signal. Class B operation is not usually designated as B1 (no grid current) or B2 (grid current) since Class B operation almost always requires that grid current be drawn to obtain maximum efficiency.

Tubes which are specifically designed for use as Class B amplifiers operate at either zero or at very low bias potential. This eliminates the need to provide a special, well-regulated bias supply, since the tubes generally operate at zero bias. With such tubes, grid current is drawn during almost the entire positive half of each cycle.

Q. 3.51. What kind of vacuum tube responds to filament reactivation and how is reactivation accomplished?

A. It is usually considered that only thoriated tungsten filaments may be reactivated. This is not necessarily true as many oxide coated cathodes have been reactivated.

The method of reactivating a thoriated tungsten filament is as follows: The filament voltage is raised to about $3\frac{1}{2}$ times normal and kept there for about 1 minute. It is then reduced to about $1\frac{1}{2}$ times normal and held there for about 1 hour. This method is not recommended for tubes with normal filament voltages above 5 volts.

D. The following method of reactivating cathodes of cathode ray tubes proved successful in at least 50% of the cases in which it was tried. A source of about 400 volts d.c. is connected in series with a milliammeter between the intensity grid and the cathode, with the positive terminal going to the intensity grid. The filament voltage is then raised by about 50% and the milliammeter is constantly observed. After some period of time, sometimes as long as 5 minutes, the milliammeter reading will be observed to be slowly and then rapidly increasing. When the reading reaches about 70 milliamperes the supply voltage should be instantly disconnected. The intensity grid may become red momentarily, but this is of little consequence.

Q. 3.52. Draw a rough graph of plate-current versus grid-voltage (I_p vs E_g) for various plate voltages on a typical triode vacuum tube.

(a) How would output current vary with input voltage in Class A amplifier operation? Class AB operation? Class B operation? Class C operation?

(b) Does the amplitude of the input signal determine the class of operation?

(c) What is meant by "current-cutoff" bias voltage?

(d) What is meant by plate-current "saturation"?

(e) What is the relationship between distortion in the output current waveform and:

(1) The class of operation?

(2) The portion of the transfer characteristic over which the signal is operating?

(3) Amplitude of input signal?

(f) What occurs in the grid-circuit when the grid is "driven" positive? Would this have any effect on biasing?

(g) In what way is the output current related to the output voltage?

A.   The plate-current versus grid voltage graph is given in Fig.
3.52(a). A transfer characteristic curve drawn for one particular value
of plate-load resistance is given in Fig. 3.52(b). The bias points for
class "A," "B" and "C" operation are shown.

D.   Class A is usually near the center of the linear portion of the
curve.

Class B can be either at actual cut-off bias or as shown in the figure
at "projected cut-off" for linear operation.

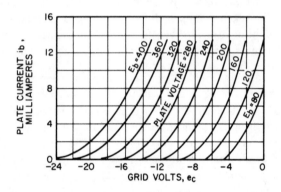

*Fig. 3.52(a).   Graph of plate current versus grid voltage for
various values of plate voltage for a typical triode. (Transfer
characteristics.)*

Class C can be any value greater than cut-off bias but is frequently
about 2 × cut-off.

(a) (1) Class A operation: A class A amplifier is one in which the
grid bias and alternating grid signal are such that plate current flows for
the entire 360° of an input sine wave voltage applied to the grid. Operation is confined as nearly as possible to the most linear portion of the
tube characteristic.

(2) Class AB operation: In class AB operation (refer to Fig. 3.52(b))
the bias is approximately half way between the class A and class B points.
In this case, plate current will flow for approximately 270 degrees of the
input wave. The *average* plate current will not be constant as with class
A operation (see (1) above), but will increase with increasing amplitudes of the input grid signal. This type of operation is most commonly
used for audio output amplifiers. In this case, two tubes in push-pull
must be used to eliminate the high level of distortion which would occur
were only one tube used.

(3) Class B operation: In class B operation, the bias is set slightly
above the actual cut-off value, so that plate current flows for slightly

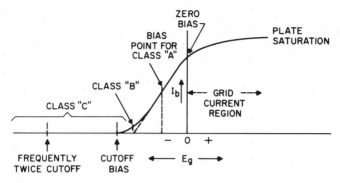

Fig. 3.52(b). Tube characteristic curve, with certain significant bias points.

more than 180 degrees of the input wave. Class B operation is frequently used in modulators and r-f amplifiers and in high-power audio amplifiers (push-pull) where low distortion is not the prime consideration. The average plate current of a class B amplifier varies normally during operation, where the input signal is not a constant amplitude, sinusoidal voltage. (It practically never is, except possibly during tests.) With no input signal applied to the class B amplifier grids, the plate current will be extremely small. (This is an advantage in portable or high power equipment where conservation of the power supply is essential.) The plate current will vary in direct proportion to the amplitude of the grid signal, and since an audio wave contains many harmonic frequencies, the shape and amplitude of the modulating signal is constantly changing. This in turn causes consequent variations of plate current. If the modulator were operated class A, the plate current would remain substantially constant, with or without excitation.

(4) Class C operation: In class C operation, the bias is set at some value greater than cut-off bias. Thus, the plate current flows for less than 180 degrees of the input wave, and is permitted to flow *only* during the time that the instantaneous value of plate voltage is at or near its *minimum* value. At all other times the tube is non-conducting. This permits a relatively small loss on the plate and high plate efficiency. However, in order that the above conditions be met, a large value of bias must be used, in some cases equal to 4 times cut-off value, but usually about twice cut-off value. Since grid current must flow at some time in each cycle, a relatively large value of grid driving power must be available from a low impedance source. Appreciable r-f power is consumed in the grid circuit. Although the plate current wave is a pulse and rich in harmonics, the plate voltage waveshape will be sinusoidal since the plate load will in most cases be a tank circuit with a reasonably high Q. An interesting feature is that the maximum positive value of grid voltage ($e_{c\ max}$), is approximately equal to the minimum

value of the plate voltage ($e_{b\ min}$). Class C amplifiers may not be used in audio amplifiers due to the high distortion, but are commonly used for r-f amplification in transmitters; they are often applied to special circuits such as clippers and peakers.

(b) No. The class of operation is determined basically by the grid-bias value. It is possible to overdrive an amplifier, but this does alter its class of operation.

(c) Theoretically, this is the value of bias which will prevent plate current from flowing (no signal input). The amount of bias needed for a given class of operation is inversely proportional to the amplification factor (μ) of the tube. For example, in class C operation where the bias is equal to twice cut-off, it may be found from the formula, $E_c = \dfrac{2\,E_b}{\mu}$.

(d) For any given filament or cathode temperature "plate saturation" occurs when the plate current is equal to the electron emission. Under normal operating conditions for an amplifier tube, the cathode temperature and plate supply voltage are fixed. Saturation effects may occur when a further positive swing of the grid can no longer produce an appreciable increase of plate current.

(e) (1) In true class A operation, the output waveform is essentially an undistorted reproduction of the input waveform. In classes AB, B and C (see (a) above), plate current flows for only a portion of the cycle. Distortion in an audio amplifier is greatest for class C and less for classes B and AB respectively. Distortion for class AB and class B audio amplifiers can be greatly reduced by using two tubes in push-pull. Where the plate load is a resonant tank circuit of reasonable Q (10 or more), single-ended class B or C amplifiers produce very little distortion in the output.

(2) The transfer characteristics are shown in Fig. 3.52(b). For minimum distortion, operation should not extend into the lower curved portion of the characteristic, for any given plate voltage. Neither should the tube be driven into the region of plate saturation.

(3) For an undistorted output signal the input signal amplitude and bias must be such that operation will occur along the linear portion of the transfer characteristic (Fig. 3.52(b)). If the grid signal is increased beyond these limits, the grid swing will extend into the regions of plate current cut-off and saturation. If this occurs, the output waveform will be distorted; the distortion increasing with further increases of the amplitude of the grid signal.

(f) (1) Grid current flows in the driven tube. This causes the tube (grid-to-cathode) to present a low impedance to the driving circuit and may cause distortion in audio amplifiers.

(2) If the input circuit were RC coupled, the input coupling capacitor would charge and this would tend to increase the stage bias. Assuming the stage to be an audio amplifier, the RC time constant of the coupling

capacitor and grid resistor would be large enough to maintain the charge between high positive peaks of the signal. The charge is therefore averaged in the coupling capacitor and the capacitor voltage is added to the normal bias voltage. The greater the positive signal peaks, the higher the average capacitor voltage will be, and the greater the increase of bias.

(g) The output current is the current in the tubes' output load, while the output voltage appears across this load. The output current is also the tubes' plate current. This current passing through the load impedance creates the output voltage. This may be expressed as,

$$E_o = I_o \times Z_o,$$

where E_o = output voltage
         I_o = output current
         Z_o = load impedance

If the plate load is purely resistive, the plate current will be in phase with the plate voltage across the load. An increase of plate current will result in a proportional increase of output voltage change across the load. If the plate load is a pure inductance, the plate current will lag the output voltage by 90 degrees. A parallel resonant circuit in the plate presents a resistive load at resonance, but acts like an inductive load when tuned above the input frequency, and like a capacitive load when tuned below this frequency.

Q. 3.53. What is meant by "space charge?" By "secondary emission"?

A. (a) "Space charge" is a charge due to the accumulation of negative electrons in the space between certain vacuum tube elements.

(b) "Secondary emission" is the emission of electrons from a material, due to the impact of high velocity electrons upon its surface. The original electrons are called primary electrons.

D. (a) In a diode which is not operating under saturation conditions, it will be found that a "cloud" of electrons exists between the cathode and the plate; the cloud is concentrated in a thin layer immediately surrounding the emitting surface. This cloud of electrons is called the "space charge" and exists due to the inability of the plate potential to attract all of the electrons leaving the emitter. The space charge has a negative potential and partially cancels the effectiveness of the plate potential in attracting electrons. Under conditions of equilibrium it is found that the space charge is continuously returning electrons to the emitter as well as receiving them from the emitter so that the total space charge remains constant.

In beam power tubes the space charge effect produces a negative gradient of potential at the plate that eliminates the necessity of utilizing a suppressor grid to reduce secondary emission from the plate. Beam power tubes are constructed so that the wires of the control and screen grids lie in the same plane. This causes the electrons to move in concentrated layers. The screen-plate distance is considerably greater than in conventional screen grid tubes, and so called "beam forming" plates are employed, at cathode potential, to assist producing the desired "beam" effect.

(b) If an electron is in an evacuated space containing a positively charged material, the electron will be attracted with ever-increasing velocity until it strikes the surface of the material. At the point of impact, the moving electron will impart its kinetic energy to other electrons and atoms within the material. If the impact is great enough, one or more electrons within the material will be dislodged with enough energy to be emitted from the surface. The number so emitted will depend upon the velocity of the primary electron and upon the type and temperature of the material. While secondary emission in an amplifier tube is usually detrimental, such is not always the case. For example, the dynatron oscillator relies upon one effect of secondary emission, called "negative resistance," for its feedback energy. Some structures are built to take advantage of this effect. For instance, in the RCA "image orthicon" television camera tube, there is incorporated an electron multiplier which deliberately produces secondary emission in order to amplify the magnitude of the camera signal.

Q. 3.54. What is meant by the "amplification factor" (mu) of a triode vacuum tube (amplifier)? Under what conditions would the amplifier gain approach the value of mu?

A. (a) The "amplification factor" (mu) of a triode vacuum tube is the ratio of a change of plate voltage which produces a given change of plate current, to the change in grid voltage which will produce the same change of plate current. It represents the theoretical maximum voltage gain of an amplifier.

(b) The amplifier gain will approach the value of mu if the ratio of plate load impedance to dynamic-tube plate impedance is high (10 or more).

D. (a) Amplification factor: The actual voltage gain of an amplifier tube can never be equal to the amplification factor because the drop across the plate impedance of the tube must be subtracted from the total available output signal. This amounts to a voltage divider with r_p in series with the plate load resistance. The only output voltage available is that across the plate load resistance. This means that in order for the voltage gain to be equal to the amplification factor, the load resistance must be infinitely large. The formula for amplification factor is $\mu = \dfrac{\Delta e_b}{\Delta e_c}|i_p|$

(b) The voltage amplification factor of a tube equals, $\mu \times E_s$, where E_s is the input grid signal voltage. Since every tube has an internal impedance some of the output voltage is "lost" in the tube impedance and is not available in the plate load. From a practical standpoint the load resistance should be relatively high with respect to the internal tube impedance (in triodes) if maximum gain is to be achieved. The mid-frequency gain may be calculated from the formula, $G_{mid} = g_m \times R_{eq}$, where g_m is the tube transconductance, and R_{eq} is the resultant parallel impedance of the internal tube impedance, the plate load resistance and the grid resistance of the following stage. This applies only to an RC coupled amplifier.

Q. 3.55. What is meant by "plate resistance" of a vacuum tube? Upon what does its value depend?

A. (a) The "plate resistance" of a vacuum tube is the ratio of a small change of plate current to the change of plate voltage producing that current. The grid voltage is a constant.

(b) The value of "plate resistance" is an indication of the effectiveness of the plate voltage in causing a change in the plate current. The plate resistance of triodes is much less than that of tetrodes or pentodes because the action of the screen grid makes the plate current relatively independent of plate voltage changes. When a screen grid is present it takes a much larger plate-voltage change to produce a given plate-current change.

D. Plate Resistance: Plate impedance or plate resistance of a vacuum tube is a function of the physical and electrical properties of the tube, and is the ratio between a small change of plate current to the change in plate voltage producing it, with the grid voltage held constant. If normal operating voltages are applied to a tube a certain definite value of plate current will flow. If the plate voltage is divided by the plate current the result is called the d-c plate resistance. Thus $R_p = \dfrac{E_b}{I_b}$. While this value is of some limited use, such

as in regulated power supplies, a more general term is needed which more accurately states the operating characteristics of a tube. This more general term is r_p or plate impedance. It represents the impedance offered by the cathode-to-plate path within a tube to a varying voltage.

Thus $r_p = \dfrac{\Delta e_b}{\Delta i_b}$, $|e_c|$ where Δ means "a small change of," r_p is the

plate impedance in ohms, e_b and i_b are the instantaneous values of plate voltage and current, and e_c is the instantaneous value of grid voltage, which is here held constant, as indicated by the parallel vertical lines enclosing e_c. The plate impedance may be considered to be the internal resistance of an equivalent a-c generator.

Q. 3.56. What is meant by the voltage "gain" of a vacuum tube amplifier? How does it achieve this gain?

A. (a) The voltage "gain" is the ratio of the output voltage to the input voltage, or

$$\text{Gain} = \frac{\text{E}_{\text{output}}}{\text{E}_{\text{input}}}$$

(b) Gain is a measure of the capability of vacuum tubes (except diodes) to produce "voltage amplification" of the input grid signal.

D. (a) Assuming normal plate and grid voltages to be present, the gain of a triode audio amplifier is a function of (1) tube transconductance, (2) plate load impedance, and (3) transformer step-up ratio (if used). While it is true that radical changes in plate supply voltage will change the voltage gain to some extent, this factor is of minor importance in comparison to those mentioned above. For resistance coupled amplifiers the gain is $G = g_m \times R_{eq}$, where g_m is the transconductance, and R_{eq} is the internal plate impedance, the plate load impedance and the grid resistance of the following stage taken in parallel. This formula only holds for mid-range frequencies, that is the *flat* portion of the frequency characteristic of the amplifier. For transformer coupled amplifiers, the gain with a triode and well-designed transformer is $G = \mu \times N$, where N is the turns ratio. Pentodes are not generally used with transformers, the usual exception being the output audio power amplifier. However, there is no question here of voltage gain. The only consideration is one of impedance matching for maximum power transfer.

(b) See Q. 3.46, Discussion (a)(b).

Q. 3.57. Draw a rough graph of plate current versus plate supply voltage for three different bias voltages on a typical triode vacuum tube.

(a) Explain, in a general way, how the value of the plate load resistance affects the portion of the curve over which the tube is operating. How is this related to distortion?

(b) Operation over which portion of the curve produces the least distortion?

A. (a) As shown in Fig. 3.57, the higher the value of plate-load resistance, the lower the position of the load line on the graph. The load line is plotted from the maximum plate current point (E_b/R_L) to the plate voltage point (E_b). When a grid signal is applied the tube operates along the load line. Thus, the value of load resistance determines the operating portion of the curves.

As indicated in Figure 3.57, load lines have been drawn in for 30,000 and 300,000 ohm plate-load resistors. Note that the 30,000 ohm load line passes through the grid-bias lines in an area where these are most linear and most evenly spaced. This of course is not true for the 300,000 ohm load line. Changes in grid voltages (input signal) produce corresponding changes in plate currents (output currents) and conse-

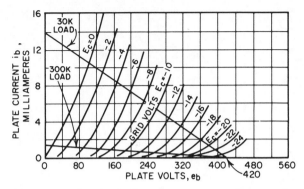

Fig. 3.57. Graph of plate current versus plate supply voltage for a typical triode.

quently in plate voltages (output voltages). The least amount of output wave distortion (versus input) will occur when the operation occurs between grid bias lines which are the most evenly spaced and most linear. Therefore, in this example (for least distortion), the 30,000 ohm load would be preferred.

(b) See (a) above.

Q. 3.58. A triode, "grounded cathode" audio amplifier has a mu (amplification factor) of 30, a plate impedance of 5,000 ohms, load impedance of 10,000 ohms, plate voltage of 300 volts, plate current of 10 ma, and cathode-resistor bias is used.

(a) What is the stage gain of this amplifier?

(b) What is the cut-off-bias voltage, E_{co}?

(c) Assuming the bias voltage is one-half the value of E_{co}, what value cathode resistor would be used to produce the required bias?

(d) What size capacitor should be used to sufficiently by-pass the cathode resistor if the lowest approximate frequency desired is 500 cycles per second?

A. (a) The stage gain = 20.

(b) The cut-off bias = -10 volts.

(c) The cathode resistor = 500 ohms.

(d) The cathode by-pass capacitor = 6.4 microfarads.

D. (a) Step 1: Find the stage gain of the amplifier,

$$A = \frac{\mu \times R_L}{R_L + R_p} \text{ where}$$

A = gain of the stage.

μ = amplification factor (mu).

R_L = load impedance, in ohms.

R_p = plate impedance of tube in ohms.

$$A = \frac{30 \times 10,000}{10,000 + 5,000} = \frac{300,000}{15,000} = 20$$

(b) Step 2: Find the cut-off bias (E_{co})

$$E_{co} = \frac{E_b}{\mu} \text{ where}$$

E_{co} = grid cut-off bias, in volts.
E_b = plate (supply) voltage, in volts.
μ = amplification factor (mu)

$$E_{co} = \frac{300}{30} = -10 \text{ volts.}$$

(c) Step 3: Find the cathode resistor value for one-half of E_{co}, or −5 volts

$$R_K = \frac{E_K}{I_p} \text{ where}$$

R_K = cathode resistor, in ohms.
E_K = cathode bias, in volts.
I_p = plate current in amperes.

$$R_K = \frac{5}{.01} = 500 \text{ ohms.}$$

(d) Step 4: Find the value of cathode by-pass capacitor.
(1) To be effective, the capacitor should have a reactance at least one-tenth or less of the value of the cathode resistor (or in this case, XC_K = 100 ohms) at the lowest frequency (or 500 cycles).

(2) $XC_K = \dfrac{1}{2\pi\, fC_K}$, or

$$C_K = \frac{1}{2\pi\, fXC_K} = \frac{.159}{500 \times 50} = \frac{.159}{25,000} = 6.4 \text{ microfarads.}$$

Q. 3.59. Why is the efficiency of an amplifier operated class C higher than one operated class A or class B?

A. In class C amplifiers the plate current is permitted to flow *only* during the time that the instantaneous value of plate voltage is at or near its *minimum* value. At all other times the tube is non-conducting. This permits a relatively small loss on the plate and high plate efficiency.

D. The outstanding characteristics of a class C amplifier are:
1. High plate circuit efficiency, up to 85%.

2. Large grid driving power.
3. Plate current exists for less than 180° of the grid excitation cycle, usually for approximately 120°.
4. Grid bias on the average is about twice cut-off value.
5. Large power output in comparison to class A.
6. Great distortion of plate current waveshape.

However, in order that the above conditions be met, a large value of bias must be used, in some cases equal to 4 times cut-off value, but usually about twice cut-off value. Since grid current must flow at some time in each cycle, a relatively large value of grid driving power must be available from a low impedance source. Appreciable r-f power is consumed in the grid circuit. Although the plate current wave is a pulse rich in harmonics, the plate voltage waveshape will be sinusoidal, since the plate load will in most cases be a tank circuit with a reasonably high Q. An interesting feature is that the maximum positive value of grid voltage ($e_{c\ max}$) is approximately equal to the minimum value of the plate voltage ($e_{b\ min}$).

Q. 3.60. The following are excerpts from a tube manual rating of a beam pentode. Explain the significance of each item:

(a) Control grid-to-plate capacitance   ...   1.1 uuf
(b) Input capacitance   ...   2.2 uuf
(c) Output capacitance   ...   8.5 uuf
(d) Heater voltage   ...   6.3 volts
(e) Maximum dc plate-supply voltage   ...   700 volts
(f) Maximum peak positive pulse voltage   ...   7,000 volts
(g) Maximum negative pulse plate voltage   ...   1,500 volts
(h) Maximum screen grid voltage   ...   175 volts
(i) Maximum peak negative control grid voltage ...   200 volts
(j) Maximum plate dissipation   ...   20 watts
(k) Maximum screen-grid dissipation   ...   30 watts
(l) Maximum dc cathode current   ...   200 ma
(m) Maximum peak cathode current   ...   700 ma
(n) Maximum control-grid circuit resistance   ...   0.47 megohm

A. Examination of an RCA tube manual shows these ratings to be almost identical for type 6CD6-GA television, horizontal-output tube. However, in two instances, the decimal points appear to have been misplaced. Input capacitance should read 22 uuf, instead of 2.2 uuf. Also maximum screen dissipation should read 3.0 watts, not 30 watts. The following is the significance of each listed item:

(a) Control grid-to-plate capacitance: The measured capacity from the control grid to the plate, with other grids connected to the cathode.

(b) Input capacitance: The sum of control grid-to-cathode, control grid-to-screen grid and control grid-to-suppressor grid (or beam plates) capacitances.

(c) Output capacitance: The sum of plate-to-cathode, plate-to-screen grid and plate-to-suppressor grid (or beam plates) capacitances.

(d) Heater voltage: The nominal cathode heater voltage. It may vary ± 10 percent.

(e) Maximum d–c plate-supply voltage: The maximum steady-state, power-supply voltage permitted to be applied to the plate to restrict the plate dissipation to a safe value.

(f) Maximum positive pulse voltage: In the TV circuit, this occurs during the horizontal flyback time (about 10 μs) when the high voltage builds up. This (7000 v) is the maximum safe value to prevent internal tube arcing.

(g) Maximum negative pulse voltage: In the TV circuit, this occurs during the horizontal trace (about 53 microseconds) and is limited for the same reason as in (f) above.

(h) Maximum screen-grid voltage (d–c): The maximum steady-state, d–c supply voltage permitted to be applied to the screen grid. The screen voltage largely determines plate current (and plate dissipation) as well as screen-grid current and dissipation.

(i) Maximum peak negative control-grid voltage: The maximum safe value to prevent control grid-to-cathode arcing.

(j) Maximum plate dissipation: The maximum safe wattage the plate can dissipate continuously, without causing tube damage (or short life).

(k) Maximum screen-grid dissipation: Same as (j) above, but for screen grid.

(l) Maximum d–c cathode current: The maximum continuous current which the cathode can supply without serious deterioration of the oxide coating of the cathode. The d–c (average) current must be limited to this value.

(m) Maximum peak-cathode current: Within the pulse-width limitations of the TV receiver operation, this is the maximum pulse current the cathode can supply without serious deterioration.

(n) Maximum control-grid circuit resistance: The maximum value of grid to ground resistance. Higher values may result in an excess positive grid voltage caused by positive ion-grid current, which would cancel out the bias and might damage or destroy the tube.

Q. 3.61.   Name at least three abnormal conditions which would tend to shorten the life of a vacuum tube, also name one or more probable causes of each condition.

A. 1. (a) Excessive heater voltage.

(b) Excessive plate current.

(c) Inadequate cooling.

(d) Excessive screen-grid current.

(e) Exceeding maximum pulse-current ratings.

2. The causes listed below are keyed to the same letters in 1, above.

(a) Line voltage too high; shorted series-dropping resistor; filament transformer voltage too high.

(b) Bias too low; plate voltage too high; screen grid voltage too high.

(c) Tube shield left off; cooling fan or other cooling scheme not operating.

(d) Bias too low; screen-grid voltage too high.

(e) Pulse-duty cycle too high. In some cases, especially where high voltages are involved, too low a heater voltage may cause cathode damage. In this case, particles of the cathode-oxide coating may be stripped off by the electrostatic field in the tube.

Q. 3.62. Name at least three circuit factors (not including tube types and component values) in a one-stage amplifier circuit, that should be considered at VHF which would not be of particular concern at VLF.

A. The following should be especially considered at VHF:

1. The possibility of circuit oscillation or regeneration due to stray capacitive feedback.

2. The use of low-loss components, such as coil forms, tube sockets, ferrite cores.

3. The use of non-inductive and low-loss by-pass and coupling capacitors, such as ceramic and mica types.

4. Neutralization may be required in some circuits.

5. Use of grounded-grid type of amplifier to reduce feedback problems.

6. Signal lead lengths must be short, to reduce lead inductance.

D. An additional circuit factor of concern at VHF and above is the manner in which the circuit is grounded. Very short and direct ground leads having negligible inductance must be used. In some cases, all grounds are returned to a common point on the chassis. This is done to avoid chassis ground currents which might result in amplifier instability. In multi-stage amplifiers, it may be necessary to run all grid, cathode and filament grounds to one part of the chassis and screen grid and plate ground to another part of the chassis. This helps to prevent feedback currents in the chassis from causing oscillation or instability of the amplifier.

In general, an amplifier for use at these high frequencies should be built in a very compact manner to minimize lead lengths and thereby assure minimum lead inductance. In addition, the effect of stray capacitance may be appreciable at the very-high frequencies involved and these too must be kept to a minimum. Stray capacitance is developed between wires, parts and ground, as well as between parts and between wires and parts. In a multi-stage amplifier, it is often necessary to shield tubes and r-f transformers to prevent regeneration or oscillation, due to coupling between these units.

Q. 3.63. What is a "lighthouse" triode? An "acorn" tube? These tubes were designed for operation in what frequency range?

A. (1) A "lighthouse" triode (or disk-seal tube) is a tube designed especially to operate at UHF and is shown in Fig. 3.63(a). The plate, grid and cathode are assembled in parallel planes instead of coaxially. Extremely close electrode spacing reduces electron transit time. In addition, the electrodes are connected to parallel discs, practically eliminating tube lead inductance. The use of small internal elements results in very low interelectrode capacities. These tubes will amplify up to about 2500 megacycles.

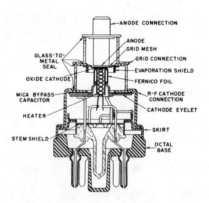

Fig. 3.63(a). Cross-section of a "lighthouse" triode tube.

(2) Acorn tubes are seldom used in modern electronic equipment. They will amplify up to about 600 megacycles. Acorn tubes are very small (about half the size of a golf ball) and have no base. Electrode connections are brought out to short wire pins which are sealed in a glass rim around the lower portion of the tube. An "acorn" tube is illustrated in Fig. 3.63(b).

D. "Lighthouse" tubes are also known as "disc-seal" and "planar-disc" tubes. The name "lighthouse" is derived from the appearance of

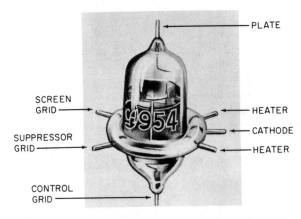

Fig. 3.63(b). A pentode-type of acorn tube. (Courtesy RCA)

the basic tube although a variety of the tubes have been made and may differ widely in appearance. The very close spacing of electrodes is exemplified by one type of lighthouse tube in which the grid and cathode are separated by only 0.004 inch. Because of the close electrode spacing, very low values of transit time are achieved. If the cathode-plate transit time is greater than one-tenth of a cycle at the operating frequency, the tube efficiency begins to drop. Efficiency decreases as the percentage of transit time to cycle increases. For a tube operating at 2500 megacycles, the time for one cycle is 4×10^{-4} microseconds and the maximum allowable transit time is 4×10^{-5} microseconds (see Q 3.64 following).

As the transit time becomes greater than one-tenth of a cycle, the plate current lags the plate voltage by greater than 36 degrees. This results in an important decrease of power output and consequent increase of tube-plate dissipation. The condition becomes worse with increasing values of transit time. In the case of oscillators, it is usually found that oscillation ceases as the transit time approaches a quarter of a cycle (90 degrees).

The physical configuration of a lighthouse tube is ideally suited for insertion into resonant coaxial-line tuners. The tuner may consist of coaxial line, cathode-grid, and plate-grid cavities. The assembly of a "lighthouse" tube in its coaxial tuner is shown in Fig. 3.63(c). Note in the figure, that the assembly comprises three concentric cylinders fitted to the end of the tube. Tuning of the cavity is accomplished by a cathode-grid shorting plunger and by a plate tuning rod which slides the plate cylinder over the plate terminal of the tube. Because of the high operating frequency (about 2500-3000 mc) mechanical problems dictate the use of tuning lines which are multiples of a quarter wavelength. As shown, the cathode line is about ¾ wavelength and the plate line about one full wavelength. (See also Q 3.62 above and Q 3.64 following.)

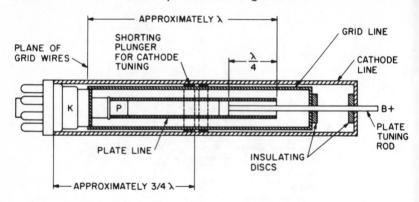

Fig. 3.63(c). Sketch of a lighthouse tube (left) mounted in its coaxial tuner (see discussion).

Q. 3.64. Why are special tubes sometimes required at UHF and above?

A.   Special tubes or tube types are usually required at UHF or higher frequencies. At frequencies above about 100 megacycles, the interelectrode capacitances of ordinary tubes will attenuate the signals greatly. In addition, the ordinary cathode-to-plate, electron-transit time of one-thousandth of a microsecond becomes excessive. At UHF this time approaches or may equal the time of one cycle of the operating frequency, causing undesirable phase shifts within the tube. In addition, the relatively large lead inductance of ordinary tubes limits their operating frequency.

D.   Desirable characteristics of UHF tubes are:
1. Closely spaced electrodes.
2. Small elements.
3. Low-inductance leads.
4. No tube base.

In special VHF and UHF tubes, such as "traveling-wave" tubes, klystrons and magnetrons, the transit time of electrons is utilized to provide proper operation. For a description of these tubes, see Q. 3.246, Q. 3.247 and Q. 3.248 following. See also Q. 3.63 above.

Q. 3.65.   Draw a diagram of each of the following power supply circuits. Explain the operation of each, including the relative input and output voltage amplitudes, waveshapes, and current waveforms.

(a) Vacuum-tube diode, half-wave rectifier with a capacitive-input "pi-section" filter.

(b) Vacuum-tube diode, full-wave rectifier with choke input (RC) filter.

(c) Silicon diode, doubler-circuit rectifier with a resistive load.

(d) Non-synchronous-vibrator power supply, with silicon diode, bridge-circuit rectifier and capacitive input "pi-section" filter.

(e) Synchronous-vibrator power supply with capacitive input "pi-section" filter.

A. (a) See Fig. 3.65(a1). The following description applies to a half-wave rectifier system as illustrated. The first problem to be considered is that of rectification, or changing alternating current into unidirectional (d-c) current. A rectifier tube is essentially a one-way path for electronic flow since its reverse (or inverse) current conduction is almost zero. The rectifier tube conducts only when its plate is positive with respect to cathode, and is a non-conductor when the plate is negative with respect to cathode. When an alternating voltage is applied to such a rectifier tube, its output consists of a series of current pulses, which are uni-directional in character. See Fig. 3.65(a2) for waveshapes of operation. Due to the action of the filter, these pulses are considerably less than ½-cycle in width and are separated by spaces more than ½-cycle in width. The output of a rectifier tube must be filtered to a large degree in order to eliminate the fundamental and harmonic frequency components from the rectifier-filter system output. The usual method for accomplishing this is to insert a suitable *LC* low-pass filter in series with the rectifier output whose cut-off frequency is well below the line frequency. The type shown in the figure is a capacitor-input "pi"-type filter. The input capacitor of the filter charges up practically to the peak value of each positive alternation applied to the plate of the rectifier tube. The rectifier tube stops delivering current to the filter until the next positive alternation exceeds the potential of the input capacitor. During this interval of time, the power is supplied by the input capacitor, whose voltage drops in a linear manner due to the constant-current action of the filter choke. The output capacitor of the filter must be large enough to offer very little reactance at the lowest frequencies to be amplified, so as to reduce the possibilities of feedback through the medium of the common power supply impedance, and also to supply peak demands from the load.

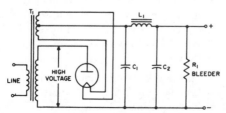

Fig. 3.65(a1). Half-wave rectifier, with "pi-section" filter.

In a half-wave rectifier, the ripple frequency is equal to the line frequency, i.e., a line frequency of 60 cycles will produce a ripple frequency of 60 cycles. A half-wave rectifier is the simplest and least expensive type. However, it is more difficult to filter and ordinarily has poorer regulation than a full-wave type. The d-c output voltage of this supply depends upon the extent of current taken from it. If the loading is light, the d-c voltage may equal the peak value (not peak-to-peak) of the secondary voltage. As the loading increases, the d-c voltage output drops

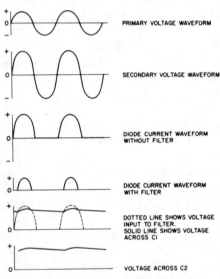

Fig. 3.65(a2). Current and voltage waveforms for a half-wave rectifier with capacitor-input filter.

and the ripple voltage increases. If the supply is heavily loaded, the d-c voltage may drop to 0.9 or less of the rms value of the secondary voltage.

(b) For diagram, see Fig. 3.65(b1). This arrangement may be used where the highest voltage taken from the power supply is at a high current drain and fed to a stage which is insensitive to a fairly high ripple voltage. Such a stage would be the power output stage of an audio amplifier. Stages of higher gain and low-current requirements require a lower ripple voltage and this may be supplied by an additional RC filter, as shown. A typical stage meeting these requirements is an audio preamplifier. (See Q. 4.24.)

The waveforms for the full-wave rectifier are shown in Fig. 3.65(b2). Referring to the schematic (Fig. 3.65(b1)) it may be seen that the high-voltage secondary is centertapped, the centertap becoming the negative side of the d-c output voltage. Note that the *total* secondary voltage must be twice that required for a half-wave rectifier, because of the centertap. (See part (d) of this question for comparison to bridge-type rectifier.) However, the tubes conduct alternately for each half of every cycle and the output voltage (ripple frequency) is applied to the filter at twice the line frequency. The ripple frequency for a 60 cycle line will be 120 cycles. The higher ripple frequency permits a less expensive filter to be employed than in the case of a half-wave rectifier having the same ripple voltage requirements. The full-wave rectifier will also have improved regulation over the half-wave type. For comparative characteristics of choke and capacitor input filters, see Q. 3.69.

(c) See Fig. 3.65(c).

CASCADE DOUBLER, FIGURE-GROUP A. During the first negative half cycle, capacitor C_1 charges through diode D1 to approximately the peak value, E, of the transformer secondary voltage (Figure A′). As soon as the negative peak has gone by and the wave starts in the positive direction, capacitor C_1 begins to charge C_2 through D2 (Figure A″). When the wave reaches its positive peak, the voltage across the transformer secondary in series with the voltage across C_1 (totalling $2E$) charges C_2 to approximately double the peak secondary voltage. This doubler is a half-wave device.

CONVENTIONAL DOUBLER, FIGURE-GROUP B. For simplicity of explanation it is assumed that the circuit has been in operation for some time and that we are considering a positive-going half cycle (Figure B′). C_2 has been previously charged through D2 and the transformer secondary to approximately the peak value of secondary voltage. As soon as the transformer voltage starts in the positive direction, C_2 begins to discharge through D1 into the load and filter. When the transformer reaches its maximum positive value, it adds its voltage to that of C_2 and charges the filter capacitor (not shown) to approximately double the peak secondary voltage. During this same positive-going half cycle, capacitor C_1 is being recharged to the peak secondary voltage through D1 and the transformer secondary.

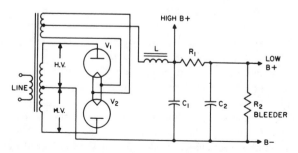

Fig. 3.65(b1). Full-wave rectifier with choke-input RC filter.

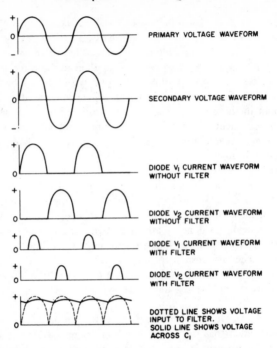

PRIMARY VOLTAGE WAVEFORM

SECONDARY VOLTAGE WAVEFORM

DIODE V₁ CURRENT WAVEFORM
WITHOUT FILTER

DIODE V₂ CURRENT WAVEFORM
WITHOUT FILTER

DIODE V₁ CURRENT WAVEFORM
WITH FILTER

DIODE V₂ CURRENT WAVEFORM
WITH FILTER

DOTTED LINE SHOWS VOLTAGE
INPUT TO FILTER.
SOLID LINE SHOWS VOLTAGE
ACROSS C₁

*Fig. 3.65 (b2). Current and voltage waveforms for a full-
wave rectifier with choke-input filter.*

As soon as the wave starts in the negative direction (Figure B″), capacitor C_1 begins discharging through D2 into the load (and filter, not shown); when the transformer reaches its maximum negative value, its voltage is added in series to that of C_1 charging the filter capacitor (not shown) to approximately double the peak secondary voltage. During this same negative-going half cycle, C_2 is being recharged to the peak secondary voltage through D2 and the transformer secondary. This completes one cycle of full-wave operation.

(d) *Note:* Although there are many vibrator power supplies in present use, it should be realized that this type of supply is rapidly being replaced by transistor power supplies which have no moving parts and are far more reliable. Refer to Fig. 3.65(d). When power is applied to the vibrator coil and transformer primary, the armature is pulled to the left. This shorts out the vibrator coil and the armature springs to the right and touches the right-hand contact, after which the magnetic field of the coil and the spring action cause it to touch the left-hand contact. This action becomes cyclical at about 150 to 250 cps. Note that the armature action causes current to flow first in the top half of the primary

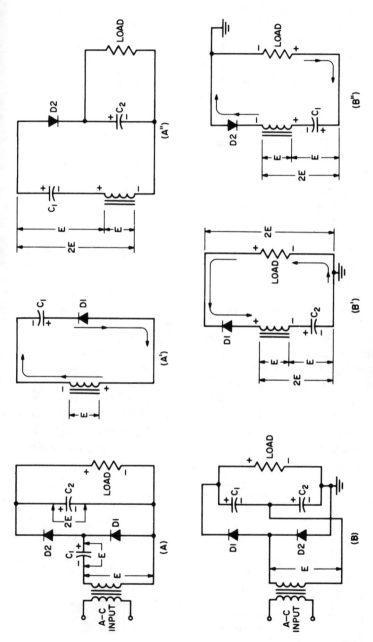

Fig. 3.65 (c). Group A shows a cascade doubler; group B shows a conventional doubler circuit.

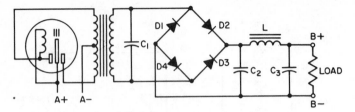

*Fig. 3.65(d). Non-synchronous vibrator with bridge
rectifier and pi-section filter.*

and then in the bottom half, but in opposite directions. This constitutes
an alternating current in the primary which is stepped up in the secondary winding to the desired value. The bridge rectifier shown is a
full-wave rectifier and operates as follows:

(1) When the top of the secondary is positive and the bottom negative, electron flow is through the secondary from top to bottom, through
D4 to B–, through the load and L, through D2 and back to the top of
the transformer.

(2) When the polarities are reversed, electron flow is through D3,
up through the secondary, through D1 to B–, through the load and L
and back to D3. For filter operation, see part (a) of this question.

(e) See Fig. 3.65(e). The usual synchronous rectifier is the synchronous vibrator, consisting of a "U" frame designed to permit the
mounting of a coil with pole piece at the closed end. A vibrating reed
and insulated side springs with contacts are mounted at the opposite
end. The reed carries contacts mounted on either side in pairs, corresponding to the stationary side spring contacts. The vibrating reed is
usually so connected as to keep it at ground potential. The "driver"
coil is a high resistance winding which is placed in series with one-half
of the centertapped primary of the transformer and the battery. Both

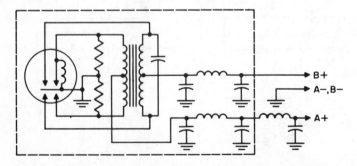

*Fig. 3.65(e). Schematic diagram of a synchronous vibrator
power supply, using capacitor-input filter.*

primary and secondary windings of the transformer are centertapped. The centertap of the primary is connected to the "hot" side of the d-c input line, while the centertap of the secondary is the take-off point for the positive high-voltage rectified d.c. The operation is as follows: All contact pairs are open normally and the starting of the reed movement depends upon the magnetic attraction of the "driver" coil. This movement is sufficient to cause the reed to make good electrical connection with a side spring contact which is connected to the same side of the transformer as the driver coil. This shorts the driver coil, destroys the magnetic field and releases the reed which now swings in the opposite direction beyond its original resting position. The reed now contacts the opposite side spring connections, and the driver-coil field pulls it back. In this manner the reed sets up vibrations, usually designed to be 135 cycles per second. As the reed moves, the secondary side spring contacts alternately reverse the primary and secondary transformer connections so that the output is a uni-directional current (d.c.). For filter operation, see part (a) of this question.

Q. 3.66. What advantage may a bridge rectifier circuit have over a conventional full-wave rectifier?

A. See Q. 3.65(d), above for diagram of bridge rectifier and (b) of that question for diagram of a full-wave rectifier. The advantages are as follows:

(a) A bridge circuit produces almost double the output voltage, using the same transformer. (Centertap of secondary is not used.)

(b) For the same output voltage, the inverse-peak voltage is only one-half as much across each tube in a bridge rectifier (4 tubes), compared to a conventional full-wave rectifier (2 tubes).

D. The same advantage is true when solid-state rectifiers are used for both (a) and (b) above. Solid-state rectifiers are preferred for bridge circuits for the elimination of the three filament transformers which would be required for vacuum tubes and for their greater reliability and lower internal drop.

Q. 3.67. What are "swinging chokes"? Where are they normally used?

A. (a) "Swinging chokes" are power-supply filter chokes, whose inductance varies inversely with the load current in the choke.

(b) They are used to improve the voltage regulation of a power supply which is operating under conditions of varying loads.

D. A swinging choke is one whose inductance varies inversely with the amount of d-c current flowing through it. The main reason for using a swinging choke is economy, as compared with the use of a conventional or smoothing choke. Where a varying load is present, less filtering is required at heavy loads. As the load decreases, it is necessary to have an increasing value of inductance if the choke is to continue to filter properly, otherwise the output voltage will rise sharply at low current values. A swinging choke may be chosen to fulfill these requirements much more economically than a smoothing choke which would have to be designed to present a constant maximum inductance under all load conditions. This would mean a large, expensive choke. A swinging choke must be the one nearest the rectifier tube, and is generally followed by a smoothing choke in order to satisfy filtering conditions. A system like this is still considerably more economical than if two smoothing chokes had to be used. The inductance is made to vary by having a very small gap, such as the thickness of a piece of fish paper, inserted in the iron core.

Q. 3.68. Show a method of obtaining two voltages from one power supply.

A.   See Fig. 3.68(a).

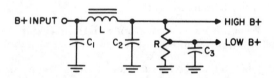

Fig. 3.68(a). A simple divider method for obtaining two voltages from one power supply.

D.   The following example illustrates the method of determining the voltage divider resistance.

A rectifier-filter power supply is designed to furnish 500 volts at 60 milliamperes to one circuit and 400 volts at 40 milliamperes to another circuit. The bleeder current in the voltage divider is to be 15 milliamperes. What value of resistance should be placed between the 500- and 400-volt taps of the voltage divider?

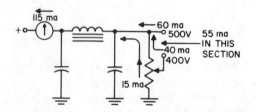

Fig. 3.68(b). A rectifier-filter system which can supply 500 volts at 60 milliamperes and 400 volts at 40 milliamperes to another circuit.

Refer to Fig. 3.68(b). It will be seen that two currents are present in the 400- to 500-volt section. These are the bleeder current of 15 ma plus the 400-volt load current of 40 ma or a total of 55 milliamperes. The value of resistance is found by Ohm's Law.

$$R = \frac{E}{I} = \frac{100}{.055} = 1818.2 \ ohms.$$

The value of resistance should be 1818.2 ohms.

The power rating is found as follows: $E \times I = 5.5$ watts actual dissipation. Use a 10-watt resistor as a safety factor.

Q. 3.69. What are the characteristics of a capacitor-input filter system as compared to a choke-input system? What is the effect upon a filter choke of a large value of direct current flow?

A. (a) The primary comparative characteristics of a capacitor-input filter are:

(1) Higher d-c output voltage. (About 1.4 times rms value of secondary voltage under light loads.)

(2) Poorer voltage regulation.

(3) Higher peak surge currents.

(4) Not suitable for use with mercury vapor tubes.

(b) The effect depends upon the original design of the choke. If it was designed to carry a large value of direct current, there would be no adverse effects. However, if the normal rating of the choke was being exceeded, d-c core saturation would occur, the value of inductance would be reduced, and the choke might overheat.

D. The characteristics of a choke-input filter as compared with a capacitor-input filter, are:

(1) Lower output voltage, about 90% of rms secondary voltage.

(2) Better voltage regulation.

(3) Lower peak current surges.

(4) More efficient utilization of tubes and transformers.

When a capacitor-input filter is used, the capacitor charges to 1.414 times the rms value of the secondary voltage of the power transformer. Neglecting any drop in the d-c resistance of the choke, this will be the output d-c voltage with a light load. If the load increases, however, this voltage may drop to .9 of the rms secondary value or less. The choke input filter starts with a d-c voltage of .9 rms secondary voltage and will vary very much less, thus affording better regulation. See Question 3.65. If the rectifier has mercury-vapor tubes, a choke-input filter must be used, as otherwise the initial current may be high enough to damage the tube. At the first starting cycle of the rectifying voltage, the input capacitor has no charge. This means that it is practically a short circuit for the initial current until it becomes charged. Thus there is nothing to limit the initial current except the impedance of the tube which is very low and the impedance of the high voltage secondary winding which is also very low. This means that the initial current value will be extremely high and may damage the tube.

Where the input capacitor is removed and a choke-input filter is used, the initial current will be very much lower. This is because, when the initial charging current flows, it must flow through the inductance of the choke oil. The sudden surge of current develops a high reactive drop across the choke coil which opposes the original secondary voltage and thus limits the current in the system to a safe value. Sometimes, in low current systems, a current limiting resistor may be used in series with the rectifier tube. This, however, has an adverse effect on the regulation.

Q. 3.70. What is the purpose of a "bleeder" resistor as used in conjunction with power supplies?

A. The primary purpose of a "bleeder" resistor in conventional power supplies is to improve the regulation of the voltage output.

D. A bleeder resistor is connected directly across the load terminals. It is usually designed to draw at least 10% of the total current. In this way the bleeder acts as a minimum load on the power supply when the normal load is removed. Since the output voltage of a rectifier tends to rise when the load is removed, the bleeder draws a constant current and prevents the voltage from rising as much as it would if no bleeder were present. The bleeder also serves the important function of discharging the filter capacitors when the power is turned off.

Q. 3.71. Would varying the value of the bleeder resistor in a power supply have any effect on the ripple voltage?

A. Varying the value of the bleeder resistor might affect the ripple voltage output of a power supply.

D. If a bleeder resistor of too low a value were employed, then the bleeder current plus the load current might exceed the normal current rating of the power supply. This would decrease the output voltage and increase the ripple voltage. The d-c current rating of the filter choke(s) might also be exceeded, reducing the choke inductance and increasing the ripple voltage.

Q. 3.72. What effect does the amount of current required by the load have upon the voltage regulation of the power supply? Why is voltage regulation an important factor?

A. (a) The greater the amount of current required by the load, the poorer the regulation will tend to be. (Of course a supply can be designed to maintain the required regulation for any practical load).
(b) Regulation is important to maintain virtually constant output

supply voltages under varying loads. This prevents inter-modulation of circuits due to power-supply voltage variations as well as possibly insufficient or excessive supply voltages.

D. "Voltage regulation" expresses the ratio between the amount of voltage drop under full load conditions from the no-load value, to the full load voltage. This ratio is multiplied by 100 to express it as a percentage. Poor regulation may be caused by:

1. High resistance filter chokes.
2. Insufficient filter capacity.
3. Saturation of iron core of filter chokes.
4. No bleeder resistor.
5. Varying drop in rectifier tube with changing load (high-vacuum type).

Regulation is usually expressed as a percentage according to the formula: $Reg. = \dfrac{E_{NL} - E_{FL}}{E_{FL}} \times 100$, where E_{NL} is the no-load voltage, and E_{FL} is the full-load voltage.

Q. 3.73. What is meant by the "peak-inverse-voltage" rating of a diode and how can it be computed for a full-wave power supply?

A. (a) "Peak-inverse-voltage" rating of a rectifier tube is the maximum safe peak voltage which can be applied in the reverse direction without causing "arc back" or "flash back."

(b) In a capacitor input full-wave rectifier power supply, the peak-inverse-voltage across the non-conducting tube equals the peak-to-peak a-c voltage of one-half the secondary winding, or the rms value of the entire secondary winding times 1.414, less the drop in the conducting tube and the d-c drop in the half of the transformer which is conducting.

D. In a half-wave rectifier system the peak-inverse-voltage is simply equal to the rms secondary voltage times 1.414.

Q. 3.74. Discuss the relative merits and limitations as used in power supplies of the following types of rectifiers:
(a) Mercury-vapor diode.
(b) High-vacuum diode.
(c) Copper oxide.
(d) Silicon.
(e) Selenium.

A. (a) Advantages of mercury-vapor rectifier tubes are:
1. A low internal voltage drop of 10 to 15 volts, which remains

constant under varying load conditions, thus making for good voltage regulation.

2. Permits the use of oxide coated cathodes, with their lower filament power requirements.

3. Cooler operation due to the low internal drop.

4. Greater efficiency and economy in high voltage, high current operation.

Disadvantages of mercury-vapor rectifier tubes are:

1. Produces radio frequency interference due to ionization of mercury or gas.

2. Relatively low peak-inverse-voltage rating.

3. Filament may be damaged if not pre-heated before plate voltage is applied.

(b) Advantages of high-vacuum rectifier tubes are:

1. Higher peak-inverse-voltage rating for a given size of tube.

2. Will stand more abuse without breakdown.

3. Does not generate r-f interference (hash).

Disadvantages of high-vacuum rectifier tubes are:

1. Voltage drop across the tube varies with load current changes making for poorer voltage regulation.

2. Higher filament power requirements.

3. Tube runs hotter due to larger voltage drop.

(c) Copper-oxide rectifiers: The merit of this type is that they can (for a given size) supply a relatively large direct current. Limitations of this type are: (1) there is a large shunt capacitance, and (2) its characteristics vary widely with temperature.

Note: These rectifiers are rapidly being replaced in many uses by germanium and silicon diodes.

(d) Silicon rectifiers: The merits of this type are:

(1) Compact size.

(2) High-current ratings (up to several amperes for larger units).

The major limitation is the relatively low peak-inverse-voltage rating of a junction. By stacking units in series, peak inverse ratings up to several thousand volts can be achieved.

(e) Selenium rectifiers: The merits of this type are:

(1) Higher junction break-down voltage than copper oxide.

(2) Lower forward resistance than copper oxide and, therefore, greater current-carrying capacity.

(3) Can be used for high-voltage applications by stacking units in series.

(4) Compact in size (for its type).

(5) Low voltage drop across rectifier (about 5 volts). Some limitations of selenium rectifiers are:

(1) Require appreciable space and special mounting facilities.

(2) Must be mounted to obtain adequate cooling.

(3) Appreciably larger size than silicon rectifiers, where they are interchangeable for the same function.

(4) High-shunt capacity, limiting use to power and audio frequencies.

D. (a) It is important to operate a mercury-vapor tube within specified temperature limits in order to realize maximum tube life and efficiency. Mercury-vapor tubes are built with an excess of liquid mercury to maintain a saturated condition of the vapor. The temperature of this vapor determines the pressure in the tube. If the pressure (or temperature) is too low, ionization is incomplete and the space charge is not sufficiently neutralized. Under these conditions the tube drop becomes excessive. With a high voltage drop, the ion velocities become very great, and bombard the cathode with enough energy to damage it. The minimum temperature at which the condensed mercury may be operated without causing disintegration of the cathode is about 20°C. If the operating temperature is excessive, an increase of vapor pressure will occur which will decrease the peak inverse voltage and may cause "flash-back." The maximum operating temperature is usually in the order of 75°C.

In a mercury-vapor rectifier tube positive ions are produced which tend to neutralize the negative space charge and thus permit higher conduction currents to take place. Electrons which are removed from the positive ions also add to the plate current. When operating two mercury-vapor rectifier tubes in parallel, small resistors must be placed in series with each plate lead.

The operating characteristic curve of a mercury-vapor rectifier tube is so steep that any slight difference in the characteristics of two tubes would cause a very large difference in the currents taken by each tube. The tube with the smaller voltage drop would take almost the entire load current. This difficulty can be overcome by connecting a small resistor in series with each tube before connecting them in parallel.

(b) For use in circuits operating under 400 volts d.c., the high-vacuum type can be designed to have an internal drop which is little, if any, greater than the internal drop of a mercury-vapor tube. However, this is not true of higher voltage operation in which high-vacuum tubes have a greater voltage drop than the mercury-vapor tube. The peak inverse voltage is the maximum safe negative voltage which can be applied to the plate of a rectifier tube without danger of arcing from plate to cathode. This value is always lower, for a given size, in a mercury-vapor tube due to the ionization of the mercury, which offers a better conduction path than a vacuum. The mercury-vapor tube generates r-f interference as a result of ionization, and it must be properly shielded and its output filtered.

(c) The most common use of copper oxide rectifiers is their use in rectifying a-c voltages of low and medium frequencies so that a-c measurements can be made with d-c meters.

(d) Silicon rectifiers are frequently being used to replace vacuum tube rectifiers. They require no filament supply or tube socket and have a very low voltage drop. It is frequently necessary to protect silicon rectifiers against peak capacitor charging surges by a small series resistor. The use of such a resistor has an adverse effect on voltage regulation and must therefore be kept to the smallest permissible value.

(e) Selenium rectifiers have definite advantages over copper oxide types (as stated above) and have replaced the latter in many instances. However, selenium rectifiers are frequently being replaced by solid-state rectifiers, such as the silicon type.

Q. 3.75. Explain the action of a voltage regulator (VR) tube.

A.   Refer to Fig. 3.75(a) and (b). A VR tube regulates by virtue of the fact that a constant (relatively) voltage drop appears across the tube as long as the tube current remains within the proper limits (usually

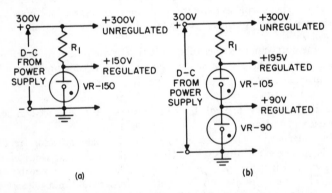

Fig. 3.75. Applications of cold-cathode electron tubes.

5 to 30 ma.). As shown in the figures, the output voltage supply is taken across the tube(s) itself. Variations in either input voltage or output-load current cause varying voltages across the series resistor (R_1), but not across the tube itself. The regulation obtained by this means is poorer than when an amplifier-type of regulator is used, but is adequate for many non-critical, low current circuits.

D.   A cold-cathode gassy-diode rectifier tube (see Q. 3.46(h)) consists of a large area cathode (coated with suitable emitting material such as barium and strontium), a small diameter rod-shaped pointed anode, and a starter anode. These elements are enclosed in an envelope containing a gas such as helium, acetylene, argon, or neon. The gas pressure is critical for correct operation. Electron emission from the cathode is due to two major factors:

1. If the electrostatic field produced by the starter anode is sufficiently great, electrons will be pulled from the cathode coating by force of attraction.

2. Any gas is always in a state of partial ionization. The existing positive ions are accelerated by the cathode to starter-anode voltage so that they strike the cathode with sufficient force to aid in the emission of electrons. The rectifying action of such a tube makes use of the fact that the current which ionization causes to exist between two electrodes in a low-pressure gas is approximately proportional to the area of the cathode. If one electrode has a very large area (cathode) and the other electrode a very small area (anode), electrons will flow in the direction from cathode to anode. Conduction occurs on that half cycle which makes the anode positive with respect to the cathode.

Q. 3.76. If the plate, or plates of a rectifier tube suddenly became red hot, what might be the cause, and how could remedies be effected?

A. If the plate of a rectifier tube became red hot, it would be due to excessive current demand upon the tube.

D. The filter components should be checked as indicated in Question 3.77. If these are in good order the current demands of all the supplied circuits should be investigated. A screen or plate bypass capacitor might be shorted. The coupling capacitor to a high power tube might be shorted. In the case of an r-f power amplifier the plate tank might be mistuned or overloaded.

Q. 3.77. If a high vacuum type, high voltage rectifier tube suddenly became red hot, what might be the cause, and how could remedies be effected?

A. The following should be checked:

(1) The filter capacitors should be checked for leakage or short circuit.

(2) If these are good the choke or chokes should be checked for possible insulation breakdown.

(3) The rectifier tube itself should be checked for gas and shorts.

D. See Q. 3.76.

Q. 3.78. What does a blue haze in the space between the filament and plate of a high-vacuum rectifier tube indicate?

A. A blue haze indicates the presence of gas in the tube.

D. The blue color is due to the ionization of free gas within the tube and is caused by electron bombardment. If the tube is operating under normal conditions, it should be replaced, as its peak-inverse-voltage rating is decreasing and it may soon become unsuitable as a rectifier under the existing conditions.

A blue color is a normal condition of operation in tubes such as mercury-vapor rectifier tubes and voltage regulator tubes.

A glow from within the tube, often a purplish color, indicates a "soft" tube. If the tube was not originally designed to be a "soft" tube, other indications would be: excessive plate current, erratic or non-operation, and a possible red heat observable in the plate. In certain applications the cathode or filament may be destroyed due to positive-ion bombardment. Sometimes fluorescence occurs in the glass itself, also bluish or purplish; this does not indicate a soft tube.

During the manufacturing processes, many precautions are taken to exclude the presence of air from tubes, even those which are designed to contain gas after evacuation. The presence of such air or other undesired gases will interfere with the normal action of the tube due to ionization under the impact of the emitted electrons. Most gases are driven off by heating the tube to a high degree during evacuation. Any gases which remain are absorbed by the "getter," usually consisting of barium, "flashed" inside the tube after evacuation is complete. Deliberate introduction of gas is then made if desired.

INDICATING INSTRUMENTS

Q. 3.79. Make a sketch showing the construction of the D'Arsonval type meter and label the various parts. Draw a circuit diagram of a vacuum-tube-voltmeter and a wattmeter.

A. (a) For the sketch of a D'Arsonval meter, see Fig. 3.79(a).

The D'Arsonval type of meter consists of three basic parts: (1) a permanent magnet, (2) a movable coil with pointer attached, rotating in jewel bearings, (3) two spiral springs, one at each side of the movable coil. The current to be measured is caused to flow through the movable coil, connection to which is made through the two spiral springs. The magnetic field set up in the movable coil is proportional to the current flowing through it, and causes the coil to turn against the two spiral springs by reacting against the field of the permanent magnet. The amount of coil rotation (and needle), therefore, depends upon the motor force developed to overcome the resistance of the spiral springs. The movable coil rotates about a stationary soft iron core, to increase the magnetic force and thus the sensitivity of the meter. The movable coil is wound of very fine silk covered copper wire upon a light aluminum frame. The frame also performs the function of damping. As the coil moves in the permanent magnetic field, eddy currents are set up in the frame which in turn produce magnetic fields tending to oppose the original field of the permanent magnet, thus tending to stop the rotation. Without such damping, the needle would oscillate many times before finally coming to rest at the proper reading.

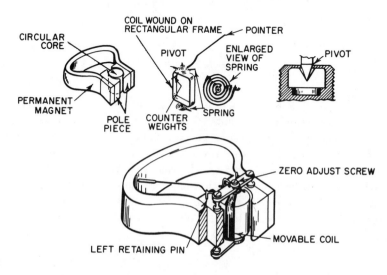

Fig. 3.79(a). Construction details of a D'Arsonval moving-coil mechanism.

(b) For the circuit diagram of a vacuum-tube voltmeter, see Fig. 3.79(b). The major advantage of a vacuum-tube voltmeter over a conventional (simple) voltmeter is the VTVM's high input resistance which is commonly 11 megohms on all scales. The vacuum-tube voltmeter thus draws negligible current from the circuit being tested and thereby avoids erroneous readings. Generally speaking, the impedance of the meter should be ten times greater than that of the circuit it is shunting for test. Contrast the 11 megohm impedance on a 1.5 volt scale of a VTVM, with the 30,000 ohm impedance of a 20,000 ohm-per-volt meter, and with the 1,500 ohm impedance of a 1,000 ohm-per-volt meter. This last meter, measuring voltage across a one megohm resistor, would provide a completely erroneous reading by changing the circuit impedance from 1,000,000 ohms to approximately 1,500 ohms.

(c) For the circuit diagram of a wattmeter, see Fig. 3.79(c).

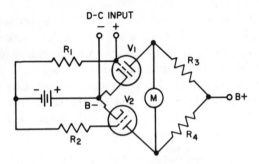

Fig. 3.79(b). Simplified diagram of a balanced triode d–c vacuum-tube-voltmeter.

A wattmeter is basically a voltmeter and an ammeter so connected that power factor is automatically compensated for in the indicating device. The usual type of wattmeter consists of two stationary coils made of a few turns of heavy wire which are connected in series with each other and with the line, and a movable coil inside of the two fixed ones, which is connected in series with a high resistance across the line as a voltmeter. The current in the stationary coils produces a field which is proportional to the line current, while the current in the movable coil

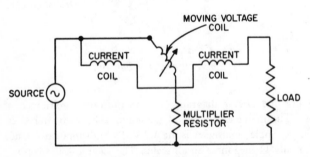

Fig. 3.79(c). Circuit diagram of a wattmeter.

produces a field which is proportional to the line voltage. The torque tending to deflect the needle of the moving coil is proportional to the product of the instantaneous line voltage and current, or to the instantaneous power. However, the moving element has sufficient damping so that the needle indicates only the *average* power, and thus compensates for power factor. Wattmeters of this type may be used on either a.c. or d.c.

Q. 3.80. Show by a diagram how a voltmeter and ammeter should be connected to measure power in a d-c circuit.

A. For the diagram, see Fig. 3.80.

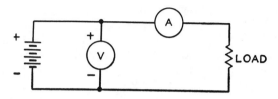

Fig. 3.80. D-c power measurement with voltmeter and ammeter.

D. In a d-c circuit, as shown, the power in watts is equal to the product of the voltage in volts and the current in amperes, or

$$P = E \times I$$

Q. 3.81. If a 0–1 d-c milliammeter is to be converted into a voltmeter with a full scale calibration of 100 volts, what value of resistance should be connected in series with the milliammeter?

A. The series resistance should equal 100,000 ohms, minus the meter resistance which is usually small enough to neglect in this case.

D. The value of series resistance can be found from the formula,

$$R = \frac{E \text{ (full scale)}}{I \text{ (full scale)}} = \frac{100}{.001} = 100{,}000 \text{ ohms.}$$

All standard voltmeters are basically milliammeters or microammeters. The resistance of the meter would probably not be known, but could be measured if equipment were available. However, the full scale current rating is always available on the face of the meter. Neglecting the meter resistance, the value of multiplier resistor could be calculated from, $R = \dfrac{E_{fs}}{I_{fs}}$, where R is the value of multiplier resistance, E_{fs} is the full scale voltage reading desired, I_{fs} is the full scale current rating of the meter in question.

Q. 3.82. A one-milliampere meter having a resistance of 25 ohms was used to measure an unknown current by shunting the meter with a 4 ohm resistor. It then read 0.4 milliampere. What was the unknown current value?

A. The unknown current was 2.9 milliamperes.

D. A basic formula to use in these problems is

$$R_m I_m = R_s I_s$$

where

R_m = resistance of the meter

I_m = current flowing in the meter

R_s = resistance of the shunt

I_s = current in the shunt.

This is because $R_m I_m$ is the voltage across the meter $(E = IR)$ and $R_s I_s$ is the voltage across the shunt. The two voltages must be the same because the two are connected.

The meter drop is $R_m I_m = 25 \times 0.0004 = 0.01$ volt.

Then $\qquad R_s I_s = 0.01;\ I_s = \dfrac{0.01}{4} = 0.0025$ amp.

Both together take 0.0025 amp. + 0.0004 amp. = 2.9 milliamperes, the total current.

Q. 3.83. An RF VTVM is available to locate resonance of a tunable primary tank circuit of an RF transformer. If the VTVM is measuring the voltage across the tuned secondary, how would resonance of the primary be indicated?

A. Resonance will be indicated by the peak reading of the meter.

D. At resonance the primary tank will offer maximum impedance to the wave and therefore the maximum voltage will be developed across it and coupled to the secondary.

Q. 3.84. Define the following terms and describe a practical situation in which they might be used.
(a) RMS voltage
(b) peak current
(c) average current
(d) power
(e) energy

A. (a) RMS (or root-mean-square) is also known as the "effective" value of a waveform. In the case of a sine wave, it equals 0.707 of the peak value of the wave. Many meters are calibrated in terms of RMS values because this is the "working" or "heating" value of the current. The effective value of an a-c current is that value which would cause the same heating effect as a d-c current of the same numerical value.

(b) The peak current of any waveform is the greatest instantaneous value of that current. For a sine wave, the peak current equals 1.414 times the RMS value.

Peak currents are important in rectifying devices. The rated peak value should not be exceeded to avoid damage.

(c) The average current in an a–c circuit is equal to 0.636 of the peak value, or 0.9 of the rms value.

The rotation of the moving coil in a d–c meter is proportional to the average value of current flowing in it. However, the scale is generally calibrated in the effective (RMS) value, which is the working or heating value of the current.

(d) Electrical power is the *rate* of doing work (the rate of expending energy) by electricity. Electrical power is measured by a unit called the *watt*. One watt is the power expended in heat in a circuit when a current of one ampere (6.28×10^{18} electrons per second) flows through a resistance of one ohm. One watt is one joule per second.

(e) Electrical energy is the *capacity* or *ability* to accomplish work by electricity. ("Work" in this sense includes production of heat, or conversion into any other form of energy.) Electrical energy is measured by a unit called the *joule*. Energy in electrical circuits is transferred into the form of heat. A joule is the *amount* of energy expended in moving one coulomb (6.28×10^{18}) of electricity through a resistance of one ohm. One joule = .7376 ft.-pound; 3600 joules = 1 watt-hour.

Q. 3.85. Describe how horizontal and vertical deflection takes place in a cathode ray oscilloscope. Include a discussion of the waveforms involved.

A.   The usual test oscilloscope has a cathode ray tube utilizing electrostatic deflection plates. (This discussion is keyed to the illustration in Fig. 3.85.)

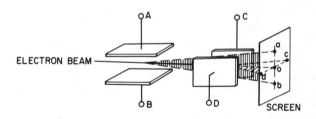

Fig. 3.85. Deflection plates for electrostatic cathode-ray tube.

There are two sets of deflection plates, the vertical deflecting plates (A–B) and the horizontal deflecting plates (C–D). The effect of these deflection plates is based on the fact that an electron beam can be deflected by an electrostatic field. The negative electron beam will be attracted toward the positive plate and repelled from the negative plate. Since the beam is accelerated toward the screen, its electrons are merely shifted in their path and are not ordinarily picked up by the positive deflection plate. If plate A is more positive than plate B, the beam will be deflected upward and will strike the point "a" on the screen. If the potentials are equal (or zero), the beam will strike point "o." Conversely, if plate B is more positive than plate A, the beam will strike at point "b." In the same manner, the beam may be moved horizontally from point "d" to point "c" on the screen.

In practice, a sawtooth deflection voltage is applied to plates C–D. This causes a relatively slow movement of the beam from "d" to "c" and a much more rapid return of the beam from "c" to "d." The rate of this movement is synchronized with the waveform repetition rate of the input waveform to be viewed. This waveform is applied to the vertical deflecting plates, and may be any wave within the limitations of the oscilloscope. The combination of the horizontal (sweep) movement and the vertical signal input causes the input waveform to be traced out on the screen.

OSCILLATORS

Q. 3.86. Draw circuit diagrams of each of the following types of oscillators (include any commonly associated components). Explain the principles of operation of each.

(a) Armstrong

(b) Tuned plate-tuned grid (series fed and shunt fed, crystal and LC controlled)

(c) Hartley

(d) Colpitts

(e) Electron coupled

(f) Multivibrator

(g) Pierce (crystal controlled)

A. *General*: All oscillators (except relaxation types) require a tuned circuit made up of inductance and capacitance for their operation. It is this tuned circuit which is actually the oscillator. The frequency of an oscillator with reasonably high Q (greater than 10) is found from the approximate formula $f = \dfrac{1}{2\pi\sqrt{LC}}$, where f is in cycles, L is in henrys, and C is in farads. A conventional type of oscillator operates as follows: when the power switch is turned on, high-frequency current surges pass through the tuned circuit (tank) and shock-excite it into oscillation. If no means were provided to make up energy losses, this oscillation would gradually die out at a rate which would be proportional to the Q of the tank, and the resultant wave train would be called a "damped wave." In order to produce sustained oscillations, it is necessary that the losses which occur in the tuned circuit be replenished from the power supply by means of a vacuum tube. These losses are mainly due to: (1) d-c resistance, (2) a-c resistance (skin effect), (3) coupling into a load, (4) grid power requirements, (5) radiation.

The function of the vacuum tube is to act as a valve which releases pulses of energy into the tank circuit in the correct phase. This energy is usually applied indirectly to the tank circuit by means of a feedback network. These networks usually consist of inductive or capacitive coupling elements which connect the tube with the tank circuit. Many oscillator tubes operate as class C amplifiers and are "cut off" for a large percentage of each cycle. When the potential at the grid side of the tank circuit is passing through its most positive values, the class C bias is overcome and the tube is permitted to conduct for a short period of time, feeding energy into the tank circuit. It should always be borne in mind that the tube itself is *not* the oscillator; the tuned circuit *is*.

Grid leak bias is developed in an oscillator by the charging of the grid capacitor from grid current and its discharging through the grid leak resistor. The average value of the capacitor voltage is the bias. Before the oscillator starts into operation there is no charge in the grid capacitor and the initial bias is, therefore, zero. When the tank circuit starts oscillating the first cycle has a small amplitude which increases at a definite rate depending upon the Q until a maximum value is reached a number of cycles later. Since the initial bias was zero, the effect of the first positive swing of the tank circuit, on the grid, is to cause grid current to charge the grid capacitor to some small value. In a like manner the grid capacitor continues to charge to the increasing positive swings of the tank circuit until the capacitor voltage is equal to some value of the steady-state tank-circuit positive swings, which depends upon the value of grid-leak resistance. The polarity of the charged capacitor is such that it is negative at the grid side, and thus provides the bias potential. The maximum steady state bias depends upon a number of factors such as type of tube, effective Q of tank circuit, amount of feedback, and tube operating voltages. One method of calculating grid bias constants is given below (assuming that the average grid current is known), is given in a tube manual, or can be found experimentally.

1. (a) For class C, $E_c = \dfrac{2E_b}{\mu}$ (for twice cut-off) where E_c is the d-c grid bias, E_b is the d-c plate voltage, and μ is the amplification factor of the tube.

(b) For class B, $E_c = \dfrac{E_b}{\mu}$ (At cut-off)

(c) For class A2, $E_c = \dfrac{0.6E_b}{\mu}$.

2. $R_g = \dfrac{E_c}{I_g}$, where R_g is the grid resistance in ohms, and I_g is equal to the average d-c grid current in amperes.

3. $C_c = \dfrac{5000}{F_r \times R_g}$, where C_c is the grid capacitor in microfarads, F_r is the lowest operating frequency in kilocycles, and R_g is the grid resistor in ohms.

(a) Fig. 3.86(a1) shows a shunt-fed Armstrong oscillator and Fig. 3.86(a2) shows a series-fed Armstrong oscillator.

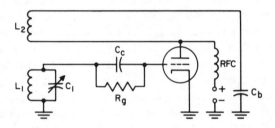

Fig. 3.86(a1). A tuned-grid Armstrong oscillator with shunt-fed plate.

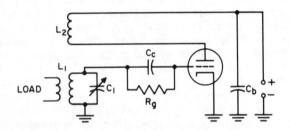

Fig. 3.86(a2). A tuned-grid Armstrong oscillator with series-fed plate.

Feedback is accomplished by magnetic coupling between L_2 and L_1 and may be varied by changing the degree of coupling. The frequency is determined mainly by L_1C_1. C_b prevents short circuiting the power supply and provides an easy path for r-f plate current to return to the cathode. The radio-frequency choke, *RFC*, prevents r-f plate current from entering the power supply; R_g-C_c is the bias network.

The transistor equivalent of the tuned-grid Armstrong oscillator, with shunt-fed plate, is shown in Fig. 3.86(a3). While the circuits are basically similar, there are some important differences.

With a vacuum-tube oscillator, employing only grid-leak bias, the tube is at maximum conduction when the bias is zero. In the case of a transistor oscillator, this would not be true, since the transistor would be biased class C at zero bias [see Q. 3.192(S)]. In order that a

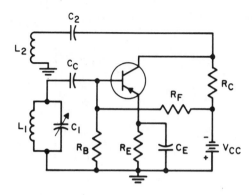

Fig. 3.86(a3). A tuned-base Armstrong oscillator with shunt-fed collector. (This circuit is similar in operation to Fig. 3.86(a1).)

transistor oscillator will be self starting, it is essential to provide some forward bias for the base-emitter circuit. Thus, most transistor oscillators are operated either class AB or class A.

In Fig. 3.86(a3), forward bias is provided by the voltage divider consisting of R_F and R_B. The emitter resistor R_E has been included to provide thermal transistor stabilization (see Q. 3.189). The emitter capacitor, C_E, is necessary to prevent degeneration from the voltage which would otherwise appear across R_E.

Note that the function of the RF choke in Fig. 3.86(a1) is performed by the resistor R_C, in Fig. 3.86(a3). The operation of the transistor oscillator is the same as the tube type.

(b) (1) For the diagram of a tuned-plate, tuned-grid, series-fed, LC controlled oscillator, see Fig. 3.86(b1).

Feedback is accomplished through the interelectrode capacitance C_{gp}. The output frequency is slightly lower than the resonant frequency of either L_1C_1 or L_2C_2. L_2C_2 is tuned slightly higher than L_1C_1. C_b offers a low impedance path for the r.f. to return to the cathode, by-passing the power supply. R_g—C_c is the bias network. Tetrodes or pentodes will not be suitable except at very high frequencies because of the low values of C_{gp}.

(2) For the diagram of a tuned-plate, tuned-grid, shunt-fed, LC controlled oscillator, see Fig. 3.86(b2). (See also part (b)(1) of this question.) C_b prevents short circuiting of the power supply. The value of the inductance of the radio-frequency choke, *RFC,* should be at least 10 times greater than the inductance of L_2 so as not to change the frequency of L_2C_2.

(3) For circuit diagrams of tuned-grid, tuned-plate, crystal-controlled oscillators, see Figs. 3.86(b3) and 3.86(b4).

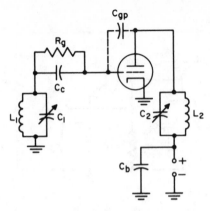

Fig. 3.86(*b1*). *A tuned-plate tuned-grid oscillator with series-fed plate.*

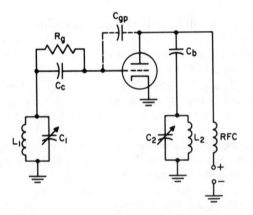

Fig. 3.86(*b2*). *A tuned-plate tuned-grid oscillator with shunt-fed plate.*

Figure 3.86(b3) is a diagram of a tuned-plate, tuned-grid oscillator with the crystal and its holder replacing the original grid tank circuit. Feedback is accomplished through C_{gp}. The bias capacitor here is C_h, the capacity of the crystal holder, and the bias resistor is R_g. The purpose of the r-f choke, *RFC*, is to maintain a high impedance across the crystal and so maintain a high Q. A pentode or tetrode has a higher power sensitivity and a much lower value of C_{gp} than a triode. This means that it is possible to reduce the amount of crystal voltage and current for a given output power and consequently reduce crystal heat-

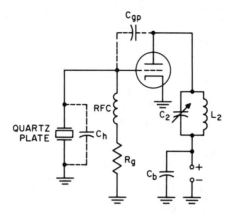

Fig. 3.86(b3). A crystal-controlled vacuum-tube oscillator.

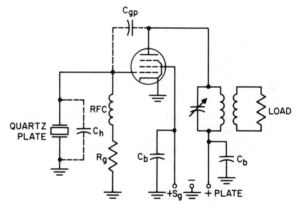

Fig. 3.86(b4). A pentode tube used as a crystal-controlled oscillator.

ing. The grid circuit is also less affected by changes in load than when a triode is used, due to the reduced C_{gp}. However, C_{gp} may be too small to allow sufficient feedback especially at the lower frequencies, and in this case a small capacitor in the order of 2 $\mu\mu$f should be connected between grid and plate.

(c) For the circuit diagram of a shunt-fed Hartley oscillator, see Fig. 3.86(c).

To find whether the oscillator or amplifier is shunt or series fed, merely trace the path of *d-c* plate current. If it passes through any part of a tuning inductance, the circuit is series fed. Otherwise it is shunt fed. Feedback is accomplished by magnetic coupling between L_a and L_b, and may be increased by lowering the tap, or decreased by raising the tap.

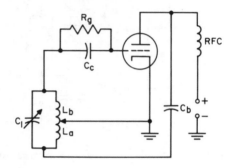

Fig. 3.86(c). A Hartley oscillator with shunt-fed plate.

The "tank" circuit which mainly determines the resonant frequency, consists of C_1 across the *entire* inductance of $L_a + L_b$. C_b offers a low impedance path for r-f plate current to return to the cathode through L_a. The radio-frequency choke, *RFC*, prevents r-f plate current from passing through the power supply. R_g-C_c is the bias network.

For the schematic diagram of a transistor, shunt-fed Hartley oscillator, see Fig. 3.283. Note the great similarity to the tube version shown in Fig. 3.86(c). The operation for the two types is the same. The discussion in part 3(a) of Question 3.86, regarding forward bias, the emitter network and resistor R_C, applies equally to this transistor oscillator.

A comparison between the Hartley oscillator shown in Fig. 3.86(c) and the Colpitts oscillator shown in Fig. 3.86(d) follows.

The basic difference between the Colpitts and Hartley oscillators is the method of adjusting the feedback. In both the Colpitts and Hartley oscillators, the tank circuit is effectively connected between the grid and plate of the vacuum tube. In both cases the amount of feedback is adjusted by varying the point at which the cathode is effectively tapped into the tank circuit. In the Hartley oscillator this is done by tapping into the coil proper, while in the Colpitts oscillator the tap is made by means of a capacitive voltage divider. This consists of two series capacitors connected across the tuning inductance, with the cathode connected between the two. By varying the *ratio* between the two capacitors, the feedback voltage may be varied. Once the feedback ratio is determined, the two capacitors may be "ganged" together for tuning. Other differences include: (1) The Colpitts oscillator *must* be shunt fed, while the Hartley oscillator may be shunt or series fed. (2) In the Colpitts oscillator the grid leak resistance must be connected from grid to cathode, while in the Hartley oscillator it may alternatively be connected across the grid capacitor. (3) The Colpitts oscillator seems to be preferred for use in the very low frequencies and the very high frequencies (ultraudion), while the Hartley oscillator is used between these two extremes.

(d) For a circuit diagram of a shunt-fed Colpitts oscillator, see Fig. 3.86(d).

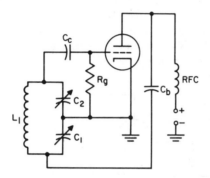

Fig. 3.86(d).   A Colpitts oscillator with shunt-fed plate.

Feedback is accomplished by a capacitive voltage divider action between C_1 and C_2. To increase feedback, decrease the value of C_2 in relation to C_1. To decrease feedback, increase C_2 in relation to C_1. R_g must be connected between grid and cathode otherwise the grid will have no d-c return to ground. C_e is often eliminated, in which case C_2 will also serve the function of bias capacitor. The frequency is determined mainly by L_1 in parallel with the series combination of C_2 and C_1. In changing frequency, C_2 and C_1 are moved simultaneously. C_b offers a low impedance path for r-f plate current through C_1 to the cathode. The r-f choke, *RFC*, keeps r-f plate current out of the power supply. See also part (c) above.

For the schematic diagram of a transistorized Colpitts crystal oscillator, see Fig. 3.286. While a crystal oscillator is shown, this could be easily changed to an LC oscillator by replacing the crystal by a coil and insuring that capacitors C1 and C2 are correct to tune the coil to the desired frequency range.

The discussion in part 3(a) of Question 3.86, regarding forward bias, the emitter network and resistor R_C, also applies to this transistor oscillator.

(e) For the circuit diagram of an electron-coupled oscillator, see Fig. 3.86(e).

The oscillator proper is a series-fed Hartley with the screen grid acting as the plate of the oscillator. Coupling into the plate tank circuit occurs by virtue of the electron stream variations caused by the swing of the control grid, hence the name "electron-coupled." The main advantage of this circuit arrangement is its excellent frequency stability. Its features are: (1) Buffer action because the oscillator tank is isolated from the load; (2) frequency multiplication may be obtained by tuning L_2C_2 to a harmonic oscillator frequency; (3) frequency is substantially independent of power supply variations; (4) combination of oscillator and amplifier using only one tube.

(f) For the circuit diagram of a symmetrical, plate-coupled, free-running multivibrator, see Fig. 3.86(f1). The waveforms used in conjunction with the explanation of its operation are given in Fig. 3.86(f2).

A multivibrator is a form of relaxation oscillator which is rather unstable in the free running condition, but which may be completely

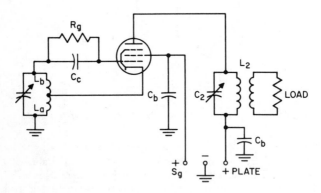

Fig. 3.86(e). An electron-coupled oscillator.

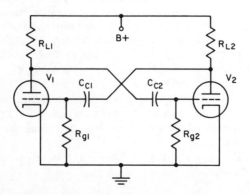

Fig. 3.86(f1). Circuit diagram of a symmetrical, plate-coupled, free-running multivibrator.

stabilized by the application of suitable synchronizing voltages. It requires two tubes for its operation and has a frequency range extending approximately from 1 cycle per minute to 100,000 (or more) cycles per second. The operation of this circuit follows.

It is assumed that V_1 initially conducts more heavily than V_2 when power-supply voltages are applied. This causes an increase in the voltage drop across R_{L1} and a *decrease* of the plate voltage of V_1 (e_{p1}). This decrease of e_{p1} voltage is coupled by capacitor C_{c2} to the grid of V_2. The negative-going voltage (e_{g2}) causes a reduction in the plate current of

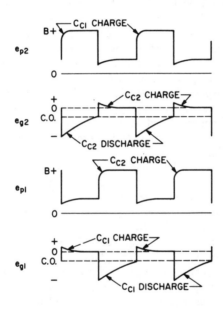

Fig. 3.86(f2). Waveforms of a symmetrical, plate-coupled, free-running multivibrator.

V_2 and an *increase* of its plate voltage, e_{p2}. The increase of e_{p2} is coupled through capacitor C_{c1} as a "positive-going" voltage at the grid of V_1, which further increases the plate current of V_1 and further decreases its plate voltage.

The action just described is regenerative and ends with V_2 being cut off and V_1 conducting at its maximum value (see waveforms). This regenerative (or switching) operation occurs in a fraction of a microsecond. Capacitor C_{c2} now begins to *discharge* to the reduced plate voltage of V_1 through R_{g2}. As C_{c2} discharges in accordance (mainly) with the time constant of C_{c2}-R_{g2}, the negative voltage at the grid of V_2 *decreases*. This discharge continues (with V_2 cut off and V_1 conducting heavily) until e_{g2} reaches the *cut-off bias* value for V_2. At this point, a new switching action begins. As e_{g2} begins to rise above the cut-off value for V_2, this tube begins to conduct. This initiates another switching action which will be concluded when V_1 is cut off and V_2 conducts heavily.

The conduction of V_2 results in a *decrease* of its plate voltage, e_{p2}. This "negative-going" voltage is coupled to the grid of V_1, reducing its plate current. The reduced V_1 plate current results in an *increase* of its plate voltage and this "positive-going" voltage change is coupled through capacitor C_{c2} to the grid of V_2, further *increasing* its plate current and further *reducing* its plate voltage. Once again the action is regenerative and results in the situation where V_1 is now cut off and V_2 is conducting heavily. The beginning of the next switching action starts when e_{g1} rises just above cut-off and completes one full cycle of operation.

Since this is a "free-running" multivibrator, the above described action continues until the power supply voltages are removed.

As can be seen in Fig. 3.86(f2), the plate waveform is basically a square wave. This arrangement, with and without additional squaring procedures, is frequently used when square wave pulses are desired. The waveforms shown are symmetrical, because both halves of each cycle are equal in time duration. This occurs primarily because the time constant of C_{c1} and R_{g1} is equal to that of C_{c2} and R_{g2}. In many applications (e.g., sawtooth generators and pulse generators), it is desirable to have the positive portion of the plate waveform either narrower or wider than the negative portion. This is accomplished by choosing unequal time constants for the two grid circuits.

A symmetrical, free-running, collector-coupled transistor multivibrator is shown in Fig. 3.86(f3). Note the great similarity to Fig. 3.86(f1). The operating principles are the same as for the tube counterpart, with one major exception. For oscillations to begin (as with a transistor LC oscillator), it is necessary to forward bias both transistors. This is accomplished by connecting the two base resistors to $-V_{CC}$. (See part 3(a) of Question 3.86 for a discussion of the requirement for forward bias.)

Some uses for multivibrators are:

1. As frequency dividers.
2. As sawtooth generators.
3. As harmonic generators.
4. As square wave and pulse generators.
5. As a standard frequency source when synchronized by an exter·nal crystal oscillator.
6. Many specialized uses in radar and television circuits.

There are two general classifications of multivibrators. These are the *free running* or non-driven type, and the *driven* or monostable type. The former type is capable of generating continuous oscillations, while

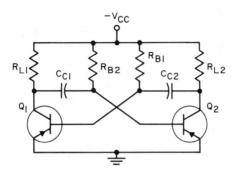

Fig. 3.86(f3). Circuit diagram of a symmetrical, collector-coupled, free running (astable) transistor multivibrator.

the latter type requires a driving pulse to start the operation after which it will complete one full cycle and then stop and wait for the next driving pulse.

Multivibrators are also classified as to the manner of feedback. These divisions generally speaking are: (1) plate coupling, where feedback is taken from the plate circuit of each tube and fed into the grid of the opposite tube, and (2) cathode coupling where feedback is provided by means of a common cathode resistor for both tubes and plate coupling for one tube. When used as a frequency divider, the free running frequency of the multivibrator is set so as to be slightly lower than a whole sub-multiple of the synchronizing frequency. A frequency division of 10:1 or so is usually considered to be the maximum obtainable with reliable stability of the multivibrator. For example, an original source of 100,000 cycles could be used to synchronize a multivibrator operating at 10,000 cycles. Due to the very high harmonic content of the non-sinusoidal multivibrator output voltage, harmonics in the order of one hundred or more may be obtained. Thus if the 100,000 cycle synchronizing voltage was supplied by a very stable crystal oscillator, a series of standard harmonic frequencies would be available ranging from 10,000 cycles (fundamental) and increasing in steps of 10,000 cycles to possibly 1,000,000 cycles. No definite simple formula may be given for the frequency of a multivibrator since there are too many variables. However, it can be said that the grid coupling elements (capacitor and resistor) have the greatest effect upon the determination of the frequency. Increasing or decreasing the time-constant of this combination causes proportional increases or decreases of frequency.

(g) For the circuit diagram of a crystal-controlled Pierce oscillator and its operation, see Figs. 3.86(g1) and 3.86(g2).

Figure 3.86(g2) is an explanatory diagram for the circuit given in Fig. 3.86(g1). The dotted lines indicate capacity between the tube

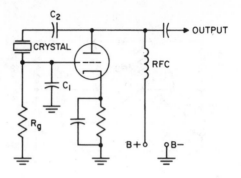

Fig. 3.86(g1). Pierce oscillator.

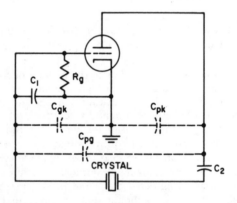

Fig. 3.86(g2). Explanatory diagram for Fig. 3.86(g1).

elements. C_2 blocks the d-c plate voltage from the crystal. C_1 decreases
the capacitive reactance between grid and cathode, to keep the feedback down to its proper value. Since the crystal acts as a tank circuit,
with the cathode returning to an intermediate point, determined by
the relation of C_{pk} to C_1 and C_{gk}, its operation is electrically equivalent
to a Colpitts oscillator (part d) above).

A transistor version of the Pierce oscillator is shown in Fig. 3.86
(g3). This circuit employs a junction, field-effect transistor (JFET),
which has certain characteristics that are very similar to a triode vacuum
tube. The gate (G) is similar to a grid; the source (S) is similar to
a cathode; and the drain (D) is similar to a plate. The similarities
apply both to their functions and to their relative impedance levels.
Like a vacuum tube, a FET has a high input impedance and a lower
output impedance. (This contrasts with the conventional transistor,
which has a low input impedance and a higher output impedance.)

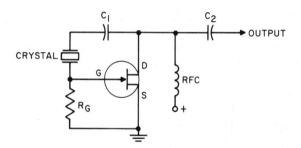

*Fig. 3.86(g3). A Pierce oscillator employing FET
(Field-Effect Transistor). (See text.)*

This transistor version of the Pierce oscillator functions in the same manner as the vacuum-tube version, previously described.

Q. 3.87. What are the principal advantages of crystal control over tuned-circuit oscillators?

A. The principal advantages of crystal control are improved frequency stability and compactness of the crystal as compared to a conventional tuned circuit.

D. The quartz crystal, its holder capacitance and associated tube and stray capacitance actually form an equivalent tank circuit of very high Q. Etched crystals with plated electrodes, mounted in a vacuum, have been found to give Q's in the order of 500,000. This is exceptional, however, and ordinary crystal installations have a Q (unloaded) in the order of a thousand or more. Crystal oscillators are generally found in two forms. One is the tuned-plate variety, in which the crystal takes the place of the grid tank circuit (Question 3.86(b)(3)). The other type is the Pierce oscillator (equivalent to the "ultraudion"), in which the crystal is the sole tuned circuit in the oscillator (Question 3.86(g)). In any event the very high Q of the crystal makes for excellent oscillator stability, especially when a constant temperature is maintained.

A serious disadvantage of crystal control is the difficulty of changing operating frequencies. This entails the use of a cumbersome crystal changing switch, or the actual plugging in of separate crystals. Small changes in the crystal operating frequency may be made by changing the pressure of the crystal holder or by having a small variable capacitor across the crystal, or by the use of a special diode whose capacity varies with a change of bias voltage.

Q. 3.88. Why should excessive feedback be avoided in a crystal oscillator?

A.   The crystal might overheat and break.

D.   In the conventional (tuned-plate, tuned-grid) crystal oscillator, discussed in Q. 3.86(b)(3), this means a relatively large value of grid to plate capacitance for the particular operating frequency. This in turn might cause excessive feedback into the crystal circuit, overheating and possibly cracking the crystal. The use of a tetrode or pentode greatly reduces this possibility because of the small value of grid to plate capacitance.

Q. 3.89.   Why is a separate source of plate power desirable for a crystal oscillator stage in a radio transmitter?

A.   To prevent "dynamic instability" of the crystal oscillator.

D.   "Frequency shift" or "dynamic instability" refers to the instantaneous changes of oscillator frequency due to corresponding changes of plate and screen grid voltages of the oscillator tubes and is caused by improper regulation of the power supply.

If a common power supply were used for the oscillator, r-f amplifiers, and modulator stages, it would be difficult to prevent "dynamic instability," especially if the modulator was not operating strictly class A. Any changes in loading due to any cause, or any changes in modulator power requirements will create a change in power supply output voltage. This in turn may cause the oscillator frequency to shift, creating undesired frequency modulation. In general, an increase of oscillator plate voltage (with screen voltage constant) will cause the oscillator trequency to increase because of a decrease of tube input capacity. A proportional increase of screen voltage would have the opposite effect on the frequency, and this factor is taken advantage of in the electron-coupled oscillator to maintain frequency stability and reduce "dynamic instability." Dynamic instability can also be reduced by: (1) using an oscillator tank circuit with a high C/L ratio, (2) by light loading of the oscillator circuit, (3) by using a high value of grid leak, (4) by using separate power supplies for oscillator, modulator, and r-f amplifiers, or at least for the oscillator.

Q. 3.90.   What may result if a high degree of coupling exists between the plate and grid circuits of a crystal controlled oscillator?

A.   See Q. 3.88.

Q. 3.91.   Explain some methods of determining if oscillation is occurring in an oscillator circuit.

A. The following methods may be used:

1. Tuning a radio receiver to the oscillator frequency.

2. Tuning a heterodyne frequency meter to the oscillator frequency. A sensitive wavemeter (loosely coupled) may also be used.

3. Certain grid-dip meters have phone jacks and provisions for detecting a zero-beat condition. When the grid-dip meter is tuned to the oscillator frequency (if operating), a "zero-beat" condition will be observed.

4. A neon bulb or low current flashlight bulb connected to a loop of wire and loosely coupled to the oscillator circuit will light if the oscillator is functioning.

5. Check the grid bias with a high-impedance voltmeter. It will be considerably higher when the circuit is oscillating than when it is not. If the voltmeter is not high-impedance, the oscillations may be stopped when the meter is applied.

6. A grid milliammeter will read grid current. This should be by-passed for r-f.

7. The d-c plate current of the oscillator is lower when the circuit is oscillating. This may be checked with a by-passed milliammeter.

Q. 3.92. What is meant by parasitic oscillations; how may they be detected and prevented?

A. (a) Parasitic oscillations are defined as "either high or low frequency oscillations occurring in circuits other than the original tank circuits, and at frequencies other than the desired output frequencies."

(b) They may be detected by tuning for them with a receiver (loosely coupled), wavemeter, or heterodyne frequency meter. Excessive or erratic grid or plate current readings, or overheating of components, sometimes indicates the presence of parasitic oscillations.

(c) Parasitic oscillations may be either high or low in frequency. High frequency parasitics are present in tuned circuits usually composed of tube and stray capacitance and lead inductance. Many times, this behaves as a tuned-grid tuned-plate oscillator. High frequency parasitic oscillations may be minimized by inserting small non-inductive resistors in series with plate and grid leads, and by making the plate leads considerably longer than the grid leads. Other methods are placing a wave trap in series with the grid, and placing small r-f chokes in series with the plate and grid leads. Low frequency parasitics are usually caused by having r-f chokes in both plate and grid circuits. These can be minimized by eliminating one of the two chokes, or by making the plate choke larger than the grid choke. Series plate and grid resistors may also help to eliminate low frequency parasitic oscillations.

D. For methods of testing for the presence of parasitic oscillations, see Q. 3.126.

Q. 3.93. What determines the fundamental frequency of a quartz crystal?

A.   The fundamental frequency of a quartz crystal is dependent upon the following factors:
1. The crystal's physical dimensions.
2. Capacitance of the crystal holder.
3. The orientation of the slab cut from the natural crystal.
4. The crystal substance.

D.   Certain crystalline substances such as quartz, rochelle salts, and tourmaline have a property known as piezo-electricity. If a pressure is applied to such a substance along one of its axes, a potential difference is developed across another axis. Conversely, a potential difference applied across one axis produces a mechanical displacement along another axis. This phenomenon is known as the "piezo-electric effect." Of all the various substances, quartz is the most generally satisfactory for use in oscillators.

There are very many different types of crystal cuts in use each having its own stability characteristics. Most of these change their operating frequency in varying degrees, with changes of operating temperature. Where extreme frequency stability is desired, the crystal may be kept in a constant-temperature oven.

Q. 3.94. What is meant by the temperature coefficient of a crystal?

A.   The "temperature coefficient" of a crystal defines the manner in which the frequency of the crystal varies with temperature change. The crystal is rated in terms of cycles per megacycle per temperature change in centigrade degrees (see discussion).

D.   A crystal may have a negative, a positive or a zero-temperature coefficient. If the crystal has a negative temperature coefficient, its operating frequency is inversely proportional to its temperature. With a positive temperature coefficient, the crystal frequency is directly proportional to the temperature. A crystal with zero temperature coefficient remains at a relatively constant frequency within stated temperature limits. A typical example involving a negative-temperature coefficient crystal follows.

A standard crystal marking may be as follows: $-50/10^6/C°/$. This means that the crystal frequency will change at the rate of 50 cycles per megacycle, per degree change of temperature in centigrade. The negative sign indicates that the crystal has a negative temperature coefficient. For example, a 7 megacycle crystal has the following marking: $-40/10^6/C°$; find the operating frequency if the temperature increases 5°C. This is done simply as follows: $40 \times 7 \times 5 = 1400$ cycles. The new frequency is 7,000,000 minus 1400 or 6,998,600 cycles.

Q. 3.95.   What are the characteristics and possible uses of an "overtone" crystal? A "third mode" crystal?

A. 1. An "overtone" crystal is one specially ground to oscillate at an odd harmonic of its fundamental frequency. Crystals are available to oscillate at frequencies up to 100 mc. Most standard crystals will oscillate on their third and fifth overtones using suitable circuitry. Overtone crystals are commonly used for oscillators in VHF transmitters (often in conjunction with frequency-multiplier stages).

2. A "third mode" crystal is one which is operated on the third harmonic of its fundamental frequency.

D.   As the fundamental operating frequency of a crystal increases, its thickness decreases. Consequently, at fundamental frequencies above about 25 to 30 megacycles, the crystal tends to become quite fragile and may be unstable. "Overtone" operation is produced when crystals are operated at much higher frequencies. While standard crystals may produce "overtone" operation, the best results are obtained with specially ground "overtone" crystals operated in circuitry designed for such operation. In "overtone" operation, a relatively low-frequency (e.g., 20 megacycles) crystal, is operated on its overtone frequency and may produce (for example) its fifth overtone frequency of 100 megacycles. This procedure permits the use of a relatively thick (and stable) crystal at frequencies not practical for crystals operating at their fundamental frequency.

Q. 3.96.   Explain some of the factors involved in the stability of an oscillator (both crystal and LC-controlled).

A.   Some of the important factors are:
1. C to L ratio of tank circuit.
2. A stable and separate power supply. See Q. 3.89 above.
3. Components with very low temperature coefficients.
4. Low loss components, including tank circuit elements, by-pass capacitors and tube sockets.
5. Constant temperature operation, such as enclosing critical circuits in a temperature-controlled oven.
6. Use of high-Q, frequency determining elements, including the important factor of stable-crystal control.
7. Isolation of the oscillator from its load.
8. The use of temperature compensating components.

D.   A major cause of oscillator "drift" is due to changes in the total tuning capacitance of the oscillator. These include such factors as tube capacitance, wiring capacitance, and reflected reactance. If the original tuning capacitor is made relatively large, then any such capacity changes will cause a smaller percentage change of the total capacitance than if the original tuning capacitance were much smaller. Thus the percentage of oscillator frequency change is less when the oscillator tank has a high C to L ratio. See also Q. 3.87, Q. 3.89, Q. 3.94, Q. 3.98, Q. 4.43, Q. 4.44 and Q. 4.93.

Q. 3.97. Is it necessary or desirable that the surfaces of a quartz crystal be clean? If so, what cleaning agents may be used which will not adversely affect the operation of the crystal?

A. The crystal surfaces must be free of dirt or grease in order to operate properly. The faces of the crystal should not be touched with the fingers, and may be cleaned with soap and water or carbon tetrachloride.

D. Any greasy film upon the surfaces of a crystal will prevent good contact being made with the holder, and will interfere with the correct operation of the crystal.

Q. 3.98. What is the purpose of a buffer amplifier stage in a transmitter?

A. A buffer amplifier is used to improve the frequency stability of the oscillator stage.

D. A buffer amplifier is located immediately following the oscillator. It has low gain and low Q circuits and draws no grid current. Thus it presents a very high impedance load upon the oscillator and does not affect the oscillator Q to any great extent. Any changes in tuning of the succeeding amplifier or antenna stages have little or no effect upon the output frequency of the oscillator. If a buffer amplifier were not present, such tuning changes, or even motion of the antenna, might change the oscillator frequency.

AUDIO AMPLIFIERS

Q. 3.99. Draw simple schematic diagrams illustrating the following types of coupling between audio amplifier stages and between a stage and a load.

(a) Triode vacuum tube inductively coupled to a loudspeaker.

(b) Resistance coupling between two pentode vacuum tubes.

(c) Impedance coupling between two tetrode vacuum tubes.

(d) A method of coupling a high impedance loudspeaker to an audio-frequency amplifier tube without flow of plate current through the speaker windings, and without the use of a transformer.

A. (a) For inductive coupling, see Fig. 3.99(a).

(b) For resistance (RC) coupling, see Fig. 3.99(b).

(c) For impedance coupling (rarely used), see Fig. 3.99(c).

(d) For high-impedance speaker coupling (rarely used), see Fig. 3.99(d).

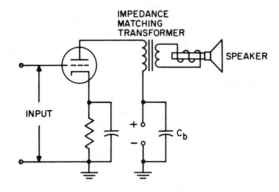

Fig. 3.99(a). An a-f amplifier inductively coupled to a loudspeaker.

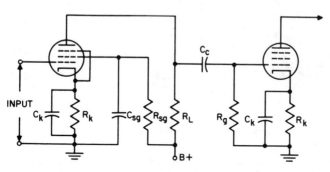

Fig. 3.99(b). Resistance (RC) coupling between two pentode vacuum tubes.

Q. 3.100. What would probably be the effect on the output amplitude and waveform if the cathode-resistor by-pass capacitor in an audio stage were removed?

A. The output amplitude would be reduced and the output waveform might be improved.

D. If the cathode by-pass capacitor is removed, a condition of negative current feedback exists in the amplifier. This is a degenerative volt-

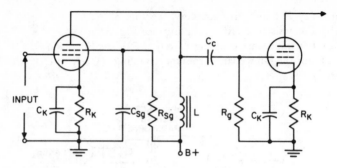

Fig. 3.99(c). Impedance coupling between two tetrode vacuum tubes.

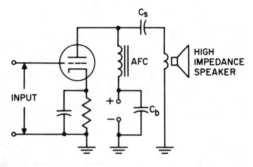

Fig. 3.99(d). Method of coupling a high-impedance loud-speaker to an a-f amplifier.

age, developed across the cathode resistor by the plate current in it. (See Q. 4.26.)

The results of degenerative feedback in audio amplifiers are:

1. Greater stability of amplifier characteristics.
2. Reduction of harmonic distortion.
3. Reduction of phase distortion.
4. Improvement of frequency response linearity.
5. Reduction of amplifier gain.
6. Reduction of noise output.
7. Reduction of effective r_p with negative voltage feedback.
8. Increase of effective r_p with negative current feedback.

The gain ratio of an amplifier with negative feedback may be deter-

mined from the formula, $a' = \dfrac{a}{1 + Ba}$, where a' is the gain with feedback, B is the fraction of the total output voltage fed back in opposition to the input signal voltage E_s, a is the gain without feedback. The low-frequency response will be affected according to the formula,

$F_1' = \dfrac{F_1}{1 + Ba}$, where F_1' is the new low-frequency response without

feedback. The high-frequency response will be affected according to the formula, $F_2' = F_2 (I + Ba)$.

If no bypass capacitor were across the cathode resistor, the amplifier would in general have improved performance but at a sacrifice in gain. Placing a capacitor of suitable value across the cathode resistor prevents degenerative effects due to instantaneous bias changes on the cathode, which are in phase with the applied signal. This is due to the fact that the capacitor charges very little on increasing plate currents and discharges very little on decreasing plate currents. This condition requires that the time constant in the cathode circuit be long with respect to the time of the lowest audio frequency desired to be passed through the amplifier without degeneration. A simple formula to cal-

culate the value of cathode capacitor is: $C_K = \dfrac{10,000,000}{2\pi f_1 R_k}$, where C_K is

cathode capacitor in microfarads, f_1 is the lowest frequency in cycles desired to be passed and R_K is the cathode bias resistance in ohms.

Q. 3.101. Why do vacuum tubes produce random noise?

A. Vacuum tube random noise (or shot-effect noise) is caused by random irregularities in the flow of electrons within the tube.

D. Shot-effect is caused by the fact that electrons are discreet particles which are emitted from the cathode in a random manner, rather than as a smooth continuous "fluid-like" flow. The current resulting from such an emission causes variations in the output circuit, commonly called "noise." The "noise" energy is distributed evenly across the entire frequency spectrum.

Q. 3.102. Why are de-coupling resistors and capacitors used in stages having a common power supply?

A. The purpose of decoupling networks is to prevent oscillations from occurring in a multistage audio amplifier.

D. It is common practice to supply plate and screen grid supply voltages for a multistage audio amplifier from a single power source. The output impedance of a power supply (unregulated) consists mainly of the reactance of the output filter capacitor. This reactance is a common impedance coupling element between all stages. If the amplifier contains high gain stages, there is a possibility of sufficient feedback voltages being developed across the reactance of the output capacitor to sustain oscillations. Since the reactance of a capacitor increases as the frequency decreases, such oscillations, if they occur, will most likely be of a very low frequency.

Q. 3.103. How would saturation of an output transformer create distortion?

A.   When saturation of an output transformer has been reached, the inductance value is greatly reduced. This causes two immediate effects:

(a) A reduction of load impedance on the output tube which reduces output amplitudes, especially at the low frequencies and thus creates amplitude distortion.

(b) The inability of a saturated transformer to pass the waveform through to the speaker, without severe change. This happens because the flux in the transformer is already at its (practical) maximum value and cannot increase to follow the waveform pattern. This causes severe audio distortion.

D.   When a transformer core is saturated, the iron contains the maximum number of flux lines it is capable of handling. A further increase in current through the primary does not produce additional flux lines and the effect is a flattening of the signal in the secondary. The transformer may respond in the normal manner to low current signals, but saturate on high current peaks.

Q. 3.104. Why is noise often produced when an audio signal is distorted?

A.   Whether or not "noise" is actually present when an audio signal is distorted depends largely upon the actual cause of the distortion. Simple amplitude or frequency distortion will not necessarily produce any noise. Some cases where noise may accompany audio distortion may result from:

1. Defective coupling capacitor.
2. Microphonic tube.
3. Microphonic connections or components.
4. Defective volume control.

D.   An apparent increase of the "noise" level of an audio signal may be a consequence of distortion. If appreciable non-linear audio amplification is present, amplitude distortion and possibly intermodulation distortion may result. Amplitude distortion causes the production of harmonics of the original wave. Intermodulation distortion is a result of the production of entirely new frequencies which were not present in the original audio wave. These may be produced by a heterodyning process (non-linear amplification) between original audio frequencies or between original audio frequencies and their harmonics produced by non-linear amplification. In either case, the resultants are the sum and difference frequencies (and harmonics of these) of the various combinations which tend to obscure the original audio tones and thus may be considered a form of audio "noise."

Q. 3.105. What are the factors which determine the correct bias voltage for the grid of a vacuum tube?

A. The following factors apply:
1. The class of operation (A, B, or C).
2. The plate supply voltage.
3. Permissible distortion.
4. Grid signal magnitude.
5. Permissible plate dissipation (in power tubes).
6. Desired amplification factor (in variable μ tubes).
7. The no-signal plate current desired.
8. The desirability or not of drawing grid current.

D. The amount of bias needed for a given class of operation is inversely proportional to the amplification factor (μ) of the tube. For example, in class C operation where the bias is equal to twice cut-off, it may be found from the formula, $E_c = \dfrac{2\,E_b}{\mu}$. See also Q. 3.52, Q. 3.58 and Q. 3.106 through Q. 3.109.

Q. 3.106. Draw schematic diagrams illustrating the following types of grid biasing and explain their operation.
(a) Battery
(b) Power supply
(c) Voltage divider
(d) Cathode-resistor

A.   (a) For battery bias, see Q. 3.50(b), above.
(b) For power supply bias, see Fig. 3.106(b) and Q. 3.50(c) and (e), above, for diagrams. In this scheme the desired value of bias is provided by means of a separate power supply. The current provided by

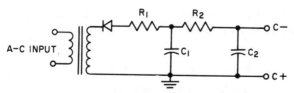

Fig. 3.106(b). A simple power supply to provide vacuum-tube bias.

such a supply is negligible, so that small solid-state rectifiers and simple RC filters may be employed in a half-wave rectifier.

(c) For a diagram of a voltage-divider bias scheme, see Fig. 3.106 (c). In this bias scheme, the center-tap of the high-voltage secondary is returned to ground only through the low end of the bleeder resistor. This provides a negative d–c voltage with respect to ground, whose amplitude is proportional to the percentage of the bleeder resistance tapped to ground.

(d) For cathode bias, see Q. 3.50(a), above.

D. See Q. 3.105.

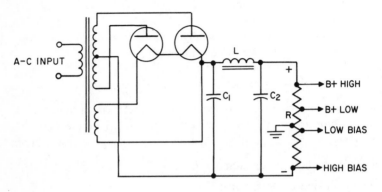

Fig. 3.106(c). Schematic showing how to obtain voltage-divider bias.

Q. 3.107. Is grid-leak biasing practical in audio amplifier stages?

A. Grid-leak biasing is not practical in audio amplifier stages.

D. The value of grid-leak bias is proportional to the amplitude of the input-grid signal. This type of bias varies whenever the signal changes and thus the operating point of the tube also changes. This condition may cause severe distortion of the audio signal. In addition, the grid current required to produce grid-leak bias causes loading on the driver stage reducing its gain and causing additional waveform distortion. See also Q. 3.52(f), Q. 3.105, Q. 3.121, and Q. 3.122.

Q. 3.108. Draw a diagram showing a method of obtaining grid bias for a filament type vacuum tube by use of resistance in the plate circuit of the tube.

A. For the circuit diagram, see Fig. 3.108.

D. This is actually a type of "cathode" bias scheme. Plate current flows from the plate, through the load resistor, through the battery, then

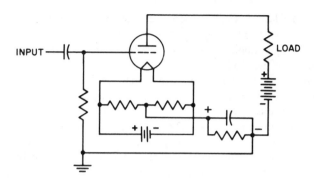

Fig. 3.108. Tube bias by series plate-return resistor.

through the series RC network to the filament center tap. The drop across the RC network is such that a positive d-c voltage appears at the filament, providing the bias.

Q. 3.109. Explain how you would determine the approximate value of cathode bias resistance necessary to provide correct grid bias for any particular amplifier.

A. The bias is equal to the *IR* drop across the cathode resistance and is found by dividing the desired d-c bias voltage by the total dc, no-signal cathode current.

D. For a triode the bias resistance will equal the d-c bias voltage divided by the no signal d-c plate current or $R_K = \dfrac{E_c}{I_{b1}}$ where E_c = d-c bias voltage as desired, and I_{b1} is the no signal value of d-c plate current.

For tetrode or pentode the screen current must be added to the plate current, giving:

$$R_K = \frac{E_c}{I_{b1} + I_{s0}}$$

Q. 3.110. Draw circuit diagrams and explain the operation (including input-output phase relationships, approximate practical voltage gain, approximate stage efficiency, uses, advantages, and limitations) of each of the following types of audio circuits.

(a) Class A amplifier with cathode-resistor biasing.

(b) Cathode-follower amplifier.

(c) At least two types of phase inverters for feeding push-pull amplifiers.

(d) Cascaded Class A stages with a form of current feedback.

(e) Two Class A amplifiers operated in parallel.

(f) Class A push-pull amplifier.

A.   (a) Class A amplifier, with cathode-resistor biasing:

(1) For diagram, see Figure 3.50(a).

(2) For operation, see Q. 3.50. The output wave is 180 degrees out of phase with the input wave.

(3) The actual voltage gain which may be achieved depends upon the tube in use and the circuitry. An example of finding the voltage gain of a stage is given in Q. 3.58.

(4) The approximate stage efficiency is 25 percent.

(5) This type of amplifier may be used as an audio pre-amplifier, audio-intermediate amplifier, or final audio amplifier. It may also be used as a receiver r–f amplifier or i–f amplifier. It also has many uses in various stages of different types of test equipment.

(6) Advantages of this circuit are:

1. Requires practically no grid driving power.

2. Provides minimum distortion of the output waveform.

3. Average plate current remains constant with or without an imput signal.

4. Has a high power-amplification ratio.

Limitations of this circuit are:

1. Low plate circuit efficiency, usually about 25 percent.

2. Plate current flows for 360 degree of each cycle (reducing efficiency).

3. Low power output compared to class B or class C.

(b) (1) For the diagram, see Fig. 3.50(d).

(2) For operation and discussion of cathode-follower, see Q. 3.50, Answer (d).

(3) The voltage gain is always less than one and depends upon the tube and circuitry in use. For the method of calculating gain, see Q. 3.50, Answer (d).

(4) Plate circuit efficiency is not a factor in a cathode follower since the output is taken across the cathode circuit. However, for a class A-biased stage, the efficiency is comparable to a class A-biased conventional amplifier, or about 25 percent.

(5) A cathode follower is most often used to drive a low-impedance device from a high-impedance input. It is frequently used to feed a low-impedance transmission line from a high-impedance source and is commonly used for this purpose in connection with pulse circuits. Because of its low-impedance output, its output is affected relatively little by the affects of shunt capacities of the load. It is sometimes used to feed a loudspeaker voice coil directly and thus eliminate the need for an output transformer. However, relatively high impedance voice coils are required (25-50 ohms) in this case.

(6) The advantage of the cathode follower lies in the fact that it is a simple but highly effective impedance reducer. It also has a very wide

frequency response and passes narrow pulses without appreciable distortion. Its only serious limitation is the fact that its voltage gain is always less than one.

(c) Two types of phase inverters: These are covered one at a time, the first one discussed is the single tube (paraphase) amplifier.

(1) For diagram, see Figure 3.110(c1).

(2) As shown in the figure, one output is taken from the plate (inverted) and one from the cathode (not inverted). In practice, R_K is made equal to R_L and equal outputs are thus obtained since the same current flows through both resistors.

(3) The voltage gain of each output is always less than one because of the negative feedback across R_K.

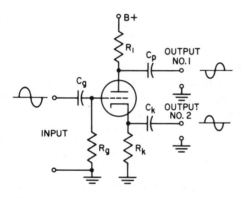

Fig. 3.110(c1). A simple method of supplying signals to double-ended audio amplifier without transformer.

(4) Plate circuit efficiency is about 25 percent.

(5) The paraphase amplifier is used to drive a push-pull amplifier from a single-ended input.

(6) The advantage of this circuit is that it requires only a single tube, and has excellent frequency response. Its limitation is that it has no voltage gain.

Note: The second type of phase inverter to be discussed below is called a cathode-coupled paraphase amplifier.

(1) For diagram, see Figure 3.110(c2).

(2) Observe in the figure that the common cathode resistor R_2 is unbypassed and that the grid of V_2 is grounded. R_2 is chosen so that the signal across it is equal to one-half of the V_1 grid-input signal. The effective signals applied to both tubes are equal since the R_2 signal is degenerative for V_1, but not for V_2. The output of V_1 is inverted with

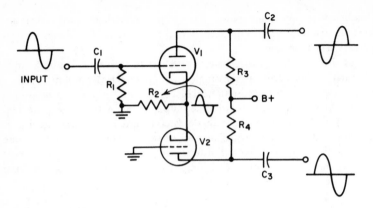

*Fig. 3.110(c2). Schematic of a cathode-coupled paraphase
inverter.*

respect to the input signal. However, the output of V_2 is not because
its input signal is applied to its cathode and not to the grid.

(3) The voltage gain of each stage is equal to one-half of its normal
gain because of the cathode signal action. For gain-calculation references, see part (a)(3) of this question.

(4) The approximate plate efficiency of each tube is 25 percent.

(5) The use of this amplifier is the same as for the paraphase amplifier discussed above.

(6) This circuit has the advantage of providing voltage gain at each
plate and good frequency response. However, the frequency response is
poorer than in the prior phase inverter and it has only one-half the gain
provided by conventional amplifier circuits.

(d) Cascaded class-A stages with current feedback.

(1) For diagram of cascaded class-A stages, see Fig. 3.110(d).

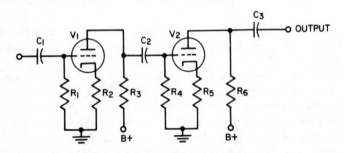

*Fig. 3.110(d). Simplified schematic of a two-stage audio amplifier
employing current feedback in both stages.*

(2) In practice, voltage feedback over two stages is generally preferred, or a combination of voltage and current feedback may be found quite often. The circuit of Fig. 3.110(d) employs current feedback in both stages by virtue of the unbypassed cathode resistors. The polarity of signal at each cathode is the same as that appearing at its corresponding grid. Therefore degeneration (negative feedback) occurs in each stage. This is current feedback because the voltage at each cathode depends upon the plate current of each tube flowing through the individual cathode resistors (R_2 and R_5).

(3) The voltage gain of each stage is modified (reduced) by the negative feedback and may be found from the equation

$$A' = \frac{\mu R_L}{(\mu + 1) \ R_K + r_p + R_L}$$

where $A' =$ Gain with feedback.

$\mu =$ Amplification factor.

$R_I =$ Plate-load resistance.

$R_K =$ Cathode resistance.

$r_p =$ Plate resistance (internal).

(4) The approximate plate efficiency of each stage is 25 percent.

(5) This type of amplifier may be used as intermediate audio-amplifier stages in various types of audio systems, or as intermediate amplifier stages in an oscilloscope, or other test equipment.

(6) Advantages of this type of amplifier include; reduced distortion, improved frequency response, improved stability from regeneration or oscillation, reduction of hum and noise. The only serious limitation is the reduced gain.

(e) Two class-A amplifiers operated in parallel.

(1) For diagram, see Figure 3.110(e).

(2) Operation is basically the same as for a single tube as discussed

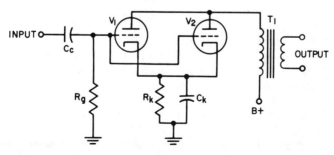

Fig. 3.110(e). Schematic diagram of two class-A amplifiers in parallel.

in part (a) of this question. However, in this case, the proper cathode bias depends upon the plate current of both tubes. Two tubes in parallel provide double the power output of one tube. Distortion remains the same as for one tube and the grid input voltage remains the same. The effective internal-plate resistance is half that of one tube and thus the required plate load impedance is cut in half.

(3) The voltage gain is unchanged by the use of two tubes in parallel. However, this factor is seldom important since power output is the reason for paralleling the two tubes.

(4) The approximate plate efficiency of each tube is 25 percent.

(5) This type of amplifier, while not popular, may be used as an audio power-output amplifier. In general the push-pull type is preferred.

(6) The principal advantage of this configuration is the elimination of the phase splitter required for push-pull operation. Limitations include: double the d-c plate current requiring a special and expensive output transformer, no reduction in distortion as with push-pull operation and the larger cathode by-pass capacitor required because of the half value of the cathode-bias resistor.

(f) Class-A push-pull amplifier.

(1) For diagram, see Figure 3.110(f).

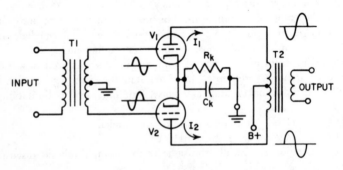

Fig. 3.110(f). Schematic diagram of a Class-A push-pull amplifier.

(2) The proper inputs could be supplied from a phase inverter (see part (c) of this question), but is here provided by a center-tapped input transformer. The two grids are fed with signals which are 180 degrees out of phase. As a result, the plate signal currents (I_1 and I_2) are also 180 degrees out of phase. However, these currents flow in opposite directions through the primary winding and so are additive in the secondary winding.

(3) Voltage gain is not a consideration here, but the power output is twice that for an amplifier using one of the same output tubes.

(4) The approximate plate efficiency of each tube is 25 percent.

(5) The most common use of this amplifier is as the audio power-output stage feeding a loudspeaker.

(6) Advantages of this circuit are:

1. Cancellation of even harmonic distortion in the output.
2. Reduction of hum.
3. Reduction of regenerative feedback.
4. Elimination of d-c core saturation, in output transformer.
5. Elimination of cathode by-pass capacitor.

Elaborating:

1. Even order harmonic currents flow out of phase in the output transformer and thus cancel. This does not apply to distortion created either before or after the push-pull stage.

2. Hum currents are out of phase in the output transformer and return circuits and, therefore, cancel.

3. There is no a-c signal current flowing through the plate supply and return circuits, and thus the tendency for regeneration in a multi-stage amplifier is reduced.

4. The d-c plate currents in the output transformer flow in opposite directions creating opposing magnetic fields which cancel. This enables the size of the iron core to be made much smaller for a given power rating.

5. The fundamental a-c signal components flow in opposite directions through the cathode resistor and cancel. Thus no by-passing is theoretically needed. However, a bypass capacitor is often included to compensate for unbalance in the tubes and for heater to cathode leakage.

Limitations of this circuit are:

1. The need to supply out-of-phase grid signals, and matched tubes and transformer windings for best results.

2. Bias controls may be required to assure perfect balancing.

Q. 3.111. Why does a class-B audio frequency amplifier stage require considerably greater driving power than a class-A amplifier?

A. A class B audio amplifier stage usually operates with a value of grid input signal sufficient to drive the grid positive with respect to the cathode, on the positive peaks of the signal. Thus grid current exists for these positive peaks and appreciable power is dissipated in the grid circuit. The usual class A amplifier does not operate in the grid current region, and, therefore, requires an insignificant amount of grid driving power.

D. As with most power tubes, it is required that the input grid impedance be kept low, especially where grid current exists. A transformer is generally used to couple into the grid circuit of the push-pull class B tubes. The turns ratio of this transformer must be correct so that the proper load impedance will be reflected back into the primary of the driver tube (or tubes). A well-regulated power supply is needed to supply the class B tubes because the average plate current varies in proportion to the grid signal.

Q. 3.112. Show by use of circuit diagrams two ways of using single-ended stages to drive a push-pull output stage.

A. (1) A paraphase amplifier, shown in Fig. 3.110(c1), is one method. The operation of this circuit is discussed in Q. 3.110(c).

(2) A second type of phase inverter is shown in Figure 3.112. The voltage divider has a ratio equal to the voltage gain of V_1.

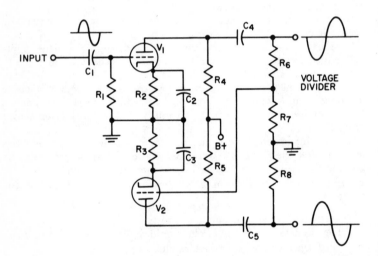

Fig. 3.112. Single-ended stages arranged to drive a push-pull output stage.

Because of this relationship, the signal output of V_1 is divided by its gain factor. The inverted output-signal amplitude from the voltage-divider is equal to the input-signal amplitude of V_1. The voltage-divider output is applied to the grid of V_2 and since V_1 and V_2 have equal gains, the output signals from V_1 and V_2 have equal amplitudes, but opposite phases.

Q. 3.113. Draw circuit diagrams and explain the operation of two commonly used tone control circuits and explain their operation.

A. See Figures 3.113(a) and 3.113(b).

(a) In the circuit of Figure 3.113(a) the tone-control elements are C_T and R_T. This is a very simple, but popular, circuit and provides high-frequency attenuation only. When the slider of R_T is at the top, C_T is fully effective in bypassing the higher audio frequencies. When R_T is at the bottom end (maximum series resistance), the effect of C_T is nullified and all high audio frequencies are passed to the grid of the tube.

(b) The circuit of Figure 3.113(b) is more complex and provides both bass and treble attenuation. When C_1 goes to the grid side of R_2, low frequencies are attenuated by the effect of the series reactance of C_1, but this effect is limited by the bypass effect of R_1. When C_1 is at the ground end of R_2 high frequencies are attenuated by the bypass effect to ground of C_1.

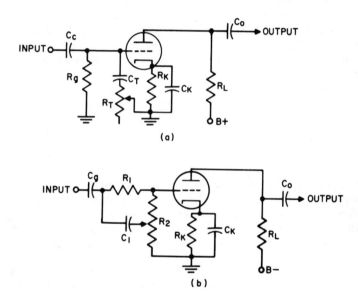

Fig. 3.113(a) and (b). Schematics of two commonly used tone-control circuits.

Q. 3.114. Name some causes of hum and self-oscillation in audio amplifiers and the methods of reducing it.

A. (a) Hum may be caused by:

(1) Heater-to-cathode tube leakage. The tube must be replaced to cure this.

(2) Filament-wire radiation. When the two wires are twisted together in close proximity, the hum radiation is largely cancelled. The reason for this is that the two wires are carrying currents in opposite directions and thus the magnetic fields will oppose and cancel out to a large degree.

(3) Open-grid circuit. The high-impedance grid is susceptible to hum-radiation pickup. The cure is obvious.

(4) Faulty filter capacitor (or resistor or choke) in the power supply filter feeding the amplifier. Again, the cure is obvious.

(5) Hum pickup from a power transformer due to its inadequate shielding or its close proximity to a high gain stage. This may be corrected by replacing the transformer or by proper shielding of the tube(s) involved and their input (grid) leads. Proper dress of the input leads may also be effective in reducing hum pickup.

(6) Hum may be reduced by the use of a push-pull amplifier. See Q. 3.110(f) for a discussion of this procedure.

(7) High-gain amplifiers, e.g., the pre-amplifier for a stereophonic audio amplifier, are more susceptible to hum pickup problems than are low-gain amplifiers. In such cases, it is common to feed the filaments of such stages with well-filtered d-c voltage. This reduces the heater-to-cathode hum pickup problem as well as reducing hum radiation from the filament wires.

(b) Self-oscillation may be caused by the following:

1. Open grid resistor (when amplifier draws grid current).

2. Coupling circuit time constant too long (when amplifier draws grid current).

3. Output power supply filter capacitor too small, or defective.

4. Decoupling filter(s) defective.

5. Output of one high-gain stage feeding back to the grid circuit of a prior high-gain stage. This can be prevented by isolating the input grid from output-plate circuits, and by shielding the tubes (and whole stages where necessary). Proper layout of the amplifier stages will provide physical separation of stages which might create oscillation problems.

D. Self-oscillation is an oscillation which is generally of the relaxation type when coupling elements are involved. If the output impedance of the power supply is relatively large and decoupling filters are not used, it represents a common impedance coupling element between the various amplifier stages and thus affords a means for feedback to sustain oscillations. See Question 3.102.

Q. 3.115. What factors should be taken into consideration when ordering a Class-A audio-output transformer; a Class-B audio-output transformer feeding a speaker of known ohmic value?

A. (a) Some important considerations when ordering a Class-A, audio-output transformer are:

(1) Operating power level in watts, including peak-power level expected.

(2) Turns ratio to match speaker voice coil to the output tube(s).

(3) Single ended or push-pull power output stage.

(4) Frequency response under normal power-output conditions.

(5) Harmonic distortion at the lowest frequency involved and at the maximum-output power.

(6) Direct current in primary winding(s).

(7) Adequate magnetic and electrostatic shielding.

(8) Source impedance and load impedance.

(b) Important considerations for a Class-B output transformer are the same as for Class-A (above) with one added consideration. Since the plate currents flow intermittently (180 degrees) in each tube, it is essential that the leakage inductance between both halves of the primary windings be very small. If this is not true, transients will be produced in the primaries, that may produce severe distortion.

Q. 3.116.   Draw a diagram of a single-button carbon microphone circuit, including the microphone transformer and source of power.

A.   For the diagram, see Fig. 3.116.

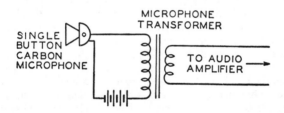

Fig. 3.116.   Single-button microphone connection.

D.   The "carbon-button" microphone depends for its operation upon the characteristics of a pile of carbon granules when subjected to varying pressures. The carbon button proper consists of a small cup completely filled with very fine carbon granules. A tightly stretched duralumin diaphragm is attached to the carbon button (or buttons) in such a way that sound vibrations cause varying pressures upon the button. The resistance of the carbon button varies in proportion to the pressures upon it. A battery supply is connected in series with the button and a resistance (or transformer primary), so that variations in resistance will cause corresponding variations in the output current from the button. These varying currents will be proportional to the character of the sound waves producing them. The frequency response of a broadcast type is inferior to most other types of microphones, and is in the order of 70 to 6000 cycles. The carbon microphone is no longer in general use because, although it has very high sensitivity, it has a number of serious disadvantages. These are: (1) it is sensitive to vibration, (2) it cannot be handled while in use, (3) it generates a hissing sound in its output, (4) the carbon granules in the buttons are subject to "packing," (5) it requires a battery power supply for operation. Carbon microphones are used wherever high output voltages with restricted frequency response characteristics are desired. A typical example is the use of carbon microphones in aircraft radio transmitters and in other mobile equipment.

Q. 3.117. If low-impedance head telephones of the order of 75 ohms are to be connected to the output of a vacuum tube amplifier, how may this be done to permit most satisfactory operation?

A. Low-impedance head telephones may be satisfactorily coupled to an amplifier tube by the use of an impedance matching transformer.

D. In order to achieve maximum output with tolerable distortion it is necessary that a certain value of plate load impedance be presented to the amplifier tube. An impedance of 75 ohms will not be satisfactory as a plate load with any of the common types of tubes. Therefore, it is necessary for the tube to work into its proper load impedance and for the phones to work into their proper impedance which is 75 ohms. This is accomplished by making use of the impedance reflecting properties of a transformer. If the load across the secondary of the transformer is 75 ohms, then the primary impedance is found by $Z_p = Z_s \times N^2$. Thus if the turns ratio, which is equal to the voltage ratio, is 10 to 1, the primary impedance will be 75×10^2 or 7500 ohms. If it is desired to find the turns ratio the following formula is applied: $N = \sqrt{\dfrac{Z_s}{Z_p}}$, where N is the turns ratio, Z_p is the correct plate load impedance and Z_s is the impedance of the driven device (headphones).

Another way of using the 75-ohm phones without a transformer is to connect them as a cathode bias resistor in the output stage. In this case, the B+ goes directly to the plate, and there is no cathode by-pass capacitor. This is the cathode-follower connection, useful for feeding low impedance loads and to reduce distortion.

Q. 3.118. Describe the construction and explain the operation of a "crystal" type microphone; a "carbon button" microphone.

A. (a) For sketch of a crystal microphone, see Fig. 4.17(c).

A "crystal" microphone depends for its operation upon the piezoelectric effect of a suitable crystalline material. Rochelle salts are most commonly used for this purpose in the crystal microphone. The crystal proper is made up of a number of crystal cells arranged so as to increase the sensitivity of the unit. One such unit consists of *two* crystal elements so arranged as to operate in phase when sound vibrations are present, but to generate out of phase potentials when subjected to shock or mechanical vibration. The entire crystal unit is impregnated in wax and enclosed in an airtight chamber. This enclosure, however, does not prevent the crystal from vibrating and thus generating emf's proportional to the sound wave components. The sound vibrations are transmitted to the crystal unit by means of a conical duralumin diaphragm either directly or by means of a resilient, intermediate member. The microphone has a flat frequency response over the entire audio range. It is lightweight, reasonably rugged, easily maintained, and requires no power supply. It has a high-impedance output, is non-directional, and has no inherent background noise level. The microphone should be protected against excessive humidity, as Rochelle salts are soluble in water. The wax impregnation of the crystal element is, however, highly efficient in protecting the crystal against moisture. See also Q. 4.17(c).

(b) For sketch of a single-button carbon microphone, see Fig. 4.17(d). For its operation, see Q. 3.116.

D. For a discussion of several types of microphones, and their construction, see Q. 4.17.

Q. 3.119. What precaution should be observed when using and storing crystal microphones?

A. The microphone should be protected against excessive heat, shock and humidity.

D. See Q. 3.118.

RADIO-FREQUENCY AMPLIFIERS

Q. 3.120. What is an RFC? Why are they used?

A. In general, an r-f choke acts as a low-pass filter which permits the passage of d-c and low frequency components but prevents the passage of radio frequencies.

D. Chokes are often used to prevent radio frequencies from entering the power supply. They are also used as coupling elements, to help maintain the Q of tank circuits, as in a crystal oscillator, and sometimes as tuning elements, as in a Pierce oscillator.

Q. 3.121. What are the advantages of using a resistor in series with the cathode of a Class-C radio-frequency amplifier tube to provide bias?

A. If the exciting signal to a Class-C radio-frequency amplifier, using grid-leak bias only, is interrupted for any reason the bias will be reduced to zero and excessive d–c plate current will flow; usually with disastrous results. If at least a portion of the total bias is obtained from a resistor in series with the cathode, the bias will not be reduced to zero because the d–c plate current, flowing through the cathode resistor, will still provide some bias.

D. This remaining bias can be made just sufficient to allow no more than the maximum allowable plate dissipation to occur under the d–c conditions of no excitation. For example, consider a type 833-A triode being used as a Class-C r-f amplifier with a plate voltage of 2500 volts. The maximum allowable plate dissipation for this tube is 300 watts. Under no-excitation conditions, all of the plate power input is converted to plate dissipation which, in this case, will reach the maximum allowable when the d–c plate current is 120 milliamperes. Reference to the characteristic curves for the tube will indicate that approximately -40 volts grid bias will produce a d–c plate current of 120 ma. Using Ohm's Law, the value of resistance to be used is found to be 40/0.120 or 333 ohms.

If the total grid bias recommended is -300 volts, the remaining 260 volts can be obtained in the usual manner by means of a grid leak.

Q. 3.122. What is the difference between r-f voltage amplifiers and r-f power amplifiers in regards to applied bias? What type of tube is generally employed in r-f voltage amplifiers?

A. (a) Usually an r-f voltage amplifier is operated as a Class-A amplifier, whereas an r-f power amplifier is operated as either a Class-B or Class-C amplifier. Therefore, an r-f voltage amplifier would normally use a bias that is approximately midway between zero and the cut-off bias for the value of plate voltage employed. For a Class-B power amplifier the bias would be approximately equal to the cut-off bias and for a Class-C power amplifier the bias would be in the order of twice cut-off bias.

(b) As power amplification is not required of r-f voltage amplifiers, receiving type tubes are normally used for this function. Commonly, these are pentodes, although triodes are sometimes used under special circumstances.

Q. 3.123. Draw schematic diagrams of the following circuits and give some possible reasons for their use.

(a) Link coupling between a final r-f stage and an antenna. (Include a low pass filter.)

(b) Capacitive coupling between an oscillator stage and a buffer amplifier.

(c) A method of coupling a final stage to a quarter-wave Marconi antenna other than link or transmission line.

A. (a) Link coupling between a final r-f stage and an antenna is most useful when the antenna is located remotely from the transmitter building as is the case in most broadcast stations. This permits placing both the building and the antenna in the most advantageous physical locations. Figure 3.123(a), illustrates the pertinent details of the system.

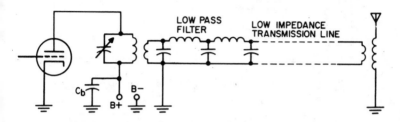

Fig. 3.123(a). *Link coupling between a final r–f stage and an antenna.*

(b) Capacitive coupling between an oscillator and its buffer amplifier is a very simple and easily adjustable method. For greater coupling, the tap on the tank coil of the oscillator may be moved closer to the plate end of the coil. Figure 3.123(b), illustrates the basic scheme for this type of coupling.

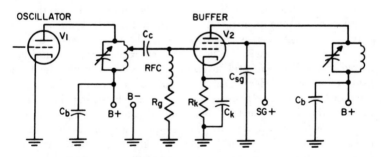

Fig. 3.123(b). *Capacitive coupling between an oscillator stage and a buffer amplifier.*

(c) For shipboard installations where the intermediate frequency ranges are used, the antenna's physical size is such that the connections to it from the transmitter necessarily are part of the complete antenna system. In such circumstances, the antenna download, which is a portion of the antenna itself, is connected directly to the transmitter output terminals. The diagrams given in Fig. 3.123(c) (1 and 2) illustrate two

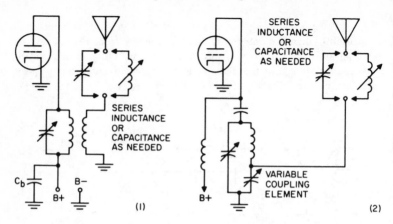

C_b B−
B+

(1)

SERIES
INDUCTANCE
OR
CAPACITANCE
AS NEEDED

SERIES
INDUCTANCE
OR
CAPACITANCE
AS NEEDED

B+

VARIABLE
COUPLING
ELEMENT

(2)

Fig. 3.123(c). Methods of coupling the r-f output of a transmitter to an antenna.

methods for accomplishing this. It should be noted that all parts shown in the diagrams are included inside the transmitter enclosure and just the antenna and ground connections are made to the transmitter.

Q. 3.124. Draw a schematic diagram of a grounded-grid r-f amplifier and explain its operation.

A. For the diagram, see Fig. 3.124. As shown in the figure, the grid is grounded and the input signal is applied to the cathode circuit.

In some circuits, bias is applied to the grid circuit either by a fixed-bias supply, or by means of a grid-leak resistor and grid capacitor connected in parallel from grid to ground. In the latter arrangement, the grid is "grounded" for signal by means of a capacitor, but is not grounded for d-c. The filament chokes prevent bypassing through the filament transformer capacity to ground of the input signal through the cathode-to-filament capacity. The output signal is taken from the plate circuit in the same manner as in a grounded-cathode amplifier. However, since the input voltage is in series with the external load impedance, this signal contains an additional component consisting of the input energy (see discussion below).

D. For an extensive discussion of grounded grid amplifiers see Q. 3.50(c).

Grounded grid amplifiers are sometimes used at very high frequencies because it is often possible to utilize triode tubes without the necessity for neutralization. In the grounded-grid amplifier the feedback capacitance is not the plate-grid capacitance, but is the much smaller plate-cathode capacitance. This smaller capacitance is less likely to cause oscillations,

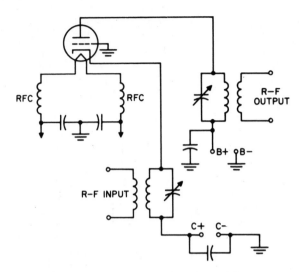

Fig. 3.124.   A grounded grid amplifier.

even at extremely high frequencies when special triodes (lighthouse type) are used. See also Q. 3.63 and Q. 3.64.

Q. 3.125.   Explain the principle involved in neutralizing an r-f stage.

A.   The purpose of neutralization in a radio-frequency amplifier is to prevent the amplifier from generating self-sustained oscillations. Without neutralization but with the tuned transformers customarily used, the circuit usually will act as a tuned-plate tuned-grid oscillator. Three common methods of neutralization are known as: (1) Hazeltine or plate neutralization, (2) Rice or grid neutralization, (3) Cross neutralization or push-pull neutralization.

D.   Conventional triode r-f amplifiers with both plate and grid circuits tuned to the same frequency invariably require neutralization. The reason for this is obvious when the r-f amplifier of Figure 4.46(a) is compared with the diagram of a tuned-grid tuned-plate oscillator as shown in Figure 3.86(b). Except for the neutralization connections, the two circuits are identical. Feedback through C_{gp} will cause the circuit to oscillate. If the amplifier is permitted to oscillate, there will be several undesirable effects: (1) Excessive plate current, (2) Overheating with possible burnout of tube, (3) Possible damage to circuit parts, such as meters, r-f chokes, etc., (4) Generation of spurious frequencies, (5) Distortion of a modulated wave (if this stage is modulated) during peaks of modulation. Since the tendency to oscillate is caused by an r-f voltage applied through C_{gp} to the grid, in phase with the original grid voltage, then a bucking voltage must be provided which is equal in amplitude and opposite in phase to the feedback through C_{gp}. The means of providing for such a bucking voltage is to tap the lower end of the plate tank circuit and feed this new voltage into the grid circuit. (1) A schematic diagram and the equivalent bridge circuit of a plate-neutralized amplifier are shown in Figures 3.125(a) and (b).

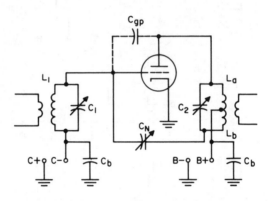

Fig. 3.125(a). Schematic diagram of a plate-neutralized amplifier.

The currents flowing into the input circuit through C_{gp} tend to cause oscillation. This effect is cancelled by opposing currents fed back to the input circuit through C_n. If the bridge is properly balanced (by adjusting C_n), no oscillations can appear in the output circuit. The relationship for balance is: $\dfrac{L_a}{L_b} = \dfrac{C_n}{C_{gp}}$

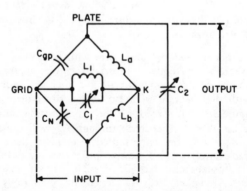

Fig. 3.125(b). Equivalent bridge circuit of a plate-neutralized amplifier.

(2) The schematic diagram and the equivalent bridge circuit of a grid-neutralized r-f amplifier are illustrated in Figures 3.125(c) and (d). This circuit operates in a manner similar to the plate neutralized system. For a balance, $\dfrac{L_a}{L_b} = \dfrac{C_n}{C_{gp}}$, as before.

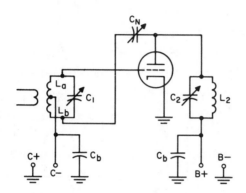

Fig. 3.125(c). Schematic diagram of a grid-neutralized amplifier.

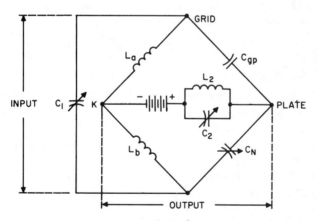

Fig. 3.125(d). Equivalent bridge circuit of a grid-neutralized amplifier.

(3) Push-pull neutralization does not require the addition of any special circuits other than the neutralizing capacitor, a schematic diagram is shown in Figure 3.125(e). It can be considered to be a form of plate neutralization. Advantage is taken of the fact that the

voltages on the two sides of a push-pull amplifier are of opposite polarity, and thus automatically provide the correct phase relations for neutralizing.

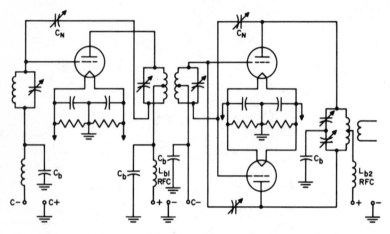

Fig. 3.125(e). Amplifier employing push-pull neutralization.

Q. 3.126. State some indications of, and methods of testing for, the presence of parasitic oscillations in a transmitter.

A. (a) Parasitic oscillations may be indicated by one or more of the following:

(1) Generation of spurious frequencies (carrier).

(2) Generation of spurious sideband frequencies during modulation.

(3) Distortion of the modulated wave.

(4) Overheating of the amplifier tube.

(5) Reduced efficiency of the amplifier tube at the desired frequency or frequencies.

(6) Change of bias (grid leak).

(7) High or erratic plate or grid-current readings.

(8) Unstable operation of an amplifier stage (or stages).

(9) Abnormal tuning characteristics of a stage (or stages).

(b) Some methods of testing for the existence of such parasitics are as follows:

(1) Using a radio receiver or sensitive wavemeter to explore the frequency spectra on either side of the desired operating frequency during both modulated and unmodulated conditions. Parasitic oscillations will show up as extra frequencies produced in addition to the desired operating frequency.

(2) Observing the modulation envelope, preferably using a trapezoidal pattern, with an oscilloscope with and without constant tone modulation. The presence of parasitics will cause unexplained nonlinearities, the degree of which will vary with differing percentages of modulation.

(3) Measuring the efficiency of the amplifier tube at the operating frequency. If the tube is operating with rated dissipation and power input, but the output at the operating efficiency is too low, the "missing" power output represents power output at a parasitic frequency.

(4) Checking for the overheating of one or more amplifier components. The radio frequency chokes and bypass capacitors are especially suspect.

D.   See Q. 3.92.

Q. 3.127.   Draw a circuit diagram of a push-pull (triode) final power amplifier with transmission line feed to a shunt-fed quarter-wave antenna and indicate a method of plate neutralization.

A.   For the diagram, see Fig. 3.127.

D.   For a discussion of transmission line feed, see Q. 3.214; for shunt feed, see Q. 3.209(b); and for push-pull neutralization, see Q. 3.125 and Q. 4.46(a).

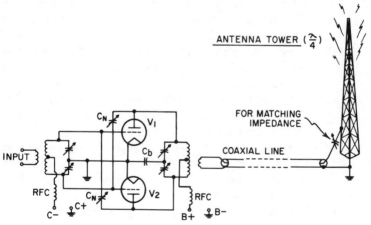

Fig. 3.127. Neutralized push-pull final amplifier; transmission-line fed to a shunt-fed quarter-wave antenna.

Q. 3.128.   Explain, step-by-step, at least one procedure for neutralizing an r-f amplifier stage.

A. Two procedures for neutralizing an r-f amplifier stage are as follows:

1. (a) Remove the plate (and screen) voltage from the stage being tested, but keep filaments lit and grid excitation present. The plate voltage should be removed in order to make the amplifier inoperative. If the amplifier were in the process of being neutralized and the plate voltage were not removed, it would be extremely difficult to determine when neutralization had taken place, since with grid excitation present there would always be r-f in the plate tank circuit. The danger of self-oscillations damaging the tube before neutralization is completed is another important factor.

    (b) If not already present, insert a d-c milliammeter of suitable range into the grid circuit of the amplifier under test.

    (c) Vary the tuning of the plate tank circuit while observing the grid current meter.

    (d) If sharp variations of grid current are observed while so tuning, the stage is not properly neutralized.

    (e) Adjust neutralizing capacitor until variations in grid current cease during plate tank tuning.

2. (a) This method requires the use of a suitable r-f indicator which may be a neon bulb, a small flashlight bulb with a loop of wire attached, a sensitive wavemeter, a sensitive thermocouple meter with a loop of wire attached, or any other suitable indicator.

    (b) Remove the plate (and screen) voltages from the stage being tested, but keep filaments lit and grid excitation present. (See 1.(a) above.)

    (c) With any of the indicators mentioned above (a), test for the presence of oscillations in the plate tank while tuning the tank capacitor through its range.

    (d) While performing the above (c), the grid circuit should be tuned for the maximum grid current, and the preceding plate circuit tuned for maximum drive, indicated by maximum grid current.

    (e) If oscillations are present in the plate tank circuit, adjust the neutralizing capacitor until they vanish or are at a minimum.

    (f) After a minimum indication has been reached, the driver and grid tanks should be retuned for maximum grid current and the neutralizing procedure repeated.

D. After the neutralizing procedure has been completed couple the load to the output of the amplifier (if not already coupled) and apply reduced plate and screen grid voltages to the neutralized stage. Tune the plate tank to resonance (as shown by a minimum plate current indication). Then apply normal voltages and readjust the plate tank for resonance. (See also Q. 3.125.)

Q. 3.129. Draw a circuit diagram of a push-push frequency multiplier and explain its principle of operation.

A. For the diagram, see Fig. 3.129. As shown in the diagram, the plates are connected in parallel. Also, the plate tank circuit is tuned to twice the frequency (second harmonic) of the grid-tank circuit. The plate circuit thus completes two cycles to every cycle of the grid circuit. However, because of the "push-push" connection the plate tank receives a pulse of current for each of its two cycles. When the grid of V_1 is positive it provides a pulse of current to the plate tank. One-half cycle of the input wave later, the grid of V_2 is positive and it provides a pulse of current to the plate tank for the second cycle occurring at this time.

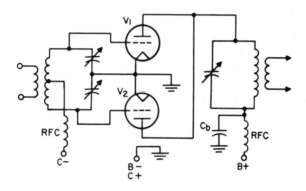

Fig. 3.129   A push-push frequency multiplier.

D. In the case of a single-tube frequency doubler (see Q. 3.131 and Q. 3.132), the plate efficiency is about 50% and the power output is about 70%, compared to a conventional class C amplifier. The reason for this is that plate current energy is supplied to the plate-tank circuit only every other cycle. For a tripler, energy is supplied only on every third cycle and the power output capability is further reduced. Thus, reduction of power output and plate efficiency becomes increasingly severe as higher orders of frequency multiplication are attempted. As a result, frequency multipliers in transmitters are generally limited to doublers and triplers. Another factor to be considered in relation to the degree of multiplication is the stability of the output wave. For a single tube tripler, the tank circuit is "running free" for two out of three cycles and is not under control of the stable driving (usually crystal) oscillator. A tank circuit with a high Q is required to maintain a stable frequency during the "free-running" time. However, if too great a frequency multiplication is attempted, frequency instability may result due to phase or frequency changes of the "free-running" cycles. To improve the efficiency of frequency multipliers, "push-push" circuits are used as frequency doublers (even-order harmonics), and "push-pull" circuits are used as frequency triplers (odd-order harmonics).

Q. 3.130. Push-pull frequency multipliers normally produce what order of harmonics; even or odd?

A.   Since the push-pull amplifier has been especially designed to reduce or eliminate all even-order harmonics, it follows that such an amplifier when used as a frequency multiplier will operate successfully only on odd-order harmonics.

D.   See Q. 3.129, Q. 3.131 and Q. 3.132.

Q. 3.131.   Draw a schematic diagram and explain the operation of a harmonic generator stage.

A.   For the diagram see Fig. 3.131.

A pure sine wave contains only one frequency, the fundamental. However, any distortion of the sine wave indicates the presence of other frequencies, which are multiples of the fundamental and are called harmonics. Thus any amplifier which distorts the input wave is actually a harmonic generator. The desired harmonic may be selected with a suitable resonant circuit. In a frequency doubler the grid tank is tuned to the fundamental while the plate tank is tuned to the second harmonic. In triodes the grid bias for most efficient doubling is 10 times cut-off value, with a plate efficiency of 50%, a relative power output (compared to ordinary class C amplifier) of 70%, and a plate current pulse length of 90°.

For a triode tripler, the grid bias is 20 times cut-off, plate efficiency

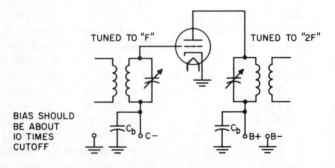

Fig. 3.131. An r-f doubler stage.

of 50%, relative power output of 36%, and a plate current pulse length of 75°.

Due to the high bias, very large values of grid excitation voltages must be used.

D. From a practical consideration, a doubler is most often used in connection with crystal oscillators. The high frequency limitations of quartz crystals are due to the fact that the crystal plate becomes thinner as its resonant frequency is increased. Thus it becomes extremely fragile and easily subject to overheating and cracking. To overcome this important limitation, the crystal frequency is kept relatively low, usually under 20 megacycles, and the crystal oscillator may be followed by one or a series of doublers to increase the output frequency.

In addition to the triode harmonic generators, beam-power pentodes are also commonly used. Because of its high transconductance, a beam-power tube may deliver a high harmonic content output with a relatively low driving signal. It should be noted that in general, frequency multipliers do not require neutralization (see Q. 3.128). This is so because the plate and grid circuits are tuned to widely differing frequencies and the feedback from plate-to-grid circuits is not of the phase necessary to sustain oscillations.

Q. 3.132. What class of amplifier is appropriate to use in a radio frequency doubler stage?

A. A Class C amplifier.

D. See Q. 3.131. See also Q. 3.129 and Q. 3.130.

Q. 3.133. Describe some factors in connection with the following items, which should be considered at VHF and above but would not be of particular concern at MF or below.
(a) Wire diameter and length.
(b) Wiring configuration (placement and bending).
(c) Coaxial cables and transmission lines.
(d) Capacitor types.

A. (a) To minimize the self-inductance of wires carrying VHF currents it is necessary to use conductors that are as short as possible and with as large a diameter as feasible. The diameter, however, should not be increased to the extent of appreciably increasing the capacitance of such conductors to ground or other conductors.

(b) Wiring configuration should be such that each conductor is separated by as great a distance from other conductors and ground as possible to minimize any distributed capacitances.

Any bends in the conductors should be minimum in number and of a maximum in radius as possible within the physical confines of the space available. This is to minimize the self-inductance of such conductors.

(c) The insulation of coaxial cables and transmission lines should be of a material having the lowest possible dielectric losses. Certain materials exhibit negligible losses at MF but have substantial losses at VHF. Insofar as is possible, such cables and lines should be air insulated. Where physical support is required, the number of such supports should be as few as possible. If standing waves are normally present on such cables and lines, it is important that insulating supports only be located at points of minimum voltage.

(d) Variable capacitors used in VHF service should be air insulated, using a minimum of solid dielectric for supporting the capacitor plates. Such dielectric that is used should have as small a dielectric loss as possible. Fixed capacitors should have low loss dielectrics, such as mica or ceramic.

D. At low r-f frequencies only the capacitance of a capacitor is considered and any inductive effects are usually discounted. However, at VHF and above, the inductance of a capacitor may represent an appreciable reactance and will modify the performance of the capacitor. At such frequencies the capacitor may represent a resonant circuit. In fact, in certain by-pass applications at VHF a capacitor may be chosen that is series-resonant at the operating frequency, thus offering minimum impedance to ground. Of course, at frequencies differing substantially from resonance, the capacitor may act as a fairly high value of either inductive or capacitive reactance. Thus, so-called "bypass" capacitors, under some conditions may not "bypass" at all and may function as a high impedance instead. In the usual case, capacitors used at VHF and above are constructed to have an exceedingly low value of self inductance, so that at the operating frequency, the inductive element can be neglected and the very-low value of capacitive reactance is the dominating factor. Typical of these are the "button" ceramic and "feed-through" coaxial-ceramic types, which are widely used in VHF transmitters and receivers. These are made in very small physical sizes with extremely low inductances and act as efficient coupling, bypass or r-f filter capacitors.

TRANSMITTERS

Q. 3.134. **Discuss the following items with respect to their harmonic attenuating properties as possibly used in a transmitter or receiver.**
(a) Link coupling
(b) Tuned circuits
(c) Degree of coupling
(d) Bias voltage
(e) Decoupling circuits
(f) Shielding

A. (a) Link coupling has, to a small degree, some attenuating properties for harmonics due to the relatively high capacitance of the low impedance transmission line connecting the two coupling coils. The capacitance will offer decreasing reactance as the frequencies increase and thus tend to bypass harmonics to a greater extent than the fundamental frequency.

A low impedance coaxial-transmission line with a grounded outer conductor is often used, and harmonics tend to be bypassed to ground to a considerably greater extent than the fundamental frequency. Another reason link coupling discriminates against harmonics is the reduction of capacitive coupling between the coils. Harmonics are coupled more readily through capacitive coupling (because of reduced reactance) than the fundamental frequency. The use of physically small link coils reduces capacitive coupling between the resonant circuits and the link coils to a greater extent than if two resonant circuits were inductively (or capacitively) coupled.

(b) Tuned circuits, resonant to the fundamental frequency, discriminate against harmonic frequencies to a remarkable degree. This discrimination, and hence harmonic attenuation, is a function of the Q of the tuned circuits and it is therefore desirable to have as high a Q as practical, if harmonic reduction is a prime consideration.

(c) In coupled-tuned circuits it is best to use loose coupling to achieve harmonic attenuation. The effect of such loose coupling is to "sharpen" the frequency response curve of the coupled circuits and increase the operating Q's of each of the tuned circuits. Not only is the Q increased but, as discussed in (a) above, the capacitive coupling between the two tuned circuits is reduced, decreasing harmonic transfer between the tuned circuits.

(d) Bias voltage in class-A, class-B, and class-B linear r-f amplifiers is extremely important from the standpoint of the reduction of harmonic generation. If the bias is incorrect in these amplifiers, a distorted output is obtained and harmonics of the input signal therefore appear. It should be noted, however, that already existing harmonics in the input signal will appear in the output undiminished and therefore the correct bias will not aid in the attenuation of such harmonics. Any harmonic attenuation in these amplifiers will be due to the action of the tuned circuits only.

(e) Since decoupling circuits are employed to reduce or eliminate positive feedback in multi-stage amplifiers, distortion in such amplifiers is reduced and, therefore, the generation of harmonics is reduced. However, if harmonics are present in the input signal, harmonics will appear in the output to the same degree despite the use of decoupling circuits. If the amplifiers are tuned, any harmonic attenuation will be due to the tuned circuits only.

(f) Shielding, when properly used, can be very effective in harmonic attenuation; especially when used as electrostatic or Faraday shields between coupled tuned circuits. Used in this manner, the shields drastically reduce the capacitive coupling between such circuits and thus reduce the transfer of harmonic energy from one circuit to the other.

D.   (a) For the diagram of one type of link coupling see Fig. 3.123(a). See also Q. 3.168(b) for another type of link coupling.

"Link coupling" is a low impedance transmission line method of coupling together two circuits which may be separated by a relatively large distance. It may be considered to be a step-down transformer and a step-up transformer interconnected. A link system consists of a very few turns of wire which is coupled to the low impedance point of a tank circuit, then connected to a length of low impedance transmission line and terminated by another few turns which is again coupled to the low impedance point of the antenna matching circuit. The amplifier low impedance point is that point to which the r-f bypass capacitor is connected. In push-pull operation, the low impedance position is at the center of the tank. Advantages of this system are extreme flexibility of mechanical construction and a reduction of tube capacitance effects on the L/C ratio of the tank circuits.

(b) A parallel resonant circuit of fairly high Q will present a high impedance at the resonant frequency and a very much lower impedance at harmonic frequencies. At harmonic frequencies the impedance will be a relatively low capacitive reactance. Thus, the gain of a stage employing a tuned-circuit load will be much lower at harmonic than at the fundamental frequencies. Of course, care must be taken to assure that harmonics are not transferred by means of capacitive coupling between stages (see also (c) and (f) above).

(c) See Q. 3.131 for the effect of bias on harmonic generation.

(d) For discussion of decoupling circuits, see Q. 3.102 and Q. 3.114.

(e) For discussion of Faraday shield, see Q. 3.137(a).

Q. 3.135. Define "transmitter intermodulation," a possible cause (or causes), its effects and steps that could be taken to reduce it.

A.   Transmitter intermodulation is the generation, by a transmitter, of a frequency, or frequencies, which is the combination of the fundamental or any of its harmonics with another fundamental or harmonics from a second transmitter that is fairly close by. One common cause of this is the picking up, by the antenna, some of the radiated energy from the second transmitter which is then fed backward into the transmitter over the transmission line. A portion of this energy can then be transferred to the grid of the power amplifier. Since at least the grid of this amplifier is a non-linear circuit, a modulation of one frequency, or its harmonics, by the second frequency, or its harmonics, takes place with resulting sideband frequencies. These sideband frequencies are known as intermodulation products and may be equal to $f_1 \pm f_2$, $f_1 \pm 2f_2$, $2f_1 \pm f_2$, etc.

One obvious manner of reducing such intermodulation would be to locate the transmitters and their associated antennas at greater distances from one another. Economic and other reasons, however, often eliminate this remedy. By placing a wavetrap, tuned to the second transmitter's frequency or offending harmonic, in the transmission line close to the transmitter, the picked up energy can be markedly reduced, with a corresponding reduction in the intermodulation. R-f power amplifiers using inductive neutralization are prone to these intermodulation effects because the neutralization is only effective for the operating frequency and energy transfer from output to input at frequencies appreciably different from the operating frequency takes place quite easily. Plate or grid neutralization, on the other hand, is effective over quite a large frequency spectrum and such energy transfer is more effectively blocked.

D.   For a discussion of the principles of intermodulation involving audio frequencies, see Q. 3.104, D. Generally, the same principles apply to intermodulation involving radio frequencies, as described above. Due to the nature of intermodulation, problems involving this phenomenon may occur within a transmitter, as well as between two transmitters. These may be produced in virtually any stage of a transmitter: audio, video, or radio frequency, if the stage operates in a non-linear fashion. This includes modulator stages, Class C r-f amplifiers and even conventional audio and video amplifiers if operated in a non-linear manner. If radiated, intermodulation frequencies may result in interference to other channels or may produce distortion in the originating signal. In the case of audio or video amplifiers, which are generally Class A types, care must be taken to see that the operation of these stages remains in the linear regions of their characteristic. This dictates, primarily, that the original design be adequate; that the components function properly; that correct bias is maintained; and that there is no overdriving of stages. (See Q. 4.37 through Q. 4.41 for discussion of "limiting" and "AGC" and "compression" amplifiers.) Many of the r-f intermodulation components generated within a transmitter are automatically eliminated by the resonant effect of the r-f tank circuits and by the antenna matching network which is normally used between the final r-f amplifiers and the antenna and transmission line. (See Q. 4.55, Q. 4.56 and Q. 4.82.) Shielding of some transmitter circuits and the use of Faraday screens (see Q. 3.134(f)) are also effective means of reducing r-f intermodulation radiation. In addition, circuits used to reduce simple harmonic radiation (see Q. 3.137), may also be effective in reducing r-f intermodulation radiation. Obviously, intermodulation components lying within the normal audio, video, or r-f pass band cannot be filtered out, but must be eliminated at the source.

Q. 3.136. State a probable cause of and method of reducing transmitter spurious emissions (other than harmonics).

A. There are three general types of spurious emissions, other than harmonics or intermodulation frequencies.

(a) Parasitic oscillations: See Q. 3.92 and Q. 3.126 for a complete discussion.

(b) Harmonic generator frequencies: Many types of transmitters employ harmonic generators. In some cases the input or output frequencies of intermediate harmonic generator stages exist at sufficiently high amplitude to feed through to the antenna. However, most of these frequencies are removed from the transmitted frequency. In many cases, therefore, such frequencies are discriminated against by the r-f tank circuits, and by the shielding and filtering normally employed against the transmission of harmonics and intermodulation frequencies (see Q. 3.135). In special cases, it may be necessary to employ resonant filters to reduce interference from an unusually strong harmonic generator, from intermediate frequency signals, or from the primary frequency generated by the stable-master oscillator. See Q. 3.128 through Q. 3.132 for a discussion of such stages. See also Q. 3.168(a) and Q. 4.89(b) and (d).

(c) Another possible type of spurious emission is due to oscillation of an improperly neutralized r-f amplifier. In this case, the stage acts as a tuned-grid, tuned-plate oscillator, with feedback occurring through the plate to grid capacitance of the tube. A similar type of oscillation may occur in a transistor r-f amplifier employing tuned input and output circuits, which are resonant to the same frequency. In this case, the feedback is through the collector-to-base capacity and the base-material resistance. For a discussion of neutralization, see Q. 3.125 and Q. 3.128.

Q. 3.137. List several frequently used methods of attenuating harmonics in transmitters and explain how each works.

A. (a) A Faraday screen may be used between the final-tank inductance and the output-coupling coil of the transmitter as shown in Fig. 3.137(a). The Faraday screen is a grounded electrostatic screen which greatly reduces the capacitive coupling between the two coils and thus reduces the transfer of harmonic frequencies. (See discussion below.)

(b) The use of tuned wave traps in the transmission line to the antenna. The diagram shown in Figure 3.137(a) shows how such traps may be connected to the transmission line. The parallel resonant traps shown connected in series with the line present a very high impedance to the harmonic frequency to which they are tuned and therefore reduce the

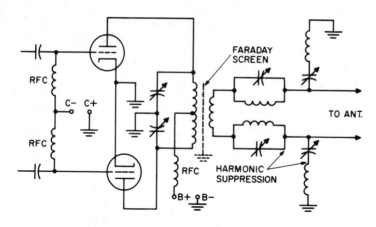

Fig. 3.137(a). R-f output of a transmitter may be coupled to a transmission line in this manner, utilizing the Faraday screen to reduce the transfer of harmonic frequencies.

amount of harmonic energy transferred to the antenna. The series resonant traps shown connected from the line to ground exhibit a very low impedance to the harmonic frequency and tend to short circuit the harmonic energy to ground, thus reducing the amount of such energy from reaching the antenna.

(c) Low pass r-f filters are sometimes used in the transmission line instead of the tuned filters discussed above. The low pass filters are designed to have a cut-off frequency somewhat in excess of the operating frequency. These filters not only reduce the harmonic radiation but have the added advantage of attenuating any other spurious emissions above the filter's cut-off frequency. For diagrams of low-pass filters, see Q. 3.35 and Q. 3.36.

(d) The use of a "pi" network for impedance matching between the plate of the output tube and the transmission line has some value in attenuating harmonic output and is shown in Fig. 3.137(d). The output or load adjusting capacitor of the network will have much lower reactance for harmonic frequencies and thus tends to bypass such energy to ground.

D.   (See Q. 3.134.)

(a) The purpose of a "Faraday" screen (or shield) is to minimize the transfer of harmonic frequencies between two inductively coupled circuits due to the capacity between the two coils. The two coils in question are usually the plate tank circuit coil of the final r-f amplifier and the coupling coil to the antenna system.

In addition to inductive coupling between the two coils, there also exists a degree of capacitive coupling due to the stray capacity existing between the two coils. The amount of capacity coupling increases as the two coils are brought closer together. This capacity coupling offers a relatively low impedance path for the transfer of harmonics, since the capacitive reactance decreases as the frequency is increased. One effective means of reducing harmonic transfer into the antenna circuit is to reduce the capacity between the two coupled coils. The method of accomplishing this is similar to the principle of a screen grid in a tetrode vacuum tube. A screen or shield which is grounded is placed between

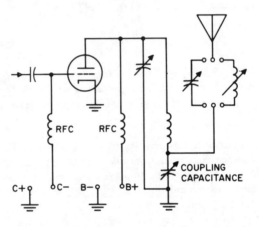

Fig. 3.137(d). Coupling to an antenna by means of a "pi" network.

the two coils. Such a device is called a "Faraday" screen. It is made up of a flat plate constructed of separate parallel conductors insulated from each other at one end, but joined together physically and electrically at the other end. The conductors are insulated at one end so that no closed circuits will appear in the screen which would also cause magnetic shielding. The insertion of this grounded screen between the two coils greatly reduces the capacitance between the coils and so minimizes harmonic coupling due to the capacitance effect.

(b) For discussions of commonly used filters, see Q. 3.35 and Q. 3.36.

(c) See Q. 4.55 and Q. 4.56 for diagrams of antenna coupling methods and discussions of these.

AMPLITUDE MODULATION

Q. 3.138. What is the meaning of the term "carrier frequency"?

A. The "carrier frequency" is the frequency of the "carrier wave."

The "carrier wave" is the output of a transmitter when the modulating wave is equal to zero.

D.   The above definitions hold true in the case of conventially modulated AM or FM transmitters. However, in the case of single-sideband suppressed carrier emission (see Q. 3.152), the carrier is not transmitted. There is a carrier frequency in this case, but it is suppressed prior to transmission.

Q. 3.139.   If a carrier is amplitude modulated, what causes the sideband frequencies?

A.   The process of modulation can be thought of as a process of heterodyning two or more frequencies and results in beat frequencies. The products of modulation are the two original frequencies plus the sum and difference frequencies. The sum and difference frequencies are known as the sideband frequencies. One of the two original frequencies (the radio frequency) appears unchanged and is termed the carrier frequency. The lower original or modulating frequency is also unchanged, but usually does not appear in the output of the modulated amplifier because the amplifier's load presents practically zero impedance to this low frequency.

D.   In a more analytical sense, the modulated wave is a distorted sine wave because its amplitude is varying. Mathematically it can be shown that this distorted sine wave is comprised of three component frequencies; the carrier plus the two sidebands. The amplitude of the modulated wave at any instant is the vector sum of the amplitudes of the three components at the same instant.

Q. 3.140.   What determines the bandwidth of emission for an AM transmission?

A.   The bandwidth of emission for an AM transmission is always equal to twice the highest modulating frequency being used.

D.   Assuming a carrier frequency of 500 kilocycles and a modulating frequency of 800 cycles, the bandwidth of emission is determined as given in the following example.

The total bandwidth is the difference between the upper and lower sideband frequencies. The upper sideband frequency equals 500,000 + 800 = 500,800 cycles. The lower sideband frequency equals 500,000 — 800 = 499, 200 cycles. The total bandwidth therefore equals 1600 cycles, or the difference between the two sideband frequencies.

Q. 3.141.   Why does exceeding 100% modulation in an AM transmission cause excessive bandwidth of mission?

A. When 100% modulation is exceeded in an AM transmission, the negative peaks of the modulation envelope are clipped. The result of this is to introduce even-order harmonics of the modulating frequencies into the wave. Since these represent higher modulating frequencies, the bandwidth of the emission is correspondingly increased and may become excessive.

D. When an r-f amplifier is modulated in excess of 100%, there are definite periods of time when the amplifier does not produce any output at all. This factor radically changes the original wavelength of the modulating signal. New frequencies are thus generated which were not present in the original modulating signal. Among these new frequencies are many harmonics, the number and intensity of which vary in proportion to the degree of overmodulation. These in effect create additional sideband frequencies which may extend far beyond the allotted bandwidth, and cause interference to adjacent channels. In addition to creating interference, the change in waveshape of the modulation component also causes distortion of the received signal, the magnitude of which increases with the degree of overmodulation.

Q. 3.142. What is the relationship between percent modulation and the shape of the waveform "envelope" relative to carrier amplitude?

A. The amplitude of the peaks of modulation, expressed as a percentage of the carrier amplitude, is the percentage of modulation. Fig. 3.142 illustrates the relationship between the audio modulating signal, the unmodulated carrier wave and the modulated carrier wave for a 50 percent modulated wave.

D. Assume the carrier amplitude to be 100 volts unmodulated, the

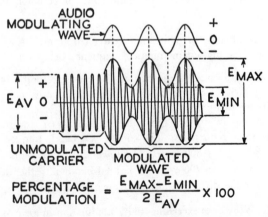

Fig. 3.142.   A 50-percent modulated wave.

value of E_{max} to be 150 volts, and the value of E_{min} to be 50 volts. The percentage modulation is found according to the formula:

$$Mod. = \frac{E_{max} - E_{min}}{2\,E_{av}} \times 100 = \frac{150 - 50}{200} \times 100 = 50\%$$

For 100% modulation E_{max} would be 200 and E_{min} would be zero.

Q. 3.143. Draw a simplified circuit diagram of the final stages (modulator, modulated push-pull linear amplifier) of a type of low-level plate modulated transmitter, utilizing a pentode tube in the modulated stage. Explain the principles of operation. Repeat using a tetrode to provide high-level modulation.

A. Figure 3.143(a) illustrates one possible configuration for a low-level Class-C plate-modulated amplifier followed by a push-pull Class-B RF linear amplifier. It is believed the question is slightly in error, as a push-pull linear amplifier is not ordinarily modulated.

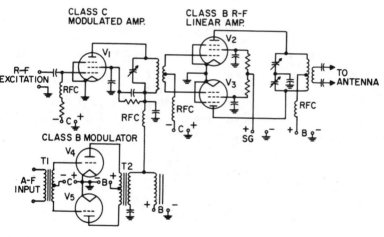

Fig. 3.143(a). Low level plate-modulated transmitter with pentode in modulated stage.

In a properly adjusted Class-C amplifier, the output voltage or amplitude is directly proportional to the applied plate voltage. Examining the diagram, it can be seen that the AF output voltage of the modulator is in series with the applied d–c plate voltage to the modulated amplifier. This results in an applied voltage that varies in accordance with the modulating frequency and therefore results in an output from the modulated amplifier whose amplitude also varies in accordance with the modulating frequency. Thus an amplitude modulated wave is created.

When a pentode is used as a modulated Class-C amplifier, it is necessary to vary the applied screen grid voltage in the same manner as the applied plate voltage. One way of doing this is shown in the figure. An inspection of the figure will reveal that the screen voltage is obtained, through a series dropping resistor, from the applied voltage and therefore both voltages will vary simultaneously.

In the circuit shown, a Class-B RF linear amplifier amplifies the already modulated wave. It is necessary to use this particular type of amplifier to prevent distortion of the modulated wave. Such an amplifier has the ability to produce an output voltage that almost exactly duplicates the exciting voltage within certain limits. A Class-C amplifier used in this position, of course, would produce intolerable distortion.

Figure 3.143(b) illustrates one possible configuration for a high level plate modulated amplifier using a tetrode. High level modulation is defined as plate modulation of the final power amplifier, hence, in this case, the output of the modulated amplifier is fed directly to the antenna instead of to a following amplifier.

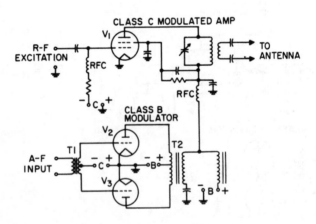

Fig. 3.143(b). High level plate-modulated transmitter with tetrode in modulated stage.

The illustrated circuit operates exactly as described for the foregoing pentode modulated amplifier. An examination of both circuits will reveal that they are similar in all respects except for the suppressor grid connection.

D. Any stages which are required to amplify a modulated wave must be operated as linear amplifiers in order that the modulation components shall not be distorted. Class-C operation cannot be used because of the extreme distortion which would result. It would be possible to employ Class A except for its very low efficiency. Thus Class-B operation is the logical choice both from the standpoint of low distortion and of efficiency. It is usually preferred to operate at least the final Class-B amplifier in push-pull. See also Q. 3.139 through Q. 3.142, Q. 3.143, Q. 4.48, Q. 4.85, Q. 4.86 and Q. 4.89(a).

Q. 3.144.   How does a linear power amplifier differ from other types?

A.   It is assumed that the question was meant to be "How does an RF linear power amplifier differ from other types of RF power amplifiers?"

Under the above assumption, the most generally used RF power amplifier is the Class-C amplifier with its high distortion produced by using a bias voltage greatly in excess of the cut-off value. As opposed to this, the RF linear power amplifier is a Class-B amplifier that uses a bias approximately equal to the projected cut-off bias. Biased in this manner, such an amplifier has an output voltage that is almost exactly directly in proportion to the exciting voltage—hence the name, linear.

D.   Occasionally, Class-A RF power amplifiers are used. These amplifiers are also linear, but are not able to generate the amount of output power that the Class-B amplifiers can, nor do they operate as efficiently. (See also Q. 3.143.)

Q. 3.145.   Draw a simple schematic diagram showing a method of coupling a modulator tube to a radio frequency power amplifier tube to produce grid modulation of the amplified RF energy. Compare some advantages or disadvantages of this system of modulation with those of plate modulation.

A.   For the diagram, see Fig. 3.145.

Some *advantages* of grid modulation vs. plate modulation are as follows:

(a) The amount of audio power required of the modulator for 100% modulation is extremely small.

(b) Very much smaller modulation transformer may be used.

Some *disadvantages* of grid vs. plate modulation are as follows:

(a) The grid modulated amplifier must use tubes having an output rating approximately equal to four times the carrier output power, whereas the plate modulated amplifier must use tubes having an output rating equal to approximately one and a half times the carrier output power. The output power ratings mentioned are those for straight Class-C unmodulated or oscillator service.

(b) Distortionless modulation, greater than about 85%, is very difficult to achieve, whereas with the plate modulated amplifier, 100% modulation without distortion is easily accomplished.

D.   The efficiency of a grid-modulated amplifier is maximum at complete modulation and minimum at zero modulation.

The plate efficiency of a grid-bias modulated class C r-f amplifier under unmodulated conditions is about ½ of the amplifier efficiency realized during the 100% modulation peaks. This averages between 30 and 40% in typical cases. When the wave is 100% modulated, the plate efficiency averages about 45 to 60%. The carrier power obtained from a grid-bias modulated stage is about ¼ of the power obtainable from the same tube operated as an ordinary class C amplifier.

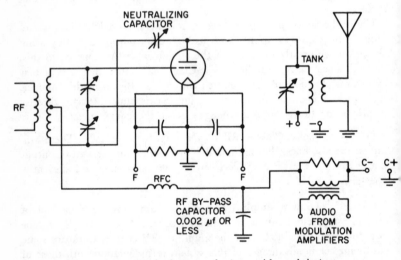

Fig. 3.145. Method of producing grid modulation.

If maximum output from a grid-modulated amplifier is to be achieved, it is necessary that the grid be driven positive (and draw current) on the modulation crests (peaks). However, it must be realized that grid current may cause distortion due to an impedance drop in the driver. It is essential, therefore, that the impedance presented by the driver be a low value to insure output voltage regulation. Where minimum distortion is desired, the grid is not permitted to draw current. This operating condition results in a reduction of both output and operating efficiency, but this is the price which must be paid for the improved quality.

The d-c grid bias is normally adjusted to a value varying from 1½ to 3 times the plate current cut-off value. The actual value of bias used is not extremely critical and is a function of the available modulating voltage, and the desired operating efficiency. The efficiency of a grid-bias modulated class C amplifier is only about half that of a properly designed unmodulated class C amplifier and therefore the output is correspondingly less.

Q. 3.146. What is meant by "frequency shift" or "dynamic instability?" with reference to a modulated r-f emission?

A. "Frequency shift" or "dynamic instability" refers to the instantaneous changes of oscillator frequency due to corresponding changes of plate and screen grid voltages of the oscillator tubes, and is caused by improper regulation of the power supply.

D. If a common power supply were used for the oscillator, r-f amplifiers and modulator stages, it would be difficult to prevent "dynamic instability," especially if the modulator were not operating strictly class A. Any changes in the loading due to any cause, or any changes in modulator power requirements will create a change in power supply output voltage. This, in turn, may cause the oscillator frequency to shift, creating undesired frequency modulation. In general, an increase in oscillator plate voltage (with screen voltage constant) will cause the oscillator frequency to increase because of a decrease of tube input capacity. A proportional increase of screen voltage would have the opposite effect on the frequency, and this factor is taken advantage of in the electron-coupled oscillator to maintain frequency stability and reduce dynamic instability. Dynamic instability can also be reduced by: (1) using an oscillator tank circuit with a high C/L ratio, (2) by light loading of the oscillator circuit, (3) by using a high value of grid leak, and (4) by using separate power supplies for oscillator, modulator and r-f amplifiers, or at least for the oscillator.

Q. 3.147. What would cause a dip in the antenna current when AM is applied? What are the causes of carrier shift?

A. (a) This is called "downward modulation."

With *plate* modulation, "downward modulation" may be caused by any of the following:

(1) Insufficient bias at the modulated r-f amplifier.

(2) Insufficient excitation into the modulated r-f amplifier.

(3) Excessive overloading of the class C modulated r-f amplifier.

(4) Incorrect load impedance for the class C modulated r-f amplifier.

(5) Faulty or insufficient value of output capacity in the power supply filter for the modulated r-f amplifier.

(6) Poor regulation of a common power supply.

(7) Defective tube.

With *grid-bias* modulation, a downward "kick" may be caused by any of the following:

(1) Excessive r-f excitation to the grid of the modulated r-f amplifier.

(2) Insufficient operating bias on the grid of the modulated r-f amplifier.

(3) Distortion in the modulator or speech amplifier.

(4) Excessive resistance in the grid bias power supply.

(5) Faulty or insufficient output capacity in the plate power supply filter to the modulated r-f amplifier.

(6) Insufficient loading of the plate circuit of the modulated r-f amplifier.

(7) Too high plate-circuit efficiency of the modulated r-f amplifier under unmodulated conditions.

(8) Defective tube.

(b) "Carrier shift" occurs when the relative amplitudes of the positive and negative modulation peaks are unsymmetrical. The shift is one of amplitude and not of carrier frequency.

D.   (a) An upward rise of antenna current when a transmitter is amplitude modulated is a normal condition. However, an upward "kick" of current may occur which is not a normal condition. With plate modulation an upward "kick" may be caused by any of the following:

(1) Parasitic oscillations in the modulated r-f amplifier.
(2) Overmodulation.
(3) Incomplete neutralization of the modulated r-f amplifier.

With grid modulation an upward "kick" may be caused by any of the following:

(1) Overmodulation.
(2) Audio system distortion.
(3) Incomplete neutralization of the modulated r-f amplifier.
(4) Excessive grid bias in the modulated r-f amplifier.

(b) The following are causes of positive carrier shift:

1. High or low frequency parasitic oscillations.

2. Excessive audio drive.

3. Incorrect tuning of final amplifier.

4. Insufficient r-f excitation.

5. Incorrect neutralization.

The following may cause negative carrier shift:

1. Distorted modulating wave due to

(a) Improper bias of modulation amplifier.

(b) Overdriving of modulation amplifier.

(c) Poor regulation of modulator power supply.

(d) Defective tube or modulation transformer.

2. Overmodulation.

3.   Incorrect load impedance presented to modulator tube by r-f amplifier.

4.   Improper tuning of tank circuits.

5.   Poor regulation of r-f amplifier power supply.

6.   Insufficient r-f excitation.

The term "negative carrier shift" does not denote a change of carrier frequency, although additional harmonic frequencies are produced. Carrier shift occurs when an unsymmetrical distortion of the modulation envelope is present. In "negative carrier shift," the negative portions of the modulation component become greater than the positive portions, resulting in a decrease of the average output power as evidenced by a decreased reading on the d-c plate milliammeter of the final r-f amplifier. In "positive carrier shift" the positive portions of the modulation component become greater in amplitude than the negative portions, resulting in an increase of the average output power as evidenced by an increased reading on the d-c plate milliammeter of the final r-f amplifier.

The d-c plate current of a modulated class C amplifier should remain constant when AM is applied. If no distortion (practically) occurs in the process of modulation, the amount of increase in class C plate current should be exactly the same as the amount of decrease and therefore the average change is zero. This applies as long as there is no overmodulation present or carrier shift.

Q. 3.148.   What is the relationship between the average power output of the modulator and the plate circuit input of the modulated amplifier under 100 percent sinusoidal plate modulation? How does this differ when normal voice modulation is employed?

A.   (a) With 100 percent sinusoidal plate modulation, the average audio output power of the modulator is equal to 50 percent of the d-c plate circuit input power of the modulated amplifier.

(b) With normal voice modulation, the average modulation percentage is only in the order of 30 percent or less. This is due to the ratio of peak to average power in the human voice. Under these conditions, the average power output of the modulator is only about 4.5 percent of the amplifier's d–c plate input power. To reproduce the peaks of speech faithfully, however, the modulator must still have the same peak power capability as when called upon to produce 100% sinusoidal modulation.

D.   Under 100% sinusoidal plate modulation conditions, the a-c power output of the modulator must equal ½ of the d-c power input to the modulated r-f amplifier. The modulator output supplies the power for the sidebands, while the d-c supply furnishes the power for the carrier wave.

Q. 3.149.   What is the relationship between the amount of power in the sidebands and the intelligibility of the signal at the receiver?

A. Since all the intelligence in an amplitude-modulated emission is contained in the sidebands and none in the carrier, the intelligibility of the signal at the receiver is directly proportional to the amount of power in the sidebands.

D. The following are advantages of high percentage modulation:

(1) A higher signal-to-noise ratio at the receiver.

(2) Greater area coverage for a given carrier power.

(3) Greater useful transmitted power for a given carrier power.

(4) Higher plate efficiency of the modulated r-f amplifier.

(5) Less interference at the receiver from other stations operating on the same channel.

It should be realized that the only *useful* power contained in a modulated carrier wave is in the sidebands. At 100% modulation the sideband power represents only 33⅓% of the total radiated power. The remainder of the power, or 66⅔%, is in the carrier wave and is of no value in transmitting intelligence. If the percentage of modulation is reduced to 50%, the amount of power in the sidebands is reduced only about 11% of the *total* radiated power. (This corresponds to an increase of 12.5% over the original carrier power.) It may be seen from the above examples that it is important to keep the average percentage of modulation as high as may be practical for any particular transmitter.

Q. 3.150. What might cause FM in an AM radiotelephone transmitter?

A. See Q. 3.146.

Q. 3.151. Draw a block diagram of an AM transmitter.

A. For the diagram, see Fig. 3.151.

D. See Q. 4.89(a).

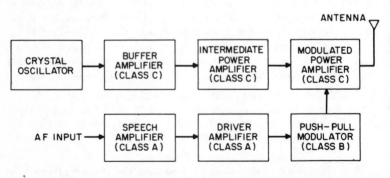

Fig. 3.151. Block diagram of an AM transmitter.

Q. 3.152. Explain the principles involved in single-sideband sup-pressed-carrier (SSSC) emission. How does its bandwidth of emission and required power compare with that of full carrier and sidebands?

A. Either a mathematical or electrical analysis of an amplitude mod-ulated wave will demonstrate that the carrier of the wave is completely unaffected by the presence or absence of modulation. Further analysis will demonstrate that *each* sideband will contain *all* the intelligence that is being transmitted. The foregoing facts lead to the conclusion, that, to successfully convey intelligence, it is only necessary to transmit but one sideband; the carrier and the remaining sideband being suppressed or not transmitted.

Since with the single-sideband suppressed-carrier (SSSC) mode of transmission, only one sideband is transmitted, the bandwidth of emis-sion is reduced to only one-half of the bandwidth required for normal amplitude-modulated transmission. The bandwidth required is equal to the highest modulating frequency used.

The signal-to-noise power ratio at the output of a radio receiver de-pends on several factors, among which are the following:

(1) The amount of power contained in the sidebands of the received wave.

(2) The width of the receiver's passband or its selectivity.

(3) The amount of noise power received by the antenna.

If the above factors are constant, then, for the same peak-power cap-abilities of the transmitter, an improvement in signal-to-noise power ratio of eight times can be obtained by the use of SSSC. For the same signal-to-noise performance at the receiver, the transmitter must be capable of handling only one-eighth the peak power that would be required of an amplitude-modulated transmitter.

On an average-power, instead of a peak-power basis, the SSSC trans-mitter must deliver only one-sixth the amount of average power required of an amplitude-modulated transmitter for the same signal-to-noise per-formance at the receiver.

D. See Q. 3.153 and Q. 3.154.

Q. 3.153. Draw a block diagram of an SSSC transmitter (filter type) with a 20-kc oscillator and emission frequencies in the range of 6 mc. Explain the function of each stage.

A. (a) For the diagram, see Fig. 3.153.

(b) The *First Balanced Modulator,* because of special circuit balanc-ing, produces a modulated wave containing upper and lower sidebands but no carrier. The carrier, if it were present, would have a frequency in this case of 20 kc and is supplied by the 20-kc *Crystal Oscillator.* The

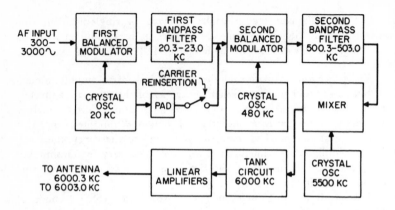

Fig. 3.153. Block diagram of a filter-type SSSC transmitter.

output of the first balanced modulator consists of the lower sideband frequencies, from 17.3 kc to 19.7 kc, and the upper sideband frequencies, from 20.3 kc to 23.0 kc.

The *First Bandpass Filter* is so designed as to pass only frequencies of 20.3 to 23.0 kc. Frequencies outside this pass band are greatly attenuated. Therefore, the first bandpass filter allows only the upper sideband frequencies to pass through and be fed to the *Second Balanced Modulator*. By this action, a single-sideband suppressed-carrier signal has been generated, but it requires further treatment as it is not of the desired frequency range as yet.

The second balanced modulator differs from the first balanced modulator only in having an input carrier frequency of 480 kc instead of 20 kc. The output of the second balanced modulator consists of lower sideband frequencies of from 457.0 kc to 459.7 kc and upper sideband frequencies of from 500.3 kc to 503.0 kc.

The second bandpass filter, because of its pass band of 500.0 kc to 503.0 kc, allows only the upper sidebands of the second balanced modulator to be presented to the input of the *Mixer*.

The mixer stage is similar to mixer stages used in superheterodyne receivers and its output consists of the original input frequencies of from 500.3 to 503.0 kc, the *Crystal Oscillator* frequency of 5500 kc, the difference frequencies from 4997.0 kc to 4999.7 kc and the sum frequencies from 6000.3 kc to 6003.0 kc.

The *Tank Circuit,* which actually is part of the mixer, is adjusted to be resonant at 6000 kc. Consequently, the output of the tank circuit is only the upper sideband frequencies of from 6000.3 kc to 6003.0 kc. All of the other responses of the mixer are discriminated against or attenuated by the tank circuit.

In actual practice, the carrier is not always suppressed completely. For use in receiving a single-sideband signal it is very useful to have a very much attenuated carrier present in the wave as a reference frequency. The carrier may be reduced as much as 20 db below the sideband power level. Propagation conditions may often dictate a carrier power level that is higher than the usual 20 db. The carrier is reinserted into the single-sideband signal at the output of the first bandpass filter as shown in the diagram. The amount of carrier reinserted is controlled by the adjustable attenuating pad.

D.   It is normal practice to operate the above-described stages at very low power levels and to use receiving type vacuum tubes in this part of the transmitter. Today, semi-conductors are beginning to replace vacuum tubes. The section of the transmitter just described is called various names, among which are "Exciter," "SSB Generator," etc., and has a final power output in the order of tenths of a watt.

The output of an exciter is insufficient to excite the antenna and further amplification is required. Since the signal is already modulated, the normal Class C amplifier cannot be used for this purpose. Therefore, Class B RF linear amplifiers are used to obtain essentially distortionless power amplification to the power level required at the antenna. In some infrequent instances, Class A RF linear amplifiers are used, but this practice is rapidly declining because of the low efficiency of this class of amplifier.

Q. 3.154.   Explain briefly, how an SSSC emission is detected.

A.   To detect a SSSC signal, the output of a low frequency (20 kc) local oscillator is applied to the final receiver detector, together with the single-sideband output of the last i-f amplifier (20.3 to 23 kc). Because of the non-linear action of the detector, an amplitude-modulated wave is produced, which is then detected in the conventional manner by the same detector.

D.   A single-sideband receiver is a superheterodyne and may be of the single-conversion (see Q. 3.155) or double-conversion (see Q. 3.180) type. The SSB receiver differs from the conventional type primarily in the manner of final detection, as described above. In order to faithfully reproduce the original audio signal, it is essential that the reinserted carrier have the same frequency as the transmitter carrier and have the correct amplitude. There are several ways of insuring proper frequency. As stated in the preceeding question, a reduced carrier (20 kc) may be transmitted together with the single-sideband signal. This reduced carrier may be extracted from the i-f signal by a sharply tuned crystal filter and can be utilized in either of two ways. One procedure is to use the reduced carrier as the reference frequency for an AFC system to stabilize the frequency of the carrier reinsertion oscillator (20 kc). Another possibility (after extraction) is to amplify the reduced carrier and to utilize it directly as the reinserted carrier. Both of these schemes add to the expense and complexity of the SSB receiver. A simpler arrangement, which is frequently used, utilizes a highly stable carrier reinsertion oscillator, operating at 20 kc.

To recover the modulation information from a single-sideband signal, it is not essential to reinsert a carrier at the original low frequency (20 kc). The carrier may be reinserted at the i-f frequency (such as 455 kc), or at the r-f transmission frequency (such as 6,000 kc, as in the preceding question). For example, in communications receivers employing a "beat-frequency oscillator" (see Q. 3.158), the BFO may be used to reinsert an i-f carrier. In this case the BFO frequency is carefully adjusted to obtain an undistorted audio output. The BFO is then tuned to the precise i-f frequency, 455 kc. As an alternative, an r-f oscillator may be tuned to the transmission r-f carrier frequency (such as 6,000 kc) and fed into the antenna input circuit of the receiver. In the latter case, the oscillator must be tuned to the exact r-f transmission frequency of the station. This condition will be effected when undistorted audio is obtained from the receiver. As was the case for the low frequency (20 kc) reinserted carrier, the oscillators used to reinsert the carrier must be highly stable. This is necessary because any oscillator drift will result in a distorted, "scrambled," or "inverted" audio output.

Q. 3.155.   Draw a block diagram of a single-conversion superheterodyne AM receiver. Assume an incident signal and explain briefly what occurs in each stage.

A.   For the diagram, see Fig. 3.155.

Using the incident frequency of 2450 kc as shown in the diagram, a brief description of what occurs in each stage is as follows:

1. The signal, with a frequency of 2450 kc, is fed by the antenna

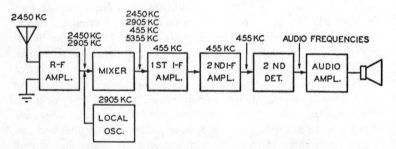

Fig. 3.155.   Block diagram of a superheterodyne AM receiver.

system into the RF amplifier where it is amplified and separated, to some extent, from other frequencies.

2. The mixer has two signals fed to it. One of these is the incoming signal of 2450 kc from the RF amplifier and the other is a signal of 2905 kc from the local oscillator. The mixer combines these two frequencies and produces in its output the two original frequencies and their sum and differences. These are shown in the diagram.

3. The 1st IF amplifier is tuned, in this case, to 455 kc and so amplifies the 455-kc output of the mixer and rejects the remaining output frequencies. The selectivity characteristics of the IF amplifiers are such as to provide the main selectivity of the receiver.

4. The 2nd IF amplifier provides further amplification and selectivity for the 455-kc IF signal and presents it to the 2nd detector.

5. The 2nd detector demodulates the 455-kc IF signal and extracts the original audio frequencies from it. The 2nd detector usually derives a d-c voltage from the carrier for use in the automatic-gain controlled stages of the receiver.

6. The audio amplifier raises the power level of the audio frequencies from the 2nd detector to a value sufficient to drive the loudspeaker of the receiver.

D. (a) The purpose of the first detector is to act as a mixer by operating in a non-linear fashion and providing the action which produces the desired intermediate frequency.

If two frequencies are applied to a perfect class A amplifier, there will be no beating action in the tube, and the only frequencies available in the output circuit will be the original two frequencies. This is because a perfect class A amplifier is a linear circuit. In order to produce "beating," which is necessary for detection or modulation, the two frequencies must be combined in a *non-linear* device. Such a non-linear characteristic may be obtained, for example, by operating a vacuum tube on the non-linear portion of its characteristic. This is exactly what is done in the first detector of a superheterodyne (and the second detector as well). The first detector is operated with a relatively large bias, so that the operation takes place along the lower curved portion of the tube characteristic. If two different frequencies are introduced into such a non-linear device, a distortion of the input voltages will take place so that new frequencies are produced in the plate circuit, which were not originally present in the input circuit. These are mainly: (1) the *sum* of the two original frequencies, (2) the *difference* between the two original frequencies, (3) various *harmonic* frequencies. In addition, the two *original* frequencies will also be present in the plate circuit of the first detector. The desired frequency, which is usually the difference frequency in radio receivers, is selected and amplified by the intermediate frequency amplifiers.

(b) Some superheterodyne receivers employ a crystal oscillator in order to insure maximum stability of receiver operation.

In a superheterodyne receiver, the correct setting and calibration of the mixer oscillator is of critical importance, since the oscillator fre- quency "beating" with the incoming signal produces the correct inter- mediate frequency. Radio-frequency circuits (r-f amplifier and mixer) do not tune very sharply and can vary considerably without causing much trouble. It is, therefore, desirable whenever practical to employ a crystal-controlled oscillator to provide maximum stability. Crystal os- cillators are frequently used in communications receivers operating on certain pre-determined channel frequencies. In this case a separate crys- tal is switched in for reception on any particular channel. This system is impractical where variable tuning is required.

(c) A "superheterodyne" receiver is subject to image interference. The intermediate frequency delivered by the first detector, and selectively amplified by the i-f stages, is the difference between the in- put signal frequency and the oscillator frequency. There are two signal frequencies which will give the same intermediate frequency for a given oscillator frequency—one higher, and one lower than the oscil- lator. The input system is designed to select one and reject the other; but it sometimes happens that, due to misalignment of the receiver or to a very strong signal, the unwanted signal will get through to the first detector. When this happens, it causes an intermediate frequency signal which passes through the receiver normally. Such a signal is called "image interference." An incoming signal causing image inter- ference is twice the intermediate frequency above or below the fre- quency to which the receiver is tuned, depending on whether the oscil- lator frequency is designed to be above or below that of the desired signal.

(d) A high intermediate frequency is desirable in order to place the image frequency as far as possible from the normal received signal so that the image frequency may be effectively suppressed in the tuned r-f amplifier and mixer circuits. This may be illustrated by the following example: Assume that the desired carrier signal is 1000 kilocycles, the oscillator frequency 1050 kilocycles, and the intermediate frequency 50 kilocycles. The image frequency equals twice the intermediate frequency plus the carrier frequency or $(2 \times 50) + 1000$ kilocycles = 1100 kilo- cycles. Since the image is removed only 100 kilocycles from the desired carrier, the r-f and mixer circuits will not offer too much rejection to the image frequency. On the other hand, if the oscillator frequency were 1500 kilocycles, the intermediate frequency would then be 500 kilocycles and the image would equal $(2 \times 500) + 1000$ kilocycles = 2000 kilocycles. The image is now removed from the desired signal by 1000 kilocycles and will be greatly attenuated by the r-f and mixer circuits.

Q. 3.156. Explain the relation between the signal frequency, oscillator frequency and the image frequency in a superheterodyne receiver.

A. (a) Assuming the oscillator frequency to be *above* the incoming frequency, the following relations prevail:

(1) Oscillator frequency = Incoming-Signal Frequency + Intermediate Frequency.

(2) Image Frequency = Incoming Frequency + 2 × Intermediate Frequency.

(b) Assuming the oscillator frequency to be *below* the incoming frequency (used mainly in some VHF receivers), the following relations prevail:

(1) Oscillator Frequency = Incoming-Signal Frequency − Intermediate Frequency.

(2) Image Frequency = Incoming Frequency − 2 × Intermediate Frequency.

D. For example, assume a receiver is tuned to an incoming frequency of 1000 kc; its oscillator frequency is 1455 kc and its intermediate frequency is 455 kc. In this case the image frequency equals the incoming frequency plus twice the i-f, or; Image = $(2 \times 455) + 1000 = 1910$ kc.

For a VHF receiver operating at 120 mc with an oscillator frequency of 109.3 mc and an i-f of 10.7 mc, the image frequency equals twice the i-f subtracted from the incoming frequency, or; Image = 120 mc − $(2 \times 10.7$ mc$)$ = 198.6 mc.

Q. 3.157. Draw a circuit diagram of an AM second detector and a-f amplifier (in one envelope), showing AVC circuitry. Also show coupling to, and identification of, all adjacent stages.

(a) Explain the principles of operation.

(b) State some conditions under which readings of AVC voltage would be helpful in trouble-shooting a receiver.

(c) Show how this circuit would be modified to give DAVC.

A. For the diagram, see Fig. 3.157(a).

(a) (1) The functioning of a diode detector depends upon the ability of an RC network (C_2, R_2, R_3) to follow the *average* diode current variations, which are directly proportional to the modulation envelope.

The secondary circuit of the last i-f transformer (which acts as a generator) is connected to the diode plate and cathode in series with the parallel RC network, C_2, R_2, R_3. Assume first that an unmodulated carrier is applied to the detector. Rectification will occur with the diode plate conducting on the positive portions of the r-f cycles. Capacitor C_2 will charge almost to the peak value of the unmodulated carrier. The plate side of C_2 will be negative and of a steady value, as long as the carrier amplitude remains constant.

Now assume that amplitude modulation is applied to the carrier wave. Charge on C_2 increases proportionally to the increased amplitude of the modulated carrier. Also, as the carrier amplitude decreases, charge on C_2 decreases. Thus, the charge across C_2 varies in accordance with the audio modulation changes (because of the time constant of C_2, R_2, R_3). However, the time constant is very long compared to the time of one r-f cycle and the network has very little response to individual r-f cycles. It does, of course, respond to the average change in amplitude of these r-f cycles, which corresponds to the audio wave.

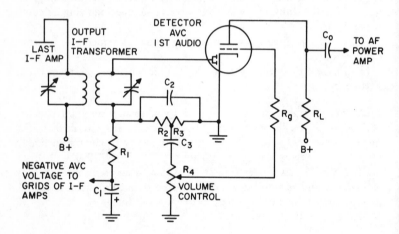

Fig. 3.157(a). Circuit diagram of AM second detector and a-f amplifier.

(2) The detected audio wave is taken from the tap of R_2 and R_3 (to reduce distortion) and fed via the volume control, R_4, to the grid of the first audio amplifier. This functions as a conventional triode audio amplifier (see Q. 3.50(a)). The output of this stage drives the audio-power amplifier, which operates a loudspeaker.

(3) As stated above, there is a rectified-negative voltage at the diode-plate side of C_2. This voltage varies at an audio rate, but its average value is proportional to the strength of the carrier wave. If this negative voltage is fed back to the control grids of the i-f (and r-f) amplifiers, it provides a method of obtaining automatic volume control.

The basis for efficient automatic volume control is the action of the variable-μ (remote cut-off) tube. This tube has a control grid which is so constructed, that changes of d-c grid bias cause corresponding variations in the tube's transconductance and thus control the gain of the i-f (and sometimes also r-f) amplifiers The transconductance decreases as the negative bias increases and vice versa. In the second de-

tector, the modulated i-f signal is rectified in such a way that the average value of the detector audio output is negative with respect to ground.
This is accomplished by grounding the cathode of the detector, and taking the output from the plate circuit. The average negative audio output
is put through a long time constant RC filter whose output is a pure,
negative d-c voltage. This voltage is fed through suitable decoupling
filters to the grids of the various i-f and r-f amplifiers involved, where
it becomes all or part of the bias for these tubes. The AVC filter output is a negative d-c voltage whose magnitude is proportional to the
average strength of the incoming modulated carrier signal. An increase
of incoming signal strength creates a larger negative bias on the various
controlling grids, thereby reducing the overall gain of the receiver and
providing a relatively constant output. A decrease of incoming signal
strength results in a *less* negative bias, an increase in overall receiver
gain, and again a relatively constant output.

(b) The amount of AVC voltage developed is approximately proportional to the signal strength expressed in db. The AVC voltage, therefore, can be a guide in determining the amplification of all the stages
preceding the 2nd detector. For example, with a relatively strong input
signal, the AVC voltage should be relatively large. If not, there is the
possibility of weak tubes, mistuned circuits, etc., in the amplifiers ahead
of the 2nd detector. In aligning a superheterodyne receiver, advantage is
taken of the AVC voltage by using it as a tuning indicator. In another
example of a *dead* receiver, the presence of AVC voltage but no audio
output would indicate troubles in the audio frequency amplifier(s) of
the receiver. This of course could be defective a-f tubes or components
or both.

(c) The modified circuit to provide delayed-automatic volume control
(DAVC) is shown in Fig. 3.157(c). Note that the two diodes are now
connected independently and that cathode bias is employed for the
triode amplifier. The upper diode is used only for detection and the
lower diode is used only to provide DAVC.

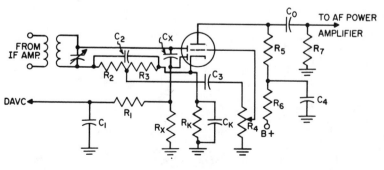

Fig. 3.157(c). Modified circuit to provide delayed AVC.

D.   In the circuit of Fig. 3.157(a), AVC voltage is developed even for very weak signals, causing a reduction in receiver gain and a loss of sensitivity. In order to obtain maximum sensitivity for weak signals, it is desirable to have zero AVC voltage. However, to maintain constant audio output, stronger signals should develop AVC. A DAVC circuit provides this action, by delaying the development of AVC voltage until the input signal level exceeds a certain pre-determined level. Note that the upper-diode circuit returns to the cathode and will detect the weakest signals. However, the lower-diode circuit is returned to ground and is affected by the triode-cathode bias. Because of the normal conduction of the triode section, a positive bias is developed at the cathode. The lower diode cannot conduct until the positive peak signal applied to its plate exceeds the amount of the cathode bias (1 to 3 volts). Because of this "delay" voltage, AVC is not developed for weak signals which develop less than the cathode-bias voltage at the lower-diode plate. However, for signals strong enough to cause lower-diode conduction, DAVC voltage is developed and regulates the receiver gain in the same manner as undelayed AVC.

Q. 3.158.   Draw a BFO circuit diagram and explain its use in detection.

A.   For the diagram, see the accompanying figure, Figure 3.158. The main function of a beat frequency oscillator is to make it possible to hear code (A-1) reception clearly. Code which is not tone modulated would otherwise be heard at the output of a receiver as a series of hissing sounds or perhaps "thumps," which would be very difficult to interpret and easily obscured by noise. When the beat frequency oscillator is turned on, a high pitched audible note is produced which is relatively easy to "read."

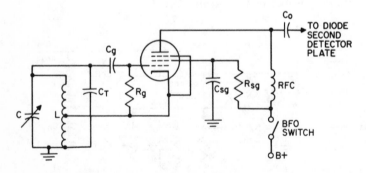

Fig. 3.158. Schematic diagram of a beat-frequency oscillator (electron-coupled Hartley).

A beat frequency oscillator may also be utilized in the detection of a single-sideband suppressed-carrier signal. See Q. 3.154.

Q. 3.159. Explain, step-by-step, how to align an AM receiver using the following instruments. In addition discuss what is occurring during each step.
(a) Signal generator and speaker.
(b) Signal generator and oscilloscope.
(c) Signal generator and VTVM.

A. Regardless of whether a speaker, oscilloscope, or VTVM is used, the alignment procedure remains the same. Since a sweep generator is not mentioned, the signal generator to be used will be an amplitude-modulated CW generator. It must be assumed that the generator is properly calibrated and that the receiver is drastically out of alignment. When the speaker is used, the ear is the indicating instrument and no special connections to the speaker are required.

In using an oscilloscope, there are several points at which it may be connected to monitor the demodulated signal generator signal. One convenient place would be across the voice-coil terminals of the speaker. When a VTVM is used (d–c type) it is convenient to connect it to the AVC bus or across the second detector load resistor. In the event an a–c VTVM is available, this may be connected across the speaker-voice coil terminals. If the AVC voltage is not being monitored, the AVC bus should be grounded or held at a nominal fixed bias with a battery. This prevents false indications of alignment due to AVC action. Regardless of the indicating device used, a maximum indication is the sign of proper alignment. The alignment procedure follows:

1. Connect the indicating instrument as described above and proceed with the I–F alignment. A common I–F frequency of 455 kilocycles is assumed in this case.

a. Set the generator to 455 kilocycles and connect through a small capacitor (0.01 uf) to the grid of the last I–F stage and ground. Set the generator for minimum usable output and peak the primary and secondary windings for maximum indication of the instrument being used.

b. Move the generator to the grid of the next-to-last I–F stage and peak the adjustments of its transformer.

c. In a like manner, all additional I–F transformers are peaked. It will be necessary to reduce the generator output as each additional stage is aligned, to prevent overloading of the amplifiers. A minimum possible generator output should always be employed.

d. The last I–F transformer to be aligned is the one in the plate circuit of the mixer. In this case, the generator is connected to the grid of the mixer (which is not tuned to the I–F frequency). At this point it is necessary to increase the generator output to obtain a usable alignment signal.

2. After completing the I–F alignment, the R–F alignment, should be undertaken. Connect the test oscillator between the antenna terminal and ground, using a small capacitor in series with the ungrounded lead. Proceed as follows:

a. Set the signal generator and the receiver dial to 1400 kilocycles.

b. At 1400 kilocycles first adjust the oscillator trimmer to obtain maximum indication.

Note: Do not attempt to adjust the low frequency "padder" adjustment at this time and always use the minimum possible generator output.

c. Next adjust the mixer and r–f trimmers for maximum response.

d. Tune the receiver dial and the signal generator to 600 kilocycles.

e. Adjust the oscillator and low-frequency tracking trimmer for maximum response.

f. Repeat steps a through e above to achieve the optimum alignment.

D. What is being accomplished in each step of the alignment when tuning for maximum response is that the circuits involved are being caused to resonate at their individual frequencies. Thus, the gain of the stages are being increased due to the increased impedance of the resonant circuits. The increased gain causes the generator signal to be amplified more, providing a greater output indication. In the case of using the AVC voltage for an indication, the greater the gain of the stages, the higher the signal applied to the AVC detector. This results in a greater negative voltage being applied to the AVC bus. (Again, a maximum response indication.)

Q. 3.160.   What would be the advantages and disadvantages of utilizing a bandpass switch on a receiver?

A.   (a) Advantages. The advantage of utilizing a bandpass switch is to reduce the I–F bandpass of a receiver. In so doing, the selectivity of the receiver is considerably improved. This characteristic is highly desirable in receiving signals from stations operating in a crowded spectrum. It permits separation, and therefore the intelligible reception of signals which might otherwise be lost in the confusion of overlapping channel signals.

(b) Disadvantages. The disadvantage of utilizing a bandpass switch is that sideband frequencies of either voice or music broadcasts will be sharply reduced, thus reducing the intelligibility of speech and music. However, in some cases using the bandpass switch is the only way to achieve any reception at all of the desired signal.

D.   By the use of regenerative I–F circuits, a controllable bandpass characteristic may be achieved. This can cut the I–F bandpass to as low as 1000 cycles for use under extremely difficult signal crowding and noise conditions. Since good double-sideband voice reproduction normally requires about a 6000 cycle bandpass, it is obvious that the intelligibility of voice (and music) will be considerably reduced. However, this technique frequently permits a signal to be received which might otherwise be covered up by interference. Since noise frequencies occupy the entire spectrum, it is seen that the sharper the bandpass, the less the noise energy that will be passed to affect the listener. In receivers used for code reception, a crystal-type I–F filter is frequently employed. With this type of filter, a bandpass of only 100 to 200 cycles is passed. This bandwidth is adequate for code, but useless for voice or music reception.

Q. 3.161. Explain sensitivity and selectivity of a receiver. Why are these important quantities? In what typical units are they usually expressed?

A. (a) Sensitivity: Sensitivity is the strength of the signal, in microvolts, at the input of the receiver required to produce a specified audio-power output.

(b) Selectivity: Selectivity is the ability of a receiver to discriminate against frequencies other than the desired frequency.

(c) Sensitivity is an important quantity because it defines the ability of a receiver to respond adequately to a weak-input signal.

(d) Selectivity defines the ability of a receiver to *select* a desired signal, which may be hemmed in by adjacent frequency (undesirable) signals.

(e) Sensitivity is expressed in microvolts for a certain audio output power.

(f) Selectivity is expressed in cycles or kilocycles, usually in terms of the i-f response curve of the receiver. The i-f response curve is basically "V" shaped, being narrow at the maximum-response point and wider at the minimum-response point. Thus, it is necessary to state at what point bandwidth is to be measured. This point differs according to the purpose of the measurement. However, for general purposes, the i-f bandwidth is measured at points 3 db (.707) down from the maximum.

FREQUENCY MODULATION

Q. 3.162. Draw a schematic diagram of a frequency-modulated oscillator using a reactance-tube modulator. Explain its principle of operation.

A. (a) For the diagram, see Fig. 3.162(a).

(b) The reactance tube operates as it does because an ordinary vacuum tube may act as an inductive or capacitive reactance. Furthermore

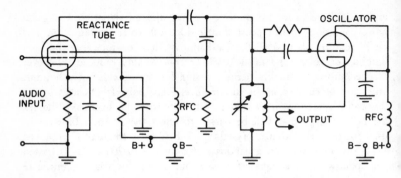

Fig. 3.162(a).   A capacitive reactance tube modulator.

the magnitude of reactance may be caused to vary in direct relationship to the speech or music which originates at the microphone. If the reactance tube is connected to the tank circuit of an oscillator, it is then possible to cause the frequency of the oscillator to vary in accordance with the modulation signal. There are several variations of the reactance tube, but only one type will be explained here. The remaining types are basically similar in operation. A basic diagram of a capacitive reactance tube modulator is shown in Figure 3.162(b). The oscillator tank circuit is made up of L and C which determines the normal frequency of the tank circuit according to the formula $f = \dfrac{1}{2\pi\sqrt{LC}}$. This formula shows that an increase of either L or C will cause a decrease of frequency, and that a decrease of L or C will cause an increase of frequency. The reactance tube V_1 is effectively in parallel with the tank, since C_b can be considered to be a short circuit at tank frequency. If a capacitance as represented by V_1 is placed across the tank and caused to vary at an audio rate, then the total tuning capacitance which is made up of C plus V_1 will cause the oscillator

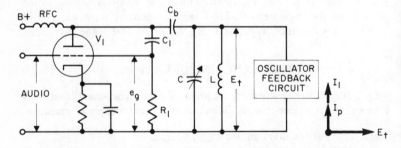

Fig. 3.162(b).   Means of modulating an FM transmitter.

frequency to vary at the same audio rate. If it can be shown that the a-c plate current of V_1 leads the a-c plate voltage by 90 degrees, then V_1 represents a capacitive reactance. The a-c tank voltage is designated as E_t. It will be seen that E_t is also the a-c plate voltage of V_1, since it is effectively applied between plate and cathode. (C_b is effectively a short.) In the vector diagram, E_t is used as the reference. Due to the applied voltage E_t, a current I_1 is caused to flow through the series circuit $C_1 - R_1$. These are so proportioned that the reactance of C_1 is made to be many times greater than the resistance R_1. Since the two are in series and the reactance predominates, we may consider $C_1 - R_1$ to be a capacitive circuit. Therefore, the current I_1 will lead E_t by 90 degrees. Remember that this current I_1 flows through both C_1 and R_1 in the same phase. The grid signal of V_1 is the voltage which is developed across R_1, or in other words the IR drop across R_1. However, this IR drop is in the same phase as I_1, which is leading the a-c plate voltage of V_1 by 90 degrees. Thus, as shown in the vector diagram, the a-c grid voltage is leading the a-c plate voltage by 90 degrees. Since the a-c plate current follows the a-c grid voltage in phase, it is apparent then that the a-c plate current also leads the a-c plate voltage by 90 degrees. Thus the tube appears to be a capacitive reactance in parallel with the oscillator tank circuit. The magnitude of this reactance is a function of the amount of a-c plate current which flows. We can say that $X_c = \dfrac{E_T}{I_p}$. Thus if the a-c plate current should increase (which would happen on the positive swing of an audio wave applied to the grid), the X_c of V_1 would correspondingly decrease and this would be equivalent to an increase of shunt capacitance across the tank, since $X_c = \dfrac{1}{2\pi f C}$ and therefore $C = \dfrac{1}{2\pi f X_c}$. That is, a decrease of capacitive reactance is equivalent to an actual increase of capacitance. Since this capacitance is added in parallel with the tank capacitance, it would cause the oscillator frequency to decrease. Therefore, the amount of frequency decrease would depend upon the amplitude of the positive swing of audio grid signal. The greater the amplitude of audio grid signal, the greater would be the effective increase of capacitance and the greater the decrease in frequency. On the other hand let us take the negative swing of the audio cycle acting upon the grid of V_1. This would cause a decrease in a-c plate current and therefore X_c of V_1 would appear larger. This is equivalent to a decrease in the shunting capacitance and to an increase of oscillator frequency. It should be remembered that the *rate* at which the oscillator frequency changes is a function of the audio frequency only and not of its amplitude. The *amplitude* of the audio determines only the amount of frequency change or deviation.

A solid-state version of an FM modulator is shown in Fig. 3.162 (c). This circuit employs a varactor diode, whose capacitance varies with

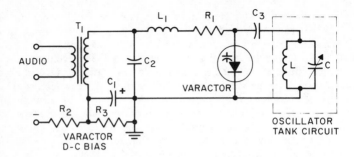

Fig. 3.162(c). A varactor (variable-reactor) FM modulator.
The varactor performs as an audio-controlled, variable capacitance
across the L-C tank circuit.

the voltage impressed across it. The varactor is reverse-biased to the center of its linear characteristic, in order for it to function as a variable capacitance. This reverse bias is supplied by the voltage divider consisting of R2 and R3. The audio modulation signal, applied through the transformer T1, is impressed across the varactor and causes it to change its effective capacitance. The amount of capacitance change (and frequency change) is proportional to the amplitude of the audio signal, while the rate of change is proportional to the audio frequency. Thus, since the varactor capacitance is across the oscillator tank circuit, a frequency-modulated wave is produced.

Q. 3.163. Discuss the following in reference to frequency modulation.

(a) The production of sidebands.

(b) The relationship between the number of sidebands and the modulating frequency.

(c) The relationship between the number of sidebands and the amplitude of the modulating voltage.

(d) The relationship between percent modulation and the number of sidebands.

(e) The relationship between modulation index or deviation ratio and the number of sidebands.

(f) The relationship between the spacing of the sidebands and the modulating frequency.

(g) The relationship between the number of sidebands and the bandwidth of emissions.

(h) The criteria for determining the bandwidth of emission.

(i) Reasons for pre-emphasis.

A. (a) When a sine wave is frequency modulated, its *instantaneous* frequency is varied according to the intelligence to be transmitted. The modulated wave consists of components made up of the original sine wave plus additional sine waves. These additional sine waves are of different frequencies from the original wave and are called sidebands and are symmetrically arranged above and below the original wave or carrier.

(b) For a given frequency deviation, the number of sidebands is inversely proportional to the modulating frequency. For example, for a frequency deviation of plus or minus 75 kilocycles and a modulating frequency of 15,000 cycles, there will be five significant sidebands on each side of the carrier. With a modulating frequency of 150 cycles and the same deviation, there will be 500 significant sidebands on each side of the carrier.

(c) For a given modulating frequency, the number of sidebands is directly proportional to the amplitude of the modulating voltage. That is, if the modulating voltage is tripled, the number of sidebands is also tripled.

(d) In FM broadcast service, one hundred percent modulation is defined as the modulating condition producing a frequency deviation of plus or minus 75 kilocycles. The number of sidebands produced, for any given modulating frequency, is directly proportional to the percent modulation.

(e) For any given modulating frequency, the number of significant sidebands is directly proportional to the modulator index or deviation ratio. [See also Discussion under (a).] .

(f) The sidebands produced by frequency modulation are separated from one another by a frequency that is equal to the modulating frequency. The sidebands adjacent to the carrier are also separated from it by an amount equal to the modulating frequency.

(g) The total number of significant sidebands multiplied by the modulating frequency equals the total significant bandwidth of emission. There are sidebands extending beyond this, but they are insignificant and contain so little power or energy that they are considered negligible.

(h) The criteria for determining the bandwidth of emission are the modulation index and the modulating frequency. The product of the modulation index and the frequency of modulation equals the frequency deviation. The bandwidth of emission is twice the sum of the frequency deviation and the modulating frequency.

(i) In speech and music very little energy is contained in the frequencies at the upper end of the audio frequency range. However, even though such components represent very little energy, they are extremely important to the naturalness of speech as they give *definition* to the consonants and add to the identification of the different types of musical instruments. Normally, these high frequency components will be lost in transmission because of *masking* by noise unless some way is found to make them override such circuit noise. One way of accomplishing this is to amplify these components more than the low frequency sounds before introducing the complete audio signal to the modulating circuits of the FM transmitter. This process is termed *pre-emphasis*—that is, the high frequencies are emphasized before modulation and thus represent more energy during transmission. At the receiver, in order to restore these components to their original amplitude relationship with the low-frequency components, it is necessary to reverse the process after detection. This latter process is termed *de-emphasis*.

D. (a) The "modulation index" is the ratio of the amount of frequency deviation to the audio modulating frequency causing the deviation. "Deviation ratio" is simply a special case of modulation index and is defined as the ratio of the *maximum permissible* frequency deviation to the *maximum permissible* audio modulating frequency. Examples of three different deviation ratios follow.

For a standard FM broadcast station the maximum permissible deviation is 75 kilocycles above or below the average; while the maximum permissible audio modulating frequency is equal to 15 kilocycles. Therefore the "deviation ratio" for a standard FM station is equal to $75/15$ or 5. The FM sound carrier of a television transmitter has a maximum deviation of plus or minus 25 kilocycles. The "deviation ratio" in this case is $25/15 = 1.667$.

In the case of narrow-band FM used in Public Safety Radio Services, the maximum deviation is 5000 cycles and the maximum audio frequency is 3000 cycles. Therefore, the deviation ratio for this service is $5000/3000 = 1.667$.

(b) In pre-emphasis, the higher audio frequencies in the modulating stages of an FM transmitter are overamplified with respect to their value and in relation to the lower audio frequencies.

Refer to Fig. 3.163(a). Studies have demonstrated that the noises which are most irritating to the listener are those which are concentrated in the upper end of the audio frequency spectrum. It is also true that these high audio frequencies represent very little energy as compared to the low frequencies. Thus it is possible in the audio stages of an FM transmitter to over-amplify the high audio frequencies without much danger of overmodulating the transmitter. In this case overmodulation would mean a deviation in excess of ± 75 kilocycles. Since there are guard bands of ± 25 kilocycles in each FM channel, occasional overmodulation would not be too serious. A practical circuit to produce pre-emphasis is shown in Figure 3.163(a). The important part of this circuit is the parallel network $R_1 - C_1$ which is in series with resistor R_g. $R_1 - C_1$ is in effect a high pass filter. At low frequencies where C_1 is practically an open circuit, we have a voltage divider made up of R_1 and R_g. Only a small portion of the input appears across R_g at low frequencies. As the frequency increases however, the impedance of the parallel network becomes less, and more of the input signal appears across R_g. Example: At 60 cycles, the reactance of C_1 is 2,670,000 ohms and the parallel combination of $R_1 - C_1$ is then 75,000 ohms. The amount of signal now appearing on the grid

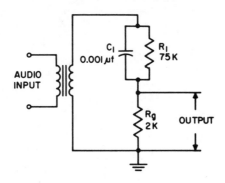

Fig. 3.163(a). A standard pre-emphasis network.

is, $e_g = E_s \dfrac{R_g}{R_1 + R_g} = E_s \times \dfrac{2000}{77,000} = E_s \times 2.56\%.$

At 15,000 cycles the reactance of C_1 is about 10,000 ohms. The parallel impedance of $R_1—C_1$ is now about 8800 ohms, and the signal voltage which appears on the grid is $e_g = E_s \times \dfrac{2000}{10,800} = E_s \times 18.5\%.$ This means that 15,000 cycles will be amplified about 7 times more than 60 cycles. The time constant for a pre-emphasis network such as $R_1 — C_1$ is standardized by the F.C.C. at 75 microseconds, $= 0.001$ (μf) $\times 75,000$ (ohms). A standard pre-emphasis chart is shown in Figure 3.163(b), and it should be noted here that the gain remains substantially constant until about 800 cycles. From then on it continues to rise until a maximum of 27 db is reached at 15,000 cycles. (Ratio of 17 db is 7:1 approx.) The fact that the higher audio frequencies are thus overemphasized makes it possible to override much of the high frequency noises which are picked up enroute to and within the receiver. However, in order to obtain the full benefits of this system and regain the correct tonal values a de-emphasis network must be incorporated into the FM receiver.

(c) Refer to Figure 3.163(c). The purpose of a de-emphasis circuit is to restore the over-amplified high frequencies to their correct value, and at the same time to greatly reduce the high frequency noise output of the receiver.

Actually the de-emphasis circuit is the exact opposite in its characteristics to the pre-emphasis circuit. Where the pre-emphasis circuit amplifies high frequencies, the de-emphasis circuit attenuates them. For example the gain at 15,000 cycles is overamplified about 7 times by pre-emphasis. In the receiver it is attenuated by the same factor of

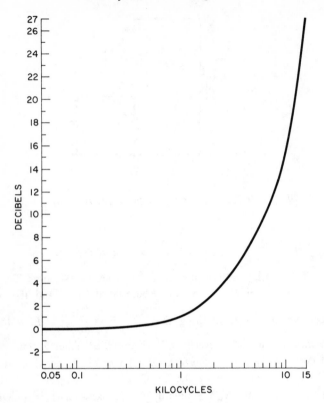

Fig. 3.163(b). A standard pre-emphasis chart.

7, thus returning the 15,000 cycle tone to its correct amplitude in comparison with low frequencies. Where the pre-emphasis circuit was a high pass filter, the de-emphasis circuit is a low pass filter. A simple de-emphasis circuit is shown in the figure. This network is usually found between the FM detector and the first audio amplifier. The time constant of a de-emphasis circuit is also 75 microseconds. It will be noted that the de-emphasis circuit works on the principle of a voltage divider with only that portion of the audio developed across C_1 being transmitted to the audio amplifier. At high frequencies the reactance of C_1 will be low and not much signal will be developed across C_1. For example at 16,000 cycles the reactance of C_1 is about 10,000 ohms. The series impedance of C_1 and R_1 equals

$$\sqrt{R^2 + X_{c1}{}^2} = \sqrt{75{,}000^2 + 10{,}000^2} = 75{,}700 \text{ ohms.}$$

The amount of voltage developed across C_1 is

$$E_{c1} = E_s \times \frac{X_{c1}}{\sqrt{R^2 + X_{c1}{}^2}} = E_s \times \frac{10{,}000}{75{,}700} = E_s \times 13.2\%.$$

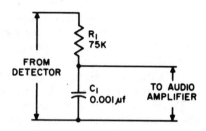

Fig. 3.163(c). A de-emphasis circuit.

At 60 cycles the reactance of C_1 is 2,654,000 ohms and the series impedance of C_1 and R_1 equals $\sqrt{R^2 + X_{c1}^2} = \sqrt{75,000^2 + 2,654,000^2}$ = 2,655,000. The amount of voltage developed across C_1 is $E_{c1} = E_s \times \dfrac{X_{c1}}{\sqrt{R_2 \times X_{c1}^2}} = E_s \times \dfrac{2,654,000}{2,655,000} = E_s \times 100\%$ which is approximately 7 times more signal than for 16,000 cycles. Thus it is seen that the de-emphasis circuit works in exactly the opposite manner to the pre-emphasis circuit. It must be remembered that at the same time the high frequencies are attenuated, all high frequency noises are also attenuated by the same degree, and it is here that the greatest noise reduction takes place. It should also be borne in .mind that while the high frequencies are being attenuated, they are simply being returned to their normal value and are not being suppressed in any way. After leaving the de-emphasis circuit, the audio signal is fed into a standard audio amplifier.

(d) The percentage of modulation of an FM station is primarily determined by the amplitude of the audio tone. For a standard FM broadcast station, 100% modulation is obtained for a modulation tone which causes a deviation of plus and minus 75 kilocycles. For any given audio tone, an increase of amplitude causes a proportional increase in the amount of frequency deviation.

(e) The rate of frequency swing of an FM broadcast station depends upon the tone frequency of the modulating signal. The rate at which the carrier deviates (swings) is a direct function of the audio frequency. Thus for an audio frequency of 10,000 cycles the carrier will deviate (or swing) at the rate of 10,000 times per second.

(f) One FM channel is 200 kilocycles wide. Of the allotted 200 kilocycles, 150 kilocycles is to be used for the actual transmission, while a guard band of 25 kilocycles is established on either end of each channel. The FM broadcast channels are allotted frequencies from 88 to 108 megacycles. The last FM channel has a center frequency of 107.9 megacycles.

Q. 3.164. How is good stability of a reactance tube modulator achieved?

A. In addition to the stability achieved by normal good design of the self-excited oscillator employed as a reactance tube modulated oscillator, further stability is obtained by operating the oscillator at a low radio frequency. The oscillator's operating frequency is at an integral submultiple of the desired antenna frequency. The oscillator is followed by frequency multipliers sufficient to obtain the desired final frequency.

A further advantage in stability is gained by operating the oscillator at a low frequency. This is because the frequency deviation, and hence the modulation index, is multiplied by the same factor as the carrier frequency when the signal is passed through frequency multiplying stages. Because of the low frequency deviation required, the effect of the reactance tube modulator on the stability of the oscillator is decreased.

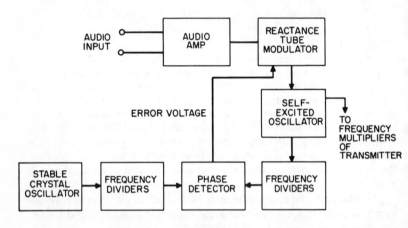

Fig. 3.164. Simplified block diagram of an AFC system used to stabilize a reactance-tube modulator.

D. Any self-excited oscillator, no matter how carefully designed is subject to some frequency drift. In addition, any variation in the parameters of the reactance tube will cause the oscillator to change frequency. To insure a completely stable reactance tube and oscillator, it is customary to employ an AFC system whose reference is an extremely stable crystal oscillator. A simplified block diagram of such an AFC system is shown in Fig. 3.164. The phase detector receives signals (divided in frequency) from both the crystal oscillator and the self-excited oscillator. The two signals are compared in the phase detector. If the frequency of the self-excited oscillator differs from that of the crystal oscillator, the phase detector develops a d–c error voltage which is fed to the reactance-tube modulator. This error voltage is of the correct polarity to bring the self-excited oscillator to its correct frequency. As the oscillator approaches the correct frequency, the amplitude of the error voltage will decrease to practically zero.

Q. 3.165. Draw a circuit diagram of a phase modulator. Explain its operation. Label adjacent stages.

A.   (a) For the diagrams, see Fig. 3.165(a) and Fig. 3.165(b).

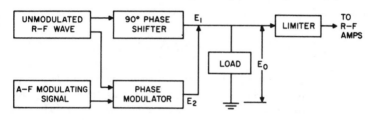

Fig. 3.165(a). Block diagram of a method of generating a phase modulated wave.

(b) For the explanation of the operation of one type of phase modulator, refer first to the block diagram of Fig. 3.165(a). An unmodulated r-f wave is applied both to the phase-modulator amplifier and to a 90 degree phase shifter. An a-f modulating signal is also applied to the phase-modulator amplifier. The latter signal causes an amplitude-modulated wave to appear at the output of the modulator. This AM wave is combined in the output load with the 90 degree shifted, unmodulated r-f wave. If the amplitude of the unmodulated wave is much greater than that of the AM wave, the resultant r-f will be phase shifted by an amount closely proportional to the amplitude of the a-f modulating signal. Thus, the resultant r-f output wave will be one whose phase is directly proportional to the amplitude of the audio modulating signal and a true phase-modulated r-f wave will have been produced.

D.   For a more detailed explanation of this phase modulator, refer to the schematic diagram of Fig. 3.165(b), and to the vector diagrams of Fig. 3.165(c). The numbers shown at the different points of the audio-sine wave are keyed to the three vector diagrams. In the schematic, an AM wave is developed in the triode and applied to the low-impedance tank circuit. This voltage is shown in the vector diagrams as E_2. A second voltage, E_1, is phase-shifted 90 degrees in passing through C_{gp} and is also applied to the plate tank circuit. These two voltages combine in the tank to produce their vector sum, E_0. Note in the three vector diagrams that the amplitude of E_1 remains fixed while the amplitude of E_2 varies in accordance with the amplitude and polarity of the audio-modulating wave. As a result of the variation in amplitude of E_2, the

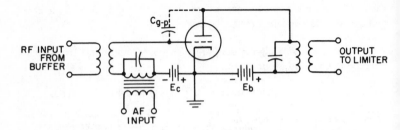

Fig. 3.165(b). Phase modulator schematic diagram.

phase angle of E_0 varies in direct proportion to the amplitude and polarity of the audio-modulating wave. In vector diagram (1), the audio signal is at zero volts and a quiescent value of phase angle (θ) results for E_0. In vector diagram (2), the audio wave is at its maximum positive value. This results in a higher amplitude of E_2 and a decreased phase angle ($\theta - \Delta$) for E_0. In vector diagram (3), the audio wave is at its maximum negative value, resulting in the minimum amplitude of E_2. Note that a greater phase angle for E_0 results ($\theta + \Delta$).

E_0 varies not only in phase, but also in amplitude. These amplitude variations are removed by the following limiter, leaving only a phase-modulated wave. As discussed in the answer above, the amplitude of E_1 is normally much greater than that of E_2. However, to more graphically illustrate the phase variations shown in the vector diagrams, these voltages are shown with comparable amplitudes.

Although the modulator shown is an unneutralized triode, self-oscillation does not occur in the stage. Self-oscillation is avoided by the use of a low Q (low impedance) tank circuit and a low value of plate voltage. As explained in Q. 3.166, phase modulation produces an equivalent frequency-modulation wave. The original phase (and frequency) modulation deviation is increased to the desired value by frequency multipliers

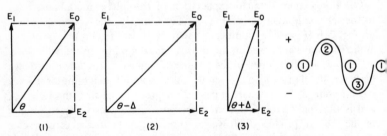

*Fig. 3.165(c). Vector diagrams and audio modulating signal
to explain the operation of the phase-shifter modulator.*

which also raise the carrier frequency to the desired final value. (See also Q. 4.89(b).)

A phase-modulator circuit employing a solid-state varactor (variable capacitance) diode is shown in Fig. 3.165(d). The operating principle of this circuit differs from that shown in Fig. 3.165(b). In the varactor circuit, a resonant tank circuit is made up of L, C and the varactor diode. The varactor is correctly biased (in the reverse direction) to the center of its characteristic curve. An audio input is applied to the anode of the varactor. This causes the varactor capacitance to vary above and below its quiescent value, as established by the dc bias. In addition, as shown, the RF wave from the oscillator is applied to the resonant tank circuit.

The RF input from the oscillator is always a single, fixed frequency. However, the effect of the audio wave on the varactor causes the tank circuit to be resonant both above and below its quiescent resonant frequency.

When the tank circuit is resonant above its quiescent (and oscillator) frequency, it looks like an inductance (inductive current predominates) to the RF signal. This produces a leading phase angle of the output voltage.

When the tank circuit is resonant to its normal (center) frequency (audio voltage passing through zero), it represents a pure resistance and no phase shift of the RF wave occurs.

When the tank circuit is resonant below its quiescent (and oscillator) frequency, it looks like a capacitance (capacitive current predominates) to the RF signal. This produces a lagging phase angle of the output voltage.

The amount of phase shift is proportional to the amplitude of the audio signal, while the rate of phase angle change is proportional to the audio frequency. Thus, a phase modulated wave is produced.

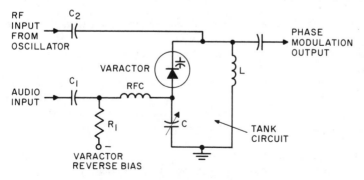

Fig. 3.165(d). A phase-modulator circuit employing a varactor (variable-reactor) diode. (Compare with Fig. 3.162(c).)

Q. 3.166.   Explain what occurs in a waveform if it is phase modulated.

A.   When a sine wave is phase modulated it becomes a distorted sine wave as illustrated in an exaggerated manner in Fig. 3.166. As a result of this distortion, additional frequencies are created and appear in the modulated wave as sidebands.

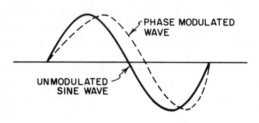

Fig. 3.166.   Effect of phase modulation on a sine wave.

Since frequency may be expressed as the rate of change of phase, the instantaneous frequency of the modulated wave is varied in exact accordance with the variation in the rate of change of phase. The net result of the foregoing is that phase modulation produces the same sort of modulated wave that is produced by frequency modulation. Actually, for the same modulating frequency and modulation index, the two waves will be identical.

Q. 3.167.   Explain, in a general way, why an FM deviation meter (modulation meter) would show an indication if coupled to the output of a transmitter which is phase modulated by a constant amplitude, constant audio frequency. To what would this deviation be proportional?

A.   Since a phase-modulated transmitter produces a wave that is frequency modulated, as explained in Q. 3.166 above, an FM deviation meter would show an indication because frequency deviation would in fact exist.

The amount of such deviation will be proportional to the amplitude *and* the frequency of the modulating signal, whereas the deviation in an FM transmitter is proportional only to the amplitude of the modulating signal and is independent of its frequency.

D.   As mentioned above, when a wave is phase modulated, the effective frequency deviation is proportional to the frequency as well as the amplitude of the audio-modulating wave. However, all FM detectors are designed to reproduce an audio wave based upon the *amplitude* only of the original audio modulating signal. As a result, when phase modulation is used in an FM transmitter, it is necessary to correct for the effect of audio *frequency* on the effective FM deviation. This is accomplished by an audio network (predistorter) which precedes the phase modulator. The "predistorter" adjusts the amplitude of the audio-modulating wave with respect to its frequency, so that the resultant effective FM deviation is proportional *only* to the *amplitude* of the audio-modulating signal. This is accomplished by making the output voltage of the speech amplifier decrease inversely with respect to the modulating frequency.

Q. 3.168. Draw a circuit diagram of each of the following stages of a phase-modulated FM transmitter. Explain their operation. Label adjacent stages.

(a) Frequency multiplier (doubler) with capacitive coupling on input and output.

(b) Power amplifier with variable link coupling to antenna. Include circuit for metering grid and plate currents.

(c) Speech amplifier with an associated pre-emphasis circuit.

A. (a) For the diagram of a doubler, see Fig. 3.168(a). The operation of a frequency doubler is explained in Q. 3.131. The degree of coupling to the intermediate power amplifier can be varied by changing the position of the tap on the coil or by changing the value of the output capacitor. Moving the tap toward the ground end of the tank coil will reduce the amount of coupling.

(b) For the diagram of a power amplifier, see Fig. 3.168(b). For the explanation of the operation of an r-f power amplifier, see Q. 3.52(a)(4). The degree of coupling to the antenna can be varied by changing the position of the small coil with respect to the tank coil. The tuned circuit at the other end of the link is resonated to the operating frequency. The taps on this coil are adjusted to match the required input impedance of the transmission line to the antenna itself.

(c) For the diagram of a speech amplifier, see Fig. 3.168(c). The speech amplifier as shown is a class A transformer-coupled stage and its operation is described in Q. 3.50(a). Following the amplifier is a network to provide pre-emphasis of the higher audio frequencies.

D. The most general use for a class A amplifier is as a voltage amplifier, although single-ended power amplifiers which feed speakers must also be class A. The average plate efficiency for triodes is about 20%, while that of pentodes is about 30 to 35%. Unlike either class B or C, the average plate current and voltage remain constant regardless of the magnitude of the grid signal. The grid signal must be so confined that

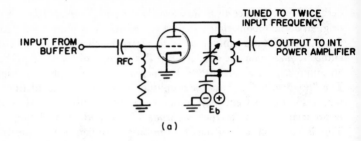

(a)

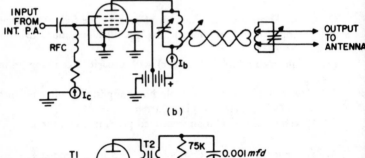

(b)

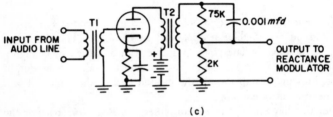

(c)

Fig. 3.168. Different stages of phase-modulated FM transmitter: (a) frequency doubler, (b) power amplifier, (c) speech amplifier.

it does not cause grid current in its positive swing, or cut off the tube in its negative swing. The power amplification ratio is high since no grid current is drawn.

$$\text{Power amplification ratio} = \frac{\text{power delivered to plate load}}{\text{power consumed in grid circuit}}$$

Following the speech amplifier in Fig. 3.168(c) is a network to provide "pre-emphasis" of the higher audio frequencies. Details of this network and its operation are given in Q. 3.163.

Q. 3.169. Discuss wide-band and narrow-band reception in FM voice communication systems with respect to frequency deviation and bandwidth.

A.   It has been shown that the highest audio frequency used in voice communication may be limited to about 3,000 cycles without seriously impairing the intelligibility of the speech. In standard FM broadcasting (88 — 108 mc) a deviation ratio of five is employed to provide the desired dynamic range. With a maximum transmitted audio frequency of 15,000 cycles, the maximum deviation will be 75 kc. However, in narrow-band FM, the deviation ratio is commonly *one* so that the deviation may be limited to the audio frequency, or to plus and minus 3,000 cycles. This is a considerable advantage over wide-band FM when many stations must operate within a crowded spectrum. In a narrow-band FM system, the FM receiver is also a narrow-band device. This not only improves the sensitivity and selectivity of a receiver with a given number of stages, but also makes it possible to improve the signal-to-noise ratio of the system. This is so because noise occupies the entire radio spectrum and the narrower the bandwidth of reception, the less noise energy will be delivered to the receiver output. Actually, for a voice-communications system, which requires limited frequency response and limited dynamic range, there would be no significant advantage in employing wide-band FM. On the contrary, this would require a greater deviation ratio, necessitating more complex modulating and multiplying circuits. In addition a much wider channel bandwidth would be required and fewer stations could be accommodated in a given spectrum assignment. A more complex receiver for an equal distance of communication would also be required for wide-band FM.

D.   Narrow-band FM may be generally defined as FM whose sidebands do not occupy a bandwidth greater than an AM signal which has the same audio-modulating frequencies. If single-tone, narrow-band FM is employed, the modulation index may not exceed about 0.6 if the bandwidth is not to exceed that of an equivalent AM signal. However, if speech modulation is used, a complex waveform is produced. In this waveform, the energy distribution is such that the modulation index is reduced for any single frequency component. Therefore, in the case of speech modulation, a somewhat higher modulation index (1.0) may be employed with no increase in bandwidth over single-tone modulation with a lesser modulation index.

In a radio communication system, the primary object of the system is the transfer of intelligence by voice. A high signal-to-noise ratio is desirable in voice reception, but an increase of this ratio above a certain definite value will not improve the readability of the received signal. For carrier wave strengths below a certain minimum value, a low-deviation system will produce a greater signal-to-noise ratio than a high deviation system. The optimum frequency deviation for an FM system which is designed to obtain maximum distance for complete readability corresponds to a deviation ratio of *one*. Since voice frequencies are not generally of importance above 3000 cycles, a deviation ratio of one means that the peak deviation frequency will be equal to 3000 cycles. (See also Q. 3.163(e) through (h), Q. 3.167, and Q. 4.59.)

Q. 3.170. What might be the effect on the transmitted frequency if a tripler stage in an otherwise perfectly aligned FM transmitter, were slightly de-tuned?

A. The tank circuit of such a tripler would present a reactive impedance to the plate of the tube instead of a resistive impedance. The value of such a reactive impedance and the resulting phase angle will depend on the frequency at any instant. Since the instantaneous frequency varies during modulation, the detuned tripler stage will inject an additional phase modulation component into the frequency modulated wave. When such a wave is finally detected at the receiver the additional frequencies will be present at the output along with the original frequencies. Such unwanted frequencies represent interference and noise.

D. When a tank circuit of reasonable Q (10 or more) is tuned to resonance, it presents a resistive impedance to the driving source (generator). However, if the tank is tuned to resonate either above or below the driving frequency, it will present either an inductive or capacitive reactance, respectively. The reactance presented by the detuned tank will depend upon the instantaneous frequency fed to it by the FM wave. For each frequency fed to the tank, an additional phase shift will occur. Thus, an extra phase modulation component will be added to the original FM wave, producing a distortion and interference component which will appear after detection at the receiver.

Q. 3.171. Could the harmonic of an FM transmission contain intelligible modulation?

A. The harmonics of FM transmission do contain intelligible modulation, the only difference between them and the fundamental is the increased deviation. The deviation is multiplied by the order of the harmonic.

D. In the usual FM transmitter, the carrier wave is generated at a relatively low r-f frequency. In addition, this low-frequency carrier is frequency modulated at a low deviation ratio. By means of frequency multipliers in the transmitter, both the deviation and the carrier are brought to the desired waveforms. (See Q. 4.89(b).) A harmonic output from the FM transmitter would merely continue this process. For example, consider an FM narrow-band transmitter operating at 31 mc with a deviation of plus and minus 3 kc. At the second harmonic of the radiated wave, the carrier would have a frequency of 61 mc and a deviation of plus and minus 6 kc. This harmonic wave contains the same intelligence as the fundamental and this intelligence may be recovered in an FM receiver tuned to 61 mc and having a bandwidth of about 6 kc (or more).

Q. 3.172.   Under what usual conditions of maintenance and/or repair should a transmitter be retuned?

A.   If tubes, RF components or RF leads are involved or disturbed during maintenance or repair, the transmitter should be retuned. Maintenance and/or repair of the power and control circuits normally do not require such retuning.

D.   See Q. 3.176(b) and (c). Note that retuning of the transmitter can be performed only by a person holding a second or first class operator's license. See Q. 4.110 through 4.114 for discussion of some FCC Rules and Regulations pertaining to the performance of FM broadcast stations. See also R & R 73.254 through R & R 73.269 in Appendix I for further information.

Q. 3.173.   If an indirect FM transmitter without modulation was within carrier frequency tolerance, but with modulation out of tolerance, what would be some possible causes?

A.   In the indirect or Armstrong system of frequency modulation, the actual modulation is obtained by employing a balanced modulator to produce sidebands, only, to be combined with the carrier only after the carrier has been shifted in phase by 90°. The carrier, during modulation, is defined as the average frequency of the whole spectrum emitted. The most probable cause of the average frequency being out of tolerance during modulation is the balanced modulator not being balanced. Such an event would result in the production of unequal sidebands which would have the effect of shifting the average frequency upward or downward. Without modulation, the average frequency or carrier would be unchanged in frequency because the sidebands being added to it at this time are zero.

D.   As explained in Q. 3.89 and Q. 3.98, two causes of oscillator frequency changes are supply voltage changes and oscillator loading variations. If the circumstances in the transmitter are such that either of these effects can be caused by the application of modulation, then carrier frequency changes may occur only in the presence of modulation. Supply voltage changes may occur due to a defective regulated power supply or defective decoupling circuits. Oscillator loading changes may occur due to a mistuned or defective buffer stage or to a defective phase modulator.

Q. 3.174. In an FM transmitter what would be the effect on antenna current if the grid bias on the final power amplifier were varied?

A. Normally, the final power amplifier of an FM transmitter is operated Class C. With such an amplifier, a change in its grid bias will produce a change in its output power and hence a change in the antenna current. Usually, a decrease in grid bias will increase the power output with an attendant increase in antenna current. An increase in grid bias will have just the opposite effect. Both of these effects can take place only over a rather limited range.

D. In the answer above, it was assumed that most of the bias was supplied from a fixed source. It is also possible to supply a considerable portion of the bias as "grid-leak bias" (see Q. 3.121). In this event there is a "self-regulating" effect on the antenna current if the driving signal varies between narrow limits. In this case, if the driving signal drops, the grid-leak bias decreases and causes an increase in amplifier gain which tends to maintain a constant output. If the driving signal increases, the grid-leak bias increases, decreasing amplifier gain, and again tending to maintain constant output. Outside of these limits however, the antenna current will tend to follow the amplitude of the driving signal.

Q. 3.175. Explain briefly, the principles involved in frequency-shift keying (FSK). How is this signal detected?

A. (a) Frequency-shift keying (F1 emission) is a means of keying a radiotelegraph transmitter by changing the frequency of its output when the key is depressed, rather than turning the transmitter on and off during keying. It may be accomplished by connecting a keyed reactance tube across the master-oscillator so that the resonant frequency is changed by about 850 cycles as keying takes place. Frequently, the shifted oscillator is at a low frequency and is only shifted a small amount to maintain good stability. The shifted oscillator frequencies are multiplied to obtain the final output frequency and the desired frequency shift.

(b) One scheme of detection which may be employed either for the aural reception of Morse code or to operate a radioteletype machine is shown in block diagram form in Fig. 3.175. The frequency-shift keying (FSK) signal passes through the usual receiver r-f and i-f circuits and is applied to the receiver detector together with the signal from a beat-frequency oscillator (bfo) (see Q. 3.158). The bfo is adjusted to heterodyne with the i-f to produce a "mark" signal of 2125 cycles and a "space" signal of 2925 cycles for a difference of 850 cycles. These are fed through individual filters to eliminate all other spurious frequencies. The output of the "mark" filter may be used directly or fed through an audio amplifier for aural copying of Morse code, since the dot and dash information is carried entirely by the "mark" signal. For operation of a radioteletype printer, the "mark" and "space" signals are fed to grid-leak detectors and current amplifiers, the output of which is used to operate the printer.

D. Frequency shift keying has several important advantages over "on-off" keying as follows:

1. A reduction of transmitted bandwidth, especially for high speed (machine) keying.

2. An increase of signal-to-noise ratio at the receiving end.

3. A possible reduction of fading.

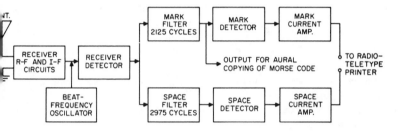

Fig. 3.175. Simplified block diagram of receiving circuits for frequency-shift keying for aural reception of Morse code, or operation of a radioteletype printer.

When a transmitter is being keyed, frequencies other than the carrier frequency are radiated. These are called sidebands and their relative amplitude and frequency depend largely upon the rate of keying, and the shape or configuration of the keyed characters. If the keyed characters have a square shape, the side frequencies will extend out on each side of the carrier for great distances. On the other hand, if the keyed characters can be rounded off and kept that way during transmission, the sidebands will be greatly attenuated. Rounding of the keyed characters in "on-off" keying cannot be easily accomplished, since clipping and limiting in class C amplifiers effectively squares up any rounding-off which might have been originally produced.

In frequency-shift keying, rounding may be accomplished by passing the square characters through a suitable low-pass filter. The keying stage produces frequency modulation of the output, and the rounded characters are able to retain their original shape.

At the receiving end a considerable increase in signal-to-noise ratio is noted in frequency-shift keying. The main reason for this is the fact that a carrier is always present (although shifted) and noise pulses are not able to actuate the signal recorder of the receiving equipment readily.

The possible reduction of fading is due to the fact that the energy in the transmitted wave is distributed over a *band* of frequencies, each frequency of which may have somewhat different fading characteristics.

An FSK signal may be passed through a limiter (or limiters) and detected by an FM discriminator. In this manner the noise reducing advantage of FM may be employed. However, in this case, the discriminator must use a d-c coupled audio output to provide a d-c output when the keying is stopped on either "space" or "mark."

Q. 3.176. Assume you have available the following instruments:

> A-C/D-C VTVM
> Ammeter
> Heterodyne frequency meter (0.0002% accuracy)
> Absorption wave meter
> FM modulation meter

Draw and label a block diagram of a voice modulated (press-to-talk microphone), indirect (phase modulated) FM transmitter having a crystal multiplication of 12.

(a) If the desired output frequency were 155.460 mc, what would be the proper crystal frequency?

(b) Consider the transmitter strip completely de-tuned; there are ammeter jacks in the control grid circuits of the multipliers and the control grid and cathode circuits of the final circuits of the final amplifier. Explain, in detail, step-by-step, a proper procedure for tuning and aligning all stages except plate circuit of final power amplifier (PA).

(c) Assume a tunable antenna with adjustable coupling to the plate circuit of the final PA. With the ammeter in the cathode circuit of the PA and with the aid of a tube manual, describe a step-by-step method of obtaining maximum output power, without damage to the tube.

(d) If the PA in (c) above were a pentode how would you determine the power input to the stage?

(e) In (c) above how would you determine if the PA stage were self-oscillating; if so, what adjustments could be made?

(f) Assume the transmitter's assigned frequency is 155.460 mc, with a required tolerance of plus or minus 0.0005 percent. What would be the minimum and maximum frequencies, as read on the frequency meter, which would assure the transmitter being within tolerance?

(g) Assume the 1 mc crystal oscillator of the frequency meter has been calibrated with WWV and that the meter is tunable to any frequency between each 1 mc interval over a range of 20-40 mc, with usable harmonics up to 640 mc. Explain in detail what connections and adjustments would be made to measure the signal directly from the transmitter; also by means of a receiver.

(h) If in checking the frequency deviation with the modulation meter, would you expect the greatest deviation by whistling or by speaking in a low voice into the microphone?

(i) If the transmitter contained a means for limiting, and were over-modulating, what measurements and adjustments could be made to determine and remedy the fault?

A. For the block diagram, see Fig. 3.176.

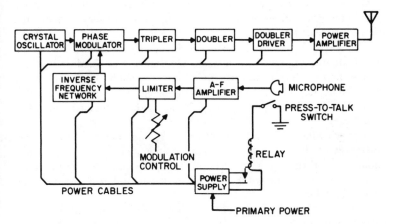

Fig. 3.176. Block diagram of a voice-modulated, phase-modulated FM transmitter.

(a) Since the transmitter employs a frequency multiplication of 12, the proper crystal frequency is the desired output frequency of 155.460 mc divided by 12, or 12.955 mc.

(b) It is assumed that the ammeter available is actually a milliammeter and is capable of being fitted with a pair of leads terminating in a suitable plug for use in measuring electrode currents in the stages by means of the jacks available. It is further assumed that the crystal oscillator is an electron-coupled Pierce oscillator.

In aligning the transmitter it is first necessary to remove the plate and screen voltages from the power amplifier. The power is then applied to the preceding stages by operating the *Press-to-Talk* switch.

The plate circuit of the oscillator is tuned to resonance by adjusting for maximum grid current in the tripler stage. At this point check the frequency of the oscillator by loosely coupling the wavemeter to the oscillator plate coil. The frequency, by this method of measurement, should be approximately 13 mc. This measurement is to assure us that the oscillator plate coil is tuned to the fundamental and not to a second or even third harmonic. This is possible in some cases due to the range of frequencies for which some oscillators are designed.

If the heterodyne frequency meter available can measure frequencies in this range, it its advisable to measure the exact frequency of the oscillator by loosely coupling the frequency meter to the oscillator plate coil. If this measurement is not feasible, the final output frequency of the transmitter can be measured later.

The milliammeter is next inserted in the jack in the control grid circuit of the first doubler and the plate circuit of the tripler adjusted for maximum grid current for this stage. Again, it is necessary to couple the wavemeter loosely to the plate coil of the tripler and check to see if the tripler output frequency approximates 39 mc. This is to assure the stage is actually tripling the frequency and not doubling or quadrupling it.

The first doubler is adjusted in a similar fashion, again tuning for maximum grid current in the following stage. The wavemeter in this case should indicate approximately 78 mc as the output frequency for this stage.

The procedure is again followed for the second doubler and the wavemeter used to be certain that its output is approximately 155 mc. At this point, more than normal grid current should be indicated by the milliammeter which is inserted in the jack for the control-grid current of the power amplifier.

(c) With the preceding stages of the transmitter aligned as in (b) above, and the coupling to the antenna reduced to the minimum, the plate and screen voltages to the power amplifier can be restored.

As soon as the power is applied to the transmitter, by operating the press-to-talk switch, the plate tank of the power amplifier must be adjusted for minimum cathode current. Following this, the antenna must be resonated as indicated by a maximum rise in cathode current. If little or no effect can be noted on the cathode current, it will be necessary to increase the antenna coupling slightly. When tuning the antenna results in a noticeable peak in cathode current, the cathode current and the grid current should be noted and the tube manual consulted. If the cathode current and the grid current are as specified by the tube manual, then the power amplifier will be delivering its maximum output power.

It should be borne in mind that the cathode current is the sum of the control grid, screen and plate currents. The control grid current can be measured independently by means of the jack in the grid circuit. If the applied screen and plate voltages are known, the screen current can be estimated from the information in the tube manual. The plate current can also be estimated with a fair amount of accuracy.

If the currents thus obtained are not sufficient, according to the tube manual, the coupling to the antenna should be increased in small increments until the desired screen and plate currents are realized without excessive grid current. After each change of coupling it will be necessary to retune the plate tank of the power amplifier to resonance as indicated by minimum cathode current. It is quite often advisable to check the tuning of the doubler driver at the same time.

(d) Since the input power to the power amplifier is the product of its plate current and its applied plate voltage, it is necessary to measure these quantities. The cathode current and the grid current can be measured with the aid of the milliammeter. If the applied screen and plate potentials are not given in the instruction manual they can be measured with the aid of the VTVM. From a tube manual, the screen current can be estimated and it and the grid current subtracted from the cathode current, leaving the amount of plate current. Since the screen current is usually only a small fraction of the plate current, this will make the plate current known to a fair degree of accuracy. If greater accuracy is desired and the screen voltage is obtained across a series dropping resistor of known value, the voltage drop across the resistor can be measured with the VTVM and the screen current determined by Ohm's law.

The power input to the stage can then be found by multiplying the plate current by the applied plate potential.

(e) Self-oscillation of the power amplifier can be detected by removing the tube in the tripler and noting the effect on the grid and cathode currents in the power amplifier. If sufficient fixed bias is used in the power amplifier to cut off the plate and screen currents in the absence of excitation, removal of the tripler tube should result in such currents being zero. If the stage is oscillating, plate and screen currents will continue to flow in the absence of excitation.

If the power amplifier is a triode, neutralizing arrangements exist. To rid the stage of self-oscillation, the neutralizing adjustments must be performed. The exact nature of such adjustments will depend on just what type of neutralizing facilities are provided.

If the stage uses a pentode or beam power tube, conditions sometimes will cause self-oscillation. Usually, insufficient loading is the cause and increasing the loading on the stage by closer coupling to the antenna will make the circuit behave more normally.

Grid and plate currents should rise and fall smoothly as the plate circuit is tuned through resonance. Erratic behavior of these currents indicate at least a tendency toward self-oscillation.

(f) Using the available frequency meter with its accuracy of plus or minus 0.0002%, it will be necessary to subtract this accuracy from the tolerance of plus or minus 0.0005% to be absolutely certain the transmitter frequency is within tolerance. Under these conditions, multiplying the carrier frequency of 155.460 mc by plus or minus 0.0003% gives an allowable variation in frequency, as read on the meter of plus or minus 0.0004664 mc. The maximum frequency would be 155.4604664 mc and the minimum 155.4595336 mc, as read on the frequency meter.

(g) It is assumed, further, that the detector of the frequency meter is also tunable only over the range of 20-40 mc. If this is so, then the meter input should be coupled to the plate coil of the transmitter's tripler and the detector (oscillating) adjusted to zero beat with the tripler's output.

The detector is then adjusted to pick up the 38th harmonic of the meter's 1-mc crystal and the detector's dial calibration adjusted to agree with this. The detector dial should then be varied to pick up the 39th harmonic and the calibration checked at this point. Returning to the frequency of the tripler output, the carrier may be read directly from the detector dial if so calibrated or interpolated if the dial is linearly divided. The frequency of the transmitter, in this case, will be four times the frequency of the tripler output (38.865×4, or 155.460 mc).

If a receiver is employed, the unmodulated transmitter is tuned in and the frequency meter's oscillating detector r-f output is also coupled to the receiver. After checking the meter's calibration as described above, the detector is adjusted so its fourth harmonic is heard in the receiver at zero beat with the transmitter. The transmitter frequency, then is four times the reading as obtained on the meter's detector dial.

(h) Since this is an FM transmitter, the amount of deviation produced is dependent only on the amplitude of the modulating signal and is independent of the modulating frequency. It is assumed that whistling into the microphone produces a louder signal than when speaking in a low voice and therefore the frequency deviation should be greater when whistling.

(i) The *modulation control* that is shown in Figure 3.176 is used to adjust the output of the limiter stage. This control should be adjusted so that when a very loud talker is speaking into the microphone, the FM modulation meter indicates the maximum allowable frequency deviation. Assurance is then had that this deviation will not be exceeded no matter which person uses the transmitter. Care should be taken to note that when the limiter output is being *reduced* the deviation also becomes less. This makes certain that the limiter is actually limiting the maximum level of speech.

The original determination of the fault, can be made with the FM modulation meter.

Q. 3.177.   Draw a schematic diagram of each of the following stages of a superheterodyne FM receiver. Explain the principles of operation. Label adjacent stages.

(a) Mixer with injected oscillator frequency.

(b) I-f amplifier.

(c) Limiter.

(d) Discriminator.

(e) Differential squelch circuit.

A.   (a) For schematic of the mixer, see Figure 3.177(a). This circuit is frequently referred to as a "mixer-oscillator" circuit. It uses one special type tube to perform the functions of both mixer and oscillator. The oscillator section of the tube is a triode, consisting of the

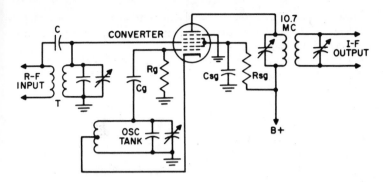

Fig. 3.177(a). Simplified schematic diagram of an FM mixer circuit with injected oscillator frequency.

control grid, cathode and screen grid. The converter section is a pentode made up of the special injector grid, cathode-screen grid, suppressor grid and plate. In this type of circuit, both the control grid (oscillator voltage) and injector grid (r–f voltage) signals are mixed electronically. Both of these signals modulate the electron stream going from cathode to plate. Since the tube is operated in a non-linear fashion, heterodyning of the two frequencies results and the desired i–f frequency of 10.7 megacycles is selected by the tuned circuit in the converter plate.

(b) For schematic of the i-f amplifier, see Figure 3.177(b). This is a Class-A amplifier with double-tuned plate and grid circuits resonated to the center i–f of 10.7 megacycles. The bandwidth of the i–f of a broadcast FM receiver will be on the order of 150 to 200 kilocycles

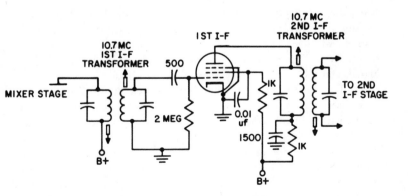

Fig. 3.177(b). Simplified schematic diagram of a first i-f amplifier stage for an FM radio.

in order to pass the required modulation sidebands. Grid bias is provided by the 2 megohm resistor which produces a space-charge bias in the order of 0.5 to 1.0 volt.

(c) For the schematic of a limiter, see figure, Fig. 3.177(c).

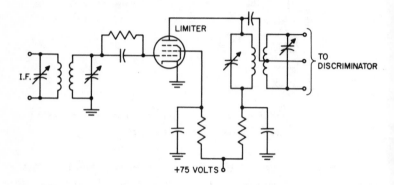

Fig. 3.177(c).   A limiter stage in an FM receiver.

The purpose of a limiter stage is to remove the amplitude variations from the intermediate frequency signal before it is detected in the discriminator. Since most noises are amplitude modulated, they can be removed by a special i-f amplifier called a limiter stage, whose output amplitude is relatively independent of input amplitude for most operating conditions. A limiter tube is easily saturated and driven below cut-off by a certain minimum value of grid swing (about .5 to 2 volts).

The limiter tube must be of the sharp cut-off type and operate with low plate and screen grid voltages in the order of 50 to 75 volts. Bias for this stage is obtained by a grid leak and capacitor network in the grid circuit. Some receivers use two limiters in cascade to improve the sensitivity of limiting action. In this case the first limiter is grid leak biased, and the second usually operates at zero bias.

(d) For the schematic of a discriminator, see Fig. 3.177(d1).

A discriminator in an FM receiver is the circuit which changes the variations in frequency of the FM wave into a conventional audio output wave which is capable of being amplified by a standard audio amplifier. The discriminator has the same relative function in an FM receiver as the second detector of a superheterodyne AM receiver. In order to detect an FM wave it is necessary to utilize a device whose d-c output voltage increases when the carrier deviates in one direction and decreases when the carrier deviates in the other direction. An FM wave from a broadcast station deviates in exact accordance with the audio modulating signal, so that the variations of d-c from the output of the discriminator will be a reproduction of the original modulating signal. The conventional type of discriminator does not reject AM and must be preceded by one or more limiter stages for noise suppression. (See also Q. 3.223.)

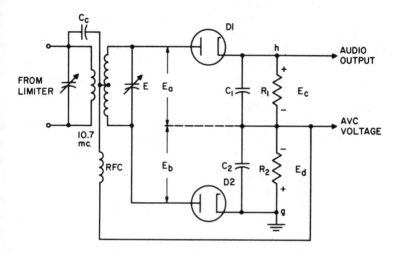

Fig. 3.177(d1). Basic circuit of the Foster-Seeley discrimitor. In practice, point g is usually grounded. The audio output appears at point h and AVC or tuning eye voltage can be obtained from the center tap of the resistors. (See text for explanation of the voltage symbols.)

To make the operation of a discriminator clear, it is necessary to review the simple relations among currents and voltages in a double-tuned i-f coil, such as that shown in Fig. 3.177(d2), when both circuits are tuned to resonance. The following fundamental facts apply:

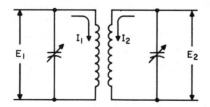

Fig. 3.177(d2). A diagram of a double-tuned i-f coil showing currents and voltages discussed in the text.

1. The resonant condition causes only resistance, and no reactance, to be reflected into the primary. The primary current I_1 will, therefore, be in phase with the primary voltage E_1.

2. The voltage across the secondary, E_2, is produced by means of a mutual reactance, M, which results from the coupling between the coils.

3. Since this mutual inductance is a reactance, *the secondary voltage E_2 is 90 degrees out of phase with the primary voltage E_1.*

4. The secondary current, I_2, is in phase with the secondary voltage E_2, because of the resonant condition. *The secondary current is, therefore, also 90 degrees out of phase with E_1.*

Now suppose the secondary is center-tapped as shown in Fig. 3.177 (d3). If the center point is considered as a reference, we now have a balanced circuit, that is, the voltage across the upper half is 180 degrees out of phase with that across the lower half. Notice that with respect to the center point, E_x and E_y are equal but opposite in phase.

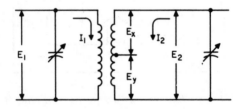

Fig. 3.177(d3). Schematic of an i-f coil with a center-tapped secondary winding such as used with Foster-Seeley and ratio discriminators.

Now consider what happens when the frequency of E_1 changes. Suppose the frequency suddenly becomes *higher*. Since we are now off resonance in the secondary, the parallel resonant circuit becomes capacitive, causing the secondary voltage to lag behind the secondary current. This means that E_x is less than 90 degrees away from E_1, and E_y is more than 90 degrees from E_1. Although these phase changes have taken place, the magnitudes of E_x and E_y are substantially the same as in the resonant case. If the frequency changes to lower than resonance, the situation will be reversed as far as phase is concerned. E_x will now have a phase angle of more than 90 degrees while E_1 and E_y will have an angle less than 90 degrees.

To summarize:

1. With a signal at the resonant frequency (normally 10.7 mc), E_x and E_y are equal and opposite, each being out of phase 90 degrees with E_1 but in opposite directions.

2. When the signal goes higher than resonance, E_x and E_y are the

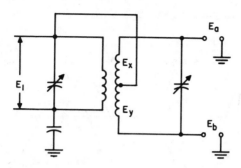

Fig. 3.177(d4). Showing how two voltages E_a and E_b are produced for application to the plates of the diodes. E_a and E_b vary in magnitude as the frequency of the input changes.

same in magnitude, but with respect to E_1, the phase of E_x is less than 90 degrees, that of E_y is more than 90 degrees.

3. With a signal lower than resonance magnitudes are still the same, but E_x's phase is more than 90 degrees while E_y's is now less than 90 degrees.

Now suppose we arrange the circuit as shown in Fig. 3.177(d4). The bottom of the primary coil has been grounded, and the top has been connected to the center tap of the secondary. Let us now investigate the voltage of the ends of the secondary with respect to ground. These voltages are labeled E_a and E_b. By tracing the circuit from the low side of the primary through the coil and then through one half of the secondary, it can be seen that at any given instant: $e_1 + e_x = e_a$ and $e_1 + e_y = e_b$. At resonance, when E_x and E_y are each 90 degrees from E_1, E_a and E_b are equal. Under off-resonance conditions, however, the changed phase relations will cause one to be larger than the other. To clarify this, refer to Fig. 3.177(d5).

In Fig. (A) of Fig. 3.177(d5) two voltages, E_m and E_n, are plotted. They are equal in magnitude, but *less* than 90 degrees apart in phase. In Fig. (B) of Fig. 3.177(d5) the same two voltages are plotted *more* than 90 degrees apart. In each case, the voltages are added, and the sum represented by the dotted line. These diagrams show that when the phase is *less* than 90 degrees, the sum is larger than when the phase is greater than 90 degrees.

The same principle applies in Fig. 3.177(d4). When the frequency is higher than resonance, the phase angle between E_1 and E_x is greater than that between E_1 and E_y. E_a, the sum of E_1 and E_x, is, therefore, greater than E_b, the sum of E_1 and E_y. When the frequency is lower than resonance, the opposite is true and E_a is less than E_b.

Another way to explain the above relations is by the use of vectors.

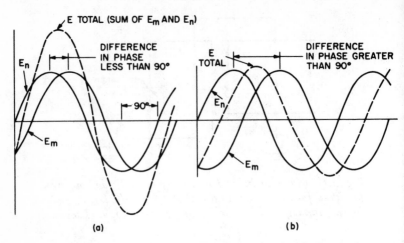

Fig. 3.177(d5). Graphs of sine waves showing how two a-c voltages can produce a sum voltage whose amplitude varies with a change of phase between them.

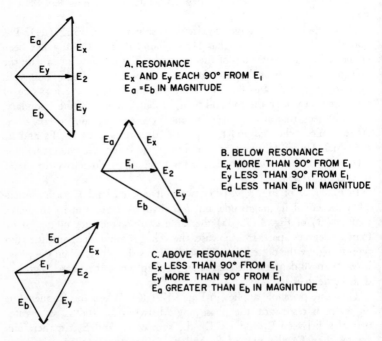

Fig. 3.177(d6). Vector relations in the Foster-Seeley and ratio discriminators.

Fig 3.177(d6) shows a vector diagram for each of the three important conditions described above. Notice E_a and E_b are made larger and smaller according to the phase of the secondary voltage.

In Fig. 3.177(d1) we have applied the voltages E_a and E_b, which are a-c to diodes D_1 and D_2, and the circuit is a Foster-Seeley discriminator. These a-c voltages are rectified and filtered and produce the d-c voltage E_c and E_d. These d-c voltages are proportional to E_a and E_b, respectively, and have the polarities indicated on the diagram.

Now the discriminator output is the voltage between points g and h. Since E_c and E_d oppose each other, the total voltage is equal to the difference in magnitude and will have the polarity of the larger voltage. At resonance these voltages are equal and the total voltage (g to h) is zero. At a frequency higher than resonance, E_c is larger than E_d. The total output voltage will then be E_c minus E_d with h positive and g negative. When the frequency is lower than resonance, the polarity of the output will be reversed, and the voltage will be E_d minus E_c.

Thus when the i-f changes above and below the resonant frequency, the discriminator output will vary in magnitude in the same way. This circuit is known as the Foster-Seeley type of discriminator.

Fig. 3.177(d7) shows the characteristic typical of a good discriminator. The curve of amplitude versus frequency should remain straight (linear) for all frequencies within the deviation range.

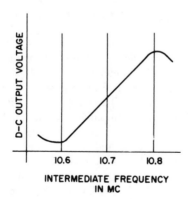

Fig. 3.177(d7). Typical discriminator characteristic.

(e) For schematic of a differential squelch circuit, see Figure 3.177(e). In the absence of a receiver-input signal, considerable noise may be amplified and heard in the speaker causing an annoying condition. With a certain minimum signal level being received, the FM receiver will achieve *quieting* and only the signal will be heard. By utilizing a squelch circuit, the no-signal "noise" is prevented from being amplified. Further, a squelch control is provided to prevent weak signals from being squelched. This control is R2 in Figure 3.177(e). In the absence of signal, the control is normally set so that the noise is barely squelched. Weak signals can then be received. However, signals in the noise level may be lost and it is sometimes desirable to operate with no squelch.

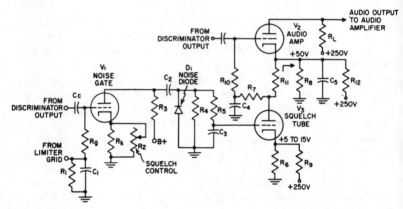

Fig. 3.177(e). Schematic diagram of a differential squelch circuit for an FM superheterodyne receiver.

In the absence of signal, noise is amplified by the noise gate. The setting of R2 and the lack of limiter grid bias applied to R1 permits V1 to amplify normally. The amplified noise is rectified by noise diode D1 and integrated by capacitor C3. The resultant, a positive d–c voltage is applied to the grid of squelch amplifier V3, causing V3 to conduct at its maximum rate. Squelch-tube current through R11, in the cathode of V2, causes V2 to be cut off and no noise output results. When a limiting signal is received, the limiter bias cuts off V1. (Capacitor C_c in the grid of V1 is very small and normally will only pass the high-frequency noise impulses.) Further, a limiting signal prevents (from the limiter or ratio detector operation) noise from appearing at V1. Under this condition, the voltage across C3 drops to zero and V3 is cut off by the fixed cathode bias across R6. With the squelch tube cut off, V2 operates normally and amplifies its audio input.

D. See Q. 3.178, 4.59 and 4.63.

Q. 3.178. Draw a diagram of a ratio detector and explain its operation.

A. For the schematic of a ratio detector see Fig. 3.178. The ratio detector operation is similar to that of the discriminator (Q. 3.177(d)). However, whereas the conventional (Foster-Seeley) discriminator re-

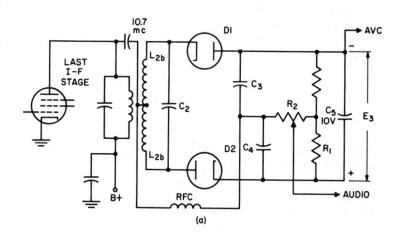

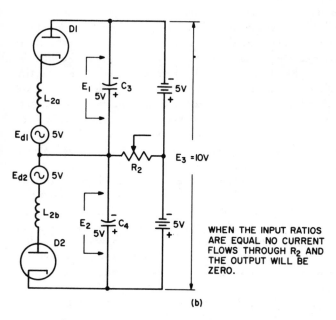

WHEN THE INPUT RATIOS ARE EQUAL NO CURRENT FLOWS THROUGH R₂ AND THE OUTPUT WILL BE ZERO.

(b)

Fig. 3.178. (a) Schematic diagram of a ratio detector;
(b) its equivalent circuit (see discussion).

sponds to amplitude variations and must therefore be preceded by one or more limiter stages if noise rejection is to be achieved, the ratio detector being very insensitive to amplitude variations does not require a limiter in its input circuit. The ratio detector derives its name from the fact that its output is proportional only to the ratio of the input i-f voltages and not to their amplitude.

Note in Fig. 3.178(a) that the major circuit differences from a conventional discriminator are:

1. The two diodes are connected in series.
2. The addition of large capacitor C_5, which provides, in conjunction with its parallel resistors, a long time constant to maintain a relatively fixed d-c voltage.

See discussion for details of the operation of this circuit.

D.   A detailed operation of a ratio detector follows. Refer to the diagrams of Fig. 3.178(a) and (b).

When the f-m wave is at the center or resting frequency, the potentials applied to both diodes are equal. When the f-m wave deviates above resonance (10.775 mc), E_{d1} is greater than E_{d2} by some ratio, say 12 volts to 8 volts. When the f-m wave deviates below resonance (10.625 mc) E_{d1} will be less than E_{d2} by a ratio of 8 volts to 12 volts. Thus, except at resonance, there always exists some ratio between the voltages applied to the two diodes. A detector whose output is made proportional only to this ratio (which is changing at an audio rate), becomes independent of amplitude variations and does its own limiting. Such a device is the *ratio detector*. An equivalent circuit, Fig. 3.178(b), will simplify the discussion. The RC network R_1C_5 is connected in series with the two diodes, the direction of electron flow being such that the top of C_5 will be negative, and the bottom positive. The time constant of R_1C_5 is quite long, about .2 of a second, so that its potential remains relatively fixed even for the lowest frequency audio variations. Actually the charge in C_5 is a function of the average carrier strength. This potential is shown as a battery of 10 volts magnitude and tapped at the center.

To this center point is connected one end of the volume control R_2. The other end of the volume control is connected to the junction of C_2 and C_4. While a fixed potential of 10 volts is used at this time, it must be remembered that this potential may vary slowly with changes in the average carrier strength. L_2 is shown in two sections with generators E_{d1} and E_{d2} representing the induced voltages for any given deviation of the f-m wave. The conditions which must be present in this circuit are as follows:

First, the ratio of E_{d1} and E_{d2} must equal the ratio E_1 to E_2:

$$\frac{E_{d1}}{E_{d2}} = \frac{E_1}{E_2}$$

Secondly; the sum of E_1 and E_2 must always equal the charge in C_5, which is E_3: $E_1 + E_2 = E_3$.

Assume that

$$\frac{E_{d1}}{E_{d2}} = \frac{5}{5}$$

If no drop exists in the diodes, then

$$\frac{E_1}{E_2} = \frac{5}{5}$$

and no current can flow through R_2. Thus at the resting frequency of the f-m wave, the d-c output will be zero.

Going above resonance now, assume that:

$$\frac{E_{d1}}{E_{d2}} = \frac{8}{2} = \frac{E_1}{E_2}$$

Under this condition current will flow through R_2, and the drop across R_2 will be 3 volts and positive at the junction of C_3 and C_4, thus producing the positive half of the audio cycle.

Deviating below resonance:

$$\frac{E_{d1}}{E_{d2}} = \frac{2}{8} = \frac{E_1}{E_2}$$

Current will now flow in the reverse direction through R_2 producing the negative half of the audio cycle.

In the rejection of amplitude modulation, the action is as follows. Suppose that a sharp increase in the carrier amplitude caused the ratio of

$$\frac{E_{d1}}{E_{d2}} \text{ to become } \frac{16}{4}$$

The ratio obviously remains the same but the amplitude has doubled. However, $E_1 - E_2$ remains fixed as determined by E_3, and the amplitude change cannot take place. E_3 *tends* to get higher, but the time constant of R_1C_5 is made so large that noise pulses or amplitude modulation are too rapid to change this voltage. If the carrier level should suddenly drop, the potential E_3 would still be maintained and this drop would not appear in the output.

Since the potential across C_5 varies with the average carrier strength, it serves as an excellent source of AVC voltage.

An important advantage is the fact that there is no "threshold" effect in the ratio detector; that is, there is no minimum carrier level necessary to cause noise attenuation as with limiter circuits.

Q. 3.179. Explain how spurious signals can be received or created in a receiver. How could this be reduced in sets having sealed untunable filters?

A. (a) Spurious signals may be received from channels adjacent to the desired one due to inadequate receiver selectivity.

(b) Spurious signals may be created in a receiver by regenerating or oscillating i–f amplifiers. They may also be generated by the two local oscillators, multipliers and mixers which may create numerous harmonic and heterodyne frequencies. (See Q. 3.180 below, for block diagram of a typical FM communications receiver.)

(c) By the use of a sealed, untunable filter it is possible to achieve an important improvement in the selectivity of the receiver and to reject many of the undesired frequencies.

D. The sealed filter is usually placed at the input to the low-frequency i–f amplifier. It has a response which is essentially flat over the necessary i–f bandwidth and which drops off very steeply (skirts) on both sides. Actually, the sealed filter establishes the i–f bandpass. The filters are sealed to avoid change due to atmospheric conditions and are designed to be relatively impervious to changes in their associated stages.

Two general classifications of radio-receiver interference and possible cures for each type are described below.

1. Interference due to static noises. The following methods may be employed to reduce the effect upon the receiver of such noises:

a. Insertion of a power line filter in series with the receiver supply cord close to the outlet.

b. Electrostatic shielding between primary and secondary windings in the power transformer.

c. Suitable filtering applied to the source of such noises whenever possible. (Motors, neon lights, etc.)

d. Use of horizontally polarized antennas if possible.

e. Use of shielded or well-balanced transmission lines.

f. Use of suitable noise limiters in receiver.

g. Use of crystal filter in receiver, if possible.

h. Use of highly directional antennas, if practical.

i. Complete shielding of entire receiver.

2. Interference due to undesired carrier waves. The following methods may be employed to reduce this type of interference:

a. Use of series or parallel resonant wave trap in antenna circuit.

b. Use of parallel resonant wave trap in cathode of first stage of receiver, and, if necessary, in some succeeding stages also.

c. Use of tuned r-f amplifier ahead of mixer stage.

d. Use of highly directional antennas if practical.

e. Complete shielding of receiver.

Q. 3.180. Describe, step-by-step, a proper procedure for aligning an FM double conversion superheterodyne receiver.

A.   A double-conversion (or double-superheterodyne) receiver is used to eliminate image interference (see Q. 3.155, Q. 3.156) from stations operating within a particular band, and to provide good adjacent channel rejection. For an FM broadcast receiver (88-108 mc) the usual i–f is 10.7 mc. With this i–f, no FM broadcast image interference is possible. Therefore, it will be assumed that the FM receiver referred to in this question is not an FM broadcast receiver, but is a VHF communications-type receiver capable of operating on one or more frequency channels. A block diagram of such a VHF receiver is given in Figure 3.180.

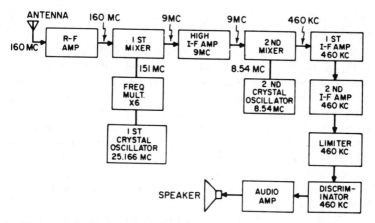

Fig. 3.180.   Block diagram of a fixed-tuned, double-conversion FM superheterodyne receiver.

This is a single channel receiver, as shown, utilizing two crystal oscillators. Additional channels might be received on such a receiver by the switching of additional crystals. An input r–f signal of 160 mc is assumed. It is also assumed that the *high* i–f is 9 megacycles and the *low* i–f is 460 kilocycles. The exact frequencies chosen are typical, but not critical, as the alignment procedure applies equally well to other frequencies.

The equipment used for the alignment will be a properly calibrated CW signal generator and a zero-center VTVM. The alignment will be performed in steps beginning with the discriminator detector (not ratio detector).

(a) Alignment of the Discriminator: Connect the zero-center VTVM between the junction of the two series-output resistors and ground. Connect the signal generator output through a small capacitor to the grid of the limiter stage and ground. Set the signal generator to 460 kilocycles. The VTVM should be set to a low scale and the generator output control adjusted to give a useful meter reading. Adjust the primary of the discriminator transformer for maximum deflection of the VTVM, reducing signal-generator output if necessary. Do not change the generator connections, but move the *hot* VTVM lead to the top of the two series-output resistors. Now, tune the discriminator secondary for a zero indication (center) between two peaks (one positive and one negative). Check the output linearity by tuning the generator equal increments on both sides of the center frequency. Equal, but opposite polarities, of voltage should occur. If this is not the case, touch up the primary adjustment to bring it about. This completes the discriminator alignment.

Note: As in most alignment procedures, use the minimum possible signal-generator output.

(b) Alignment of the Limiter: Connect the VTVM between the grid of the limiter and ground. Set the meter to read a low negative voltage. Connect the signal generator (through a small capacitor) tuned to 460 kc (unmodulated), between the grid and ground of the last i–f stage preceding the mixer. The signal generator output should be the minimum possible to obtain a meter reading, in order to prevent limiter saturation which would cause broad tuning. (Maintain this low generator output throughout the entire alignment process, reducing it as necessary when the circuits come into resonance.) Now tune the secondary of the last i–f transformer for maximum meter deflection. Next, tune the primary in a similar manner.

(c) Alignment of the I–F's: (Two i–f stages are present.) Maintain the meter in the limiter grid circuit. Move the signal generator (at 460 kc) to the grid of the first i–f stage (through a small capacitor). Peak first the secondary and then the primary of the i–f transformer between the first and second i–f stages. Next, without changing the meter position, move the signal generator (at 460 kc) to the grid of the second mixer stage (through a small capacitor). The generator output may have to be increased at this point since the second mixer grid circuit is resonated at 9 megacycles (not 460 kc). Peak the secondary and then the primary of the i–f transformer between the second mixer and first i–f stages.

(d) Set the signal generator to 160 megacycles and connect it to the antenna input of the r–f amplifier through a small capacitor. Maintain the VTVM at the grid of the limiter. As before, use the lowest possible signal-generator output. The frequency multiplier adjustments will result in the highest amplitude 151 mc signal being applied to the first mixer. This in turn will cause a 9 megacycle output from the first mixer and a 460 kilocycle output from the second mixer. Therefore, peak the multiplier adjustments for maximum VTVM readings. Next, peak the adjustments at the input and output of the *high* i–f amplifier. Following this, peak the adjustments at the input and output of the r–f amplifier. This completes the alignment procedure.

In the event the receiver has several channels, obtained by crystal switching, the *front-end* alignment will be slightly different. In this event, the r–f amplifier and first mixer will be somewhat broadbanded and tuned to the center of the channels. Selectivity will be provided by the i–f amplifiers, as usual.

D.   See also Q. 3.155 through Q. 3.161.

Q. 3.181.   Discuss the cause and prevention of interference to radio receivers installed in motor vehicles.

A.   Interference to radio receivers in motor vehicles comes primarily from the following sources:
1.   Generator brush sparking.
2.   Opening and closing of breaker points.
3.   Spark gap between rotor and distributor contacts.
4.   Spark gap in spark plugs.
5.   Static charges built up in tires and tubes while vehicle is moving.
6.   Incorrect gap settings of spark plugs and breaker points.
7.   Momentary interference from switches, such as dome switch, ignition switch, and heater switch and rheostat.
8.   Interference from the vibrating contact points of the voltage regulator.

D.   Most modern vehicles are completely bonded and so this is usually not a problem for servicemen. It is not practical to shield the ignition wires in the ordinary type of motor vehicle, but this is generally unnecessary. The following methods may be employed to minimize interference:
1.   Use a by-pass capacitor across the generator output. (Usually provided by vehicle manufacturer.)
2.   Have breaker points and spark plugs cleaned and correctly gapped.
3.   Use anti-static springs in hub of wheels, and conducting powder inside of tire tubes, or tubeless tires.
4.   By-pass all switches and long connecting wires.
5.   Shield antenna transmission line.
6.   Locate antenna well away from ignition system.
7.   Use suppressor resistors if necessary at all spark plugs and distributor rotor connection. Some plugs (such as "Auto-Lite") have built in suppressors.
8.   A capacitor is normally across the distributor breaker points, and will take care of interference at this point. The value is somewhat critical and should not be varied.
9.   A large part of voltage-regulator interference comes from the vibrating voltage (F terminal) and current-coil (G terminal) contacts. The

reverse current relay (B terminal) rarely operates and is generally not a source of important interference. Use of a bypass capacitor at the "B" terminal of the regulator will generally eliminate this type of interference when it does occur. A small series resistor and capacitor (10 ohms and 2500 μμf) from the "F" terminal of the regulator to ground will reduce interference from this point. The "G" terminal of the regulator connects to the armature of the generator which is generally bypassed. However, additional filtering (at the regulator) may have to be installed in the "G" line since the run of wire may act as a radiating antenna.

TRANSISTORS

Q. 3.182. Describe the difference between positive (P-type) and negative (N-type) semiconductors with respect to:

(a) The direction of current flow when an external emf is applied.

(b) The internal resistance when an external emf is applied.

A.   (a) As shown in Fig. 3.182(a), in P–type semiconductors, the major-current carriers are *holes* (positive charges). Hole current within the semiconductor moves from the end connected to the positive battery

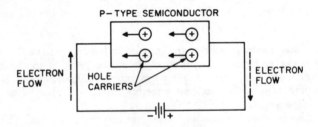

Fig. 3.182(a). Illustrating the direction of hole current flow in P-type semiconductor.

terminal to the end connected to the negative battery terminal. In N–type semiconductors, the majority current carriers are electrons. Electron current within the semiconductor moves from the end connected to the negative battery terminal to the end connected to the positive battery terminal. This is shown in Fig. 3.182(b)

(b) In both the P- and N-types, the internal resistance may be considered to be low in the direction of the majority current carriers and high in the opposite direction.

D.   The actual resistance of any semiconductor is primarily dependent upon the number of current carriers (holes or electrons) available within the material. The number of available carriers, in turn, depends upon the amount of impurities which have been added to the pure crystalline material (germanium or silicon). "Donor" materials, such as arsenic, phosphorus and antimony provide *excess electron carriers* for the crystal and classify the crystal as an "N" type. On the other hand, "acceptor" materials such as aluminum, gallium and indium cause "holes" to appear in the crystal and classify the crystal as a "P" type. Generally,

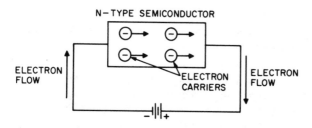

Fig. 3.182(b).   Illustrating the direction of electron current flow in N-type semiconductor.

a semiconductor which contains a higher degree of impurities than another semiconductor, will display a lower resistance in the direction of major carrier current flow. It is assumed that the same voltage is applied to the semiconductor in both cases.

Q. 3.183.   What is the difference between forward and reverse biasing of transistors?

A.   (a) When a transistor junction is *forward* biased, a continuous current flows through the junction due to the movement of the majority carriers through the P- and N-type material. (Holes in P-type and electrons in N–type constitute the majority carriers.) Fig. 3.183(a) illustrates forward biasing of the emitter-base junction and reverse biasing of the collector-base junction.

(b) Reverse biasing of a transistor junction in effect prevents current from flowing in that junction. In practice a small current (in microamperes) will flow in the junction due to the movement of minority carriers. Minority carriers consist of a relatively small number of excess holes found in N–type crystals and a relatively small number of excess electrons in P–type crystals. It should be noted that the conditions of forward and reverse biasing are normal operating conditions as shown in Fig. 3.183(a). This shows a PNP transistor. For an NPN transistor, both battery polarities would be reversed.

D.   Forward and reverse biasing terminology may also be applied to the base-to-emitter bias of a transistor. In this case, forward biasing of a transistor means that the bias polarity from base-to-emitter is such as to permit relatively large current flow from the emitter to the collector.

Note: For a PNP–type the base is made negative with respect to the emitter. Opposite polarity bias is used for an NPN–type.

In this same general case, reverse bias means that the base-to-emitter bias is such as to prevent emitter-to-collector current flow (except for leakage current).

Note: For a PNP–type the base is now made positive with respect to the emitter. Opposite polarity bias is used for an NPN–type.

The junction transistor is made with wafer-type construction, the complete transistor consisting of three wafers. The wafers may be arranged in positive-negative-positive sequence in the P–N–P type, or in negative-positive-negative sequence in the N–P–N type. The middle layer, or wafer of the junction transistor is called the base. On either side of the base are found the very much smaller emitter and collector wafers. The emitter corresponds to the cathode of a vacuum tube, the base to the control grid, and the collector, to the plate.

An enlarged cross-sectional view of a *P–N–P* junction transistor with grounded base circuit is shown in Figure 3.183(a). This view illustrates the internal operation of the unit. The *P-N-P* transistor utilizes "holes" (which may for simplicity be considered as positive charges) for conduction.

In the case of the *P–N–P* junction transistor, any voltage or current variations in the input (emitter) circuit cause corresponding variations in the number of holes in the base. Any variations in the supply of holes from the emitter can vary the number of holes traveling through the

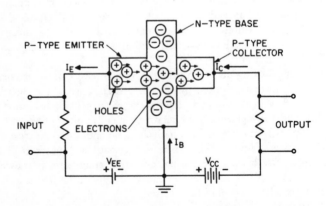

Fig. 3.183(a). Forward and reverse biasing of a junction transistor (PNP). Arrows indicate electron flow.

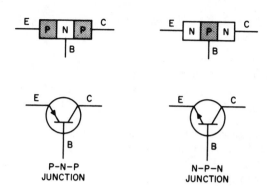

*Fig. 3.183(b). The physical and symbolic representations
of PNP and NPN junction transistors.*

base and to the collector element. It is found that any change in emitter current produces a substantially equal change in collector current; however, the emitter circuit has *low* impedance, while the collector circuit has *high* impedance. If the currents in the two circuits are substantially equal, it follows that the voltage (or power) variations in the collector circuit will be greater than the variations in the emitter circuit. It is by virtue of this effect that amplification is obtained in the *P-N-P* junction transistor.

Important characteristics of the junction transistor are: high power gain, low input power requirements and a low noise factor.

For the convenience of the reader, Fig. 3.183(b) shows the generalized physical structure and the corresponding schematic diagram for the junction *P–N–P* and the *N–P–N* transistors.

Q. 3.184. Show connections of external batteries, resistance load and signal source as would appear in a properly (fixed) biased, common-emitter transistor amplifier.

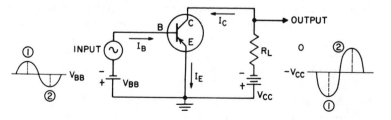

*Fig. 3.184(a). Schematic diagram of a PNP common-emitter
transistor amplifier using fixed bias batteries. Arrows indicate
electron flow.*

A. See Fig. 3.184(a). For an NPN transistor, the polarity of both batteries would be reversed.

D. In the simplified schematic shown (Fig. 3.184(a)), the signal input is applied between the base and emitter and the output is taken across R_L, which is connected between the collector-to-emitter circuit. As explained in Q. 3.183, the base-to-emitter junction is forward biased and the base-to-collector junction is reverse biased. The common-emitter transistor amplifier is similar in circuit arrangement to the conventional grounded cathode triode amplifier (see Q. 3.50(a)); an equivalent-tube circuit is shown in Fig. 3.184(b). Note in both the tube and transistor circuits, that a polarity reversal takes place between the input and output circuits. This polarity reversal would also occur for a common emitter NPN amplifier. (For a common base, or common collector amplifier, no polarity reversal occurs. This situation is similar to the grounded grid and cathode follower tube amplifiers.)

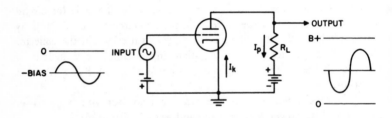

Fig. 3.184(b). Grounded cathode, triode-amplifier circuit. The common emitter amplifier (Fig. 3.184(a)) is similar.

The electron flow through a PNP common-emitter amplifier is shown by the arrows in Fig. 3.184(a). Consider the input signal going in the positive direction (point 1). This signal *opposes* the forward bias of the battery, thereby *decreasing* the total current (I_E) flowing through the emitter. The base and collector currents are now *decreased* by corresponding amounts. The decreased current in R_L will now permit the collector to become more negative (toward the negative battery potential). This effect is indicated at the output waveform by a corresponding point 1. (Note: the polarity is opposite that of the input.) Assume the input waveform to be going in the negative direction (point 2). The signal now *aids* the forward bias, *increasing* the emitter current. Corresponding increases take place in the base and collector currents. An increased current through R_L causes the collector to become less negative (more positive) which is again opposite in polarity to the input signal.

Q. 3.185. The following are excerpts from a transistor handbook describing the characteristics of a PNP-alloy-type transistor as used in a common-emitter circuit configuration. Explain the significance of each item.

Maximum and Minimum Ratings:
(a) Collector-to-base voltage (emitter open)   — 40 max. volts
(b) Collector-to-emitter voltage
      (Base-to-emitter volts = 0.5) .... — 40 max. volts
(c) Emitter-to-base voltage .... — 0.5 max. volts
(d) Collector current .... 10 max. ma
Transistor Dissipation:
(e) At ambient temperature of 25° C
      For operation in free air .... 120 max. mw
(f) At case temperature of 25° C
      For operation with heat sink .... 140 max. mw
(g) Ambient-temperature range:
      Operating and storage .... — 65 to + 100°C

A. (a) Collector-to-Base Voltage: The maximum voltage which can be applied between these elements without danger of a breakdown of the collector-to-base junction.

(b) Collector-to-Emitter Voltage: The maximum safe voltage which can be applied between collector and emitter (with a reverse bias of 0.5 volt between base and emitter), without breakdown occurring from collector-to-emitter.

(c) Emitter-to-Base Voltage: The maximum safe forward-bias voltage, to limit emitter-to-collector current and base-to-emitter current.

(d) Collector Current: The maximum permissible collector current at which the transistor may be operated without adverse effects.

(e) Transistor Dissipation in Free Air: The maximum safe thermal rating at which the transistor may be operated without a heat sink.

(f) Transistor Dissipation with Heat Sink: The maximum safe thermal rating at which the transistor may be operated with a heat sink.

(g) Ambient-Temperature Range: The design limits for ambient temperature operation or storage of the transistor.

Q. 3.186. Draw a circuit diagram of a method of obtaining self-bias, with one battery, without current feedback, in a common-emitter amplifier. Explain the voltage drops in the resistors.

A. For the circuit diagram, see Figure 3.186. The base-to-emitter bias (negative) is obtained by a voltage-divider scheme. Because of the dc base-to-emitter bias, emitter-to-collector current will flow through R3. Additional current flows through R3 and takes the path through

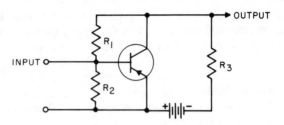

Fig. 3.186. Simplified schematic diagram of a PNP common-emitter amplifier using one battery and self bias.

R1 and the parallel combination of R2 and the base-to-emitter resistance. (Since the transistor is forward biased, current flows through the base-to-emitter junction, resulting in a low value of base-to-emitter resistance.) Because of this voltage divider action, the correct amount of base-to-emitter current is permitted to flow, thus establishing the desired forward bias. (Remember that a transistor is basically a current operated device and that we are interested in the forward bias *current,* rather than the forward bias voltage. However, these are obviously related and this current can also be established by the voltage appearing across the parallel combination of R2 and the base-to-emitter resistance.) The forward bias voltage, from base-to-emitter, has the required negative potential for a PNP transistor.

D. See Q. 3.184, Q. 3.187 and Q. 3.190(c).

Q. 3.187. Draw a circuit diagram of a common-emitter amplifier with emitter bias. Explain its operation.

A. For the circuit diagram, see Figure 3.187(a). The input signal is applied across resistor R2 to the base-emitter circuit. Bias for the base-

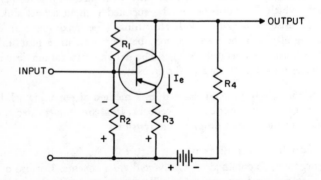

Fig. 3.187(a). Schematic diagram of a PNP common-emitter amplifier using emitter bias.

emitter circuit is the difference of two bias voltages. One is the voltage divider scheme described in Q. 3.186 above and the other is the drop across R3 (similar to a cathode resistor for a vacuum tube). R3 is introduced into the circuit for the purpose of bias stabilization. Reliable operation of a transistor over a wide range of temperatures, requires that the bias voltage and current remain stable. Variations of emitter-to-base junction resistance with temperature tend to cause bias changes unless external compensating circuits are used (such as R3).

Figure 3.187(b) shows the same common emitter amplifier as in Figure 3.187(a), but modified to provide fixed emitter bias originating from an external source (V_{EE}). In Fig. 3.187(a), the drop across R3 is in opposition to the forward bias. However, in Fig. 3.187(b) an external source (V_{EE}) provides a forward bias ($+$) at the emitter. (This bias adds to the forward bias ($-$) applied to the base.) The bias at the

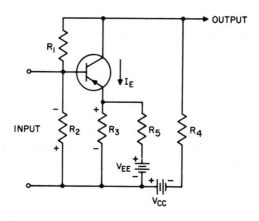

Fig. 3.187(b). The circuit of Fig. 3.187(a) modified to provide a fixed value of emitter bias from an external source (V_{EE}).

emitter is determined by the voltage divider action of R3 and R5 in conjunction with V_{EE}. Actually, the emitter current (I_E) flows through R5 and tends to reduce the forward bias for the emitter. However, R3 and R5 can be easily adjusted to overcome this effect, based on the quiescent value of I_E. In addition, bias stabilization is provided by the fixed-bias supply and by the "swamping" resistor, as explained in the discussion. The use of an emitter resistor also tends to stabilize the quiescent collector current. Any tendency to increase collector (and emitter) current, causes a voltage drop in the emitter circuit which *reduces* the forward bias and tends to oppose such an increase. Conversely, a tendency to decrease collector current, reduces the drop in the emitter circuit and increases the forward bias. This tends to oppose the decrease of collector current. This emitter resistor function is applicable to the circuits of Fig. 3.187(a) and Fig. 3.187(b).

D. The emitter-base junction resistance has a negative temperature coefficient of resistance, which causes a bias variation with temperature changes. One method of reducing the effect of this type of bias variation is to place a large value of resistor in series with the emitter lead. This resistor is called a *swamping* resistor. It causes the variation of the emitter-base junction resistance to be a small percentage of the total resistance in the emitter circuit. This technique stabilizes the bias and provides collector current stability over a wide range of temperatures (for example, $-65°C$ to $+125°C$). For best results in this technique, the base-circuit resistance should be as near zero as possible. One method of accomplishing this is to use a low-resistance transformer input to the base.

Q. 3.188. Explain the usual relationship between collector-to-base voltage and the alpha-cutoff frequency of a common emitter transistor amplifier.

A. The alpha-cutoff frequency is only indirectly related to the collector-to-base voltage. [Refer to Q. 3.192(G) for an explanation of alpha-cutoff frequency.] This frequency is a function of the physical thickness of the base and increases as the base becomes thinner. As the base becomes thinner, the allowable base-to-collector voltage decreases. Thus it may be said that the alpha-cutoff frequency ordinarily increases as the permissible collector-to-base voltage decreases.

D. The alpha-cutoff frequency is the high frequency at which the current gain of the transistor decreases by 3 db compared to its mid-frequency (flat) gain. The alpha-cutoff frequency is inversely proportional to the square of the base width and directly proportional to the minority carrier mobility. On this basis, NPN transistors are superior to PNP–types, because electrons have greater mobility than holes. To achieve the lowest base transit time, the base should be as thin as possible. However, this is limited by the permissible base-to-collector voltage. In transistor design, a tradeoff must be made between permissible base-to-collector voltage and the alpha-cutoff frequency.

Q. 3.189. Why is stabilization of a transistor amplifier usually necessary? How would a thermistor be used in this respect?

A. (a) Stabilization is usually necessary because transistor parameters, such as reverse-bias collector current and emitter-base junction resistance (see also Q. 3.187 above), vary with temperature. These cause changes in the transistor operating characteristics with respect to temperature. Specifically, emitter current increases with an increase of temperature.

(b) A thermistor is used as part of a voltage divider in the emitter (or base) circuit. The thermistor causes the transistor bias to change with temperature, such that changes in collector current due to temperature variations, are cancelled by opposing changes in transistor bias.

D.   The operation of the thermistor stabilization circuit is explained in detail with the aid of Fig. 3.189. Forward bias for the base is obtained by means of a voltage divider consisting of resistors R1 and R3. This voltage remains constant regardless of temperature variations. A reverse bias is applied to the emitter through another voltage divider consisting of RT1 and R2. The thermistor used for this purpose has a negative-temperature characteristic. That is, its resistance decreases with an increase of temperature and increases with a decrease of temperature.

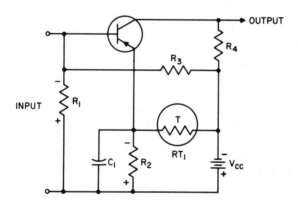

Fig. 3.189. Schematic diagram of a PNP common-emitter amplifier using thermistor control of the emitter bias.

Ordinarily (without stabilization), the collector current would tend to increase with an increase of temperature. This increase can be counteracted by increasing the reverse bias applied to the emitter through the voltage divider consisting of the thermistor and the emitter resistor. An increased temperature causes a decrease in resistance of the thermistor. This in turn raises the negative reverse bias applied to the emitter and decreases the net emitter forward bias. Consequently, the tendency of the collector current to increase is counteracted.

Q. 3.190.   **Draw simple schematic diagrams of the following transistor circuits and explain their principles of operation. Use only one voltage source; state typical component values for low power—10 mc operation:**

(a) **Colpitts-type oscillator**

(b) **Class-B push-pull amplifier**

(c) **Common emitter amplifier**

(d) **A PNP transistor directly coupled to an NPN type.**

A. (a) For the schematic of the Colpitts oscillator, see Figure 3.190(a). For basic discussion and vacuum tube schematic, see Question 3.86(d). In the transistorized oscillator shown in the figure, positive feedback is provided by placing the resonant tank circuit (L–C) in parallel with the collector-to-base circuit. The circuit now becomes voltage, rather than current controlled. The feedback is taken from the junction of the two series capacitors, C1 and C2, which are effectively across the tank. R2 and C3 provide forward base bias and a degree of oscillator-amplitude stability.

(b) The principle of a Class-B push-pull transistor amplifier is basically the same as for this type of amplifier using vacuum tubes (see Q. 3.50(c) for a discussion of its principles). For a schematic of the transistor push-pull, Class-B amplifier, see Figure 3.190(b). Resistors R1 and R2 are proportioned so that both transistors are operated at the collector-current-cutoff point. Both transistors will amplify only the negative portions of the applied base voltages. In this case, Q1 amplifies only the second half (2) of the sine wave and remains at cutoff during the first half (1). Q2 amplifies the first half (3) of the sine wave and is cut off during the second half (4). Note that the top and bottom of the output tank circuit receive voltage pulses of the same polarity (negative). However these occur a half cycle apart and so are correctly phased. The resulting tank circuit output is a complete sine wave, which is coupled to the succeeding circuit by means of the output portion of T2. Resonating the two transformers increases

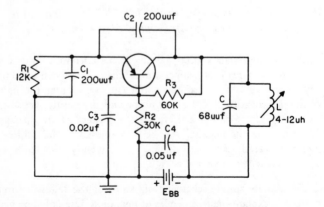

Fig. 3.190(a). Schematic diagram of a Colpitts oscillator for 10-mc operation.

circuit efficiency and provides improved waveform (less distortion and harmonics) in the output.

The output transformer is designed to match the low-impedance input to the following transistor, from the output impedance of the driving transistor. In general, the transistors used have a low value of input impedance. This prevents self-oscillation, due to feedback, from each collector to its associated base. (This is similar to plate-to-grid feedback in a vacuum-tube amplifier as explained in Q. 3.125 and Q. 3.128.) However, in the case of certain low-power transistors having higher values of input

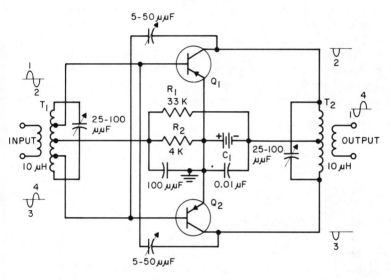

Fig 3.190(b). Schematic diagram of a Class-B push-pull amplifier for use at 10-mc.

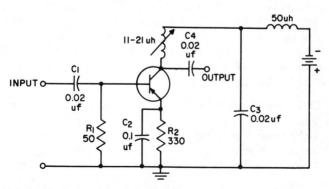

Fig. 3.190(c). Common-emitter amplifier with components for 10-mc operation.

impedance, it may be necessary to employ "push-pull" neutralization, as is explained in Q. 3.125, part (3) of the discussion, and is illustrated for vacuum tubes in Figure 3.125(e). In the circuit of Figure 3.190(b) the same scheme is used, with each neutralizing capacitor connected from the collector of one transistor to the base of the other one.

(c) For the schematic of a common emitter amplifier, see Figure 3.190(c). For principles of operation, see Q. 3.186 and 3.187 above.

(d) For a schematic of a PNP-transistor directly coupled to an NPN–type, see Figure 3.190(d). This scheme operates by virtue of the fact that the polarity of an input signal necessary to increase the conduction of the PNP–transistor is opposite to that required to increase the conduction of the NPN transistor. Since a signal polarity reversal occurs in Q1 from base to collector, this condition is satisfied. The proper bias for Q1 is established by the action of the voltage divider consisting of R1 and R2. The bias for Q2 is established by the collector current of Q1 flowing through the emitter to base circuit of Q2. The polarity of the base of Q2 is positive with respect to its emitter, thus providing forward

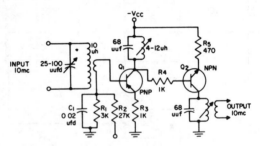

Fig. 3.190(d). A PNP transistor directly coupled to an NPN-type for 10-mc operation.

base-to-emitter bias. Note that the collector of Q2 is grounded for d–c and the collector-to-base potential is actually applied in reverse polarity to the emitter of Q2. This is similar to a vacuum tube amplifier wherein the plate voltage is actually applied as a negative potential to the cathode.

Transistor bias stabilization is provided by resistor R3 for Q1 and by resistor R5 for Q2.

Q. 3.191. **Discuss etched-wiring printed circuits with respect to the following:**

(a) **Determination of wiring breaks.**

(b) **Excessive heating.**

(c) **Removal and installation of components.**

A. (a) Wiring breaks are determined by point-to-point continuity checking with an ohmmeter. (If voltage exists in the circuit involved, voltage tracing could be used with the aid of an ohmmeter. Signal tracing with an oscilloscope is sometimes· desirable.) Since there may be many common points permanently connected to the wire in question, a physical layout of the printed circuit board would be desirable to assist in locating the break. In many cases, the break can be repaired by soldering or by connecting an external wire across it.

(b) Etched wiring printed circuit boards are constructed of various materials such as epoxy and mylar. The etched wiring is attached to the board with a cement or other bonding agent. Such boards are subject to damage caused by excessive heat. Such heat can cause distortion of the board, or stresses which may result in cracks, wire breaks, or lifting of the etched wire from the boards.

(c) The components may be mounted on the boards by placing the component leads directly on a printed circuit finger and welding or soldering to the finger. Alternatively, the lead may be placed through a printed-circuit hole or eyelet. Generally, components are mounted only on one side of the board with their leads inserted into holes or eyelets. The other side of the board may then be dip soldered, or wave soldered, accomplishing all soldering in one operation. The leads of a defective component are usually removed with a small soldering iron. If the leads are welded, they are cut and the surface is cleaned in preparation for a new weld or for a solder repair. In removing transistors having three (or four leads) special attachments are available to a soldering iron so that all leads can be unsoldered simultaneously and the transistor pulled out of the board. Otherwise, one lead at a time can be unsoldered and the transistor gradually *rocked* out of the board.

Q. 3.192. What is a junction tetrode transistor? How does it differ from other transistors in base resistance and operating frequency?

A. (a) A tetrode transistor is one which is constructed in the same manner as a three-terminal PNP or NPN transistor except for the addition of an extra terminal to the base region, as shown in Fig. 3.192.

The normal emitter, base and collector terminals are labelled (1), (2) and (3). The additional terminal to the base is labelled (4) and is supplied with a small negative voltage (0.4V). The normal base terminal (2) is grounded as shown.

(b) The base resistance is substantially lower than in a three-terminal transistor and the operating frequency is increased considerably.

D. As shown in the figure, the voltage in all portions of the emitter and collector is constant. However, because the base is supplied with 0.4 volts at the top and is grounded at the bottom, a voltage gradient appears from top to bottom of 0.4 to 0 volts. As discussed in Q. 3.183, forward biasing of an NPN transistor requires that the base be positive with respect to the emitter. Note in Figure 3.192 that this condition oc-

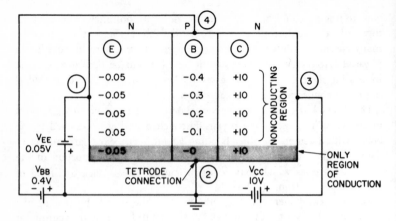

Fig. 3.192. Diagram of a tetrode (NPN) transistor, illustrating the voltage gradient of the base.

curs only at the very bottom portion and conduction takes place only within this very restricted region of the transistor. This applies to emitter-to-base current as well as to emitter-to-collector current. Because of the small conduction areas involved, the base resistance is substantially reduced. In addition, the input and output transistor capacitances are reduced. Since both of the above factors largely determine a transistor's high frequency response, the response is substantially increased.

Note to Students: The following questions on transistors do not appear in the current FCC Study Guide, but have been added here to improve the students' knowledge of transistor principles. It is felt that this added information will assist the student in answering certain questions on transistors which may appear on FCC examinations.

Q. 3.192(A). What is the meaning of the term "alpha" as applied to the performance of a transistor?

A. The term "alpha" (a) is applied only to common-base amplifiers, and is a measure of the "current gain" of the circuit. The current gain is always less than one in a common-base circuit and may be commonly 0.91 to 0.99.

D. The term alpha (common-base only) is expressed by the simple equation

$$a = \frac{\Delta I_t}{\Delta I_e}$$

This equation shows that alpha may be defined as the ratio of a change of collector current to the change of emitter current which produced the collector current change.

As an example, assume that in a common-base circuit, a change of collector current of 1 ma. is caused by a change of emitter current of 1.05 ma. The alpha of this transistor is

$$a = \frac{1}{1.05} = 0.95$$

Note that a common-base circuit may be compared to a grounded-grid vacuum tube circuit, which has somewhat comparable operating characteristics.

Q. 3.192(B). How is the term "alpha," as applied to transistors, expressed more specifically in terms of both dc and small-signal (ac) current ratios?

A. Alpha is a general term, referring to both dc and small signal (ac) current ratios. To distinguish between these two types of ratios, the dc ratio is commonly designated as "H_{FB}" and the small signal (ac) ratio, as "h_{fb}."

D. In electronic terminology it is common to represent dc values by capital letters and ac values by small letters. In the above designations, "H" (or "h") represents current amplification; "F" (or "f") stands for forward current; and "B" (or "b") indicates a common base configuration.

Q. 3.192(C). What is the meaning of the term "beta" as applied to the performance of a transistor?

A. The term "beta" (β) is applied only to common-emitter amplifiers and is a measure of the "current gain" of this circuit. The current gain is always greater than one in a common-emitter circuit and some common values lie between 25 and 100.

D. The term beta (common emitter only) is expressed by the simple equation

$$\beta = \frac{\Delta I_c}{\Delta I_b}$$

This equation shows that beta may be defined as the ratio of the change of collector current to the change of base current which produced the change of collector current.

As an example, assume that in a common-emitter circuit, a change of collector current of 50 microamperes is caused by a change of base current of one microampere. The beta of this transistor is

$$\beta = \frac{50}{1} = 50$$

Note that a common emitter circuit may be compared to a conventional grounded-cathode vacuum tube circuit and that in this case, beta may be compared to the amplification factor of the tube, which relates the change in plate voltage caused by a lesser change in grid voltage.

Q. 3.192(D).   How is the term "beta," as applied to transistors, expressed more specifically in terms of both dc and small signal (ac) current ratios?

A.   Beta is a general term, referring to both dc and small signal (ac) current ratios. To distinguish between these two types of ratios, the dc ratio is commonly designated as "H_{FE}" and the small signal (ac) ratio as "h_{fe}."

D.   In the above designations, "H" (or "h") represents current amplification; "F" (or "f") stands for forward current; and "E" (or "e") indicates a common emitter configuration. [See also Q. 3.192 (B).]

Q. 3.192(E).   A certain transistor has a small signal (ac) emitter-current gain of 0.99. What is the small signal base-current gain?

A.   The small-signal, base-current gain, h_{fe}, is 99.

D.   The base-current gain is beta, which for the ac case is designated h_{fe} [see Q. 3.192(D)]. The emitter-current gain is alpha, which for the ac case is designated h_{fb} [see Q. 3.192(B)]. The question requires that we relate beta in terms of alpha (small signal, or ac cases). Beta is related to alpha by the simple equation

$$\text{Beta} = \frac{\text{alpha}}{1 - \text{alpha}}$$

or for the ac case

$$h_{fe} = \frac{h_{fb}}{1 - h_{fb}} = \frac{.99}{1 - .99} = 99$$

Q. 3.192(F).   A certain transistor has a small signal (ac) base-current gain of 49. What is the small signal emitter-current gain?

A.   The small signal, emitter-current gain, h_{fb}, is 0.98.

D.   (See also the preceding discussion.) The question requires that we relate alpha (emitter-current gain) in terms of beta (base-current gain) for small signal (ac) cases. Alpha is related to beta by the simple equation

$$\text{Alpha} = \frac{\text{beta}}{1 + \text{beta}}$$

or for the ac case

$$h_{fb} = \frac{h_{fe}}{1 + h_{fe}} = \frac{49}{1 + 49} = 0.98$$

Q. 3.192(G). What is meant by the alpha cut-off frequency of a transistor?

A. The alpha cut-off frequency is the high frequency at which a transistor connected in the common-base configuration drops in gain to 0.707 (−3db) of its value at 1,000 cycles.

D. Note that the alpha cut-off frequency refers only to the common-base configuration (h_{fb}) emitter-current gain. Also note that the alpha cut-off frequency of any given transistor is always greater than the beta cut-off frequency (see next question) of the same transistor. This situation is somewhat comparable to the characteristics of the grounded-grid amplifier (compared to common-base), which is useful to frequencies appreciably higher than the same tube used as a grounded-cathode amplifier (compared to the common emitter). See also Q. 3.188.

Q. 3.192(H). What is meant by the beta cut-off frequency of a transistor?

A. The beta cut-off frequency is the high frequency at which a transistor connected in the common-emitter configuration drops in gain to 0.707 (−3db) of its value at 1,000 cycles.

D. In the cases of the beta cut-off frequency and the alpha cut-off frequency (discussed in the preceding question), the values refer only to the transistor proper and do not take into account the external circuit. As in the case of most amplifiers, the external circuit usually has the effect of further reducing the value of useful high-frequency response.

Q. 3.192(I). With reference to transistors, what is meant by the "gain-bandwidth" product?

A. The gain-bandwidth product of a transistor is a number whose magnitude is equal to the frequency (in cycles) at which the common-emitter current gain (beta) is equal to unity. Thus, if the common-emitter gain becomes equal to one at 5 megacycles, the gain-bandwidth product is 5,000,000 cycles or 5 mc.

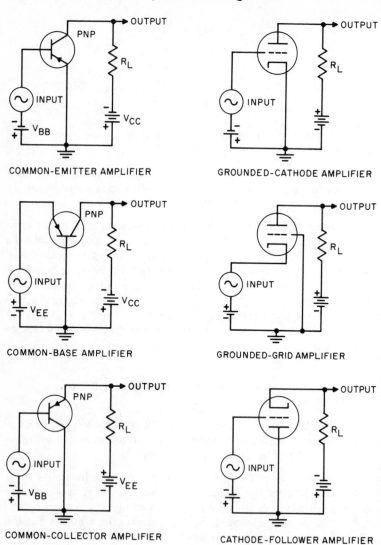

Fig. 3.192(J). The three transistor-amplifier configurations and
their comparable vacuum-tube amplifier configurations.

D. The gain-bandwidth product is a commonly used measure of
the approximate useful frequency range of any given transistor. It is
also called a "figure of merit" for transistors.

Q. 3.192(J). Draw simple schematic diagrams comparing the common-emitter, common-base, and common-collector transistor amplifier configurations with their similar vacuum-tube configurations.

A. The diagrams are shown in Fig. 3.192(J). Note that the common-emitter amplifier is similar to the grounded-cathode amplifier; the common-base amplifier is similar to the grounded-grid amplifier; and the common-collector amplifier is similar to the cathode-follower amplifier.

D. For a comparison of the operating characteristics of the three transistor amplifier configurations, see the next question.

Q. 3.192(K). Compare the operating characteristics of the common-emitter, common-base and common-collector transistor amplifier configurations, with respect to the following: power gain; voltage gain; current gain; input resistance; output resistance; and signal inversion.

A. The various characteristics are tabulated in Fig. 3.192(K).

Characteristic	Common Emitter	Common Base	Common Collector
Power Gain	25–40 db	20–30 db	10–20 db
Voltage Gain	250–1000	500–1750	Less than 1
Current Gain	25–55	Less than 1	25–55
Input Resistance	500–1500 ohms	30–150 ohms	25k–500k ohms
Output Resistance	30k–50k ohms	300k–1M ohm	50–1000 ohms
Signal Inversion	Yes	No	No

Fig. 3.192(K). Table showing typical values of transistor characteristics for the three amplifier configurations. Values are typical for selected medium-power transistors.

D. Examining the table of Fig. 3.192(K) points up several important facts. The common-emitter configuration has intermediate values of input and output resistance, the highest level of power gain, and a fairly high value of voltage gain. It is also the only configuration which produces a voltage inversion of the output signal.

The common-base configuration has the lowest value of input resistance, but the highest value of output resistance. It has an intermediate value of power gain, but the highest value of voltage gain. It is the only configuration that has a current gain less than one.

The common-collector configuration has the highest value of input resistance, but the lowest value of output resistance. It has the lowest value of power gain and the only configuration with a voltage gain less than one. (See also the preceding question for a comparison of the three transistor amplifier configurations to similar vacuum-tube amplifier configurations.)

Q. 3.192(L). In a common-emitter transistor amplifier, it is found that a change in the base voltage of 0.01 volts results in a change in collecting voltage of 4.0 volts. What is the voltage gain of this amplifier?

A. The voltage gain (A_v) is 400.

D. The voltage gain of a common-emitter amplifier is equal to the ratio of the change of collector voltage which is caused by a change of base voltage. The simple equation for voltage gain is

$$A_v = \frac{\Delta V_c}{\Delta V_b} = \frac{4}{.01} = 400$$

Q. 3.192(M). Figure 3.192(M)(1) shows a low-to-medium power silicon transistor, with a beta of 110, connected in a common-emitter circuit and employing "fixed" bias. It is desired to operate this circuit in class A amplification. Determine the following: (1) The required value of R_B; (2) The collector current at the "Q," or quiescent condition (dc); (3) The collector voltage at the "Q" condition.

A. (1) The required value of R_B is 200,000 ohms.
    (2) The collector current (I_C) is 4.4 ma.
    (3) The collector voltage (E_C) is 3.6 volts.

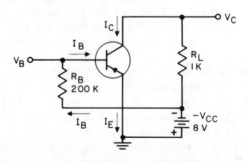

Fig. 3.192(M)(1).   Common-emitter amplifier connected for "fixed" bias.

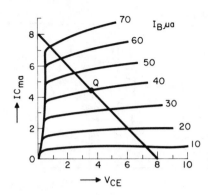

Fig. 3.192(M)(2). Load line representing d-c operating conditions of the schematic in (1).

D. *Note:* In this discussion, refer also to the simplified transistor characteristic curves, showing the collector-to-emitter voltage vs. the collector current for various values of base current, given in Fig. 3.192 (M) (2). These curves and the load line are used in the calculation of the required values.

In order to determine class A operation for this transistor, it is necessary to first draw the dc load line. This load line is drawn in a manner similar to that for a vacuum tube as shown in Fig. 3.57. The transistor load line is drawn from the point of maximum collector current to the point representing the collector supply voltage. The maximum collector current occurs when the transistor is in saturation and here the collector is assumed to be shorted to the emitter. This current is

$$I_{C \text{ max.}} = \frac{V_{CC}}{R_L} = \frac{8}{1000} = 8 \text{ ma}$$

The collector supply voltage, V_{CC}, is given as 8 volts.

Once the load line is drawn, the Q point is chosen such that the base current can be varied above and below this value by an approximately equal amount. This will insure that the corresponding variations in collector current will be practically distortionless. In Fig. 3. 192(M) (2), this Q point has been chosen at the intersection of the load line and the base current curve representing 40 ua. Having established the required dc base-current bias, the value of R_B is found (to a very close approximation) by

$$R_B = \frac{V_{CC}}{I_B} = \frac{8V}{40\mu a} = 200,000 \text{ ohms}$$

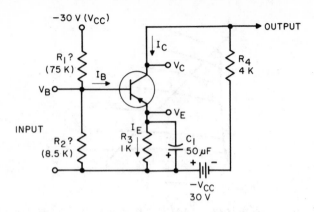

*Fig. 3.192(N).   Common-emitter amplifier using voltage-divider,
base bias and employing a bias-stabilizing emitter resistor.*

(Since dc base-to-emitter diode resistance is a small fraction of R_B, it
may be ignored in this calculation.)

The collector current is easily found now, and is

$$I_C = \text{beta} \times I_B = 110 \times 40 \ \mu a = 4.4 \ \text{ma}$$

The collector voltage is also easily found. It is

$$E_C = V_{CC} - (I_C \times R_L) = 8V - (4.4 \ \text{ma} \times 1000) = 3.6 \ \text{volts}$$

Note that both the collector current and the collector voltage can
be found to a very close approximation from the characteristics curves
and these points on the curves should be checked to verify the calculated values. These values are found on the curves by extending a
line from the Q point, horizontally to the left to obtain the collector
current. The collector voltage is obtained by extending a vertical line
down from the Q point, to obtain the collector voltage.

Q. 3.192(N).   Fig. 3. 192(N)(1) shows a low-to-medium power
germanium transistor with a beta of 90, connected in a common-
emitter circuit, employing voltage-divider type base bias, and an emitter bias-stabilizing resistor, R3. It is desired to operate this circuit in
class A amplification. Determine the following: (1) The magnitude
of V_B required to bias the transistor class A; (2) The values of
the base-bias resistors, R1 and R2 required to provide the base-
bias voltage (V_B) for class A operation; (3) The dc (no-signal)
collector current.

A. (1) The class A, base bias (V_B) is, –3 volts.
    (2) R1 = 75,000 ohms. R2 = 8500 ohms.
    (3) The dc collector current is 3 ma.

D.   While the solution requires several steps, it is not difficult if the steps are taken in logical order, as presented below.

STEP 1: DETERMINE THE CLASS A BASE-BIAS VOLTAGE (V_B)

To determine this, we must first find the limits of the emitter voltage (V_E), at cut-off and saturation.

(a.) At cut-off, with no current in R3, V_E is at ground potential, or is zero.

(b.) At saturation, $V_{E\ max}$ is found by

$$V_{E\ max} = \frac{R3}{R3 + R4} \times (-V_{CC}) = \frac{1000}{1000 + 4000} \times (-30) = -6V$$

Halfway between zero volts and –6 volts is –3 volts (V_E) which is the optimum base bias for class A operation. However, $V_E = V_B$, so $V_B = $ –3 volts.

STEP 2: DETERMINE THE VALUES FOR R1 AND R2

Resistors R1 and R2 may be selected with reasonable accuracy by assuming a value for R2 and calculating R1 on this basis.

For germanium transistors of the general type discussed in this question (beta can be greater or less), a value of R2 such as chosen here (8500 ohms) can be assumed. (Actually any value between 5000 and 10,000 ohms could be chosen.) Having selected R2, R1 is chosen so that the desired bias will appear at the base.

In this problem, having selected a value of 8500 for R2, R1 is chosen at 75,000 ohms to provide the required –3 volts at the base (using practical resistors).

Note: If the transistor in question was a silicon transistor of the same general type, the value of R2 would be about 7 times greater (35,000 to 70,000 ohms). (The base-input resistance of a silicon transistor is about 7 times greater than that of a germanium transistor.)

The answer to part (2) of the question is R1 = 75,000 ohms; R2 = 8500 ohms.

STEP 3: WHAT IS THE DC COLLECTOR CURRENT?

In step 1(b), it was determined that V_B was −3 volts based on a halfway point of −3 volts for the emitter voltage. [While not stated at that time, it can be assumed for germanium transistors (only), that the dc emitter voltage is always equal to the dc base voltage because of the very small (.1 − .2 volts) base-to-emitter drop.]

Thus, there is a 3 volt drop across R3, and the emitter current is

$$E_C = \frac{V_E}{R3} = \frac{3}{1000} = 3 \text{ ma}$$

But, practically, $I_C = E_C = 3$ ma.

Q. 3.192(O).   In Fig. 3.192(N)(1), what is the voltage gain of the circuit?

A.   The voltage gain, $A_v = 460$.

D.   If there is no unbypassed emitter resistance, as in this case, the voltage gain is found by

$$A_v = \frac{R4}{r_e}$$

However, r_e is found by dividing the constant .026 by the dc emitter current, thus

$$r_e = \frac{.026}{3 \text{ ma.}} = 8.7 \text{ ohms}$$

and

$$A_v = \frac{4000}{8.7} = 460$$

Note: If the circuit contains an unbypassed emitter resistance, this must be included in the equation for voltage gain, as

$$A_v = \frac{R4}{r_e + R_E}$$

Q. 3.192(P).   A two-stage common-emitter transistor audio amplifier is RC coupled. The low frequency response (determined by CB only), is to be down 3 db at five cycles (F_1). The total output impedance (r_g) of the driving stage (Q1) is 3370 ohms and the total input impedance (r_i) of the driven stage (Q2) is 2080 ohms. Determine the value of the interstage coupling capacitor, C_B, which will provide the desired low frequency response.

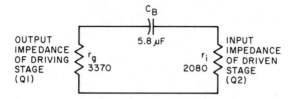

Fig. 3.192(P). Simplified diagram of a two-stage transistor audio amplifier, to facilitate calculation of the value of the interstage coupling capacitor, C_B.

A.   The required value of C_B is 5.8 μF. (A commercial value of 6 μF is available.)

D.   The value of C_B can be easily found from the simple equation

$$C_B = \frac{1}{2\pi\,F_1 \times R_T}$$

[Refer to the simplified diagram of Fig. 3.192 (P).] We know F_1 since this is given at 5 cycles (3 db down), but we must first solve for R_T, as follows:

$$R_T = r_g + r_i = 3370 + 2080$$

$$= 5450 \text{ ohms}$$

$$C_B = \frac{1}{6.28 \times 5 \times 5450} = 0.0000058 \text{ Farads} = 5.8\ \mu\text{F}$$

Note: This problem has been deliberately simplified for the purpose of answering similar questions as they might be asked on FCC examinations. In practice, the values of r_g and r_i would have to be calculated for the particular amplifiers involved. This process is somewhat more complicated than the simplified example given above.

Q. 3.192(Q).   A transistor audio amplifier, of the common-emitter type, employs an emitter resistor and bypass capacitor. It is desired that the emitter circuit response will be −3 db at 50 cycles (F_1). What is the required value of the emitter bypass capacitor if the *effective* value of the emitter resistance, R_{ET}, is 48 ohms?

A.   The required value of the emitter bypass capacitor, C_E, is 66.3 μF. (A 60 μF capacitor would generally be adequate.)

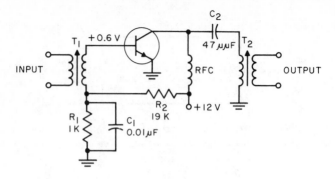

Fig. 3.192(R).   A 30 mc, common emitter amplifier, biased class B. A low-power silicon transistor is used (see text).

D.   The value of C_E can be easily found from the simple equation

$$C_E = \frac{1}{2\pi \, F_1 \times R_{ET}}$$

$$= \frac{1}{6.28 \times 50 \times 48} = 0.0000663 \text{ Farads}$$

$$= 66.3 \, \mu F$$

Note: As in the case of Q. 3.192(P), this problem has been simplified for the purpose of answering similar questions as they might be asked on FCC examinations.

Q. 3.192(R). The schematic diagram given in Fig. 3.192(R) is a 30 mc, low-power RF amplifier, employing a silicon transistor. Calculate the value of R1 and R2 necessary to provide class B bias for this amplifier. Also, discuss the requirement for the value of capacitor C1.

A.   The value of R1 is 1,000 ohms and R2 is 19,000 ohms. (This combination provides a forward bias of 0.6 volt.) Capacitor C1 must provide an ac ground at the bottom of the secondary of T1 and thus it must have a very low value of reactance at 30 mc.

D.   Unlike vacuum tubes, most similar transistors have an almost identical value of junction-barrier voltage. For low-power silicon transistors, the barrier voltage for the base-to-emitter junction is about 0.6 volt. This voltage, which is due to the physics of the transistor, is a "back voltage," which tends to oppose the flow of base-to-emitter current.

Base-to-emitter current cannot begin to flow until this barrier voltage is overcome (this is true also of collector current). Thus, to bias a transistor at class B, it is necessary to supply a forward-bias voltage which will just overcome the barrier voltage of 0.6 volt. (This is equivalent to biasing a vacuum tube at cut-off bias.)

The voltage divider consisting of R1 and R2 is chosen so that it will provide a forward bias of 0.6 volts to the base. Obviously, there are an infinite number of combinations which will provide this voltage. Since the signal is grounded (for ac) by the low reactance of C1 (0.5 ohm), the value of R1 is not critical. However, the overall divider should not draw appreciable current from the power supply and for this case a bleeder current of 0.6 ma was chosen. R1 and R2 values were then based upon this bleeder current. [See also Q. 3.190(b). In the figure, if V_{CC} was 6 volts, the forward bias would be 0.66 volt.]

In some cases of class B operation, it is desirable to provide a small additional forward bias, since this reduces the required amount of drive.

Germanium transistors have a much lower base-to-emitter barrier voltage. For low power germanium transistors, the barrier voltage is about 0.1 volts. In this case class B operation can be easily achieved by operating the transistor with zero forward bias.

High power silicon transistors have a barrier voltage in the order of 0.5 volt, while high power germanium transistors have a barrier voltage in the order of 0.2 volt.

Q. 3.192(S). What is the approximate class C bias for medium power, silicon, and germanium transistors?

A. The approximate class C bias is 0 volts between the base and emitter.

D. The usual class C bias is set so that approximately 120 degrees of collector current will flow per cycle. For typical, medium power silicon and germanium transistors, this condition occurs (approximately) when the dc bias between the base and emitter is 0 volts.

A typical medium power silicon transistor [see Fig. 3.192(S)] has a base-to-emitter barrier voltage [see D. for Q. 3.192(R)] of 0.6 volt. This type of transistor reaches collector-current saturation with a base-emitter voltage of 1.5 volts. With zero bias, the signal swings around this value and varies from zero to 1.5 volts, to zero, to minus 1.5 volts. However, from zero to 0.6 volts (forward-bias direction), there will be no collector current, which will flow only when the for-

	SILICON TRANSISTORS		GERMANIUM TRANSISTORS		APPROX. B-E, CLASS C BIAS VOLTAGE	
	Base-Emitter, Barrier V.	Base-Emitter, Ic saturation V.	Base-Emitter, Barrier V.	Base-Emitter, Ic saturation V.	Silicon	Germanium
Low Power	0.6	0.8	0.1	0.25	0.5 (forward)	0
Medium Power	0.6	1.5	0.2	0.55	0	0
High Power	0.5	2.0	0.2	2.0	0.25 (reverse)	0.7 (reverse)

Fig. 3.192(S). Typical characteristics for low, medium, and high-power silicon and germanium transistors.

ward bias voltage is between 0.6 and 1.5 volts (produced by higher amplitudes of the input signal). Thus class C operation is achieved.

The same general principle applies to the medium power germanium transistor, except that the barrier is 0.2 volt and the collector current saturation occurs at 0.55 volt.

Fig. 3.192(S) gives the values of barrier voltage, collector saturation current, and approximate class C bias voltages for low, medium, and high-power silicon and germanium transistors. This table is based upon typical transistors used in the three power ranges.

Note that while zero bias, transistor class C amplifiers are frequently used, this is not the only method of obtaining class C bias. One disadvantage of this scheme is that it is not self-adjusting and thus cannot readily accommodate varying levels of input signal. The use of grid-leak bias (see Q. 4.46) in vacuum tubes operated as class C amplifiers permits the bias to vary with the amplitude of the input signal. This method minimizes changes of output power which might occur due to variations of input power. Similar schemes are also used with transistor class C amplifiers, as described in Q. 3.192(T).

Q. 3.192(T). It is desired to operate a high power germanium transistor in a 30 mc. class C amplifier, using a base self-bias RC network. The peak base current (at collector saturation) is 20 ma. Determine the required values of the resistor and capacitor for the bias network.

A.   The resistor, $R_B = 35$ ohms.
     The capacitor, $C_B = .01 \ \mu F$ (not critical).

D.   Refer to the simplified schematic diagram of Fig. 3.192(T). Base current flows only during the positive portions of the RF input signal. It flows through the bias network in the direction shown, producing a reverse bias across the network. The value of the resistor is

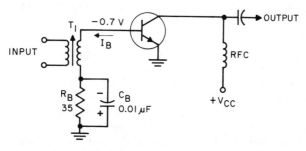

Fig. 3.192(T). Simplified schematic diagram of a germanium transistor, 30 mc high-power class C amplifier, with base-self bias (see text).

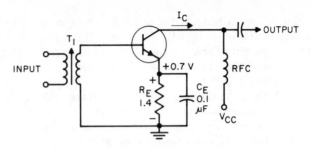

Fig. 3.192(U). Simplified schematic diagram of a germanium transistor, 30 mc high-power class C amplifier, with emitter-self bias (see text).

$$R_B = \frac{V_B}{I_{B\ max}} = \frac{.7}{.020} = 35 \text{ ohms}$$

The value of the capacitor is not critical, but it must present a very low reactance at the operating frequency. A .01 μF capacitor is chosen, with a reactance of 0.5 ohms.

Q. 3.192(U). Using the same transistor and operating conditions as in Q. 3.192(T), but employing an emitter-bias network, determine the required values of the resistor and capacitor for the bias network. The peak collector current is 500 ma.

A. The resistor, $R_E = 1.4$ ohms.
The capacitor, $C_E = 0.1$ μF (not critical).

D. Collector current as well as base current flows only during the positive portions of the input RF signal. The collector current flows through the emitter-bias network in the direction shown in Fig. 3.192 (T), producing a reverse bias across the network. The value of the resistor is

$$R_E = \frac{V_E}{I_{E\ max}} = \frac{.7}{.500} = 1.4 \text{ ohms}$$

As in the previous question the value of C_E is not critical. However, its reactance must be small compared to R_E in order to avoid degeneration in the emitter circuit. A value of 0.1 μF has been chosen, since it has a reactance at 30 mc of only .05 ohms.

The base self-bias scheme shown in the previous question is quite widely used, but has the disadvantage that too high a value of R_B limits the usable collector-to-emitter breakdown voltage. On the other hand, the emitter self-bias arrangement described in this question does not affect the transistor breakdown characteristic and also provides thermal stability.

Some class C amplifiers employ a combination of both the base and the emitter-bias schemes. In this design, the required bias is provided partially by each bias network.

As mentioned in the discussion of Q. 3.192(S), both the base and the emitter self-bias methods have the advantage of being self-adjusting to changes of input signal level. With either (or both) of these schemes, an increase of input signal will result in an increase of bias and a decrease of signal level will result in a decrease of bias, with the output power remaining fairly constant.

ANTENNAS

Q. 3.193. **Explain the voltage and current relationships in one-wavelength antenna; half-wavelength (dipole) antenna; quarter-wavelength "grounded" antenna.**

A. (a) In a one-wavelength antenna, the current is minimum at both ends and at the center of the antenna. Simultaneously, the voltage is maximum at these points. This may be seen clearly in the accompanying figure (Fig. 3.193(a)).

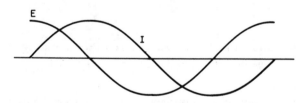

Fig. 3.193(a). Voltage and current distribution along a one-wavelength antenna (full-wave antenna).

(b) As shown in Fig. 3.193(b), the voltage is maximum and the current minimum at both ends of a half-wavelength antenna. In addition, the impedance is maximum at both ends (2500 ohms) and minimum (73 ohms) at the center. Half-wavelength antennas are invariably fed at the center with a low-impedance transmission line.

(c) For a quarter-wavelength "grounded" antenna, the ground acts as a *mirror* to supply the second half of a half-wave antenna. The maximum current is therefore at the ground point, as is the minimum voltage. At the top of the antenna, the current is minimum and the voltage maximum.

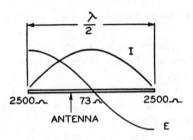

Fig. 3.193(b). Current and voltage distribution on Hertz antenna.

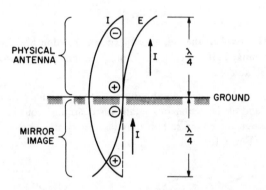

Fig. 3.193(c). Current and voltage distribution along a quarter wavelength, "grounded" antenna.

The current and voltage distribution for a "grounded," quarter-wave antenna is shown in Fig. 3.193(c).

D. *General*: An antenna is a special type of resonant circuit. In the familiar type of resonant circuit where coils and capacitors are used, the dimensions of these circuit elements are generally a small percentage of a wavelength at the operating frequency. When this is the case, very little radiation takes place from the resonant circuit. On the other hand, if the resonant circuit has dimensions which are an appreciable part of a wavelength (¼, ½, or one wavelength or greater), a good deal of radiation of the electromagnetic energy will take place and for all practical purposes, the circuit represents an antenna. In practice, to achieve the greatest radiation efficiency, antennas are composed of straight resonant wires (or rods), or combinations of such elements. As in any resonant circuit, the greatest current will flow when the circuit is resonated to the applied frequency. When an antenna is resonant, it achieves the greatest amount of radiation because maximum current then flows in the conductor(s). The *shortest* length of antenna wire that can be made resonant to any given frequency is one-half wavelength. Such an antenna is commonly known as a "dipole." (See part (b) of this discussion. See also Q. 3.14.D. for a discussion of radiation fields from an antenna.)

If an antenna wire was infinitely long and excited at some frequency, the r-f energy would travel down the wire and would be dissipated in the form of radiation and heating of the wire. However, when the wire has a finite length and is short in terms of wavelengths, the original excitation energy (incident wave) reaches the end of the antenna with very little attenuation. At this point, it sees an open circuit and is reflected back (reflected wave) toward the feed point. However, the incident wave is continuously present and the two waves combine to create "standing" waves on the wire. (See Q. 3.215 and Q. 3.216.) In the three figures for this question the "standing" waves of voltage and current are shown for three antennas of different wavelengths.

(a) In Fig. 3.193(a), the antenna illustrated is an *electrical* wavelength long (see Q. 3.203(d)). As such, a full wavelength of voltage and current standing waves appear on the antenna. The distribution of the voltage and current is sinusoidal. Also, note that they change polarity at certain fixed points along the antenna. The voltage changes polarity at the one-quarter and three-quarter wavelength points. However, the current changes its polarity at the half-wavelength point and is always 90 degrees out of phase with the voltage. Note that the voltage and current radiated fields (Q. 3.14) are also 90 degrees out of phase. An interesting fact is that identical transmitting and receiving antennas have the same standing wave pattern, impedance distribution and directivity pattern.

The impedance along any point of an antenna (see Q. 3.194) is determined by the *ratio* of the voltage to the current at that point. Examination of Fig. 3.193(a) indicates that a full-wavelength antenna has maximum impedance at the center and both ends of the antenna, and minimum impedance at the one-quarter and three-quarter wavelength points.

(b) The simple dipole antenna is the basis of practically all antenna systems. As shown in Fig. 3.193(b), it is an electrical half wavelength long. The actual length of a dipole in feet may be computed from the formula

$$L = 492 \times .95/f \text{ (mc)} = 468/f \text{ (mc)}$$

The factor .95 is necessary because the velocity of propagation on the antenna is less than the velocity in free space. Impedance values measured at any point on an antenna are a function of the magnitude of the current and voltage at that point. At the center of a dipole where the current is a maximum and the voltage a minimum, the impedance is equal to 73 ohms. At the ends, the impedance is about 2500 ohms. Since dipoles are usually fed at the center, the value of 73 ohms is of great importance because it must be matched to the transmission line. A common impedance for one type of coaxial line is 72 ohms and this type of line is frequently used to match correctly to the center of a dipole antenna (see D. of Q. 3.211).

(c) The quarter-wave "grounded" antenna operates with its lower end closely coupled to ground, or to a metal ground plane (see Q. 3.204). The quarter-wave rod acts as one half of a half-wave antenna. The earth or ground plane (see Q. 3.204) acts as a mirror and supplies the other quarter-wave section, as shown in Fig. 3.193(c). This type of antenna is frequently referred to as a Marconi antenna. If a vertical grounded antenna is to show a resonant (resistive) impedance at its base, it must be an odd number (1, 3, 5, etc.) of quarter-wavelengths long. This antenna is fed at its base where there is a low impedance of about 38 ohms. (See Q. 3.209 for methods of feeding such antennas.) If an antenna is *less* than one-quarter wavelength high, it presents a capacitive reactance at its base. In this case an inductance must be added in series with the antenna to make it resonant. On the other hand, an antenna having a length between one-quarter and one-half wavelength will look inductive at the base. Such an antenna may be resonated with a series capacitor which will "tune-out" the inductance and make the base-input impedance, resistive. (See also Q. 3.203(c) and (d).)

The concept of a "mirror" or "image" antenna is a convenient one to describe the effect of the ground plane in reflecting the original wave from the physical antenna back into space. This ground-plane reflection causes a reflected wave to occur, which has the same characteristics as if this reflected wave originated at a second antenna. This second antenna would be identical to the real antenna, but situated under the ground directly below it. As shown in Fig. 3.193(c), the "mirror-image" antenna exhibits a "mirror-image" of the voltage polarity which appears across the real antenna. As a result, the current in each portion of the "antenna" flows in the same direction, producing a reinforced transmitted wave. In physical terms, what actually happens is that the vertically-polarized waves will be reflected from a highly-conductive ground plane without any appreciable change in phase, and tend to reinforce the wave from the physical antenna.

Q. 3.194. **What effect does the magnitude of the voltage and current, at a point on a half-wavelength antenna in "free space" (a dipole), have on the impedance at that point?**

A. The impedance measured at any point on a dipole in free space, is equal to the ratio of the voltage to the current at that point. (The actual magnitude of the values of voltage and current is of no consequence, other than to establish the ratio, $Z = \dfrac{E}{I}$.)

D. See Q. 3.193(b), Answer and Discussion.

Q. 3.195. How is the operating power of an AM transmitter determined using antenna resistance and antenna current?

A. The operating (output) power is found by multiplying the square of the antenna current by the antenna resistance (radiation resistance).

D. See Q. 4.102. See also Q. 4.113 and Q. 4.124.

"Radiation resistance" is a fictitious quantity of resistance which, while not present physically in the antenna, is equivalent to a resistance which if inserted in the antenna would dissipate an amount of power equal to that radiated from the antenna.

In defining the radiation resistance it is necessary to refer it to a particular point in the antenna. This point is usually taken at a current loop (maximum). The radiation resistance must be such that the square of the current times the radiation resistance will equal the power radiated. The grounded end is frequently used as the current reference point. Radiation resistance, $R_{rad} = \dfrac{\text{radiated power}}{I_{max}^2}$. To determine antenna or radiation resistance by the resistance substitution method, a known value of non-inductive resistance is placed in series with the antenna and antenna ammeter, and a shorting switch is connected across the resistance. All circuits should be correctly tuned and the driver power and output voltage should be maintained constant during the readings. The "antenna resistance" is found from the formula, $R_{rad} = \dfrac{I_2}{I_1 - I_2} \times R_1$, where R_1 is the known resistance, I_2 is the antenna current with R_1 in the circuit, I_1 is the antenna current with R_1 shorted out.

Q. 3.196. What kinds of fields emanate from a transmitting antenna and what relationships do they have to each other?

A. Two kinds of fields emanate (radiate) from a transmitting antenna. These are (1) the electric field, which lies mainly along the plane of the antenna and (2) the magnetic field, which lies mainly perpendicular to the plane of the antenna. (An "induction" field having the same relationship described above exists in proximity to the antenna wire, but is not *radiated*. Its amplitude varies inversely as the square of the distance from the antenna.) A graphical representation of the magnetic and electric fields emanating from a vertically-polarized antenna is shown in Figure 3.196. These fields are varying in magnitude and

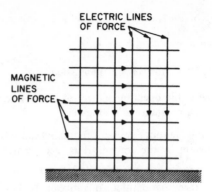

Fig. 3.196. Graphical representation of the electric and magnetic fields from a vertically-polarized antenna.

direction in a sinusoidal fashion at the rate of the transmitted frequency. The arrows indicate the instantaneous directions of both fields for a wave which is traveling toward the reader. A radiated wave in *free space* decreases in strength inversely with the distance from the antenna. In practice, the attenuation is greater, due mainly to absorption of the energy by the ground and by atmospheric conditions.

D.   See the discussion for Q. 3.14.

Q. 3.197.   Can either of the two fields that emanate from an antenna produce an emf in a receiving antenna? If so, how?

A.   This question is of a highly theoretical nature since it appears that the two fields are always present in a radiated wave (see Q. 3.196 above), and are interdependent. However, if it is assumed, for example, that only the electromagnetic wave intercepts a receiving antenna (correctly polarized) a voltage will be induced in the receiving antenna. However, this immediately sets up an electrostatic field in the receiving antenna, causing current to flow and thus produce its own electromagnetic field. This locally restores the condition of the two interdependent fields. Similarly, it might be considered that the electrostatic field only intercepts a correctly polarized receiving antenna. A potential difference will be induced across the antenna, causing current to flow in the antenna. As above, the twin and interdependent fields will again be produced.

Q. 3.198.   Draw a sketch and discuss the horizontal and vertical radiation patterns of a quarter-wave vertical antenna. Would this also apply to a similar type of receiving antenna?

A. (a) The patterns are given in Figs. 3.198(a) and 3.198(b). Note that the horizontal radiation pattern is omnidirectional and radiation is equal for all azimuth angles. In Figure 3.198(b) (vertical pattern), observe that the strength of radiation is greatest along the horizon and is reduced practically to zero at an angle of 90 degrees above the horizon.

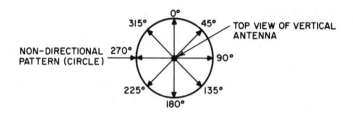

Fig. 3.198(a). Horizontal radiation pattern of a quarter-wave vertical antenna.

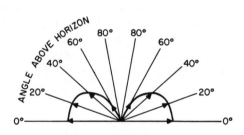

Fig. 3.198(b). Vertical radiation pattern of a quarter-wave vertical antenna.

(b) The same basic patterns apply to transmitting and receiving antennas.

D. See Q. 3.193(c).

Q. 3.199. Describe the directional characteristics, if any, of horizontal and vertical loop antennas.

A. (a) A horizontal loop antenna is non-directional along the plane of the loop. It has minimum radiation or reception vertically. A loop antenna is rarely used in the horizontal plane since its primary function is to provide direction-finding. This requires a directional pattern which is discriminatory in the azimuth (horizontal) plane. (See Part (b).)

(b) A vertical loop antenna has a bi-directional pattern which is maximum in the directions in the plane of the loop, and minimum in the directions broadside to the loop. This directional pattern is clearly shown in Fig. 3.199.

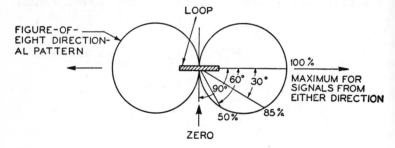

Fig. 3.199. Directional pattern (bilateral) of loop antenna.

Loop antennas are shielded in order to minimize "antenna effect" and provide a sharper indication of direction. "Antenna effect" causes a broadening of the null points because of the unsymmetrical capacity balance between the loop antenna and ground. The shield must be electrostatic only and, therefore, is electrically broken by a small section of insulating material.

D. See Q. 3.210.

Q. 3.200. In speaking of radio transmissions, what bearing does the angle of radiation, density of the ionosphere and frequency of emission have on the length of the skip zone?

A. See Figure 3.200.

(a) Angle of radiation: The smaller the angle of radiation at which a wave leaves the earth, the greater will be the length of the skip zone.

(b) Density of the ionosphere: The greater the density of the ionosphere, the more wave refraction (bending) takes place and the shorter will be the length of the skip zone.

(c) Frequency of emission: In general, the higher the frequency (below a critical value) the longer will be the skip zone.

D. (a) (Refer to the figure.) If radio waves are propagated at relatively low angles (to the earth), they require less refraction by the ionosphere to return them to earth and consequently have a relatively long "skip zone." Higher-angle radiated waves are returned to earth by greater refraction angles, producing shorter skip zones. At still higher angles (above a critical angle for the particular frequency used) the wave may pass completely through the ionized layer and may not be returned to earth at all. In this case, only the *ground wave* is effective in providing communication.

(b) The amount of wave bending is proportional to the density of the ionization of a particular layer, so that shorter skip zones occur for higher densities. However, some of the wave energy is absorbed in the ionosphere and only a portion is returned to earth. The amount of absorption increases with the density of ionization, with the density of the ionized atmospheric region, and with a *decrease* of frequency.

It is interesting to note that the ionization may exist in several layers, which are designated by letters. Thus, the "D" layer exists from 30 to 55 miles high and exists only in sunlight. The "E" layer is the lowest, making possible long-distance communication and is about 65 miles high. It is minimal around midnight. The most intensely ionized layer is the F2 layer, which varies from 150 to 250 miles in height. The F2 layer maintains the most constant density over the 24-hour period and is important in long-distance communication. At high frequencies (15 to 30 mc) the waves may pass completely through the "D" and "E" layers, but may be returned to earth by the denser F2 layer.

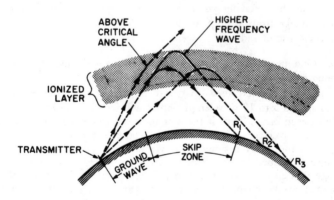

Fig. 3.200. Illustrating the refraction of radio waves and the "skip zone." Note that higher frequency wave, or lower radiation angle may increase the "skip zone."

(c) As the emission frequency increases, the amount of "wave bending" decreases, resulting in longer skip zones. However, for a given angle of radiation, as the frequency is increased, a frequency will be reached where the wave bending is not sufficient to return the wave to the earth (see the figure) and no "skip" reception is possible. However, under this condition "skip" reception may sometimes be possible by lowering the radiation angle. It should be noted in connection with "skip" reception that frequencies above about 50 megacycles are seldom of value for reliable reception.

The subject of "skip zone" is of necessity covered very inadequately by this question. Many variables and special conditions affect the phenomena of "skip." For more detailed information, it is recommended that the reader consult a book specializing in radio transmission. An excellent discussion may also be found in the ARRL Handbook, or other amateur radio handbooks.

Q. 3.201. Why is it possible for a sky wave to "meet" a ground wave 180 degrees out of phase?

A. Since the paths traveled by the sky wave and ground wave are of different lengths, the combined waves at a receiving antenna are usually out of phase. If the sky wave arrives at the receiving antenna such that its path is exactly one-half wavelength longer (or an odd multiple thereof) than the path of the ground wave, the two waves will be 180 degrees out of phase and severe fading will occur. Because of periodic changes in the strength and the path length of the sky wave, the signal strength at the receiving point may go through variations as the two signals change from an in-phase to an out-of-phase condition. This is a frequent cause of fading.

D. One method of minimizing fading effects is the use of a diversity antenna receiving system.

It has been determined that signals which are induced in antennas spaced 5 to 10 wavelengths apart will fade in and out independently of each other. Thus if three or more such antennas are connected to separate receivers with a combined output, the chances are very small that the received signal will ever fade out completely. The AVC voltages developed by the three receivers are added and the combined voltage is used to control the gain of three receivers simultaneously. In this manner the channel receiving the strongest signal at any instant is the one which is contributing most to the output, the other two being relatively inoperative at that instant.

Q. 3.202. What is the relationship between operating frequency and ground-wave coverage?

A. In general, ground-wave coverage decreases with increasing frequencies. For frequencies above 5 to 10 megacycles, the reliable ground-wave coverage may be only a few miles.

D. Ground-wave coverage for a given frequency may be increased by a substantial increase in transmitter power. Also, for high-frequency transmission, locating the transmission antenna at a high point will increase ground coverage. Typical examples of the latter are TV and FM broadcast antennas. Ground-wave coverage is limited by the energy absorption of the ground and other conducting mediums. The effect increases as the frequency increases and ground-wave coverage is not valuable above about 5 to 10 mc. (See also Q. 3.200.)

Q. 3.203. Explain the following terms with respect to antennas (transmission or reception):
   (a) Field strength
   (b) Power gain
   (c) Physical length
   (d) Electrical length
   (e) Polarization
   (f) Diversity reception
   (g) Corona discharge

A. (a) Field strength (or field intensity): The signal voltage induced in an antenna, measured in millivolts or microvolts per meter.

(b) Power gain: The power gain of a given transmitting antenna is the ratio of the power radiated (in its maximum direction of radiation), compared to the power radiated by a standard (usually dipole) antenna. Both antennas must have the same polarization.

(c) Physical length: The "physical" length of an antenna is its material length as measured in inches or feet. This is generally slightly shorter than the "electrical" length of the antenna. (See discussion.)

(d) Electrical length: The "electrical" length of an antenna is a descriptive and not a physical measurement. Rather, it is the wavelength (or fraction of a wavelength) to which a given antenna is resonant. In the case of a half-wave dipole, the "electrical" half-wavelength in meters is slightly (5%) longer than the actual physical length of the rod. (See discussion.)

(e) Polarization: The polarization of an antenna is determined by its position with respect to the earth. (The polarization is determined by the direction of the electric field which is parallel to the physical plane of the antenna.) Thus, a vertical antenna is vertically polarized and a horizontal antenna is horizontally polarized.

(f) Diversity reception: See D. of Q. 3.201.

(g) Corona discharge: Corona discharge is an electrical discharge which generally takes place between a conductor and its surrounding medium, which may be the atmosphere or an insulating material.

D. (a) The field strength of a standard broadcast station varies inversely as the distance from the antenna.

The field strength is a measure of the magnitude of the voltage (not power) in millivolts or microvolts per meter. The power would vary as the square of the voltage or inversely as the square of the distance. The value of field strength at moderate distances from the transmitter is found from the formula, $E = \dfrac{188\,hI}{\lambda r}$ millivolts per meter, where

$h =$ effective antenna height in meters.
$I =$ antenna current in amperes.
$\lambda =$ operating wavelength in meters.
$r =$ distance from antenna in meters.
(See also Q. 4.57.)

(b) Antenna "field gain", which is a *voltage* ratio is sometimes used instead of antenna "power gain."

"Antenna field gain" is the ratio of the voltage induced into a receiving antenna under two separate transmitting conditions. The first condition is when a relatively complex transmitting antenna system is used and the second case is when a simple ·dipole transmitting antenna is used.

The ratio is usually taken with respect to a dipole antenna as a reference value. The actual power output of the transmitting antenna is not increased to produce a field gain. Rather the available energy is concentrated or focused in the desired directions. According to a definition of the FCC, "antenna field gain" is defined as the "ratio of the effective free space field intensity, produced at one mile in the horizontal plane and expressed in millivolts per meter or one kilowatt antenna input power, to 137.6 microvolts per meter." The figure of 137.6 microvolts per meter is the figure used to represent an average value of field strength, at a point one mile from the antenna, which would be produced by one kilowatt radiated from a simple dipole at the mean height of the antenna being measured.

(c) The physical length of an antenna is actually somewhat less than its electrical length due to "end effect," which results from the capacitance between the ends of the antenna and the earth. The end effect varies with the height of the antenna, the diameter of the antenna, and the excitation voltage. As an average figure the physical length is usually about 5% less than the electrical length.

(d) The following discussion illustrates the reason why in the practical case, the "electrical" length is always greater than the "physical" length of an antenna.

An antenna can be considered to be a resonant circuit. Taking a half-wave (dipole) antenna in free space as a basic example, it will be found that the antenna will resonate at a frequency whose wavelength is equal to *twice* the *physical* length of the antenna. In free space the velocity of wave travel from one end of the antenna to the other and back is almost equal to the velocity of light (if wire is very thin) which is 300,000,000 meters per second. Thus in *free space* the *physical* length

of a *half-wave antenna* in *meters* may be calculated from the formula,
$l = \dfrac{300,000,000}{2\times(\text{freq. in cycles})}$. This is so because the antenna will resonate
at a frequency determined by the length of time required for a wave
to travel from one end of the antenna to the other (180°) and to return
(360°). From the above, it must be realized that the resonant frequency of any antenna is a direct function of the velocity of the wave along
the antenna wire. In the practical case, the antenna is never completely
isolated from the surrounding objects, and this causes the velocity of the
wave along the antenna wire to *decrease* somewhat. Thus the *physical*
length of the antenna must be *shortened* if it is still to resonate at the
same frequency as in free space. The exact amount of the reduction of
length is difficult to state, but a rough approximation of 5% may be
used as a starting point. The approximate *physical* length of a *half-
wave* antenna in *feet* may then be found from the formula $l = \dfrac{468}{f\,(\text{mc})}$.

(e) The physical positioning of an antenna with respect to the
earth determines the polarization of the emitted wave. An antenna
which is positioned vertically with respect to the earth radiates a
wave which is vertically polarized, while a horizontal antenna radiates
a horizontally polarized wave. If the antennas are located close to the
ground, vertically polarized waves will provide a stronger signal close
to the earth than will horizontally polarized waves. If the transmitting
and receiving antennas are more than one wavelength above the earth,
there will be little difference in signal strength caused by the two types
of polarization. If the transmitting antenna is located at least several
wavelengths above ground, horizontally polarized waves will result
in the greatest signal strength close to the earth.

(f) An important source of static produced on mobile antennas
(ground or aircraft) is the corona (electrical) discharge from such
antennas. Static charges may build up on antennas, as well as on other
conducting surfaces and tend to discharge when their potential is high
enough for the existing conditions. Discharges tend to occur from
pointed or small dimensional surfaces because the voltage stress is greatest at such points. To reduce corona effects, pointed items may be balled
or capped. In addition, the use of uninsulated and small diameter (or
braided) wire should be avoided.

Q. 3.203(A). The field intensity of a 1 kW transmitter measured at a distance of one mile from the transmitter is 200 μv/
meter. The power at the transmitter was increased so that at four
miles, the field intensity became three times as great as the original
field intensity at one mile. What power increase was made at the
transmitter?

A. The power was increased to 144 kW.

D. As stated in Q. 3.203, the field intensity (or field strength) varies inversely with the distance from the transmitting antenna. Thus, if the distance were doubled, the field intensity would be halved and if the distance were quadrupled, the field strength would be cut to $\frac{1}{4}$.

Starting with the original field strength of 200 μv/meter at one mile, if the distance were increased to four miles, the field intensity would then be $\frac{1}{4}$ of 200, or 50 μv/meter.

With the increased transmitter power, the field intensity has been increased to three times the original value, or $3 \times 200 = 600$ μv/meter (at four miles).

The ratio of the increased value of field intensity at four miles to the original field intensity at one mile is $\dfrac{600 \ \mu\text{v/meter}}{50 \ \mu\text{v/meter}} = 12:1$. Remember that this is a voltage ratio increase (not a power ratio increase).

This means that the antenna voltage (or current) at the transmitting antenna has increased by 12 times. Since the transmitter power is proportional to the square of the voltage (or current), the ratio of the transmitter power increase is $12^2 = 144$ times.

The original power of the transmitter was 1 kW and the new power is therefore 144×1 kW = 144 kW.

Note: The above question does not appear in the current FCC Study Guide, but has been added to enhance the student's ability to solve problems of this type as they may appear on FCC License Examinations.

Q. 3.204. What would constitute the ground plane if a quarter-wave grounded(whip) antenna, 1 meter in length, were mounted on the metal roof of an automobile; mounted near the rear bumper of an automobile?

A. (a) If this antenna were mounted on the metal roof, the roof would act as the ground plane since the length of the roof is an appreciable part of a wavelength (4 meters).

(b) If the antenna were mounted on or near the rear bumper, the bumper would act partially as the ground plane. Capacitive coupling to the earth would enable the earth to also act as part of the ground plane. The effectiveness of the bumper alone would depend largely upon its being an appreciable portion of a wavelength, at the frequency involved.

D. See Q. 3.193(c), Q. 3.194 and Q. 3.209.

Q. 3.205. Explain why a "loading coil" is sometimes associated with an antenna. Would absence of the coil mean a capacitive antenna impedance?

A. (a) A "loading coil" is required to operate an antenna at a lower frequency than its actual length would normally permit.

(b) Absence of a "loading coil" would mean that the antenna input would *look* like a capacitive reactance and depending on the magnitude of the reactance it might not be possible to feed power into the antenna.

D.　As stated in Q. 3.203, D.(d), the resonant frequency is dependent upon the velocity of the wave along the antenna. Thus any factors tending to *reduce* the velocity along a given *length* of wire will cause the antenna to resonate at a *lower* frequency. The addition of series *inductance* will produce this effect and thus reduce the resonant antenna frequency. Any factors tending to *increase* the velocity along a given length of wire will cause the antenna to resonate at a higher frequency. The addition of series *capacitance* will produce this effect and *increase* the resonant frequency of the antenna.

The following method, while possibly not strictly accurate, will provide a means of remembering the above facts. Consider the resonant frequency of an antenna as expressed by the formula, $f = \dfrac{1}{2\pi\sqrt{LC}}$.

Now if *inductance* is added in *series* with the antenna (and its inductance) the effect is to *increase* the total antenna inductance. If L *increases* in the formula, the frequency *decreases*. If *capacitance* is added in *series* with the antenna (and its capacitance), the total antenna capacitance is *decreased*. If C *decreases* in the formula, the frequency *increases*. (See also Q. 3.203(c) and (d) and Q. 3.209.)

Q. 3.206.　What radio frequencies are useful for long distance communications requiring continuous operation?

A.　The most reliable frequencies for long distance radio communication are in the order of 15 to 30 kc. Communication at these low frequencies is usually accomplished by means of ground waves. This requires the generation of extremely high power outputs for reliable and continuous operation.

D.　These frequencies are usually produced by high speed mechanical generators. These generators are capable of producing very large output powers. Such very low frequencies are not used much at present, because of the size of antenna required to radiate a significant amount of power. Another reliable communications system operates on VHF or UHF frequencies. This makes use of radio-relay stations operating at very high power levels. The radiation takes place by means of "scatter" propagation through the "troposphere." The "troposphere" is that layer of the atmosphere close to the earth and extending perhaps two miles above it. Wave bending in the troposphere occurs increasingly for frequencies above 50 mc and occurs when masses of air exist in layers having differing dielectric constants. This may be caused by layers having sharply different water-vapor contents or abnormal temperature vs. altitude variations. Since the radiated waves must strike the boundaries between the layers at low (grazing) angles, the transmitting antenna is designed for maximum horizontal radiation.

Q. 3.207. What type of modulation is largely contained in "static" and "lightning" radio waves?

A. "Static" and "lightning" radio waves are mostly amplitude modulated.

D. While some frequency modulation is also present in static and lightning radio waves, the majority of the modulation components are amplitude modulated. Most of these waves are also vertically polarized. Polarization of a radio wave is determined by the direction of the electrostatic field. Antennas which are horizontally polarized reject to some extent interference caused by static and lightning radio waves.

Q. 3.208. Will the velocity of signal propagation differ in different materials? What effect, if any, would this have on wavelength or frequency?

A. (a) The velocity of propagation of radio waves differs according to the type of medium involved. It is always less than the speed of light (300,000,000 meters per second) by a factor "K" which is determined by the type of transmission material (see discussion).

(b) Assuming the wave has been generated externally to the material through which it is being transmitted; the type of material has no effect on its frequency. However, considering a constant frequency and materials exhibiting a lesser propagation velocity than free space, the measured wavelength along the material will be shorter than in free space.

D. (a) The factor "K" mentioned above, expresses the ratio of the actual velocity of a wave through a given medium, to the velocity of light. For example the following values of K express the ratio of the actual velocity of the energy on the line to the velocity of light.

Line	*K*
Parallel line	0.975
Parallel tubing	0.95
Concentric line	0.85
Twisted pair	0.56 to 0.65

(b) It was stated above that the measured wavelength along the material will be shorter than in free space. This is equivalent to the characteristics of "physical" and "electrical" lengths of antennas, wherein the physical length is shorter than the equivalent electrical free-space wavelength. This occurs because the transmission of energy along the

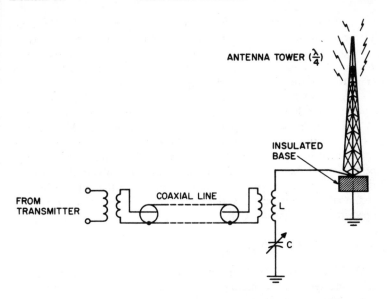

Fig. 3.209. Illustrating series-feed of a quarter-wave vertical antenna. The series LC network provides a means of impedance matching.

antenna conductor is *slower* than the transmission of energy through free space (or through the atmosphere). See also Q. 3.203(c) and (d).

Q. 3.209. **Discuss series and shunt feeding of quarter-wave antennas with respect to impedance matching.**

A. Although not specifically stated, the question refers to vertical, quarter-wave antennas, ungrounded for series feed and grounded for shunt feed. For diagram of a series-fed antenna, see Fig. 3.209. For a diagram of a shunt-fed antenna, see Fig. 3.127.

(a) In the series fed case, the bottom of the quarter-wave antenna must be insulated from ground. The impedance at the base (to ground) of the antenna is about 38 ohms. If maximum efficiency is not required, the antenna can be fed directly with a 50-ohm coaxial cable. The outer conductor is grounded (to the ground radials) and the center conductor connects to the insulated base of the antenna. For greater efficiency and lines of greater impedances, a tunable series LC network is connected between the base of the antenna and ground. The input power is inductively coupled to the series coil, which is resonated with the series capacitor to the operating frequency. This provides an excellent impedance match to the antenna, since maximum series antenna current will then be present.

(b) By the use of a shunt-feed system, it is possible to ground the base of the antenna, resulting in a savings of construction costs. In this system, the transmission line is terminated at a specified distance from the base of the antenna. A wire from the center conductor of the coaxial-transmission line is then stretched upward at an angle of approximately 45 degrees to a predetermined point on the antenna. The outer conductor of the line is grounded at its end to the ground radial system. A voltage is induced into the antenna by a magnetic field set up by a loop, consisting of the slant-wire, the lower portion of the antenna and the ground return from the base of the antenna, to the outer conductor of the coaxial line. A correct impedance match is obtained by varying the height at which the slant wire is connected to the antenna. For the common 70-ohm coaxial line, this connecting point will be approximately one-fifth of the total tower height.

D. See Q. 3.193(c) and Q. 3.198.

Q. 3.210. Discuss the directivity and physical characteristics of the following types of antennas:
 (a) Single loop
 (b) V-beam
 (c) Corner-reflector
 (d) Parasitic array
 (e) Stacked array

A. (a) Single loop (Fig. 3.210(a)): The usual type of loop antenna consists of several turns of wire enclosed in an electrostatic shield. The shape of the loop is generally circular. The loop may be considered to be an inductance coil having a large ratio of diameter to length. This inductance is frequently resonated by a variable capacitor to form the tuned-input circuit of the loop receiver. The directional characteristics are described in Q. 3.199(b).

(b) V-beam (Fig. 3.210(b)): Consists of two heavy wires in the

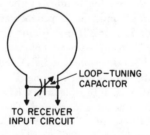

*Fig. 3.210(a). Illustration of a vertical-loop antenna.
Minimum pickup is perpendicular to the page.*

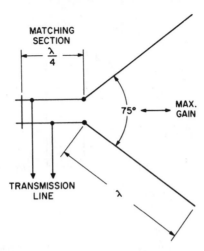

Fig. 3.210(b). A one-wavelength "V" antenna with quarter-wave impedance-matching section.

form of a horizontal "V." (This is one form of a so-called, "longwire" antenna.) When each leg of the "V" is made one-wavelength long, the angle between the wires should be about 75 degrees. The directivity of the "V" antenna is along a line bisecting the "V" (bi-directional). However, the ends of the wires can be terminated resistively and the antenna becomes unidirectional in the direction of the open "V." Terminated "V" antennas have a wide bandwidth and gains in the order of 10 to 15 db. The angle of radiation is largely in the horizontal direction and the pattern may be quite sharp (highly directive) if wires several wavelengths long are employed.

(c) Corner reflector (Fig. 3.210(c)): This antenna consists of the reflector and a half-wave dipole antenna. The reflector is made of two flat conducting sheets which are joined (for highest gain) at an angle of about 45 degrees. The reflector is mounted like an open book held vertically. The dipole is mounted vertically, a half wavelength from the joined sheets, along a line bisecting the 45 degree angle, inside of the "V" formed by the two sheets. This antenna has greater gain than the parabolic reflector type and is easier to construct. Maximum directivity is along the bisector of the corner angle and is mainly confined to the horizontal plane. This antenna is unidirectional.

(d) Parasitic array (Fig. 3.210(d)): The simplest consists of a half-wave horizontal driven dipole and a reflector. The reflector is a rod (or tubing) about five percent longer than the dipole and mounted about one-quarter wavelength behind it on the same horizontal plane. How-

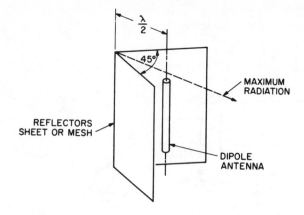

Fig. 3.210(c). Corner reflector excited by a single dipole. (The entire assembly may also be mounted horizontally to provide horizontal polarization.)

ever, the reflector has no direct electrical connection to the antenna and receives its energy entirely by induction. The practical length of the reflector may be determined by the formula

$$L = \frac{492}{f(mc)} feet$$

The length of a dipole may be determined by the formula

$$L = \frac{468}{f(mc)} feet$$

Addition of a reflector has the following effects on the normally bi-directional directivity of a simple dipole:

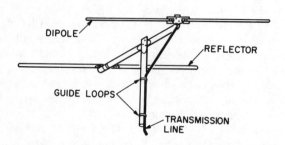

Fig. 3.210(d). Simple parasitic array consisting of a dipole and a reflector.

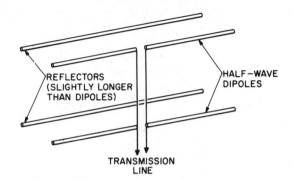

Fig. 3.210(e). Simple stacked array employing dipoles and reflectors.

1. The array becomes basically unidirectional (in the direction opposite to the reflector).

2. The gain of the antenna is increased.

3. The unidirectional pattern is sharper than for the simple dipole.

4. The bandpass is reduced.

5. The dipole input impedance is reduced. The radiation of either the simple dipole or the parasitic array is mainly in the horizontal plane.

(e) Stacked array (Fig. 3.210(e)): May be formed by mounting one driven dipole above another and is generally used with a reflector mounted behind each dipole. (Much more elaborate stackings are possible with numerous vertically stacked dipoles and reflectors. These are also frequently expanded in a broadside manner.) Stacking has the following effects compared to a single driven dipole:

1. Sharper directivity in the vertical plane.

2. Increase in gain of about 1.5 to 1.

3. Discrimination against rearward reception of about 3 to 1.

4. An increase in the dipole driving impedance.

5. Improved bandpass, compared to the single parasitic array. For a single-frequency band antenna, the vertical stacking of the elements will be about one-half wavelength. This is basically a unidirectional antenna.

Q. 3.211. Draw a sketch of a coaxial (whip) antenna; identify the positions and discuss the purposes of the following components:

(a) Whip
(b) Insulator
(c) Skirt
(d) Trap
(e) Support mast
(f) Coaxial line
(g) Input connector

A. See Fig. 3.211.

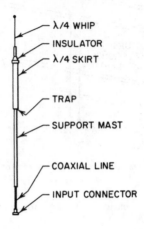

Fig. 3.211. Coaxial (whip) antenna showing all component parts.

(a) Whip: The top half (quarter-wavelength) of the radiating elements. (The other half of the radiating elements is the skirt, described below.) The whip is an electrical extension of the inner conductor of the coaxial-transmission line.

(b) Insulator: Required to insulate the center-conductor whip from the conducting skirt.

(c) Skirt: A metal cylinder mounted just below the insulator, and which is a quarter-wavelength long. This element, plus the whip completes the half-wave dipole radiator.

(d) Trap: A portion of the skirt forming a shorted quarter-wave transmission line section as shown in the illustration. The open end of the quarter-wave section represents a very high impedance at the operating frequency. This effectively insulates the bottom of the skirt from the outer conductor of the coaxial line (going through its center) permitting the skirt to act as a radiating element. The skirt receives its excitation energy at the center-feed point of the coaxial-line outer conductor, which is at the extreme top of the skirt.

(e) Support Mast: The mast supports the antenna structure. When a rigid coaxial line is employed, this item may be used as the support mast. However, for greater mechanical strength, the support mast may be a thick metal tubing or pipe, insulated from the skirt, surrounding either a rigid or flexible coax line. If a flexible coax line is used to feed the antenna, it may be supported at the skirt, using an insulated mounting support.

(f) Coaxial Line: A transmission line which guides the r–f energy from the transmitter to the coaxial-whip antenna. This is a shielded unbalanced transmission line (see discussion).

(g) Input Connector: A coaxial-type connector for connecting the coaxial line (from the transmitter) to the coaxial-whip antenna.

D. A 72 ohm coaxial line is commonly used to feed the coaxial-whip antenna. The skirt is connected to the outer conductor of the coaxial line at its extreme upper portion, while the inner conductor continues for an additional one-quarter wavelength (electrical). Thus, effectively, the co-axial transmission line is "terminated" at the junction of the skirt and the quarter-wave, center-conductor radiator. The line feeds an actual half-wave antenna at its center point (72 ohms) and thus the impedance of the line is matched and there are practically no standing waves on the line. This helps to keep the radiation angles low, raising the efficiency of the antenna.

Q. 3.212. Why are insulators sometimes placed in antenna guy wires?

A. Insulators are placed in guy wires in order to reduce the efficiency of the guy wires in acting as unwanted radiators and reflectors of radio-frequency energy, and to reduce r-f losses in these wires.

D. The guy wires should be broken up into lengths of such dimensions that they will not resonate at the fundamental or harmonics thereof of the transmitted frequency. It is considered common practice to insert an insulator near the top of each guy wire, and then cut each section of wire between the insulators so as to be non-resonant. The insulators should preferably be of the so called "egg" type which operate under compression, so that the guy wire will not separate even if an insulator breaks.

TRANSMISSION LINES

Q. 3.213. What is meant by the *characteristic* (surge) impedance of a transmission line; to what physical characteristics is it proportional?

A. (a) The characteristic (surge) impedance of a transmission line is the input impedance of a theoretically infinitely long line. In addition, if an impedance equal to this value is used to terminate a line of any given finite length, the same value of impedance appears at the input terminals of the line. The characteristic impedance also, is equal to the ratio of the voltage to the current along an infinite line, or a line terminated in its own characteristic impedance. This type of termination makes any line look like an infinitely long line.

(b) The surge impedance (or characteristic impedance) of any 2-wire transmission line is dependent upon three factors. These are: (1) the diameter of the conductors, (2) the spacing between the conductors, (3) the dielectric constant of the insulating material.

D. For a two wire parallel transmission line with air dielectric the characteristic impedance is given by the formula:

$$Z = 276 \log \frac{b}{a}$$

where Z = characteristic impedance in ohms.
  b = spacing between conductors (center to center) in inches.
  a = radius of one conductor in inches.

It may be seen from the above that the wider the spacing and the smaller the diameter of the conductors, the greater will be the characteristic impedance. However, an increase of dielectric constant above that of air will *reduce* the characteristic impedance. In this case the value obtained above is multiplied by a factor 1 over the square root of K, where, K is equal to the dielectric constant. For example, for polyethelene dielectric, the value of characteristic impedance in free air must be multiplied by the factor 0.675.

For a coaxial line with air dielectric, the impedance is given by the formula:

$$Z = 138 \log \frac{b}{a}$$

where Z = characteristic impedance in ohms.
  b = inner diameter of the outer conductor in inches.
  a = outer diameter of the inner conductor in inches.

If polyethelyne is used as the dielectric, multiply the characteristic impedance by 0.675.

A generalized formula frequently used to describe the characteristic impedance, is:

$$Z = \sqrt{\frac{L}{C}}$$

where L = Inductance per unit length.
  C = Capacitance per unit length.

The values of characteristic impedance may vary between 25 and 600 ohms, depending upon the type of line. Coaxial lines are generally in the range from 25 to 90 ohms. Parallel lines may vary from 100 to 600 ohms.

Q. 3.214. Why is the impedance of a transmission line an important factor with respect to matching "out of a transmitter" into an antenna?

A.   For maximum power transfer from the transmitter to the trans-mission line, the input impedance of the transmission line must match the output impedance of the transmitter. Also, for maximum power transfer from the transmission line to the antenna, the transmission line impedance must match the input antenna impedance. This principle is no different than impedance matching for maximum power transfer in other types of circuits (i.e., audio power output circuits).

D.   See Q. 4.55 and Q. 4.56 for methods of impedance matching to a standard broadcast antenna and discussions relating thereto.

Q. 3.215.   What is meant by "standing waves"; "standing-wave ratio (SWR)," and "characteristic impedance" as referred to transmission lines? How can standing waves be minimized?

A.   (a) "Standing" waves are apparent stationary waves of voltage or current appearing on a transmission line (or antenna). They are sta-tionary from the point of view that their maxima and minima always oc-cur at the same physical points along the line (or antenna). Standing waves are created when a line is not terminated in its characteristic im-pedance. In this event, the incident waves from the generator are reflected to some degree at the end of the line. The reflected waves combine con-tinuously with the incident waves causing *standing waves* to be formed along the line.

(b) "Standing-wave ratio" (SWR) is the ratio of maximum current (or voltage) along a line to the minimum current (or voltage) along the line. The ratio is commonly expressed as a number larger than one.

(c) For characteristic impedance, see Q. 3.213 above.

(d) Standing waves along a line can be minimized by terminating the line in an impedance equal to the characteristic impedance of the line. If this impedance is a pure resistance, there will be no standing waves and the line will be *flat,* or will appear to be infinitely long.

D.   See Q. 3.213 and Q. 3.216.

Q. 3.216.   If standing waves are desirable on a transmitting antenna, why are they undesirable on a transmission line?

A.   Standing waves are generally undesirable on a transmission line because of the following:

(a) Their presence indicates a mismatch at the antenna and, thus, a loss of power being fed to the antenna.

(b) In the case of open-type lines, radiation will occur from the line, modifying the antenna pattern.

(c) A high standing-wave ratio on a transmission line may cause over-heating, or arcing on the line, or in its associated circuits and traps.

(d) The higher the standing-wave ratio, the greater will be the losses on the transmission line.

D. A simple straightforward answer to this question is not possible. It is true that for many antenna designs, a high standing-wave ratio is necessary and desirable. These are antennas of the "resonant" type, such as quarter-wave, half-wave, or similar antennas. On the other hand there is a class of "long-wire" antennas which may be resistively terminated to have no standing waves. Examples of these are the straight-long wire, the "V" antenna and the rhombic antenna.

On the other hand, where space is at a premium (for example, on shipboard), particularly at low frequencies, the "lead-in" to the antenna may be made a resonant portion of the antenna proper. Then again, some high frequency transmission lines are deliberately operated as "tuned" or "resonant" lines and normally require the presence of standing waves for proper operation and impedance matching. In addition, some antennas are operated on several widely varying frequencies (frequently harmonically related), causing the antenna input impedance to vary greatly. In such cases, the line is usually "tuned" (resonant) to match the antenna input impedance and standing waves necessarily exist on the line.

Q. 3.217. What is meant by "stub-tuning"?

A. "Stub-tuning," (or "stub-matching) refers to the use of short (tuned) lengths of transmission line, which are connected to the main transmission line near the antenna. Such stubs are used to reduce or eliminate standing waves on the main transmission line. See Figure 3.217 for illustrations of stub tuning for parallel and coaxial lines.

D. If a long transmission line is used to feed an antenna, it is not always feasible to match the transmission line properly to the antenna. However, to reduce line losses, it is desirable to reduce standing waves by matching the load to the line. At some fraction of a wavelength (less than a quarter wavelength) from the antenna, the line appears as a reactance of a definite value. If a stub (shorter than one-quarter wavelength) is attached to the main line at the chosen point, it will have an equal and opposite reactance to that on the main line. Thus, the effective line reactance at the attachment point is cancelled, and the main line *sees* only a resistance equal to the characteristic-line impedance. Thus, the line is matched and minimum standing waves result.

Q. 3.218. What would be the considerations in choosing a solid-dielectric cable over a hollow pressurized cable for use as a transmission line?

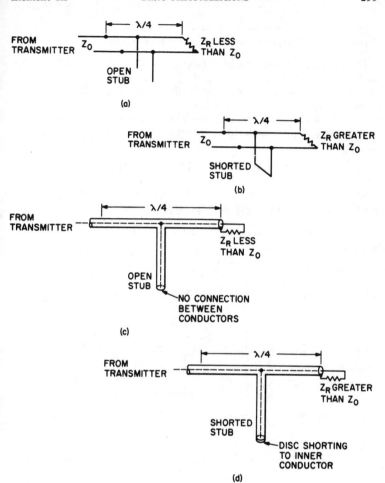

Fig. 3.217. Illustrations of "stub" tuning. Parts (a) and (b) show "stub" tuning of parallel lines. Parts (c) and (d) show "stub" tuning for coaxial lines. Z_0 is the characteristic impedance of the line. Z_R represents the antenna input impedance.

A. The question appears to be worded in reverse since the performance of the pressurized cable is superior. However, considerations for choosing a solid-dielectric cable (coaxial) would include the following:
  (a) Less expensive.
  (b) Easier to install, since it is more flexible.

(c) Tolerance to the higher losses.

(d) Does not require special plumbing-type connections.

D.   Certain types of coaxial cables are evacuated then filled with an inert gas under pressure and sealed. The reason for this is to prevent moisture from accumulating within the cable. Such moisture would reduce the normal voltage breakdown rating as well as cause increased losses within the cable. Another method sometimes used, is to continuously pump dry air under pressure through the concentric cable.

FREQUENCY MEASUREMENTS

Q. 3.219.   Draw a simplified circuit diagram of a grid-dip meter; explain its operation and some possible applications.

A.   (a)   For the circuit diagram, see Fig. 3.219.

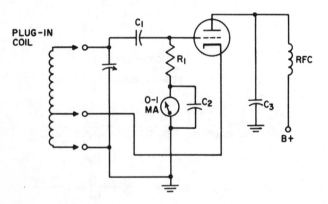

Fig. 3.219. Simplified diagram of a grid-dip meter.

(b)   The grid-dip meter is basically an oscillator (Hartley in this case) with a coil conveniently mounted so it can be easily coupled to the circuit under test. A set of plug-in coils are provided to cover a wide band of frequencies. Its operation is quite simple. When it is desired to measure the resonant frequency of a non-operating tank circuit, the probe coil is coupled loosely to the tank coil and the capacitor is varied until the meter dips to its lowest point. The frequency is then read directly from the grid-dip meter tuning dial. The meter dips because the tank circuit absorbs energy from the oscillator at the resonant frequency. This reduces the amplitude of oscillations and the oscillator grid current decreases causing a dip on the meter.

The circuit of Fig. 3.219 could easily be changed to a transistorized circuit by substituting an FET transistor (see Fig. 3.86(g3) and accompanying text) for the vacuum tube triode. The operation of the grid-dip meter remains the same.

(c) Some possible applications are:

(1) To measure resonant frequency of a tuned circuit.

(2) To find undesired resonances in receiver or transmitter circuits.

(3) Use as a signal generator to align receivers.

(4) Can be used to measure r–f inductances and capacitances in conjunction with a standard capacitance or standard inductance.

D.   See also Q. 3.220 and Q. 3.222.

Q. 3.220.   Draw a simplified circuit diagram of an absorption wavemeter (with galvanometer indicator); explain its operation and some possible applications.

A.   (a) For schematic see Fig. 3.220. The wavemeter consists of a calibrated-tuned circuit (L, C1) and a simple vacuum-tube voltmeter circuit (D1, C2 and meter). In operation, the pickup coil (L) is loosely coupled to the source of r-f energy and capacitor C1 tuned to provide maximum indication (resonance) on the meter. At this point, the calibrated capacitor is read in terms of the frequency of the unknown source. This may be by direct reading or taken from a calibration chart.

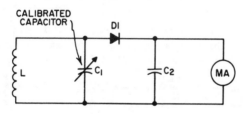

Fig. 3.220.   Absorption-type wavemeter. D1 and C2 provide dc for the galvonometer.

(b) Some applications are:

(1) To measure the frequency of a self-excited oscillator.

(2) To find parasitic oscillations in transmitters.

(3) To determine the frequency of operation of r–f amplifiers and/or frequency multipliers.

(4) To function as a general purpose r-f indicator for tuning and neutralizing a transmitter.

D.   In general a wavemeter is a resonant circuit which is tuned by a variable capacitor. A calibrated dial is provided on which is indicated the resonant frequency of the wave meter in terms of capacitor settings. A suitable r-f indicator is connected in series or parallel

302   *Radio Operator's License Q and A*

with the wavemeter tuned circuit to indicate resonance. When a series connected indicator is used, the indicator may be a sensitive flashlight bulb or thermocouple meter. A better (but more complex) arrangement is the use of a diode-type vacuum-tube voltmeter connected across a portion of the tuned circuit, or a solid-state crystal detector. The advantage of this type of indicator is that it consumes very little power and thus permits a higher value of Q to be developed in the wavemeter circuit. This is important because the accuracy with which readings can be made depends upon the Q.

A disadvantage of absorption type wavemeters in general is the reflected impedance they cause to appear in the measured circuit, which changes the tuning of the measured circuit and reduces the accuracy of readings.

The pickup coil of the absorption type frequency meter should be coupled as loosely as possible to the circuit under measurement in order to reduce errors in the readings. (See also Q. 3.79(b), Q. 3.83, Q. 3.91, Q. 3.92 and Q. 3.126 through Q. 3.128.)

Q. 3.221. Draw a block diagram, showing only those stages which would illustrate the principle of operation of a secondary frequency standard. Explain the functions of each stage.

A. For the block diagram, see Figure 3.221. The multivibrator (10 kc) is the basic oscillator and is accurately synchronized by the

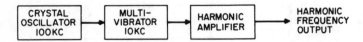

Fig. 3.221. Simplified block diagram of a secondary-frequency standard.

100 kc crystal oscillator. The harmonic amplifier may have switchable tuned circuits to amplify the higher harmonic frequencies which normally decrease rapidly in amplitude. Harmonics of both 100 kc and 10 kc are provided, with the 100 kc harmonics exceeding 30 megacycles in frequency.

D. To determine the operating frequency of a transmitter, the secondary-frequency standard should first be accurately calibrated as explained below.

The usual type of secondary-frequency standard will employ an accurately calibrated 100-kc crystal oscillator with a multivibrator providing harmonics of 10 kc. Thus, harmonics of 100 kc and 10 kc are provided, the 100-kc harmonics being useful beyond 30 mc and the 10-kc harmonics being useful beyond 3 mc.

1. Operate the transmitter and all test equipment for about 15 minutes to insure stability.

2. Measure the fundamental frequency of the transmitter by means of the frequency meter, obtaining an accurate zero-beat.

3. Turn off the transmitter and introduce the signals from the secondary-frequency standard into the heterodyne-frequency meter.

4. From the heterodyne-frequency meter chart and its dial setting, determine the approximate transmitter frequency, and from this determine the harmonic of the 100-kc oscillator from the secondary standard. (The calibration of the heterodyne-frequency meter may be checked by zero-beating it against the 100-kc harmonics and observing the dial calibration.)

5. Using the harmonics of the 10-kc oscillator, an audible beat will be present between the frequency of the heterodyne-frequency meter and that of the secondary-frequency standard. This will indicate the exact frequency within a few cycles by providing a figure from zero to 5000 cycles, to be used as the final digits of the reading provided by the heterodyne-frequency meter.

6. The exact value of the audible-beat frequency obtained in (5) above can be determined by matching this audio-frequency against that of a well-calibrated audio (or interpolation) oscillator, either by the zero-beat method or using an oscilloscope.

7. To check if the unknown frequency is greater or less than the 10-kc frequency being used for measurement, increase the frequency of the heterodyne-frequency meter slightly. If the audio-beat frequency increases, the unknown frequency is greater than the 10-kc harmonic involved. If the audio-beat frequency decreases, the unknown frequency is less than the 10-kc harmonic involved.

8. In the case of frequencies above about 3 mc, harmonics of the 10-kc multivibrator may be too weak to be useful. In this case, set the heterodyne-frequency meter to provide a suitable harmonic to beat with the transmitter frequency. Measure the frequency of the heterodyne-frequency meter, as described above and multiply the result by the appropriate harmonic.

A step-by-step explanation of how a secondary-frequency standard could be calibrated against a WWV signal is given below:

1. Using the operating frequencies of 2.5, 5, 10, 15, 20, 25, 30, and 35 mc, select that which provides a good readable signal and tune it in accurately on the receiver. (The receiver should be warmed up for about 15 minutes to insure stability.)

2. Turn on the secondary-frequency standard (usually a 100-kc crystal oscillator with a 10-kc multivibrator) and allow about a 15-minute warm-up period to insure stability.

3. Wait for the transmission period during which modulation is absent. (Receiver bfo should be off.)

4. Adjust the calibration control of the secondary-frequency standard until its harmonic is in exact zero-beat with the WWV frequency (as heard on the receiver).

5. The secondary-frequency standard is now calibrated.

Q. 3.222. Draw a block diagram of a heterodyne-frequency meter, which would include the following stages:

Crystal Oscillator
Crystal Oscillator Harmonic Amplifier
Variable Frequency Oscillator
Mixer
Detector and AF Amplifier
AF Modulator

Show RF input and RF, AF, and calibration outputs. Assume a band-switching arrangement and a dial having arbitrary units, employing a vernier scale.

(a) Describe the operation of the meter.

(b) Describe, step-by-step, how the crystal could be checked against WWV, using a suitable receiver.

(c) Under what conditions would the AF modulator be used?

(d) Describe, step-by-step, how the unknown frequency of a transmitter could be determined by use of headphones; by use of a suitable receiver.

(e) What is meant by calibration check-points; when should they be used?

(f) If in measuring a frequency, the tuning dial should show an indication between two dial-frequency relationships in the calibration book, how could the frequency value be determined?

(g) How could this meter be used as an RF generator?

(h) Under what conditions would it be necessary to re-calibrate the crystal oscillator?

A. For the block diagram, see Fig. 3.222.

(a) The unknown signal is fed to the *mixer* via the RF input where it is combined with a signal from the *variable frequency oscillator*. Due to the action in the mixer, the output not only contains the two original frequencies, but the sum and difference frequencies as well. This combination of frequencies, then, is fed to the *detector* whose output contains a signal equal to the difference of the two original frequencies— the original frequencies and their sum being bypassed. If the two original

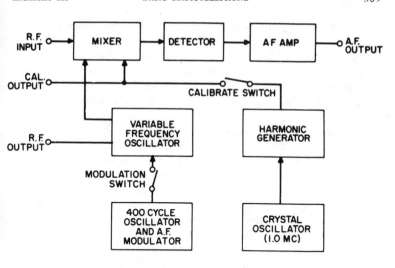

Fig. 3.222. Block diagram of a heterodyne-frequency meter.

signals are close enough in frequency, the difference frequency will be in the audio range and may be heard in the output of the *AF amplifier* by means of a suitable speaker or headphones. If the variable frequency oscillator is adjusted to make the difference frequency or beat become lower and lower in pitch until it disappears, the difference in frequencies is zero and the signal from the variable frequency oscillator has the same frequency as the unknown frequency. If the variable frequency oscillator has an accurately calibrated dial, the unknown frequency will now be known by reading the dial. The process of making the difference between the two frequencies zero is known as *zero beating*.

In order to be certain of the calibration of the variable frequency oscillator dial, facilities have been incorporated into the meter to provide signals of accurately known frequency to the mixer. In the meter shown in the block diagram, a 1.0 mc *crystal oscillator* with exceptionally good stability is used as a frequency standard. Means are provided to adjust the frequency of this oscillator to exactly 1.0 mc when required.

The output of the crystal oscillator is delivered to a *harmonic generator* for the purpose of obtaining harmonics of the 1.0 mc standard frequency that are of sufficient amplitude for use in the frequency range of the meter. If the meter is intended for use as high as 300 mc, the 300th harmonic must be strong enough to be heard in the *AF output* when beat with the variable frequency oscillator. By this method, the calibration of the variable frequency oscillator dial can be checked. If the calibration is faulty, means are provided for adjusting the dial, mechanically or electrically, so that the calibration is correct at the 1.0 mc harmonic check points.

It is often desirable to have the output of the variable frequency oscillator modulated with an audio frequency to assist in making accurate measurements. For this purpose, a *400 cycle oscillator and AF modulator* are provided. When such modulation is desired, the *modulation switch* is closed.

As shown on the diagram, an RF output terminal is shown. This output is useful for such purposes as receiver alignment, etc.

(b) If a suitable HF receiver is available, the meter can be calibrated against WWV by coupling the calibration output of the meter to the antenna input of the receiver and tuning the receiver to WWV on 5, 10, 15, 20, 25 or 30 mc. The frequency choice depends on the location of the receiving site, time of day, etc. With the receiver in the AM or phone mode, the calibrate switch of the meter is closed. If the crystal oscillator is *not* on frequency, a beat note will be heard which will be the difference between WWV and the 5th, 10th, 15th, 20th, 25th or 30th harmonic of the crystal oscillator. Which harmonic is heard will depend on which WWV frequency is being received.

By adjusting the trimmer provided on the crystal oscillator its frequency can be varied until zero beat is obtained with WWV. The crystal oscillator now is within approximately plus or minus 20 cycles of being correct *at that harmonic*. For better accuracy, it is well to adjust the crystal oscillator when the WWV signal is being modulated by its 440 cycle tone. Any frequency difference will be evidenced by an apparent waxing and waning of WWV's modulation, exact zero beat being obtained when the modulation remains steady in amplitude.

(c) Since the human ear cannot hear frequencies below approximately twenty cycles, the method of zero-beating the unknown signal against the output of the variable frequency oscillator produces results that are correct only to within approximately plus or minus twenty cycles. By modulating the variable frequency oscillator greater accuracy can be obtained. When the difference in the two frequencies is below audibility, the modulation of the variable frequency oscillator will grow stronger and weaker at a rate equal to the difference frequency. By observing this and adjusting the variable frequency oscillator so that the modulation is maintained at a constant amplitude, exact equality of the known and unknown signals can be obtained. The final accuracy of the measurement is limited only by the accuracy of a frequency standard and the calibration of the dial of the variable frequency oscillator.

(d) The process of using the meter and headphones to determine the frequency of a transmitter has already been described in the operation of the meter in the first paragraph of (a) above.

The unknown frequency of a transmitter, especially a distant one, can also be measured by using the meter in conjunction with a suitable receiver. This can be accomplished by first tuning in the transmitter on the receiver and then coupling the RF output of the meter to the antenna input of the receiver. Adjusting the variable frequency oscillator of the meter will produce a beat note in the output of the receiver between the distant transmitter and the variable frequency oscillator. Zero-beating the two signals will result in the variable frequency oscillator and the transmitter having the same frequency. The unknown frequency is read from the dial of the meter in the normal manner.

(e) Calibration check points are points or dial settings at which the 1.0 mc harmonics of the frequency standard should be heard at zero beat. They are used to assure that the frequency dial of the variable frequency oscillator is correctly adjusted to agree with the dial setting and frequency chart supplied with the meter.

For accurate and consistent results with the meter, these checkpoints should be used to check and adjust the calibration of the variable frequency oscillator *every* time a frequency is measured.

(f) The calibration information usually supplied with a meter of this type is in the form of a chart where specific dial settings are listed for discrete frequencies; the frequency spacing normally being uniform (100 cycles). It very often happens that the unknown frequency falls somewhere in between two listed adjacent frequencies and it is desired to know the unknown frequency more accurately than to the nearest 100 cycles. This may be determined by a process known as interpolation.

Let us suppose that the unknown frequency is zero beat at a dial setting of 173.6. Referring to the calibration chart, it is found that the dial setting for a frequency of 13248.3 kc is 173.1 and that for 13248.4 kc, the dial should read 174.2. It should be apparent that the unknown frequency is somewhere between 13248.3 and 13248.4 kc. On the assumption the dial setting vs frequency is a linear function over this small range, then the number of dial divisions per 100 cycles is 174.2—173.1 or 1.1. The number of dial divisions between 13248.3 kc and the unknown frequency is 173.6—173.1 or 0.5. The number of *cycles* between these two points, then, is $\frac{0.5}{1.1} \times 100$, or 45 cycles. This is added to the lower of the two listed frequencies so that the final frequency has been determined to be 13248.345 kc.

(g) The meter may be used as an RF generator for receiver alignment, etc., by using the RF output terminal coupled to the receiver under test. The variable frequency oscillator is an accurate frequency source but may be checked for accuracy by using the normal calibration check facilities as previously described.

Either a pure continuous wave or an amplitude-modulated wave can be obtained by proper positioning of the modulation switch.

(h) Normally the crystal oscillator's frequency should be checked on a routine basis; the period being determined by observation of the crystal's tendency to drift in frequency.

However, should the meter be used under unusual conditions such as high or low supply voltage or unusual climatic conditions, the crystal frequency should be checked against WWV and reset if found necessary.

Rough handling of the unit such as encountered in carrying it or shipping it dictates frequent crystal frequency checking. Any time the oscillator tube is replaced or any maintenance performed on the components of the oscillator circuit its frequency should be checked. It is good practice, also, to check the frequency when batteries are replaced in battery-powered use.

Q. 3.223. Draw a block diagram of an FM deviation (modulation) meter which includes the following stages:
Mixer
I–f amplifier
Limiter
Discriminator
Peak reading voltmeter
(a) Explain the operation of this instrument.
(b) Draw a circuit diagram and explain how the discriminator would be sensitive to frequency changes rather than amplitude changes.

A. For the block diagram, see Fig. 3.223(a).

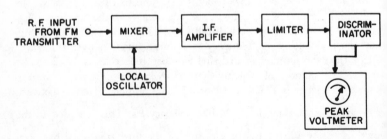

Fig. 3.223(a). Block diagram of an FM deviation meter.

(a) Essentially, the FM deviation meter is a very simple FM receiver. Referring to the block diagram, a sample of the output of the FM transmitter and a signal from the local oscillator are combined in the mixer and the difference frequency is selected by a tuned circuit and passed to the I-F amplifier. The I-F amplifier provides the required amplification and selectivity for the signal and feeds the limiter. The function of the limiter is to provide an output of constant amplitude regardless of the amplitude of its input. The output of the limiter is a signal of fixed amplitude but varying in frequency according to the modulation of the original signal. The discriminator recovers the original A-F modulating signal from the modulated wave and delivers it to the peak reading voltmeter for measurement.

Since the frequency deviation is defined as the maximum instantaneous excursion of the signal frequency from the carrier frequency it corresponds to the peak amplitude of the modulating frequency. The peak amplitude of the A-F output from the discriminator is proportional to the frequency deviation. A suitable voltmeter, responding only to the *peak* amplitude of the discriminator A-F output, can be calibrated directly in terms of frequency deviation.

(b) Figure 3.223(b) illustrates a typical schematic of a discriminator, while the graph in Fig. 3.223(c) shows the response of such a discriminator to varying frequency.

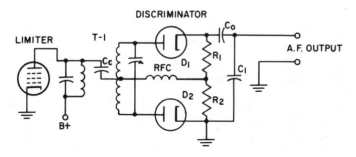

Fig. 3.223(b). Schematic diagram of an FM discriminator circuit.

The response, as shown, is the actual voltage obtained across resistors R_1 and R_2, in series. As can be seen, the instantaneous voltage output is dependent on the instantaneous frequency input. The conditions shown are for sine-wave modulation.

The dashed response curve shown would be that obtained if the amplitude of the input was somewhat reduced. This would result in a reduced output for the same frequency deviation. This possibility is eliminated by the use of a limiter ahead of the discriminator, thus assuring constant amplitude input.

D.   See also Q. 3.177(a) through (d).

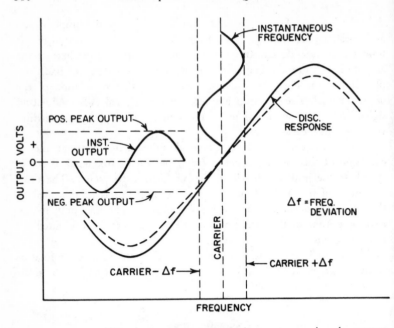

Fig. 3.223(c). The response of a discriminator to varying frequency.

Q. 3.224. Describe a usual method (and equipment used) for measuring the harmonic attenuation of a transmitter.

A.   One common method of measuring the harmonic attenuation of a transmitter is by use of a field strength meter. This instrument is an accurately calibrated receiver, whose output, indicated on a db meter, is proportional to the logarithm of the input voltage. The input to the instrument is normally derived from a short wire, used as an antenna, and is thus proportional to the field strength of the signal being measured.

The actual procedure is very simple. At some distance from the transmitter site, the meter is first tuned to the fundamental frequency and the output db noted. The meter is then tuned to the desired harmonic and the output db again noted. The difference in the two readings, indicates the harmonic attenuation of the transmitter.

D.   See Q. 3.203(a).

Q. 3.225. Why is it important that transmitters remain on frequency and that harmonics be attenuated?

A. (a) Each commercial transmitter is assigned a specific operating frequency and bandwidth channel. The purpose of such assignment is to insure that each broadcaster or broadcast service does not interfere with other stations on their assigned frequencies.

(b) Harmonic frequencies must be attenuated to prevent interference with stations in the same or other services.

D. For an example of harmonic interference, an AM broadcast station operating on 660 kilocycles might cause severe interference on 1320 kilocycles, a frequency which might be assigned to another AM broadcast station. This would occur in the case of appreciable second-harmonic radiation. In a similar manner, higher order harmonics might create interference with stations operating on the higher-harmonic frequencies. While the AM broadcast band was given as an example, harmonic radiation can occur (if not adequately suppressed) from any transmitter, causing possible interference with other services. An interesting fact, is that depending on the frequencies involved, harmonic frequencies may travel much further than the fundamental frequency, if not suppressed at the source.

BATTERIES

Q. 3.226. How does a primary cell differ from a secondary cell?

A. See Figure 3.226. A primary cell cannot be recharged after use, while a secondary cell can.

D. A primary cell cannot be recharged because the substance of one of the electrodes is chemically eroded; this occurs because the products of the chemical reaction are soluble in the electrolyte. An attempt to recharge it would not restore it to its first condition.

A secondary, or storage, cell, when it is discharged, has undergone a chemical change, but the new products are not soluble in the electrolyte. When the charging current is supplied, the chemical action is reversed; since the electrode material has not been dissolved, the cell will be restored to its charged condition.

Q. 3.227. What is the chemical composition of the electrolyte of a lead-acid storage cell?

A. The electrolyte is a dilute solution of sulphuric acid (H_2SO_4) in distilled water, which reaches a specific gravity of about 1.300 when fully charged.

D. See also Q. 3.228 and Q. 3.229. Ammonium hydroxide (ammonia), baking soda (sodium bicarbonate), or washing soda (sodium carbonate) may be used to neutralize acid electrolyte. Great care must be taken to allow none of these substances to get inside the battery.

The level of the electrolyte in a lead-acid cell should be kept about ¼ inch above the top of the plates. During charge and discharge some of the water (not acid) evaporates and so must occasionally be replaced with pure water. If the level is allowed to be continously low, the useful plate area will diminish and the capacity of the battery will be reduced.

Q. 3.228. Describe the care which should be given a group of storage cells to maintain them in good operating conditions?

A. The following items should be carefully checked in order to maintain a group of storage cells in good operating condition.

(1) Electrolyte should be kept about ¼ inch above plates by adding pure water when needed.

(2) Cells should always be kept fully charged, and on trickle charge when not in use.

(3) Cells should be frequently checked to determine state of charge.

(4) Any cell showing unusual conditions should be removed from the circuit.

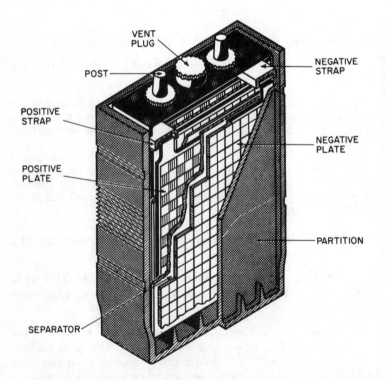

Fig. 3.226. Sectional view of storage cell.

(5) If electrolyte is spilled, it should be replaced after the battery is fully charged, using electrolyte of the rated specific gravity.

(6) Proper ventilation must be provided.

(7) Observe correct charge and discharge rates.

(8) Overcharge somewhat about once each month to remove sulphation.

(9) Keep exterior of battery dry and terminals coated with vaseline or other suitable lubricant.

(10) Keep all terminal connections clean and tight.

D. In general, the capacity of a lead-acid battery is decreased when low temperatures are present.

An important factor to be considered when lead-acid batteries are used under conditions of very low temperature is the specific gravity of the electrolyte. If the specific gravity is permitted to fall too low, there is a strong possibility that the electrolyte may freeze and split the battery. If the battery is kept fully charged, the freezing temperature is very low.

Q. 3.229. What may cause "sulphation" of a lead-acid storage cell?

A. Sulphation is a normal process in a lead-acid cell. However, excessive sulphation will be caused by overdischarging and by local action through improper charging.

The battery should be given an overcharge about once a month if in continual use, or kept on trickle charge when not in use for any extended period.

D. The effects are: (1) reduced terminal voltage, (2) increased internal resistance, (3) reduced power output, (4) possible buckling of the plates.

Sulphation is the formation of lead sulphate on the positive and negative plates of a battery during discharge. It is a normal process in the lead-acid cell and is caused by sulphuric acid molecules combining with lead dioxide and sponge lead to form lead sulphate ($PbSO_4$). If proper charging is neglected, the sulphate eventually hardens on the surface of the plates and prevents proper contact of the electrolyte with the active material of the plates. Sulphation is increased by allowing the battery to remain in a discharged condition, and by adding acid instead of properly charging the cells.

Q. 3.230. What will be the result of discharging a lead-acid storage cell at an excessively high current rate?

A. The effects are:

1. Reduction of output power. If the discharge rate is 8 times normal, the output power is only 50% of the normal output power.

2. Excessive heating.

3. Excessive evaporation of water.

D. If the battery is also overdischarged; this will result in the formation of excessive sulphation which will probably be difficult to remove with normal charging.

Q. 3.231. If the charging current through a storage battery is maintained at the normal rate, but its polarity is reversed, what will result?

A. In an Edison cell, reversing the polarity of the charge will cause no damage as long as the electrolyte temperature is kept below 115°F. The cell will charge slightly the reverse way. The battery should be completely discharged and then recharged correctly.

In a lead-acid cell reversing the charging polarity will cause no damage if the discharging effect is not permitted to become excessive. If permitted to continue in reverse direction, the battery will take on a reverse charge and become very sulphated. It should be fully discharged and then charged correctly at a low rate for as much as 48 hours. If the reverse charge is excessive the negative plates will be ruined.

D. See Q. 3.228 and Q. 3.232.

Q. 3.232. What is the approximate fully charged voltage of a lead-acid cell?

A. The fully charged terminal voltage is about 2.06 volts.

D. The cell is considered to be fully discharged when the terminal voltage drops to 1.75 volts. The actual fully charged voltage depends upon temperature and individual cell characteristics, but is close to the figure given.

Q. 3.233. What steps may be taken to prevent corrosion of lead-acid storage cell terminals?

A. The cell terminals should be occasionally cleaned and coated with vaseline or other suitable lubricant.

D. Connections should be made before the terminals are coated and care must be taken to see that all terminal connections are tight. See also Q. 3.228.

Q. 3.234. How is the capacity of a battery rated?

A. In ampere-hours.

D.   A typical auto battery may have a capacity of 120 ampere-hours. Such a battery can theoretically deliver 10 amperes continuously for 12 hours or 120 amperes for one hour. In practice, the performance may be somewhat less due to heating and chemical changes in the battery.

MOTORS AND GENERATORS

Q. 3.235. What is "power factor"? Give an example of how it is calculated. Discuss the construction and operation of dynamotors.

A.   (a)   Power factor is the factor by which the product of volts by amperes must be multiplied to obtain the true power. For an example of power factor, see the discussion.

(b)   A dynamotor is a combination motor and generator which utilizes a common field winding (or permanent field magnets). The two armatures (motor and generator) are mounted on a single shaft and require only two bearings. The motor is generally run by battery power, but may also be run from a-c or d-c lines, depending upon design requirements. The output from the generator is d-c. Typical output values are 200 volts at 50 ma., 300 volts at 200 ma., and 600 volts at 300 ma.

D.   (a)   If a circuit is purely resistive, or the voltage is d.c., its actual power consumption may be found by the formula $P = E \times I$. This is also the *apparent* power of a circuit, since E and I would be measured by a voltmeter and ammeter, respectively. However, a pure reactance consumes *no power,* so that if a circuit contains both resistance and reactance, E being alternating, the product of $E \times I$ (apparent power) is not the actual power being consumed. This is so because there is now a phase angle introduced between the voltage and current in the resistance. In order to find the "true" power, the apparent power $(E \times I)$ must be corrected by a factor which takes into account the effect of the phase angle. To find the true power of a circuit multiply the apparent power $(E \times I)$ by the cosine of the phase angle, which equals $\dfrac{R}{Z}$ Thus true power equals $E \times I \times \dfrac{R}{Z}$. For example, a circuit may have one ampere flowing through an inductance and a 3 ohm resistance. If it is d.c., the voltage is 3 volts, the power is 3 watts. If the inductance is such that 5 volts, a-c, is required to give one ampere, the power is still 3 watts $(= I^2 R)$, but the volt-ampere product is $1 \times 5 = 5$. The power factor to give 3 watts is therefore $3/5 = 0.6$.

The power factor is equal to $\dfrac{R}{Z}$, where Z is the a-c impedance, in this case 5 ohms $= \dfrac{5 \text{ volts}}{1 \text{ ampere}} \cdot \dfrac{R}{Z} = \dfrac{3}{5} = 0.6$, as before.

Since the phase-angle, A, between the current and voltage is such that $\cos A = 0.6$, A is about 53°.

True power is measured directly with a wattmeter, which automatically takes the phase-angle into account.

(b) Normally, the output voltage of a dynamotor may be regulated only by changing the speed of the motor. A series resistance in the output line could be used to reduce the available output voltage.

The principal advantages of a dynamotor are its compactness and operating efficiency. It is possible to operate dynamotors from storage batteries. One disadvantage of a dynamotor is that its voltage output is dependent on the stability of the source voltage.

Dynamotors are used extensively in aircraft and other portable installations to supply plate and screen grid power. A dynamotor has a higher efficiency than a motor-generator set, but its output voltage cannot be readily varied, and its regulation is poor.

Q. 3.236.   List the comparative advantages and disadvantages of motor-generator and transformer-rectifier power supplies.

A.   The advantages of motor-generator power supplies are as follows·

(1) Simple output voltage control.

(2) Little filtering required, due to high ripple frequency.

(3) Very rugged in construction and will stand much abuse.

(4) Self-rectifying, requires no tubes.

(5) Can be operated from either a-c or d-c lines,

Disadvantages of motor-generator power supplies are:

(1) High initial cost.

(2) Difficult to repair.

(3) Subjected to bearing troubles and other difficulties attendant with rotating machinery.

(4) Equipment is noisy and causes vibration.

(5) Large bulk and weight.

(6) Requires comparatively frequent inspection and service, as to lubrication, brushes and commutator.

(7) Limited high voltage available.

(8) Causes radio frequency interference from brush sparking.

The advantages of transformer-rectifier power supplies are:

(1) Low initial cost.

(2) Practically unlimited high voltages available.

(3) Simple to repair and replace components, compared with motor generator.

(4) Completely electronic—no moving parts to service.

(5) Quiet and practically vibrationless in operation.

(6) Clean.

(7) Can be built as an integral portion of transmitter.

(8) Usually lighter and smaller than equivalent motor-generator.

(9) Requires no inspection, except when trouble occurs.

Disadvantages of transformer-rectifier power supplies are:

(1) Voltage output not easily controlled.

(2) Requires large filter components.

(3) Tubes are fragile.

(4) Usually must be operated only from a-c lines.

(5) Tubes must occasionally be replaced.

(6) High voltage windings cannot stand much overload.

D. See Q. 3.65, Q. 3.66.

Q. 3.237. What determines the speed of a synchronous motor? An induction motor? A d-c series motor?

A. (a) The speed of a synchronous motor is determined by the number of pairs of poles and the line frequency. (b) The speed of an induction motor is determined by the number of pairs of poles, the frequency, and to some extent, the load. (c) The speed of a d-c series motor is determined chiefly by the load.

Q. 3.238. Describe the action and list the main characteristics of a shunt d-c generator?

A. The main characteristic of a shunt-wound d-c generator (Fig. 3.238) is the good voltage regulation under varying load conditions. The starting of such a generator takes advantage of the residual magnetic field of the field poles. As the armature starts rotating, an emf is induced into it due to the residual field. The first emf causes some

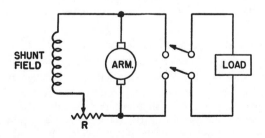

Fig. 3.238. Voltage control of shunt d-c generator.

current to flow through the high resistance field, thus increasing the field strength and the output voltage to normal value. Most of the current is delivered to the load, due to the high field resistance. The field is composed of very many turns of fine wire. A series field rheostat is used to control the output voltage.

D.   See also Q. 3.245.

Q. 3.239.   Name four causes of excessive sparking at the brushes of a d-c motor or generator.

A.   Several causes are:
1.   Brushes not properly set at neutral point.
2.   Weak spring tension on brushes.
3.   Worn brushes.
4.   Motor overloaded or started too rapidly.
5.   Open or short circuit in armature coil.
6.   Dirt on commutator or worn brushes.
7.   Commutator worn eccentric.
8.   High (protruding) mica insulation between commutator bars or commutator bars of uneven height.

D.   (a) "Commutating poles" or "interpoles" are added in order to reduce brush sparking without the necessity of moving the brushes.

Commutating poles are small field poles consisting of a few turns of heavy wire which are located between the main field poles of the machine. The commutating poles are connected in series with the armature, and in a motor are of the same polarity as the preceding main field pole. In a simple motor, as the load increases, the brushes have to be pushed backward to keep them in a neutral position for sparkless commutation. The commutating poles in a motor effectively twist the field forward, in proportion to the current taken, to keep the neutral position at the fixed brushes. ("Neutral position" refers to the position of the brushes on the commutator of a d-c motor or generator, relative to the field poles, at which minimum brush sparking will occur.)

When the motor or generator is stationary and no current flows through the armature, the neutral position occurs when the armature coil in contact with a brush is exactly half way between two adjacent field poles. At this position no emf is induced in the armature coil. In any other position, as the brush transfers to another commutator segment, it is momentarily shorting the armature coil and causes a strong magnetic field to be set up which collapses when the brush reaches the next commutator segment. It is this collapsing field which induces a large counter-emf and causes sparking. If a heavy current is flowing through the windings, the inductance will maintain a current flow, regardless of absence of external field poles; the brushes must leave the commutator segment at the time that the induced voltage has brought the current to zero. This position is not the same for different loads. As the load increases, the brushes should be moved forward in the direction of rotation to reduce sparking, in the case of a generator, while in a motor the brushes should be moved backwards against the rotation. The commutating poles keep the neutral position fixed, by effectively shifting the field.

(b) When a d-c motor is first starting, a very large armature current exists due to the lack of sufficient armature cemf. This large armature current exists only until the armature reaches sufficient speed so that the cemf becomes effective in limiting the current. If too long a time is taken in starting the motor with a hand starter, the large current value will overheat and possibly burn out the starting resistors which are only rated for intermittent operation. The starter handle should be held in each position only long enough to bring the motor speed up to the value which is normally present at that particular setting.

(c) A short circuit in an armature coil will cause excessive sparking at the commutator brushes, overheating of the machine, reduction of speed under load and excessive armature current.

The effects of a short circuit in an armature coil are similar to the effects of a short circuit in the windings of a transformer. A very large circulating current would be set up in the shorted portion, and the magnetic field thus produced would be in such a direction as to cancel the normal magnetic field of the armature. This would result in a decreased amount of torque and speed and an excessive armature current with attendant overheating.

Q. 3.240. How may radio frequency interference, often caused by sparking at the brushes of a high-voltage generator, be minimized?

A. By the use of brush by-pass capacitors, and high and low frequency filters.

D. Sparking interference is usually caused by the fact that certain elements within the generator form tuned circuits of various frequencies, and that connections and power leads behave as antennas to radiate these frequencies. The action of the spark in this case is similar to a regular spark transmitter, supplying the energy to keep the tuned circuits oscillating. If spark interference suppression is to be successful, the radiating leads must be effectively terminated (as far as radiating frequencies are concerned) very close to the generator.

If a commutator motor is being used, a low-pass filter should be installed close to it, in the motor supply line. With respect to the generator proper, a ripple filter (low-pass) should be connected in the high voltage line, as close to the generator as possible. Shielding of long connecting leads will reduce radiation and interference. Brush by-pass capacitors should be connected from each brush to ground. If some interference is still present, a "pi" filter made up of an r-f choke and two r-f by-pass capacitors can be located close to the generator in the high-voltage line and ahead of the ripple filter.

Q. 3.241. How may the output voltage of a separately excited a-c generator, at constant output frequency, be varied?

A. The most practical means would be to vary the output of the d-c exciting generator by means of a series field rheostat.

D. The output voltage of an a-c generator depends upon (among other things) the magnetic strength of the generator field. A simple method of varying the output voltage, therefore, would be to vary the current of the exciter supply by means of a series rheostat. Any other means of varying the alternator field current would have equivalent effect.

Q. 3.242. What is the purpose of a commutator on a d-c motor? On a d-c generator?

A. The function of the commutator is to periodically change the armature coils which contact the brushes and thus maintain a condition of uni-directional current in the output of a generator, and an alternating current in the armature of a motor.

D. All generators and motors are essentially a-c devices, and thus the commutator is really a mechanical inverter. In a d-c generator, the windings have a.c. induced, and the output would normally be a.c., were it not for the fact that the commutator action switches in a new set of armature coils just when the current in the original coil starts to reverse direction.

In a motor the switching action is such that the current in the armature is made to reverse periodically, and thus becomes a.c., so that as an armature coil leaves one field pole, it will be repelled from it and attracted to the next.

Q. 3.243. What may cause a motor-generator bearing to overheat?

A. The most obvious cause would be lack of lubrication or incorrect type of lubrication. Other causes might be: consistent overload, lack of ventilation, dirt in bearings, or misalignment which may result from warping or distortion of base or frame.

D. The first rule in treating an overheated bearing is never to stop the machine, as the bearings might seize (or "freeze") when contraction takes place. If possible, remove the load and slow down the machine considerably. While running slowly make every effort to cool the machine by forced air cooling or other means available. A large quantity of oil and graphite, if available, should be continuously applied while the machine is running slowly. Continue this treatment until the bearing cools to normal temperature. Flush out with flush oil or kerosene, and then lubricate with the proper grade of oil. If the heating has not been too severe the bearing will still remain in good condition. If the cause of overheating was due to any overload condition, the overload should be removed before bringing the machine back to normal speed.

Q. 3.244. What materials should be used to clean the commutator of a motor or generator?

A. The commutator may be cleaned with a piece of very fine sandpaper or commutator polishing paste; never use emery.

D. A commutator polishing agent is available, which is applied with a clean cloth. The commutator is then polished while the machine is running.
Care should be taken in the handling of any rotating machinery, and especially in the handling of high voltage generators, in order to avoid injury and shock.

Q. 3.245. If the field of a shunt wound d-c motor were opened while the machine is running under no load, what would be the probable result(s)?

A. The motor would race at an ever-increasing speed; and if unchecked it may destroy itself due to centrifugal forces, provided that fuses or circuit breakers did not act sooner to protect it.

D. Ordinarily the armature current is greatly limited due to the counter-emf developed in the armature as the field is cut by the windings. Since the armature current is limited, the torque and thus the speed is limited. If the field coil opens, most of this cemf disappears, and the armature current rises to very high values, increasing the torque and speed almost without limit.

MICRO-WAVE EQUIPMENT

Q. 3.246. Describe the physical structure of a klystron tube and explain how it operates as an oscillator.

A. See Q. 8.48.

D. See also Q. 3.251, Q. 3.248, Q. 8.42, Q. 8.46 and Q. 8.47.

Q. 3.247. Draw a diagram showing the construction and explain the principles of operation of a traveling-wave tube.

A. See Fig. 3.247. A traveling-wave amplifier is a micro-wave amplifier which may be used at frequencies well in excess of 7500 megacycles. The tube in the figure was designed for a mid-frequency of 3600 megacycles and a bandwidth of 800 megacycles. Bandwidths up to 5000 megacycles or more are possible using tubes with higher mid-frequency design.

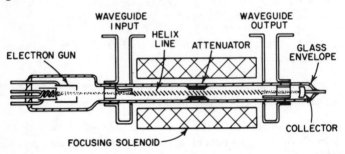

Fig. 3.247. The details of construction of a traveling-wave amplifier. (Courtesy of International Telephone and Telegraph Corp.)

The tube is made up of the following major components:
1. Electron gun.
2. Helix line.
3. Focusing solenoid.
4. Collector anode.

The length of the helix may be 6 inches or more and consists of tightly wound wire. When in use, the tube is inserted into two waveguides as shown; one for input and one for output. Input and output coupling is accomplished by short stubs connected to each end of the helix and mounted so as to provide or receive energy from each waveguide (see the figure). The helix winding and collector are operated at a high positive potential (in this case, about 1600 volts) with respect to the cathode of the electron gun. The electron gun forms a beam of electrons which is focused electrically at the gun end and magnetically along the length of the helix by the focusing solenoid. The focused and accelerated beam is shot through the inside of the helix and parallel to its axis. It is picked up by the collector anode, located at the far end of the tube.

Energy in the form of electromagnetic waves are introduced to the tube via the input waveguide, travel along the helix wire and are coupled to the output waveguide. Because the waves follow the helix wire, their actual forward velocity is only about one-tenth that of light. At the acceleration voltage chosen, the beam of electrons inside the helix moves forward at a velocity slightly greater than that of the wave. (This is the condition of maximum tube gain.) The amplification of the tube occurs by virtue of the interaction of the electrostatic component of the electromagnetic field and the electron beam. The polarity of the electrostatic component will have the effect of producing velocity modulation of the electron beam (similar to klystron operation). When the electron beam is caused to speed up (positive electric field) it removes energy from the wave. When it is caused to slow down, it supplies energy to the wave (negative electric field). Now remember that the electron beam velocity is slightly greater than the wave velocity. A portion of the beam originating during a positive electric field will be further accelerated and will move relatively quickly out of the positive field and into the negative field farther down the tube. It will be slowed down by the negative field, giving up energy to it. Since it remains longer (slower) in the negative field, more energy is given up to the wave than was taken from it and amplification results. Amplification is governed by the relative velocity of the beam with respect to the wave and also (within limits) by the length of the helix. A longer helix produces greater gain. An attenuator is situated at the approximate middle of the helix line. The function of this attenuator is to prevent self-oscillation from occurring in the traveling-wave tube. It does this by reducing the magnitude of feedback components to a level which is incapable of sustaining oscillations.

D.   See also Q. 3.246 and Q. 3.248.

Q. 3.248.   Describe the physical structure of a multianode magnetron and explain how it operates.

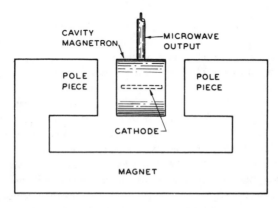

Fig. 3.248(a). Typical assembly of a multianode magnetron. The magnetic field is perpendicular to the electric field from cathode to plate(s).

A. (a) A multianode magnetron consists basically of a multiple-cavity assembly, a centrally located cathode, an output-power coupling device and a very-powerful permanent magnet. A typical magnetron assembly is shown in Fig. 3.248(a).

The body of the magnetron tube is the cylindrical anode. It consists of a copper cylinder in which resonant cavities are cut with high precision and which largely determine the operating frequency of the magnetron. The frequency is influenced to a lesser extent by the strength of the magnetic and electric fields within the tube. The general arrangement of the components within the anode cylinder are shown in Fig. 3.248(b).

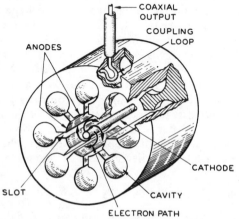

Fig. 3.248(b). Sketch illustrating the construction of the anode cylinder of a typical magnetron.

(b) Because of the interacting electric and magnetic fields, electrons which are emitted from the cathode trace circular paths just outside of the slots leading to each cavity. Initially the cavities are shock-excited into oscillation by this electron motion. Once the cavities are oscillating, the field produced by each cavity plays an important part in the continued oscillation of the magnetron. When an electron stream is moving past one of the cavities, the field across the cavity must have a polarity capable of *slowing* down the electron stream. When this occurs, the stream *gives up energy* to the cavity to sustain oscillations. If the cavity field is such as to *speed up* the electron stream, the electrons will *remove* energy from the cavity and *reduce* the amplitude of oscillations. In practice, more electrons give up energy to the cavities than remove energy. As a consequence, magnetrons operate with efficiencies varying from 20 to 50 percent, depending upon the type of magnetron and the manner in which it is operated.

D. Magnetron oscillators (they are not used as amplifiers) are widely used in radar sets as pulsed-power oscillators of high-peak power. Moderate-power magnetrons transmit in the order of 50 to 105 kw of peak power, while peak outputs of 1 mw or more are found in high-power radar sets. (Klystrons having peak-output powers of 1 mw or more are also used in some high-power radar sets.) The frequency ranges in which magnetrons are used, range from about 1,000 mc to well over 30,000 mc.

In order to obtain high peak-power outputs without overloading, most magnetrons are operated at a low-*duty cycle* (see below). Typically, a moderate-power magnetron may be pulsed (at its cathode) with a negative 15,000 volt pulse, having a duration of about 1 microsecond and a pulse repetition-rate of about 1000 cps. It may require a peak pulse current of about 20 amperes. The duty cycle may be calculated as, Duty Cycle = Pulse width × Pulse Repetition Frequency.

For the example above:

$$\text{Duty Cycle} = 1 \ \mu s \times 1000 = 1 \times 10^{-6} \times 10^{3} = 10^{-3} = .001$$

Duty cycles in the order of .001 are very common in pulsed magnetron operation.

While Figure 3.248(b) shows a coaxial power output, it is perhaps even more common to feed a waveguide output directly from the magnetron. In this event, the coupling loop from the cavity may lead directly to a quarter-wave radiator coupled inside of a waveguide. Power is then transferred through a length of waveguide to the radar antenna. It is interesting to note that the output coupling loop is only present in one of the multiple cavities. However, the cavities are so tightly coupled together that all of the power is extracted from the magnetron.

Q. 3.249.   Discuss the following with respect to waveguides:
(a) Relationship between frequency and size.
(b) Modes of operation.
(c) Coupling of energy into the waveguide.
(d) General principles of operation.

A. (a) For a rectangular waveguide, the wider dimension must be greater than one-half wavelength, while the narrow dimension should be less than one-half wavelength (see discussion). The length is not critical, however, as in any conductor, the losses increase in proportion to the length of the waveguide run.

(b) The mode of operation of a waveguide defines the manner in which the electric and magnetic fields arrange themselves inside of the waveguide. Each field configuration is called a "mode." Different modes may be excited by using different schemes of excitation. (Generally, probes of some type.) The possible modes are determined by the shape of the waveguide. Modes are separated into two groups, as follows:

(1) The *transverse magnetic* (TM) group has its magnetic field in the direction transverse to the direction of propagation.

(2) The *transverse electric* (TE) group has its electric field transverse to the direction of propagation and has a component of magnetic field in this direction.

Each particular mode is identified by the letters for the group followed by two numerals. Examples are $TM_{1,0}$ or $TE_{1,0}$.

Figure 3.249(a) illustrates the distribution of the electric and magnetic fields in a rectangular waveguide excited in the $TE_{1,0}$ mode. Note in the end view that one-half wavelength of electric field lines appears across the wider dimension. The electric field is strongest at the center

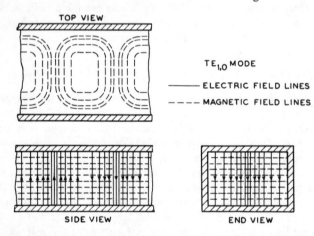

TOP VIEW

$TE_{1,0}$ MODE

——— ELECTRIC FIELD LINES

— — — MAGNETIC FIELD LINES

SIDE VIEW

END VIEW

Fig. 3.249(a). Illustration of the electric and magnetic fields in rectangular waveguide excited in the $TE_{1,0}$ mode.

and weakest at the two ends. The electric-field lines are the vertical solid lines with arrows, while the magnetic-field lines are dashed and are perpendicular to the electric-field lines. (See also Q. 3.14, Q. 3.196 and Q. 3.197.)

(c) Coupling of energy to a waveguide may be accomplished in one of three principal ways, as follows:

(1) Insertion of a small loop of wire which couples to the electromagnetic field, as shown in Fig. 3.249(b).

(2) Insertion of a small straight probe which couples to the electrostatic field, as shown in Fig. 3.249(c).

(3) Linkage of the fields within the waveguide by external fields via the use of slots or holes in the wall of the waveguide.

(d) The waveguide operates on its ability to conduct electromagnetic waves within its boundaries. The energy is considered to be completely contained in these waves and is not carried as a current in wires. Be-

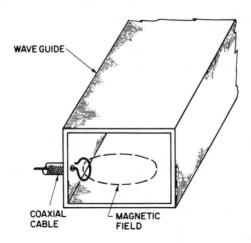

Fig. 3.249(b). Excitation of a waveguide by means of a magnetic loop of wire.

cause of skin effect, no energy escapes through the waveguide walls. Energy is introduced into and removed from a waveguide by one of the three methods described in (c) above.

D. (a) In rectangular waveguides, one mode (the $TE_{1,0}$) is considered to be superior. A rectangular waveguide can easily be constructed to be excited only in this mode. As mentioned in A.(a) above, the wide dimension must be greater than one-half wavelength, but not greater

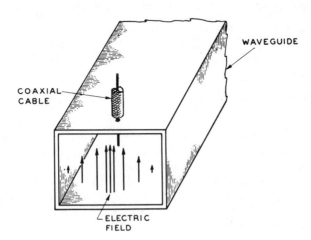

Fig. 3.249(c). Excitation of waveguide by means of electrostatic probe.

than one wavelength. Also the narrow dimension must be less than one-half wavelength. (This condition is illustrated in Fig. 3.249(a).) This mode is frequently called the "fundamental" mode. Its uses ensures that no unwanted, spurious modes will exist to waste power in the system. (See also Q. 8.31.)

(b) For a comparison between waveguides and coaxial lines, see Q. 8.30.

(c) Some advantages of waveguides are as follows:

1. Lowest losses of any conventional transmission line at the frequencies for which they are practical.

2. A hollow waveguide can transmit higher power than a coaxial line of the same size.

3. A hollow waveguide is more rugged than a coaxial line because there is no inner conductor or supports.

4. Simpler construction than a coaxial line.

5. Complete shielding.

(d) Some disadvantages of waveguides are as follows:

1. The minimum size is proportional to the wavelength used. **For a rectangular guide the height must be approximately ½ wavelength or more.**

2. Because of the size, waveguides are not extensively used below about 3000 megacycles (10 cm). For 10 meter waves the pipe would have to be 25 feet wide.

3. Installation and operation of hollow waveguides is considerably more difficult than for other types of lines.

Q. 3.250. Describe briefly the construction and purpose of a waveguide. What precautions should be taken in the installation and maintenance of a waveguide to insure proper operation?

A. (a) For construction, see Q. 8.28.

(b) For purpose and characteristics, see Q. 8.30 and 3.249.

(c) For installation and maintenance, see Q. 8.27, 8.28, 8.29, 8.33, 8.34, 8.35.

Q. 3.251. Explain the principles of operation of a cavity resonator.

A. A cavity resonator is a resonant circuit device, having very high Q and capable of being efficiently operated in the microwave frequency region. A cavity resonator is actually a measured section of waveguide whose resonant frequency depends upon its dimensions. Typical shapes for cavities are rectangular, cylindrical, spherical and doughnut. Cavities are energized in the same manner as waveguides, as described in Q. 3.249(c), above. Two of the more commonly used types of cavities are illustrated in Fig. 3.251(a).

D. A resonant cavity may be considered as merely another type of tuned circuit, but one which is able to function efficiently at microwave

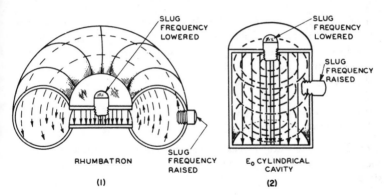

Fig. 3.251(a). Two common types of resonant cavities, showing electric-field lines (solid) and magnetic-field lines (dashed) and means of adjusting the frequency. Part (1) shows a "rhumbatron (or doughnut) type. A cylindrical type is shown in part (2).

frequencies, where the conventional coil and capacitor circuit becomes virtually useless. However, as shown in Fig. 3.251(b), the resonant cavity may be considered as developed from a single turn of wire and a capacitor. Additional turns are added in parallel until a complete rhumbatron (doughnut) cavity is formed. Placing additional turns in parallel, as shown, has the effect of reducing the inductance, thereby increasing the resonant frequency and the Q of the circuit. (Note that this type of development is not strictly accurate, but is a helpful concept in the introduction to the study of resonant cavities.) Cavities are used as resonant

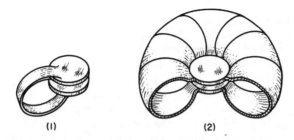

Fig. 3.251(b). The development of a resonant cavity can be considered as starting with a single turn of wire and a capacitor, as in (1), and putting turns in parallel until a completely enclosed volume results, as in (2); this is called a rhumbatron cavity.

circuits at frequencies from about 1000 mc to frequencies in excess of 30,000 mc. The Q of a cavity may be in the order of several thousand.

Cavities are commonly used as the resonant circuits for:

1. Magnetrons (see Q. 3.248).
2. Klystrons (see Q. 3.246 and Q. 8.48).
3. Echo boxes (see Q. 8.38).
4. TR and ATR tubes (see Q. 8.51).
5. Microwave wavemeters.

Q. 3.252.   How are cavities installed in vertical waveguides to prevent moisture from collecting? Why are long horizontal waveguides not desired?

A.   (a) To prevent moisture accumulation, the cavity may be mounted through a choke joint employing moisture-sealing gaskets. The same technique may be used at each choke-coupling flange of a waveguide run to prevent the introduction of moisture into the waveguide. In addition, pressurizing the waveguide with dry air or an inert gas will prevent the entrance of moisture.

(b) See Q. 8.29.

D.   (a) For description of choke joint, see Q. 8.35.

Choke joints are also commonly used to join such items as magnetrons, echo boxes, TR and ATR tubes and klystron outputs to waveguides (see Fig. 8.41(c)).

(b) See also Q. 8.33, Q. 8.41 and Q. 3.250.

RULES AND REGULATIONS

Q. 3.253.   Define the following words and phrases listed under Section 2.1 of the Commission's Rules. (R & R 2.1)

A.   R & R 2.1: Definitions:

(a) Authorized frequency. The frequency assigned to a station by the FCC and specified in the instrument of authorization.

(b) Carrier: In a frequency stabilized system, the sinusoidal component of a modulated wave whose frequency is independent of the modulating wave; or the output of a transmitter when the modulating wave is made zero; or a wave generated at a point in the transmitting system and subsequently modulated by the signal; or a wave generated locally at the receiving terminal which, when combined with the sidebands in a suitable detector, produces the modulating wave.

(c) Base station: A land station in the land mobile service carrying on a service with land mobile stations.

(d) Coast station: A land station in the maritime mobile service.

(e) Earth station: A station in the earth-space service located either on the earth's surface or on an object which is limited to flight between points on the earth's surface.

(f) Fixed station. A station in the fixed service.

(g) Space station. A station in the earth-space service or the space service located on an object which is beyond, or intended to go beyond, the major portion of the earth's atmosphere and which is not intended for flight between points on the earth's surface.

(h) Harmful interference: Any emission, radiation or induction which endangers the functioning of a radio-navigation service or of other safety services or seriously degrades, obstructs, or repeatedly interrupts a radio-communication service operating in accordance with this chapter.

(i) Land mobile service. A mobile station in the land mobile service capable of surface movement within the geographical limits of a country or continent.

(j) Land station. A station in the mobile service not intended to be used while in motion.

(k) Mobile service. A service of radio communication between mobile and land stations, or between mobile stations.

(1) Primary standard of frequency. The primary standard of frequency for radio frequency measurements shall be the National Bureau of Standards, Department of Commerce, Washington, D.C. The operating frequency of all radio stations will be determined by comparison with this standard or the standard signals of stations WWV, WWVH, or WWVB, of the National Bureau of Standards.

Q. 3.254. What is the frequency range associated with the following general frequency subdivisions? (R & R 2.101)

  (a) VLF
  (b) LF
  (c) MF
  (d) HF
  (e) VHF
  (f) UHF
  (g) SHF
  (h) EHF

A. (a) VLF (very low frequency). Below 30 kc/s.
  (b) LF (low frequency). 30 to 300 kc/s.
  (c) MF (medium frequency). 300 to 3000 kc/s.
  (d) HF (high frequency). 3 to 30 Mc/s.
  (e) VHF (very high frequency). 30 to 300 Mc/s.
  (f) UHF (ultra high frequency). 300 to 3000 Mc/s.
  (g) SHF (super high frequency). 3 to 30 Gc/s.
  (h) EHF (extremely high frequency). 30 to 300 Gc/s.

Q. 3.255. What is meant by the following emission designations? (R & R 2.201)

(a) A3

(b) A3A

(c) A5C

(d) F3

(e) F5

(f) P3D

A. (a) A3: Amplitude modulation, telephony, double sideband transmission.

(b) A3A: Amplitude modulation, telephony, single sideband, reduced carrier.

(c) A5C: Amplitude modulation, television, vestigial (partial) sideband.

(d) F3: Frequency (or phase) modulation, telephony.

(e) F5: Frequency (or phase) modulation, television.

(f) P3D: Pulse modulation, telephony, amplitude modulated pulses.

Q. 3.256. What is the basic difference between type approval and type acceptance of transmitting equipment? (R & R 2.551)

A. Type approval contemplates tests conducted by FCC personnel. Type acceptance is based on data concerning the equipment submitted by the manufacturer or the individual prospective licensee.

Q. 3.257. Define the following words and phrases listed under Section 89.3 of the Commission's Rules.

A. (a) Authorized bandwidth: The maximum width of the band of frequencies, as specified in the authorizations, to be occupied by an emission.

(b) Bandwidth occupied by an emission: The width of the frequency band (normally specified in kilocycles) containing those frequencies upon which a total of 99 percent of the radiated power appears, extended to include any discrete frequency upon which the power is at least 0.25 percent of the total radiated power.

(c) Station authorization: Any construction permit, license, or special temporary authorization issued by the Commission.

Q. 3.258. May stations in the Public Safety Radio Services be operated for short periods of time without a station authorization issued by the Commission? (R & R 89.51)

A. No radio transmitter shall be operated in the Public Safety Radio Services except under and in accordance with a proper station authorization granted by the Federal Communications Commission.

Q. 3.259. What notification must be forwarded to the Engineer in Charge of the Commission's district office prior to testing a new radio transmitter in the Public Safety Radio Service (which has been obtained under a construction permit issued by the Commission)? (R & R 89.53)

A. Procedure for obtaining a Radio Station Authorization and for Commencement of Operation:

(a) Persons desiring to install and operate radio transmitting equipment should first submit an application for a radio station authorization.

(b) When construction permit only has been issued for a base, fixed or mobile station and installation has been completed in accordance with the terms of the construction permit and the applicable rules of the Commission, the permittee shall proceed as follows:

(1) Notify the Engineer-in-Charge of the local radio district of the date on which the transmitter will first be tested in such manner as to produce radiation, giving name of the permittee, station location, call sign, and frequencies on which tests are to be conducted. This notification shall be made in writing at least two days in advance of the test date. FCC Form 456 may be used for this purpose. No reply from the radio district office is necessary before the tests are begun.

Q. 3.260. Where may standard forms applicable to the Public Safety Radio Services be obtained? (R & R 89.59)

A. To assure that necessary information is supplied in a consistent manner by all persons, standard forms are prescribed for use in connection with the majority of applications and reports submitted for Commission consideration. Standard numbered forms applicable to the Public Safety Radio Services may be obtained from the Washington, D.C. Office of the Commission, or from any of its engineering field offices.

Q. 3.261. In general, what type of changes in authorized stations must be approved by the Commission? What type does not require Commission approval? (R & R 89.75)

A. Authority for certain changes in authorized stations must be obtained from the Commission before these changes are made, while other changes do not require prior Commission approval. The following paragraphs describe the conditions under which prior Commission approval is or is not necessary.

(a) Proposed changes which will result in operation inconsistent with any of the terms of the current authorization require that an application for modification of construction permit and/or license be submitted to the Commission. The request for authorization shall be submitted on FCC Form 400, or, in the case of microwave stations, on FCC Form 402, and shall be accompanied by exhibits and supplementary statements as required by R & R 89.63.

(b) Proposed changes which will not depart from any of the terms of the outstanding authorization for the station involved may be made without prior Commission approval. Included in such changes is the substitution of various makes of transmitting equipment at any station provided the particular equipment to be installed is included in the Commission's "List of Equipment Acceptable for Licensing." In addition it must be designated for use in the Public Safety, Industrial, and Land Transportation Radio Services. The substitute equipment must employ the same type of emission and must not exceed the power limitations as set forth in the station authorization.

Q. 3.262.   The carrier frequency of a transmitter in the Public Safety Radio Service must be maintained within what percentage of the licensed value? Assume the station is operating at 160 Mc/s with a licensed power of 50 watts. (R & R 89.103)

A.   The carrier frequency must be maintained within .0005 percent.

Q. 3.263.   What is the authorized bandwidth and frequency deviation of Public Safety stations operating at about 30 Mc/s? At about 160 Mc/s? (R & R 89.107)

A.   (a) For 30 megacycles, the authorized bandwidth is 20 kilocycles and the frequency deviation is 5 kilocycles.

(b) For 160 megacycles the specifications are the same as (a) above.

Q. 3.264.   What is the maximum percentage modulation allowed by the Commission's rules for stations in the Public Safety Radio Services which utilize amplitude modulation? (R & R 89.109)

A.   The maximum is 100 percent on negative peaks.

Q. 3.265.   Define "control point" as the term refers to transmitters in the Public Safety Radio Service. (R & R 89.113)

A.   A control point is an operating position which:

(a) Must be under the control and supervision of the licensee.

(b) Is a position at which the monitoring facilities are installed.

(c) Is a position at which a person immediately responsible for the operation of the transmitter is stationed.

Q. 3.266.   Outline the transmitter measurements required by the Commission's rules for stations in the Public Safety Radio Service. (R & R 89.115)

A.   Transmitter measurements. (a) The licensee of each station shall employ a suitable procedure to determine that the carrier frequency of each transmitter, authorized to operate with a plate input power to the final radio-frequency stage in excess of 3 watts, is maintained within the tolerance prescribed. This determination shall be made, and the results thereof entered in the station records, in accordance with the following:

(1) When the transmitter is initially installed:

(2) When any change is made in the transmitter which may affect the carrier frequency or the stability thereof;

(3) At intervals not to exceed one year for transmitters employing crystal-controlled oscillators.

(4) At intervals not to exceed one month for transmitters not employing crystal-controlled oscillators.

(b) The licensee of each station shall employ a suitable procedure to determine that plate power input to the final radio frequency stage of each base station or fixed station transmitter, authorized to operate with a plate-input power to the final radio frequency stage in excess of 3 watts, does not exceed the maximum figure specified on the current station authorization. Where the transmitter is so constructed making a direct measurement of plate current in the final radio frequency stage impracticable, the plate input to the final radio frequency stage is determined from a measurement of the cathode current. The required entry shall indicate clearly the quantities that were measured, the measured values thereof, and the method of determining the plate-power input from the measured values. This determination shall be made, and the results thereof entered in the station records, in accordance with the following:

(1) When the transmitter is initially installed;

(2) When any change is made in the transmitter which may increase the transmitter power input;

(3) At intervals not to exceed one year.

(c) The licensee of each station shall employ a suitable procedure to determine that the modulation of each transmitter authorized to operate with a plate input power to the final radio-frequency stage in excess of 3 watts does not exceed the limits specified. This determination shall be made and the results thereof entered in the station records, in accordance with the following:

(1) When the transmitter is initially installed;

(2) When any change is made in the transmitter which may affect the modulation characteristics;

(3) At intervals not to exceed one year.

(d) The determinations required by paragraphs (a), (b), and (c) of this section may, at the option of the licensee be made by any qualified engineering measurement service, in which case, the required record entries shall show the name and address of the engineering measurements service as well as the name of the person making the measurements.

(e) In the case of mobile transmitters, the determinations required by paragraphs (a) and (c) of this section may be made at a test or service bench: *Provided,* the measurements are made under local conditions equivalent to actual operating conditions; That after installation the transmitter is given a routine check to determine that it is capable of being satisfactorily received by an appropriate receiver.

Q. 3.267. What are the general requirements for transmitting the identification announcements for stations in the Public Safety Radio Service? (R & R 89.153)

A.   Station identification.

(a) Except as provided in paragraph (b) of this section, the required identification for stations in these services shall be the assigned call signal.

(b) In lieu of meeting the requirements of paragraph (a) of this section, mobile units in the Police, Fire, Forestry-Conservation, Highway Maintenance, and Local Government Radio Services operating above 30 Mc/s may identify by means of an identifier other than the assigned call signal: *Provided,* that such identifier contain, as a minimum, the name of the governmental subdivision under which the unit is licensed; that the identifier is not composed of letters or letters and digits arranged in a manner which could be confused with an assigned radio station call signal; that the licensee notifies, in writing, the Engineer in Charge of the District in which the unit operates concerning the specific identifiers being used by the mobile units.

(c) Nothing in this section shall be construed as prohibiting the transmission of additional station or unit identifiers which may be necessary for systems operation: *Provided,* such additional identifiers are not to be composed of letters or letters and digits arranged in a manner which could be confused with an assigned radio station call signal.

(d) Except as indicated in paragraphs (e), (f), and (g) of this section, each station in these services shall transmit the required identification at the end of each transmission or exchange of transmissions, or once each 30 minutes of the operating period, as the licensee may prefer.

(e) A mobile station authorized to the licensee of the associated base station and which transmits only on the transmitting frequency of the associated base station is not required to transmit any identification.

(f) Except as indicated in paragraph (e) of this section, a mobile station shall transmit an identification at the end of each transmission or exchange of transmissions, or once each 30 minutes of the operating period, as the licensee may prefer. Where election is made to transmit the identification at 30 minute intervals, a single mobile unit in each general geographic area may be assigned the responsibility for such transmission, thereby eliminating any necessity for each unit of the mobile station to transmit the identification. For the purpose of this paragraph the term "each general geographic area" means an area not smaller than a single city or county and not larger than a single district of a state where the district is administratively established for the service in which the radio system operates.

(g) A station which is transmitting for telemetering purposes or for the actuation of devices, or which is retransmitting by self-actuating means a radio signal received from another radio station or stations, will be considered for exemption from the requirements of paragraph (d) of this section in specific instances, upon request.

Q. 3.268. When a radio operator makes transmitter measurements required by the Commission's rules for a station in the Public Safety Radio Service what information should be transcribed into the station's records? (R & R 89.175)

A. The results and dates of the transmitter measurements and the name of the person or persons making the measurements.

Q. 3.269. What are the Commission's general requirements regarding the records which are required to be kept by stations in the Public Safety Radio Service? (R & R 89.177)

A. Form of station records. (a) The records shall be kept in an orderly manner and in such detail that the data required are readily available. Key letters or abbreviations may be used if proper meaning or explanation is set forth in the record.

(b) Each entry in the records shall be signed by a person qualified to do so having actual knowledge of the facts to be recorded.

(c) No record or portion thereof shall be erased, obliterated, or willfully destroyed within the required retention period. Any necessary correction may be made only by the persons originating the entry who shall strike out the erroneous portion, initial the correction made and indicate the date of the correction.

APPENDIX TO ELEMENT III

TROUBLESHOOTING RADIOTELEPHONE CIRCUITS

Some questions on analyzing circuit troubles appear on the Element III examination. These questions test the applicant's ability to analyze the effects of part failure on circuit operation. Other questions require the student to complete schematic diagrams or to identify mistakes in schematic diagrams. To assist the student in answering these questions, the following section presents in question and answer form a review of the effects of part failure on the operation of various basic circuits employing both vacuum tubes and transistors. Most of the troubleshooting questions contain references to discussions in other portions of this book. The student is strongly urged to refer to these discussions to help him attain a better understanding of the principles involved in each troubleshooting problem.

To simplify the presentation, all transistor circuits in this appendix are shown as *PNP* types. However, the same operating principles and troubleshooting procedures apply to *NPN* transistor circuits. If NPN transistors were used, it would be necessary merely to reverse all battery polarities.

OSCILLATORS

Q. 3.270 In the circuit of the tuned-plate, tuned-grid (TPTG) oscillator shown in Fig. 3.270, what will be the effect on the reading of Meter M1, if C1 becomes shorted or open?

A. Meter M1 will read 0.

D. The TPTG oscillator, like most other tube LC oscillators, employs grid-leak biasing. Grid-leak bias is developed only when the grid tank circuit is oscillating. During the positive swing of the tank circuit, the grid draws current to charge C2. During the negative swing of the tank circuit, C2 discharges through R1 to provide a negative grid-bias voltage. (See Q. 3.86.) Typically this voltage is about —3 to —5 volts. If C1 shorts or opens, oscillations will cease, and grid-leak bias can no longer be developed. Therefore, M1 will read 0. (See also Q. 3.284.)

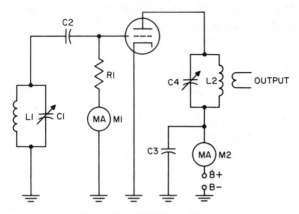

Fig. 3.270. TPTG oscillator.

Q. 3.271 In Fig. 3.270, what will be the effect on the reading of Meter M2 with C1 shorted or open?

A. The reading of Meter M2 will increase.

D. As discussed in answer of 3.270, oscillations will cease if C1 shorts or opens and a negative bias can no longer be developed. The control grid, which was negative with respect to the cathode, will be at approximately the same potential. Therefore, plate current will increase, as indicated by an increase in the meter reading.

Q. 3.272 In the TPTG oscillator (see Fig. 3.270), what will be the effect on the reading of Meter M1 if R1 opens?

A. Meter M1 would read 0, because no current can flow through the meter with the grid circuit open.

Q. 3.273 In Fig. 3.270, what would be the effect on the reading of Meter M1 if C4 becomes shorted or open?

A. Meter M1 would read 0.

D. Oscillations in the grid tank circuit are sustained by regenerative feedback from the plate tank circuit. If C4 shorts or opens, oscillations in the plate tank circuit will cease, and no feedback will be present. This will also cause the grid tank circuit to stop oscillating. And, as explained in Q. 3.270, negative grid-leak bias is no longer produced when the grid tank circuit stops oscillating, so that no current flows through Meter M1. In addition, the reading on Meter M2 will increase because of the loss of grid-leak bias.

Q. 3.274 In Fig. 3.270, what would be the effect on oscillator operation if C2 shorted or opened?

A. In both cases, oscillation would cease. Meter M1 would read 0 and Meter M2 would show increased plate current.

D. If C2 shorted, grid-leak bias could not be developed (see Q. 3.86). The tube would operate at saturation plate current and oscillations could not build up and be sustained.

If C2 opened, the r-f connection to the grid would be disconnected and L1C1 would be isolated from the oscillator circuit. Oscillations could not occur in the circuit, since C2 normally offers a low-impedance r-f path between L1C1 and the grid.

Q. 3.275 In Fig. 3.270, what would be the effect on oscillator operation if L1 or L2 opened or shorted?

A. Under the conditions stated in the question, oscillations would cease.

D. If either tank coil opened or shorted, one tuned circuit would cease to function and oscillations could not be developed. (See Q. 3.86.) In addition, if L2 opened, the plate voltage would be removed from the oscillator tube.

Q. 3.276 In Fig. 3.270, what would be the effect on oscillator operation if C3 opened or shorted?

A. If C3 opened, oscillations would cease; M1 would read 0, and M2 would show increased plate current. If C3 shorted, oscillations would cease; M1 would read 0, and M2 would show an excessive current.

D. Capacitor C3 normally provides a low-impedance path for the oscillator frequency signal to return to the cathode (r-f plate current). If C3 opened, the only r-f return path to the cathode would be through the relatively high r-f impedance of the power supply to ground, which would greatly reduce the plate circuit r-f current and the r-f voltage across L2C4. As a result, the feedback to the grid circuit would be inadequate to sustain oscillations.

If capacitor C3 shorted, no plate voltage would be applied to V1 and the circuit would be inoperative. Meter M1 would read 0. However, a very high current would flow through M2 and capacitor C3, and the meter might be damaged.

Q. 3.277 What is a simple test to determine if an oscillator is operating?

A. Assuming no built-in meters are present (as in Fig. 3.270), the simplest test is to measure the negative grid bias of the oscillator tube with a high-resistance voltmeter.

D. The "correct" bias for any oscillator must be determined for each individual circuit. It may sometimes be obtained from manufacturer's voltage charts or may be measured and recorded when the oscillator is operating *normally*. In measuring the grid bias, a high-resistance voltmeter should be used. This should have a rating of at least 20,000 ohms per volt. A better choice is an electronic voltmeter having an input resistance of 11 megohms on all scales. Using a low-resistance voltmeter will give erroneous readings, because it will shunt the grid resistor, reducing its effective value and thus the bias (see Q. 3.86). Also, a low-resistance voltmeter will severely load the tank circuit, giving erroneous information about the condition of the oscillator. (For additional methods of checking oscillation, see Q. 3.91.)

Q. 3.278 What conditions may cause weak output from an oscillator and how is this condition determined?

A. Weak output may be caused by:
    (1) Weak oscillator tube.
    (2) Low power supply voltage.
    (3) Increased value of plate (or screen) circuit resistor, or defective r-f choke.
    (4) Defective tank coil or capacitor.
    (5) Defective grid capacitor or grid resistor.
Weak output is most easily determined by measuring the grid bias (see Q. 3.277) and comparing it with the known good value.

D. In some cases, the oscillator output may be almost normal at higher frequencies and may decrease severely or stop entirely at lower frequencies. This occurs because in most oscillators, the amount of feedback increases as the frequency increases. Some of this effect is normal, but if it should be excessive, the troubles are usually those described above for weak oscillations.

Q. 3.279 In the crystal oscillator circuit of Fig. 3.279, what would be the effect on oscillation if C2 shorted or opened?

A. If C2 shorted, there would be no change in oscillator operation. If C2 opened, oscillations would cease; M1 would read 0, and M2 would read increased current. (See Q. 3.274 D.)

D. In Fig. 3.279, a resonant crystal has been substituted for the grid

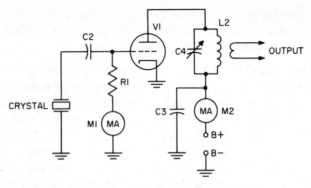

Fig. 3.279. Crystal oscillator circuit.

tank circuit L1C1 in Fig. 3.270. (See Q. 3.93, Q. 4.42, and Q. 3.86 (b) (3) for a discussion of the operation of this type of oscillator.)

If C2 shorted, oscillator operation would not change because the crystal holder constitutes a capacitor and would assume the function of C2. Actually, the crystal holder capacitance and C2 are normally in series, and the effective grid-leak capacitance is the series resultant of the two capacitances. Thus, if C2 is appreciably larger than the crystal holder capacitance, very little change in the total grid-leak capacitance will take place if C2 shorts. In many crystal oscillator circuits, C2 is not used. The time constant of R1 and the total grid-leak capacitance must be at least five times as great as the period of the waveform at the oscillating frequency. If this is true, the grid-leak bias will be sustained virtually unchanged between the positive peaks of each r-f cycle. (See also Q. 3.95, Q. 4.43, and Q. 4.44.)

Q. 3.280 In the crystal-oscillator circuit of Fig. 3.279, what would be the effect on circuit operation of the following:
(a) R1 open?
(b) C4 open or shorted?
(c) L2 open or shorted?
(d) C3 open or shorted?

A. For (a), above, see Q. 3.272.
For (b), above, see Q. 3.273.
For (c), above, see Q. 3.275.
For (d), above, see Q. 3.276.

Q. 3.281 In a crystal oscillator, what would be the effect(s) of defective crystal?

A. The effect(s) might be:

1. Cessation of oscillations.
2. Variations of oscillator frequency.
3. Weak oscillations.

D. For other causes of weak oscillations, see Q. 3.278, and also Q. 3.93 and Q. 3.97.

Q. 3.282 In a crystal oscillator, what might cause the oscillator frequency to be incorrect?

A. 1. Incorrect operating temperature of the crystal.
   2. Cracked or dirty crystal.
   3. Improperly tuned plate tank circuit.
   4. Incorrect pressure of the crystal holder.

D. 1. See Q. 3.93 and Q. 3.94.
   2. See Q. 3.97.
   3. Improper tuning of the plate (or screen grid in electron-coupled type) circuit may cause minor frequency changes in a crystal oscillator and may also affect its stability. The phase and amplitude of the oscillator feedback voltage are controlled by varying the tuning of the plate tank circuit. This is the *main* function of the plate tank. Thus, both the optimum *stability* and the exact operating frequency of this crystal oscillator may be achieved only if the plate tank is tuned correctly. The plate tank is tuned correctly when it is tuned *inductively,* that is, when the natural resonance frequency of the tank is higher than the operating (crystal) frequency. This is achieved by reducing the tuning capacitance (C4) *below* the value which provides resonance at the crystal frequency.

The correct method of adjusting crystal oscillators utilizing a plate (or screen-grid) tank circuit is shown in Fig. 3.282 and Fig. 3.279. With the aid of meter M2, capacitor C4 is adjusted first for minimum plate current, shown by Point C in Fig. 3.282. At this point, the tank is practically resistive and offers maximum impedance because it is tuned to the grid (crystal) circuit frequency. This is a critical point of operation, because any small increase in C4 will make the plate tank *capacitive* instead of inductive. This will cause the feedback to be out of phase to the grid circuit, and oscillations will cease. To render the oscillator stable, capacitor C4 is decreased in value somewhat from the point of minimum plate current, and the plate current is permitted to rise as in Points A to B in Fig. 3.282. When the oscillator is adjusted in this manner, it is operating away from the unstable point at C. At the same time, the amount of feedback is reduced, further improving oscillator stability. (In practice, the plate tank should be tuned 4 to 6 per cent above the crystal frequency.)

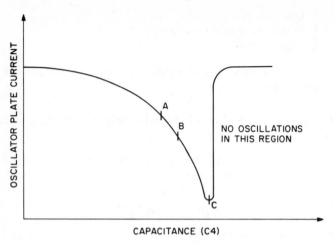

Fig. 3.282. Tuning curve for a crystal oscillator (see text).

4. Correct operation of an oscillator crystal depends upon the correct pressure being applied to the crystal. There must be adequate pressure to maintain good electrical contact during vibration. If the pressure is excessive, the crystal may stop oscillating or may oscillate at a reduced amplitude or at a different frequency. In general, the correct pressure is established by using a crystal holder specifically designed for the particular cut of crystal in use.

Q. 3.283 A schematic diagram of a transistorized (PNP), shunt-fed Hartley oscillator is given in Fig. 3.283. Describe several ways to detect oscillation in this circuit.

A. Any of the following methods may be used:

1. Tuning a radio receiver to the oscillator frequency. (If the receiver has a BFO (Q. 3.158), turn it on to hear a whistle.)

2. Tuning a heterodyne frequency meter to the oscillator frequency. A sensitive wavemeter (loosely coupled) may also be used.

3. Certain grid-dip meters have phone jacks and provisions for detecting a zero-heat condition. When the grid-dip meter is tuned to the oscillator frequency (if operating), a zero-beat condition will be observed.

4. A neon bulb or low-current flashlight bulb connected to a loop of wire and loosely coupled to the oscillator circuit will light if the oscillator is functioning.

5. Connect a voltmeter (low scale) to measure the emitter-to-base bias voltage. Now, load down the oscillator. (A simple way to do this is to touch the base or collector end of the oscillator coil.) If the

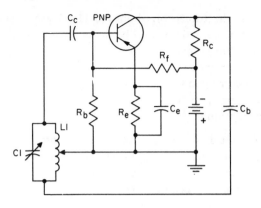

Fig. 3.283. Schematic of a transistorized, shunt-fed Hartley oscillator.

oscillator is working, there will be a noticeable change in the bias voltage. If not, the voltage will remain constant. The magnitude of the bias is not important for this test; only the change (or lack of change) of bias voltage is looked for.

D. Most vacuum-tube oscillators employ grid-leak bias. (See Q. 3.86 A. General and Q. 4.46 (b) and (d).) With this type of circuit, it is a simple matter to determine if oscillations are present by measuring the bias. (See Q. 3.277.) Unfortunately, this simple test is not applicable to transistor oscillators, since their input resistance is very low and only a low value of "grid-leak" bias can be developed. Thus, with transistor oscillators, one of the methods described above should be used to detect the presence of oscillations.

Although the circuit shown in Fig. 3.283 is a Hartley *transistor* oscillator, the basic principles of operation are the same as described in Q. 3.86(c) for a vacuum-tube Hartley oscillator. In addition, note that the amlpifier portion of Fig. 3.283 is identical (except for RT_1) with the common-emitter amplifier circuit shown in Fig. 3.189.

An important feature of low-input resistance, transistor oscillators is that, to be self-starting, they must always operate with at least a small forward bias. If the transsistor initially was biased beyond collector-current cutoff (Class B or C), no current would be available to initially shock the tank circuit into oscillation. A transistor oscillator must have at least a small forward bias placing the quiescent operating point in the class AB region. After the oscillations build-up, the oscillation signal through base-to-emitter current may cause a class B or class C bias to build up in C_c. This is the same principle as developing grid-leak bias in a vacuum tube (see Q. 3.86).

Q. 3.284 In the transistor, shunt-fed Hartley oscillator circuit shown in Fig. 3.283, what would be the effect on circuit operation of each of the following:
(a) Shorted or open C_b.
(b) Shorted or open C_e.
(c) Shorted or open C_c.
(d) Shorted or open C1.

A. (a) A shorted or open C_b would render the oscillator inoperative.

(b) A shorted C_e may make the oscillator unstable, and the collector current would increase. An open C_e would reduce the amplitude of oscillations, and in extreme cases, oscillations might cease.

(c) A shorted or open C_c would cause oscillations to cease.

(d) A shorted or open C1 would cause oscillations to cease.

D. (a) A shorted C_b would ground the collector for d.c. through the lower portion of L1, preventing the transistor from operating. If C_b opens, the a-c feedback path to L1C1 would be open and oscillations would cease. If the transistor was initially biased near cutoff, the collector current will decrease.

(b) A shorted C_e will short out R_e. The effect of R_e as a swamping resistor (see Q. 3.187) will be lost, which would tend to make the transistor characteristics unstable, with a possible resultant instability of oscillations (amplitude and frequency). Also, the shorting of R_e will increase the collector current.

If C_e opens, the a-c voltage appearing across R_e will cause degeneration, which will reduce the amplitude of oscillations. If oscillation conditions were normally marginal, oscillations might stop.

(c) A shorted C_c would ground (for d.c.) the base through the upper half of L1. This would remove the forward bias and the oscillator could not be self-starting (see Q. 3.283). The collector current would go to 0. An open C_c would disconnect the tank from the base and oscillations would stop.

(d) A shorted or open C1 would destroy the effectiveness of the tank circuit and cause oscillations to stop. If C1 opened, L1 would be resonated with the stray capacities across it, and the oscillator *might* operate at a much higher frequency. This frequency would be unpredictable and generally of no practical value.

Q. 3.285 In the transistor, shunt-fed Hartley oscillator circuit, shown in Fig. 3.283, what would be the effect on circuit operation of each of the following:
(a) Open R_b.
(b) Open R_f.

(c) **Open R_e.**

(d) **Open R_c.**

(e) **Shorted or open L1.**

A. (a) An open R_b will not stop oscillations, but may affect oscillator stability and will increase average collector current.

(b) An open R_f will prevent oscillations from starting. There will be little or no collector current.

(c) An open R_e will stop oscillations. Collector current will be 0.

(d) An open R_c will stop oscillations. Collector current will be 0.

(e) A shorted or open L1 will stop oscillations. Collector current will be reduced.

D. (a) R_f and R_b form a voltage divider to apply forward bias to the transistor base. If R_b opens, the forward bias will increase, increasing the average collector current. This may cause overheating of the transistor, some instability of transistor characteristics, and oscillator instability.

(b) If R_f opens, forward-base bias will be lost, and collector current will fall to 0 (practically). Oscillations cannot start, since there will be no current impulse through the tank circuit when the oscillator is first turned on.

(c) If R_e opens, the emitter-collector current path is opened and no collector current can flow. Oscillation cannot occur since the transistor is now inoperative.

(d) If R_c opens, collector voltage is lost and the circuit will be inoperative.

(e) If L1 shorts or opens, there will be no tank circuit and oscillations will cease. Forward bias provided by R_f and R_b will be present, resulting in a reduced value of collector current.

Q. 3.286 In the transistor, Colpitts-type crystal oscillator shown in Fig. 3.286, what would be the effect of each of the following:

(a) Shorted or open C1.

(b) Shorted or open C2.

(c) Defective crystal.

A. (a) A failure of C1 or C2 in either the open or shorted condition would prevent the oscillator from operating.

(b) See Q. 3.281.

D. The basic transistor circuit of Fig. 3.286 is very similar to that of Fig. 3.283 and the amplifier section operates in the same manner (see Q. 3.189). The major differences are: (1) in Fig. 3.286, the LC tank of Fig. 3.283 is replaced with a crystal, and (2) feedback is provided by

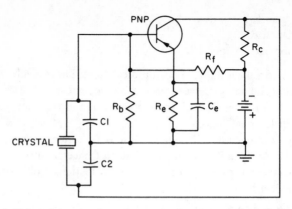

Fig. 3.286. Schematic of a transistorized, Colpitts crystal oscillator.

a Colpitts arrangement. (For an explanation of the operation of a Colpitts oscillator, see Q. 3.86(d). See also Q. 3.86(c), and Q. 3.86(g). The equivalent circuit of a crystal is discussed in Q. 4.42.)

A shorted or open C1 or C2 would prevent the feedback circuit from operating. Thus, oscillations could not be sustained. The effects of failures of the remaining components are the same as those described in Q. 3.284 and Q. 3.285 for the corresponding parts. The methods used to detect oscillations are given in Q. 3.283.

Q. 3.287 What conditions may cause weak output from a transistor oscillator and how is the condition determined?

A. Weak output may be caused by:
  (1) Weak transistor (low gain).
  (2) Defective crystal (if used).
  (3) Defective tank circuit (if used).
  (4) Leaky base coupling capacitor (if used).
  (5) Open emitter-resistor, by-pass capacitor.
  (6) Low supply voltage.
  (7) Leaky collector coupling capacitor.
  (8) Reduced feedback from any other cause.

Output may be determined by measuring the amplitude of oscillations at a convenient point, such as the base or collector. A vacuum-tube voltmeter (a-c) or oscilloscope may be used. The reading thus obtained can be compared with a reference value obtained during normal operation of this oscillator.

D. See Q. 3.91, Q. 3.278, Q. 3.281 and Q. 3.282.

AMPLIFIERS

Q. 3.288 In the triode-amplifier circuit shown in Fig. 3.288, what would be the effect of each of the following:

(a) Shorted or open C_c.
(b) Shorted or open C_k.
(c) Shorted or open C_f.
(d) Shorted or open C_o.

A. (a) A shorted C_c will probably distort the output signal and may also reduce amplifier output. An open C_c will cause either a total loss of output signal or an output of higher frequency components only.

(b) A shorted C_k will distort output and may result in excessive plate dissipation. An open C_k will reduce the output amplitude, but will not cause distortion.

(c) A shorted C_f will result in a total loss of amplifier output and may burn out R_f. An open C_f may distort output and possibly cause low-frequency oscillation (motorboating).

(d) A shorted C_o will distort and reduce amplifier output and will also affect the following stage by shunting plate voltage to it. An open C_o will result in no output or in an output of only the higher-frequency signal components.

D. (a) If C_c shorts, the driving circuitry will be connected directly to the grid of the amplifier tube. If the driver is another amplifier stage, the plate voltage of the driver will be applied to the grid of the amplifier tube. This will cause loading of the driver by the grid-to-cathode resistance. The normally extremely high input resistance will now become very low, because the positive-driver plate voltage applied to the grid will cause it to draw a substantial amount of current. Loading of the driver will greatly reduce and distort its output. The (now) positive

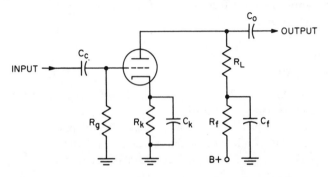

Fig. 3.288. Schematic of an RC coupled triode amplifier.

A12

grid bias will drive the amplifier to saturation, and its output will be weak and highly distorted.

If C_c opens, there may be no output, or low output, from the amplifier, the exact effect depending upon the nature of the input signal. If the signal contains a wide band of frequencies, some of the higher frequency components may be coupled through the stray capacitance of C_c (and other strays), but lower frequency components will not appear in the output.

(b) If C_k shorts, the bias will go to 0 and the tube will saturate (plate current), causing a highly distorted output. The rated plate dissipation may be exceeded.

If C_k opens, degeneration will occur across the now unbypassed cathode resistor R_k. For an explanation of this effect, see Q. 3.100 and also Q. 4.26. The degeneration does not alter the d-c operating voltages, so any distortion present will be reduced, but output will be decreased.

(c) If C_f shorts, the tube will not receive plate voltage. This will disable the amplifier. The full B+ voltage will be applied across R_f and may burn out or severely overheat R_f. A severely overheated carbon composition resistor increases in value, sometimes drastically.

If C_f opens, it no longer places an r-f ground at the bottom of R_L, and the resistance of R_f is added to R_L to form the total plate-load resistance. The amplifier load line (see Q. 3.57) will be lowered. Although the amplifier gain will increase, the output may be distorted since the grid can now only accept a lower input signal if distortion is to be avoided. In addition, the high frequency response of the amplifier will be reduced. C_f and R_f are required to decouple this amplifier stage from other stages. The loss of C_f will remove this decoupling and may result in motorboating. (See Q. 3.102 for a discussion of this effect).

(d) For the effects of a shorted or open C_o, see (a) above.

Q. 3.289 In the triode amplifier circuit shown in Fig. 3.288, what would be the effect of each of the following:

(a) Open R_g.

(b) Open R_k.

(c) Open R_L.

(d) Open R_f.

A. (a) An open R_g will result in a distorted output, and hum or other pickup will appear in the output.

(b) An open R_k will produce no amplifier output.

(c) An open R_L will produce no amplifier output.

(d) An open R_f will produce no amplifier output.

D. (a) If R_g opens, the grid loses its d-c ground return, leaving the grid at an extremely high impedance level. The grid-to-cathode bias will revert to the space-charge potential value. In most cases, this bias is improper for amplifier operation and will result in a distorted output. Also, the high grid-circuit impedance will make is susceptible to electro-static pickup of hum or other extraneous voltages near the grid circuit.

(b) If R_k, R_L, or R_f opens, the d-c plate current circuit will be opened and the amplifier will be inoperative.

(c) See Q. 3.50(a) for discussion of triode amplifier. See also Q. 3.46(b), Q. 3.47, and Q. 3.48.

Q. 3.290 In the pentode amplifier shown in Fig. 3.290, discuss the effects of shorted and open component parts.

A. Except for C_{sg} and R_{sg}, the effects of the components are as de-scribed in Q. 3.287 and Q. 3.288.

(a) A shorted C_{sg} will result in little or no amplifier output. An open C_{sg} will result in a reduced amplifier output, without distortion.

(b) An open R_{sg} will have the same effect as a shorted C_{sg}.

D. (a) If C_{sg} shorts, screen-grid voltage will be removed. In a pen-tode, plate current depends largely upon the screen grid potential. In this case, the screen grid will be *grounded* by the shorted C_{sg}. This effectively shields the plate from the control grid and cathode, resulting in a greatly reduced plate current. As a result, there will be little or no amplifier output.

If C_{sg} opens, screen-grid degeneration occurs across R_{sg}. The effect is basically the same as with cathode degeneration (see Q. 3.100), but is considerably reduced because the screen grid is spaced relatively far from the control grid, compared to the cathode. The effect of screen-grid degeneration is only about 10 to 15 per cent as great as cathode degen-eration.

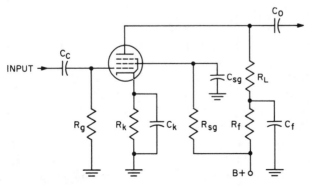

Fig. 3.290. Schematic of an RC coupled pentode amplifier.

(b) If R_{sg} opens, the screen-grid voltage will be removed. The screen grid will acquire a negative space-charge potential, resulting in little or no plate current, and there will be little or no amplifier output.

(c) For a discussion of pentode amplifier operation, see Q. 3.50(b), Q. 3.46, Q. 3.47, and Q. 3.48.

Q. 3.291 In the pentode, class C r-f amplifier shown in Fig. 3.291, what would be the effect of each of the following:
(a) Shorted or open C1.
(b) Shorted or open C_c.
(c) Shorted or open C_{sg}.
(d) Shorted or open C_o.
(e) Shorted or open C2.

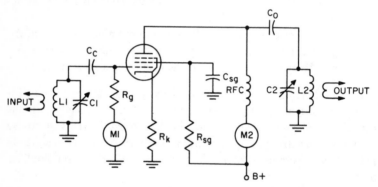

Fig. 3.291. Schematic of a pentode, class C r-f amplifier.

A. (a) A shorted C1 would result in no amplifier output. Meter M1 would read 0, while Meter M2 would read a high plate current.

An open C1 would result in a greatly reduced amplifier output. Meter M1 would read a low value of grid current and Meter M2 would show increased plate current.

(b) A shorted C_c will result in a reduced output, increased plate current, and reduced amplifier efficiency. Meter M1 will read 0, and Meter M2 will show increased plate current.

An open C_c will result in no amplifier output. Meter M1 will read 0, and Meter M2 will show increased plate current.

(c) A shorted C_{sg} will result in little or no amplifier output. Meter M1 will show a normal or slightly increased reading; Meter M2 will read very low or 0.

An open C_{sg} will result in reduced amplifier output and a slight efficiency loss. M1 will read normally, but M2 will show an increased plate current.

(d) A shorted C_o will result in no amplifier output. Meter M1 will read normally, but Meter M2 will read off scale (high side) and may burn out.

An open C_o will result in no amplifier output. Meter M1 will read normally, but Meter M2 will show an appreciable increase in plate current.

(e) A shorted or open C2 will result in a small output from the amplifier. Meter M1 will read normally, but Meter M2 will show an appreciable increase in plate current.

D. (a) If C1 shorts, there will be no grid drive, and therefore no grid current and no output. Without grid-leak bias (see Q. 3.86 and Q. 4.46), the plate current rises substantially. A small-value resistor, R_k, is in the cathode circuit to protect the tube against excessive plate dissipation (see Q. 3.121). However, R_k does not provide operating bias, since this is a class C amplifier and the normal operating bias is provided through grid current rectification.

If C1 opens, the resonant circuit consisting of L1C1 is lost and the impedance of the input circuit is appreciably reduced. This reduces the grid signal and may also cause loading of the driver stage. The net result is reduced output, reduced grid current and increased plate current. The plate current increases because the negative portion of the r-f plate voltage swing does not go down as much as when full output is achieved. In class C operation, plate current is drawn only at this time, and since the instantaneous plate voltage is higher, the plate current will increase. (This effect is explained in Q. 3.52(a)(4).)

(b) If C_c shorts, grid-leak bias is lost and the only bias is the small amount developed across R_k. Because of the low bias, a high plate current is drawn and, although grid current is flowing, Meter M1 cannot read it, since it normally only reads the discharge current of C_c. The output will be low and the efficiency very poor.

If C_c opens, L1C1 is disconnected from the grid circuit. There can be no output, and, of course, grid-leak bias is lost (see above).

(c) For a discussion of the effects of a shorted or open C_{sg}, see Q. 3.290 D.(a).

(d) If C_o shorts, the plate will be grounded (for d-c) through L2 and there will be no output. There will be a low resistance path to ground through M2, RFC, shorted C_o, and L2. A high current will flow through this path, which may damage M2 and possible RFC.

If C_o opens, the plate-tank circuit L2C2 will be disconnected from the plate. There will be a low value of signal across the RFC, but this will not appear in the output. The input circuit will not be affected and M1 will read normally. However, because of the very low r-f plate voltage swing, the average plate current will increase appreciably, as shown by M2. (See Q. 3.52(a)(4).)

(e) If C2 shorts, the plate tank is shorted out and no amplifier output is possible. Since there is now no r-f plate voltage swing, a high B+ value is continuously applied to the plate, resulting in a high reading on M2. However, the input circuit is unaffected, and M1 will read normally.

If C2 opens, the a-c plate load will consist of the RFC in parallel with L2. While this combination offers some impedance, it is appreciably less than the resonant impedance of the plate tank circuit. Thus, a small output will appear and, since no tank is present, it will be very rich in harmonics, because of the class C operation of the tube. The input circuit is unaffected and Meter M1 will read normally.

Q. 3.292 In the pentode, class C r-f amplifier shown in Fig. 3.291 what would be the effect of each of the following:
(a) Shorted or open L1.
(b) Shorted or open L2.
(c) Open R_g.
(d) Open R_k.
(e) Open R_{sg}.
(f) Shorted or open RFC.

A. (a) A shorted or an open L1 would result in no amplifier output. Meter M1 would read 0, and M2 would show a high-plate current.

(b) A shorted L2 would result in no amplifier output, and an open L2 would result in very low amplifier output. In both cases, Meter M1 would read normally, and M2 would show a high-plate current.

(c) An open R_g would result in a reduced amplifier output. If the input signal was suddenly reduced, there may be no amplifier output. Meter M1 would read 0.

(d) An open R_k would result in no amplifier output. Both meters would read zero.

(e) An open R_{sg} would result in little or no amplifier output.

(f) A shorted RFC would result in no amplifier output. Meter M1 would read normally, but M2 would show an increased plate current.

An open RFC would result in no amplifier output. Meter M1 would read normally, but M2 would read zero The screen-grid would draw excessive current.

D. (a) If L1 shorts, there can be no inductive coupling into the tank circuit. Also, the grid of the amplifier tube will be grounded for r-f. As a result, no grid signal appears at the grid; there is no amplifier output. There is no grid current, and grid-leak bias cannot be developed. Because of the low bias across R_k, both the plate and screen-grid currents will be high.

If L1 opens, there will be no inductive coupling into the tank circuit. The amplifier operation will be as described immediately above.

(b) If L2 shorts, the amplifier plate will be at a-c ground potential and no r-f signal can be developed at the plate; therefore, no output occurs. The average plate voltage will now be maximum, resulting in a high plate current. The input circuit is unaffected and Meter M1 will read normally.

If L2 opens, the plate load will consist of the RFC in parallel with the series combination of C_o and C2. This provides a relatively low impedance plate load for r-f, resulting in a very low amplifier output. Because of the low-amplitude plate r-f voltage present, plate current will be high. Again, the input circuit is unaffected and grid current remains normal.

(c) If R_g opens, C_c will charge to the *peak* value of the r-f voltage across the grid tank. The bias will be *higher* and the grid will not be driven (practically) into the positive conduction region, thus reducing amplifier output. Assuming no leakage in C_c and a constant amplitude of input signal (all other parameters held constant), the amplifier will continue to operate with reduced output. However, if for any reason the grid drive were *appreciably* reduced, the high bias would remain across C_c and no amplifier output would be present. Since the amplifier is cut off under these reduced grid-drive conditions, M2 would read zero, and there would be no screen-grid current. A lesser degree of reduced drive would result in a low amplifier output, with low plate and screen-grid currents. In either case, because of the open R_g, M1 will read 0.

(d) If R_k opens, the circuit will be opened for control grid, screen grid, and plate currents. Therefore, M1 and M2 will read 0, and the amplifier will be inoperative.

(e) If R_{sg} opens, screen-grid voltage will be removed from the amplifier, resulting in little or no output. (See discussion of Q. 3.289(b).)

(f) If the RFC shorts, it will effectively (through C_o) short out the plate tank. The plate circuit impedance will be practically 0. The d-c path to the plate will not be interrupted, but a high average plate voltage will be present for conduction because of the absence of an r-f plate swing. (See discussion of Q. 3.290(a).) Meter M2 will read high, and Meter M1 will read normally.

If the RFC opens, the d-c plate current path is open and Meter M2 will read 0. Because of the absence of plate voltage, electrons normally attracted to the plate will be repelled to the screen grid, resulting in excessive screen current. This is frequently observed (glass tube) in the form of a red- or white-hot screen grid. If there is not sufficient screen-current limiting, the tube may be destroyed.

Q. 3.293 In the pentode, class C r-f amplifier shown in Fig. 3.291, discuss the effects of a loss of input-driving signal on amplifier operation.

A. Meter M1 would read zero and M2 would show a considerably increased plate current reading. There would be no amplifier output.

D. The r-f driving signal normally would be provided by an oscillator or intermediate r-f amplifier. If the driving source failed, grid-leak bias would be lost. The only bias remaining would be the small safety bias developed across R_k. As a result, the plate current would rise to a high value.

Q. 3.294 In the class A, common-emitter amplifier shown in Fig. 3.294, what would be the effect of each of the following:
  (a) Shorted or open C_c.
  (b) Shorted or open C_e.
  (c) Shorted or open C_o.

A. (a) A shorted C_c will probably produce distortion of the output signal and may also reduce output. An open C_c will result either in a total loss of output signal or in an output of higher frequency components only.

  (b) A shorted C_e may cause distortion in the output. An open C_e will reduce the output amplitude, but no distortion will result.

  (c) A shorted or open C_o will produce results similar to those described in (a) above.

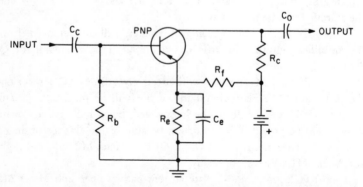

Fig. 3.294. Schematic of an RC coupled common-emitter amplifier.

D. (a) If C_c shorts, the circuitry of the driving source will be applied directly to the transistor base. In most cases, this will change the forward bias on the transistor, which may distort the output signal. In addition, a C_c short may cause loading of the driving stage, changing its operating characteristics as well. This may distort or reduce the output from the driver stage, which would be applied to the transistor stage in question.

If C_c opens, there may be weak or no amplifier output, depending upon the nature of the signal applied to C_c. If the signal contains a wide band of frequencies, some of the higher frequency components may be coupled through the stray capacitance of C_c (and other strays). However, lower frequency components will not appear in the output.

(b) If C_e shorts, it will short out "swamping" resistor R_e. (See Q. 3.187 and Q. 3.284 (b).) The loss of the emitter resistance and the emitter-to-base junction resistance changes with temperature will result in base-to-emitter bias changes, which may distort the output. The gain will not change unless a *radical* change of bias results..

If C_e opens, degeneration will occur due to the unbypassed resistor R_e. This action is basically the same as that which occurs when a vacuum-tube cathode resistor is unbypassed. (See Q. 3.100 and Q. 4.26.) Since the d-c operating voltages remain, no distortion occurs (actually distortion decreases), but the degeneration results in a reduced output.

(c) For the effects of a shorted or open C_o, see (a) above.

Q. 3.295 In the class A, common-emitter amplifier shown in Fig. 3.294, what would be the effect of the following:
(a) Open R_b.
(b) Open R_f.
(c) Open R_e.
(d) Open R_c.

A. (a) An open R_b will distort amplifier output and may reduce the gain.

(b) An open R_f will result in severe distortion and reduced gain.

(c) An open R_e will result in no amplifier output. Collector current will be 0.

(d) An open R_c will result in no amplifier output. Collector current will be 0.

D. (a) If R_b opens, the forward bias will increase substantially. (See Q. 3.284 and D. (a).) The quiescent transistor operating point will be shifted to a region of high collector current, resulting in a distorted output. Since the operating point may be on the upper curved portion of the transfer characteristic curve, the transistor gain will also be reduced.

(b) If R_f opens, forward-base bias will go to 0. The quiescent operating point will be in the class B region and only (practically) the negative input half-cycles will be amplified, resulting in severe distortion. Since the quiescent operating point is now on the lower curved portion of the transfer characteristic, the transistor gain will be reduced.

(c) If R_e opens, there can be no collector or base current and the amplifier will be inoperative.

(d) If R_c opens, collector voltage and current are lost, and there will be no amplifier output.

Q. 3.296 In the class C, common-emitter r-f amplifier shown in Fig. 3.296, what would be the effect of each of the following:
(a) Shorted or open C_c.
(b) Shorted or open C_e.
(c) Shorted or open C1.
(d) Shorted or open C2.

A. (a) A shorted C_c would result in reduced power output and reduced amplifier efficiency. An open C_c would result in no amplifier output. Collector current would practically fall to zero.

(b) A shorted C_e would have practically no effect on amplifier output. An open C_e would slightly decrease amplifier output. Operating conditions remain the same (practically).

(c) A shorted C1 would result in no amplifier output. An open C1 would result in a small amplifier output. In both cases, collector current would increase appreciably.

(d) A shorted C2 would result in no amplifier output; collector voltage and current go to zero. An open C2 would reduce r-f output; the d-c collector current would increase.

D. (a) If C_c shorts, the class C bias would be lost. C_c in conjunction

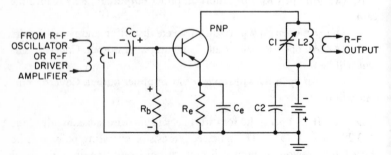

Fig. 3.296. Schematic of a transistor class C, common-emitter r-f amplifier.

with R_b provides this bias for the amplifier (R_e has a negligible effect on bias, since it is a very low value, such as 20 to 50 ohms).

For practical purposes, the emitter may be considered grounded, since R_e is very small and C_e grounds the emitter for r-f. When a negative-going signal is applied to the base, current passes through the base-to-emitter diode, through C_e, and through L1 (the generator), causing C_e to charge with the polarity shown in Fig. 3.296. This results in a positive bias being applied to the base. (See Q. 3.86 for a discussion of grid-leak bias.) In a PNP transistor, positive base bias cuts it off and the transistor operates as a class C amplifier. Thus, a short circuit of C_e produces a loss of class C bias. Since there is no fixed-forward bias provided, the transistor will now operate with substantially 0 bias, and would operate either class B or class AB. Since these classes are less efficient than class C, the power output would be reduced. (See Q. 3.59. The same basic principles apply to transistor operation.)

If C_e opened, the r-f voltage across L1 would not be able to influence the transistor base. There would be no base drive; since no forward bias is provided, the collector current would fall to 0 (practically).

(b) If C_e shorted, it would short out the very low value of R_e (emitter swamping resistor). The effect on base-to-emitter or emitter-to-collector currents would be negligible. However, the bias would be subjected to greater changes from temperature variations, which might shift the amplifier operating point.

If C_e opened, a *minor* amount of degeneration would occur across R_e; the loss of output would be slight because of the low value of R_e.

(c) If C1 shorts, the collector would be grounded for r-f, and no amplifier output would result. Since there is no r-f swing on the collector (see Q. 3.59), the collector current will increase considerably.

If C1 opens, the r-f collector load consists of only the impedance of L2. Since this is much smaller than the tank impedance, only a small output will result. Because of the small r-f collector swing, collector current will increase appreciably. (See also Q. 3.290 D.(e).)

(d) If C2 shorts, the power supply is shorted out, the collector is grounded for a-c, and no output is possible. Damage to the power supply may result.

If C2 opens, the r-f current-return path to the emitter would be through the power supply rather than through the very low impedance of C2. Since the power supply impedance to r-f is generally much higher than the impedance of C2, the r-f current through the tank would be considerably reduced, which may substantially reduce amplifier output. In addition, some of the r-f energy is dissipated in the power supply and lost as useful output.

Q. 3.297 In the class C, common-emitter r-f amplifier shown in Fig. 3.296, what would be the effect of each of the following?

(a) Shorted or open L1.

(b) Open R_b.

(c) Open R_e.

(d) Shorted or open L2.

A. (a) A shorted or open L1 would result in no amplifier output. The collector current would drop to 0 (practically).

(b) An open R_b would result in reduced amplifier output. Collector current would increase. Amplifier bias would be unable to follow changes in the r-f input from the oscillator.

(c) An open R_e will result in no amplifier output. Collector current will be 0.

(d) A shorted or open L2 would result in no amplifier output. Collector current would increase.

D. (a) If L1 shorted or opened, there would be no inductively coupled signal fed to the transistor base. Class C bias is lost and since no fixed-forward bias is provided, the collector current would drop to 0 (practically).

(b) If R_b opens, C_c would have no discharge path. It would charge to the peak value of the input signal and the transistor would not be driven as hard, somewhat reducing r-f input. Modulation distortion may result if the output is sufficiently reduced. Without a discharge path, the bias could not follow input drive variations (See also Q. 3.291 D. (c) and Q. 3.298 D. (d).)

(c) If R_e opened, there could be no input or output transistor currents and, therefore, no amplifier output would be possible.

(d) If L2 opened, the d-c collector current path would be open, resulting in a total loss of amplifier output. If L2 shorted, the collector would be at a-c ground potential (through shorted L2 and C2). No output signal would be developed. Because of the lack of r-f·swing at the collector, the average collector current will increase.

Q. 3.298 In the class C, common-emitter r-f amplifier shown in Fig. 3.296, discuss the effects of a loss of input-driving signal on amplifier operation.

A. If the driving signal were lost, collector current would go to 0 (practically), and there would be no amplifier output.

D. This operational condition is quite different from the situation where a vacuum tube is used. (See Q. 3.293.) In that case the loss of grid-leak bias resulted in high plate current. In the transistor circuit, however, no fixed forward bias is provided, and when the driving signal is removed, the base-emitter bias becomes 0 and the collector current drops to 0 (practically).

TRANSMITTERS

Q. 3.299 An amplitude (plate) modulated transmitter is shown in Fig. 3.299. Describe the effects on transmitter operation of parts defect(s) in each stage.

A. 1. The effect of defects of each part in the individual stages of the transmitter are given in the following questions:

(a) TPTG Crystal Oscillator: Q. 3.279 through Q. 3.282
(b) Class C r-f amplifier: Q. 3.291 and Q. 3.292
(c) Modulator preamplifier: Q. 3.288 and Q. 3.289
(d) Modulator stage: For the effect of defects of C_o, C_k, C_{sg}, R_k, R_g, and R_{sg}, see Q. 3.290. Except for the fact that R_g is a potentiometer and the plate load consists of a modulation transformer (T1), the modulator stage is the same as the pentode amplifier shown in Fig. 3.290. Additional faults which may occur in the modulator stage are slider-contact defects of R_g and open or short circuit conditions of T1.

(1) R_g contact defects (noisy potentiometer) may result in intermittent modulation of the r-f carrier or may introduce audio-frequency noise into the transmission. The function of R_g is to adjust the amount of audio drive applied to the grid of the modulator stage, and thus to regulate the percentage of modulation.

(2) A shorted T1 primary will result in a loss of modulator stage output and thus a loss of modulation of the r-f carrier. However, this will *not* affect the transmission of the r-f carrier.

A shorted T1 secondary will produce the same effects as a shorted primary since the shorted secondary reflects a short into the transformer primary. There will be no audio voltage variation across the secondary and no modulation.

An open T1 primary would result in a loss of modulator stage output and a loss of r-f carrier modulation. The modulator-stage plate will be open circuited and can produce no output. The r-f carrier output is unaffected. An open T1 secondary would result in a loss of modulation supplied to the r-f, class C amplifier. However, this is somewhat academic since the B+ supply to the plate and screen grid of the r-f amplifier will be interrupted. This stage will now be completely inoperative, resulting in a total loss of r-f output from the transmitter.

D. (a) For a discussion of plate modulation of a class, r-f amplifier,

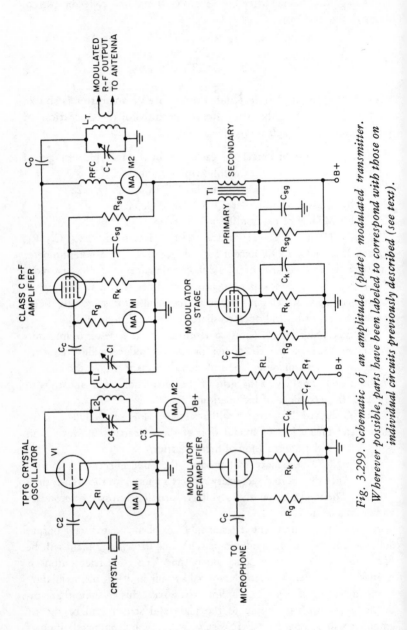

Fig. 3.299. Schematic of an amplitude (plate) modulated transmitter. Wherever possible, parts have been labeled to correspond with those on individual circuits previously described (see text).

see Q. 3.143. For a discussion of modulation problems, see Q. 3.147, Q. 3.148, Q. 3.149, Q. 4.54 (transmitter tuning), Q.4.58, Q. 4.85, and Q. 4.86.

(b) A totally disabled crystal oscillator (or r-f amplifier) will result in no transmitter output. However a weak input into the r-f amplifier or a weak output from the amplifier will result in a weak modulated r-f wave (see Q. 3.147) and will cause "downward" modulation or negative carrier shift.

(c) Defects either in the modulator preamplifier or the modulator stage will in general produce:

(1) No modulation, caused by a loss of output from either amplifier.

(2) Overmodulation, caused by excessive output from the modulator. (For a discussion of the effects of overmodulation, see Q. 3.141. See also Q. 3.142 and Q. 4.58.

(3) Undermodulation, the result of a weak (but undistorted) audio being applied to the class C r-f amplifier. This does not produce any undesired sidebands in the output, but it does reduce the area consistently covered by the transmitter. (For a discussion of this effect, see Q. 3.149.)

(4) A distorted audio-modulation output, causing a distorted audio at the receiving end and unwanted additional-sideband frequencies which may result in adjacent-channel interference. (See also Q. 3.139, Q. 3.140 and Q. 3.141.) Distortion of the audio output may cause negative-carrier shift (see Q. 3.147).

(d) To achieve symmetrical amplitude modulation of an r-f carrier wave, it is essential that the instantaneous amplitude of the r-f wave follows faithfully the instantaneous amplitude of the audio-modulating voltage. Under 100 per cent modulation conditions, the instantaneous positive peak of the r-f envelope should reach twice the amplitude of the unmodulated r-f carrier wave (see also Q. 3.142). If the r-f modulated wave goes to 0, but is not able to achieve twice the unmodulated wave amplitude, the modulation wave will be compressed on the positive peak. This distorts the audio component, resulting in the radiation of undesirable harmonic-sideband frequencies. A condition of "downward" modulation or negative carrier shift will be present (see Q. 3.147). Some conditions which may prevent the instantaneous r-f amplitude from achieving its required positive-peak value are as follows (class C amplifier considered):

(1) Insufficient grid excitation.

(2) Insufficient bias.

(3) Weak tube or excessive d-c input to the r-f amplifier (cannot attain desired maximum r-f output).

(4) Improperly tuned, plate or grid circuits.

(5) Excessive loading of plate-tank circuit.

(6) Inadequate regulation of power supply.

(7) Insufficient screen grid and/or plate modulation.

(e) If a class C amplifier is modulated symmetrically, the plate-current reading will remain constant, with or without modulation. Any change of plate current when modulation is applied indicates a lack of modulation symmetry.

Q. 3.300 An amplitude (collector) modulated transmitter is shown in Fig. 3.300. Describe the effect(s) on transmitter operation of parts defects in each stage.

A. 1. *Crystal Oscillator:* For the effect of a defect on oscillator operation, see Q. 3.284 and Q. 3.285; C_e, R_b, R_f, R_e.

The effect of defects in the remaining parts follow.

(a) Crystal defective: Oscillations cease. Collector current is reduced.

(b) C_c shorted: Oscillations cease. Collector current drops to 0 (practically). C_c open: Little or no effect on oscillator operation.

(c) C_T shorted or open: Oscillations cease. Collector current is reduced.

(d) L_T shorted or open: Same as (c) above.

2. *Class C, R-F Amplifier:* For the effect of defects in all the parts of this amplifier, see Q. 3.296, Q. 3.297. See also Q. 3.298 (loss of drive).

3. *Modulator Preamplifier:* For the effect of defects in this amplifier, see Q. 3.294 and Q. 3.295. The only difference here is that R_e is a potentiometer instead of a fixed resistor. As such, it is likely to become noisy or intermittent. The modulation will be affected in the same way. (See Q. 3.299 1.(d) (1).)

4. *Modulator Stage:* For the effect of defects of C_o (C_c), C_e, R_b, R_f and R_e see Q. 3.294 and Q. 3.295. Except that the plate load of the modulator stage is a transformer (T1) instead of a resistor, this stage has the same basic configuration as Fig. 3.294. Also, the modulator stage would employ a *power* transistor to provide the modulating power for the class C, r-f amplifier.

Additional problems in the modulator stage can be caused by a shorted or open modulation transformer (see Q. 3.299 1. (d) (2).)

D. Note the similarity of the vacuum-tube transmitter of Fig. 3.299 (A) and the transistor transmitter of Fig. 3.300. The stages are basically the same and the tpye of modulation (plate) is the same. Each stage of the transistor transmitter performs the same function as its corresponding stage in the vacuum-tube transmitter. For problems

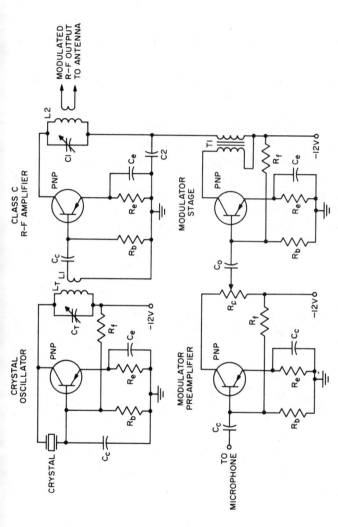

Fig. 3.300. Schematic of an amplitude (collector) modulated transmitter. Wherever possible, parts have been labeled to correspond with those on individual circuits previously described (see text).

which might arise from an overall transmitter (including modulation) point-of-view, see Q. 3.298. The basic principles apply equally well for a transistorized transmitter as for a vacuum-tube transmitter.

TRANSISTOR TESTING

Q. 3.301 Describe a simple method of testing transistors using an ohmmeter.

A. The method of testing a transistor with an ohmmeter is described with the aid of Fig. 3.301. The two diodes (base-to-collector and base-to-emitter) are first tested individually and will respond to an ohmmeter test basically the same as any simple solid-state diode. If the diodes are good, there will be a high ratio between the forward and back resistance (100 to 1 or greater is common). Place the ohmmeter leads across the base-to-emitter diode (ignoring ohmmeter polarity) and record the reading. Next, reverse the ohmmeter leads and again note the reading. A ratio of less than 100 to 1 (approximately) probably indicates a leaky diode section. The same test should be made on the base-to-

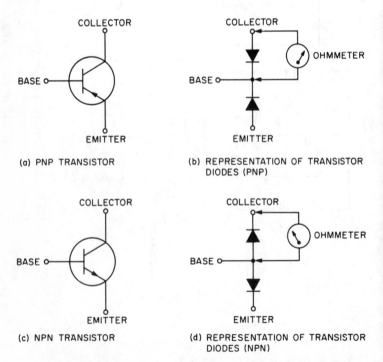

(a) PNP TRANSISTOR

(b) REPRESENTATION OF TRANSISTOR DIODES (PNP)

(c) NPN TRANSISTOR

(d) REPRESENTATION OF TRANSISTOR DIODES (NPN)

Fig. 3.301. PNP and NPN schematics and their diode equivalents.

collector diode. Again, if a low ratio exists, the transistor should be rejected.

A short or leakage test should be made between the emitter and collector. Both readings should be quite high (may exceed several hundred thousand ohms), but one of the readings will be somewhat higher than the other. Note that with an emitter-to-collector short, the two diodes measured individually may seem perfectly normal. Therefore, the emitter-to-collector test is essential to determine the condition of the transistor.

D. In making the above tests, the ohmmeter voltages and currents should not be excessive. This is not a problem when measuring power transistors, but low-power transistors may be damaged if proper precautions are not taken. It is interesting to note that the output voltage of a typical d-c, vacuum-tube voltmeter (ohmmeter function) on the R × 1 scale may be 1.5 volts and the available current 100 milliamperes or more. On the R × 10,000 scale, the voltage drops to about 0.2 volt and the available current to only 20 microamperes. A good rule to remember is to use only the high-resistance scales for low-power transistors. The low scales may be used for testing high-power transistors.

In testing transistor diodes (or other diodes), the *ratio* of forward-to-back resistance is more important than the *actual* readings. The forward resistance should always be low, usually not more than several hundred ohms. When diode resistance is measured and the ohmmeter scales are switched, different voltages and currents are applied to the diode. Thus, scale switching may result in appreciably different resistance readings on the same diode for a given polarity of the connections.

FCC-TYPE SAMPLE TEST FOR ELEMENT III

III-1. A "difference of potential" may also be described as: (Q. 3.01)
  (a) Electrical power.
  (b) Voltage.
  (c) Electron drift.
  (d) Amperage.
  (e) Conductance.

III-2. An insulator, or non-conductor, is characterized by: (Q. 3.04)
  (a) A large number of free electrons.
  (b) Very few free electrons.
  (c) Lightly bound electrons in the outer ring of the atom.
  (d) High energy dissipation.
  (e) Large amount of skin effect.

III-3. An ac series circuit is composed of a series resistance of 20 ohms, an inductive reactance of 40 ohms, and a capacitive reactance of 15 ohms. A current of 1 ampere is flowing. What is the applied voltage? [Q. 3.09(B)]
  (a) 320 volts.
  (b) 16 volts.
  (c) 28 volts.
  (d) 32 volts.
  (e) None of the above.

III-4. A loudspeaker with a voice coil impedance of 6 ohms is fed from an emitter circuit with an impedance of 600 ohms. What is the turns ratio of a transformer which will match these two impedances? (Q. 3.13)
  (a) 10:1
  (b) 100:1
  (c) 25:1
  (d) 1000:1
  (e) 1:1

III-5. The ratio of the amount of magnetic flux linking a secondary coil, compared to the flux generated by the primary coil, is known as the: (Q. 3.27)
  (a) Coefficient of magnetic lines of force.
  (b) Coefficient of coupling.
  (c) Coefficient of magnetism.
  (d) The magnetic coefficient.
  (e) Coefficient of self-inductance.

III-6. A filter which permits all frequencies above a predetermined cut-off frequency to be passed is called a: (Q. 3.36)
  (a) Constant-k filter.
  (b) M-derived filter.

(c) Band-stop filter.

(d) Power-supply filter.

(e) High-pass filter.

III-7.   The grid, in a vacuum tube, which returns secondary electrons to the plate is the: (Q. 3.46 D)

(a) Control grid.

(b) Suppressor grid.

(c) Screen grid.

(d) Shield grid.

(e) Beam grid.

III-8.   For a vacuum tube operating class C, the bias should be approximately: (Q. 3.52)

(a) Cut-off bias.

(b) 10 times, cut-off bias.

(c) Twice, cut-off bias.

(d) Four times, cut-off bias.

(e) One-half cut-off bias.

III-9.   A triode, grounded cathode amplifier has a mu of 50, a plate impedance of 10,000 ohms, and a plate load impedance of 25,000 ohms. What is the stage gain of this amplifier? (Q. 3.58)

(a) 35.7

(b) 45.7

(c) 25.7

(d) 53.7

(e) None of the above.

III-10.   Two factors which limit the use of vacuum tubes at VHF and UHF frequencies are: (Q. 3.64)

(a) Cathode emission and space charge.

(b) Transit time and envelope size.

(c) Transit time and interelectrode capacities.

(d) Interelectrode capacities and shape of tube base.

(e) Interelectrode capacities and plate voltage.

III-11.   A full-wave rectifier system operating from a line frequency of 60 cycles will have a ripple frequency of: (Q. 3.65)

(a) 60 cycles.

(b) 120 cycles.

(c) 180 cycles.

(d) 240 cycles.

(e) 90 cycles.

III-12.   If a power supply has poor voltage regulation, the effect will be: (Q. 3.72)

(a) An increased voltage under load.

(b) A constant voltage with varying loads.

(c) Appreciably varying voltage under varying loads.

(d) A decrease in output current with increasing loads.

(e) An increase in the ripple voltage with decreasing loads.

III-13.   In a D'Arsonval meter movement, damping of the meter motion is accomplished by: (Q. 3.79)

(a) The two opposing springs.

(b) The jeweled meter bearings.

(c) Eddy currents in the permanent magnet.

(d) Eddy currents in the movable coil frame.

(e) Eddy current in the two springs.

III-14.   A wattmeter automatically compensates for: (Q. 3.79)

(a) Overdamping.

(b) Power factor.

(c) Inductive reactance.

(d) Line resistance.

(e) None of the above.

III-15.   A 0-1 dc milliameter is converted to a dc voltmeter with a full-scale reading of 50 volts. What value of resistance must be connected in series with the meter? (Q. 3.81)

(a) 50,000 ohms.

(b) 500,000 ohms.

(c) 5000 ohms.

(d) 20,000 ohms.

(e) 2000 ohms.

III-16.   A one-milliampere meter with a resistance of 50 ohms is used to measure a current by shunting the meter with a 3 ohm resistor. The meter reads 0.5 milliampere on its original scale. What is the true value of the current being measured? (Q. 3.82)

(a) 2.9 ma.

(b) 29 ma.

(c) 8.8 ma.

(d) 0.88 ma.

(e) 88.0 ma.

III-17.   RMS voltage is related to peak voltage by the decimal: (Q. 3.84)

(a) 0.707

(b) 0.0707

(c) 0.636

(d) 0.9

(e) 0.7376

III-18.   In the usual test oscilloscope, vertical deflection takes place by virtue of: (Q. 3.85)

(a) Electromagnetic deflection.

(b) The internally generated sawtooth wave.

(c) A 60 cycle sine wave obtained from the line voltage.

(d) The input signal being measured.

(e) The Lissajou effect.

III-19. In a Hartley-type oscillator, feedback is obtained by the use of: (Q. 3.86)

(a) A tapped capacitive circuit.

(b) A tapped resistive circuit.

(c) A tapped inductive circuit.

(d) Plate-to-grid feedback.

(e) Bridge-type feedback.

III-20. A Pierce oscillator operates in a manner similar to a: (Q. 3.86)

(a) Electron coupled oscillator.

(b) Transitron oscillator.

(c) Colpitts oscillator.

(d) Tuned-grid, tuned-plate oscillator.

(e) Armstrong oscillator.

III-21. In a multivibrator oscillator, the main frequency determining elements are: (Q. 3.86)

(a) The tubes or transistors.

(b) The RC coupling elements.

(c) The supply voltage and plate resistors.

(d) The plate and grid resistors.

(e) The plate resistors and the coupling capacitors.

III-22. The improved frequency stability gained by using a crystal in an oscillator is obtained because: (Q. 3.87)

(a) The crystal has a high positive temperature coefficient.

(b) The crystal has a high negative temperature coefficient.

(c) The crystal feedback must be strictly limited.

(d) The crystal has a very high Q.

(e) The crystal has a very low Q.

III-23. The major purpose of using a buffer amplifier in a transmitter is: (Q. 3.98)

(a) To provide a high order of RF amplification.

(b) To provide a low order of RF amplification.

(c) To isolate the final RF amplifier from the intermediate power RF amplifier.

(d) To act as a frequency multiplier.

(e) None of the above.

III-24. An overtone crystal is one which is specially ground to operate: (Q. 3.95)

(a) In a high power circuit.

(b) In an exceptionally high-stability circuit.

(c) In an audio oscillator, for precision measurements.
(d) At an odd harmonic of its fundamental.
(e) At an even harmonic of its fundamental.

III-25.   In multistage audio amplifiers, decoupling networks are used: (Q. 3.102)

(a) To increase the overall gain.
(b) To provide negative feedback.
(c) To prevent audio oscillations.
(d) To prevent RF oscillations.
(e) To increase the high-frequency response.

III.26.   If the cathode bypass capacitor in an audio amplifier had a value considerably smaller than normally required, the effect would be: (Q. 3.100)

(a) Increased gain at low frequencies only.
(b) Decreased gain at low frequencies only.
(c) Audio oscillations.
(d) Decreased gain at high frequencies only.
(e) Motorboating.

III-27.   The effect of saturation of an audio output transformer on the audio output would be: (Q. 3.103)

(a) No effect.
(b) Transformer would burn out.
(c) Transformer core would be permanently magnetized.
(d) A reduction of audio distortion.
(e) Severe audio distortion.

III-28.   In true class A operation, the output waveform is: (Q. 3.52)

(a) A perfect reproduction of the input waveform.
(b) Always a perfect reproduction of 180 degrees of the input waveform.
(c) Always inverted by 180 degrees.
(d) Always transformer coupled.
(e) Always RC coupled.

III-29.   In a class A, push-pull, audio power amplifier, the power output is: [Q. 3.110(f)]

(a) Four times the power output of one tube.
(b) The same as the power output for one tube.
(c) Twice the power output for one tube.
(d) Two and one-half times the power output for one tube.
(e) None of the above.

III-30.   A carbon microphone has the disadvantage that it: (Q. 3.116)

(a) Has too high sensitivity.
(b) Has an excessive high-frequency response.
(c) Cannot be used in mobile equipment.

  (d) Has a relatively poor frequency response.

  (e) Does not use a power supply.

III-31. Fig. III-31 shows the schematic of a low-power r-f amplifier with an incomplete cathode circuit. The only bias desired is grid-leak bias. The cathode should be connected: (Q. 3.86)

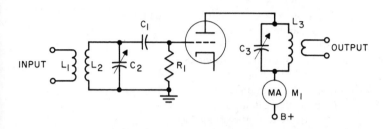

Incomplete schematic diagram of a low-power, r-f amplifier.

  (a) To the grid.

  (b) To ground.

  (c) To a source of negative voltage.

  (d) To the B+ supply.

  (e) None of the above.

III-32. In Fig. III-31, assuming the cathode circuit to be properly connected, a complete loss of input signal would cause: (Q. 3.298)

  (a) An increase of grid-leak bias.

  (b) A decreased reading on meter M1.

  (c) No change in plate or grid currents.

  (d) A change of grid current only.

  (e) None of the above.

III-33. An r-f voltage amplifier, as opposed to an r-f power amplifier, usually employs: (Q. 3.122)

  (a) Class C bias.

  (b) Class A bias.

  (c) Cut-off bias.

  (d) Saturation bias.

  (e) Zero bias.

III-34. Grounded-grid amplifiers are sometimes used at very high r-f frequencies because: (Q. 3.124)

  (a) Of the low bias required.

  (b) They employ positive feedback.

  (c) They usually require neutralization.

  (d) Of the relatively high, plate-to-cathode capacitance.

  (e) They usually do not require neutralization.

III-35. Conventional triode r-f amplifiers frequently require neutralization because of: (Q. 3.125)

(a) Cathode-to-grid feedback.

(b) Out-of-phase, plate-to-grid feedback.

(c) In-phase, plate-to-grid feedback.

(d) Their high values of gm.

(e) The low value of plate-to-grid capacitance.

III-36. In a single tube, frequency multiplier, the output may consist of: (Q. 3.131)

(a) Either odd or even harmonics.

(b) Only odd harmonics.

(c) Only even harmonics.

(d) Only double the input frequency.

(e) Only triple the input frequency.

III-37. A Faraday screen in a transmitter is used for: (Q. 3.137)

(a) Cooling of the power tubes.

(b) Reduction of transmitted harmonics.

(c) Increasing the output power.

(d) Reducing the output power.

(e) Improving the output waveform.

III-38. Link coupling has attenuating properties for harmonic frequencies because of: (Q. 3.134)

(a) The use of physically large coupling coils.

(b) The large amount of capacity coupling.

(c) The large amount of inductive coupling.

(d) The small capacitive coupling between the link coils and the resonant circuits.

(e) The small amount of inductive coupling.

III-39. Transmitter intermodulation may occur if: (Q. 3.135)

(a) A particular transmitter has any of its stages operating above its rated power.

(b) Parasitic oscillations are occurring in any stage.

(c) The transmitter antenna is picking up energy from a second transmitter close by.

(d) The transmitting antenna is picking up energy from a second, very distant, transmitter.

(e) The transmitting antenna is not correctly matched to the final stage of the transmitter.

III-40. The following is considered a spurious emission from a transmitter: (Q. 3.136)

(a) Oscillation from an improperly neutralized r-f amplifier.

(b) Radiation from the basic transmitter power supply.

(c) Radiation from a directional antenna.

(d) Oscillation of the normal transmitter oscillator.

(e) Oscillation from the modulator.

III-41.   High or erratic plate or grid current readings in an r-f amplifier may be caused by: (Q. 3.126)
  (a) A shorted power supply.
  (b) The use of a dynamotor.
  (c) Run-down batteries.
  (d) Excessive grid bias.
  (e) Parasitic oscillations.

III-42.   Harmonic frequency transfer in the antenna coupling circuit of a transmitter may occur by: (Q. 3.137)
  (a) Means of inductive coupling of the coils.
  (b) Capacitive coupling between coils.
  (c) Passing through the low-pass filter.
  (d) Passing through the pi network between the final stage and the transmission line.
  (e) Means of the capacitor between the output stage and the transmission line.

III-43.   In amplitude modulation, the sideband frequencies consist of: (Q. 3.139)
  (a) The carrier frequency and the modulation frequency.
  (b) The heterodyne frequency resulting from the sum of the upper sideband frequency and the lower sideband frequency.
  (c) The sum and difference frequencies between the carrier and the modulation frequencies.
  (d) The sum and difference frequencies between the single sideband frequencies and the modulation frequency.
  (e) The modulation frequency, plus and minus the upper and lower sideband frequencies.

III-44.   Given a carrier frequency of 1000 kc and a modulating frequency of 1000 cycles, the total bandwidth of emission is: (Q. 3.140)
  (a) 2000 cycles.
  (b) 1000 cycles.
  (c) 20,000 cycles.
  (d) 10,000 cycles.
  (e) 900 kc.

III-45.   Given an amplitude-modulated wave with a peak-to-peak amplitude (E_{max}) of 200 volts, a minimum modulated amplitude of 100 volts (E_{min}) and an unmodulated carrier amplitude of 150 volts, the percentage of modulation is: (Q. 3.142)
  (a) 25
  (b) 100
  (c) 75
  (d) 50
  (e) None of the above.

III-46.   A linear class B r-f power amplifier normally operates with a bias approximately equal to: (Q. 3.144)

(a) Projected cut-off.
(b) Twice cut-off.
(c) Ten times cut-off.
(d) 50% of cut-off value.
(e) The class A bias value.

III-47. The sensitivity of a receiver is an important quality because it: (Q. 3.161)

(a) Defines the usable receiver bandwidth.
(b) Defines the receiver's ability to discriminate against image frequencies.
(c) Defines the receiver's ability to discriminate against adjacent-channel interference.
(d) Defines the receiver's ability to respond efficiently to a weak signal input.
(e) Defines the i-f bandwidth of the receiver.

III-48. A receiver is tuned to an incoming frequency of 800 kc. Its oscillator frequency is 1255 kc and its intermediate frequency is 455 kc. The image frequency is: (Q. 3.156)

(a) 1710 kc.
(b) 2615 kc.
(c) 345 kc.
(d) 455 kc.
(e) 910 kc.

III-49. In a capacitive type, reactance-tube modulator, connected across an oscillator tuned circuit, a more negative voltage on the grid of the reactance tube will cause: (Q. 3.162)

(a) An increase of the oscillator frequency.
(b) A decrease of the oscillator frequency.
(c) An increase of the reactance-tube capacitance.
(d) A decrease of the effective capacitive reactance of the reactance tube.
(e) An increase of the reactance tube, ac plate current.

III-50. In the process of pre-emphasis: (Q. 3.163)

(a) The higher frequencies are overemphasized after detection at the receiver.
(b) The lower frequencies are overemphasized at the transmitter, before modulation.
(c) The higher frequencies are overemphasized at the transmitter, before modulation.
(d) The higher frequencies are attenuated at the transmitter, before modulation.
(e) The higher frequencies are caused to be at the same amplitude as the lower frequencies, before modulation.

III-51.   If an FM deviation meter was coupled to the output of a phase-modulated transmitter: **(Q. 3.167)**
(a) It would show no indication at all.
(b) It would show an indication proportional to the amplitude and frequency of the modulation.
(c) It would read exactly the same, as if the transmitter were frequency modulated.
(d) It would show a reading proportional only to the amplitude of the modulation.
(e) It would show a reading proportional only to the frequency of the modulation.

III-52.   In a narrow-band FM system the deviation ratio is commonly one and the highest audio frequency is generally limited to:
(a) 15,000 cycles.
(b) 300 cycles.
(c) 10,000 cycles.
(d) 7500 cycles.
(e) 3000 cycles.

III-53.   In an FM ratio detector, the output audio signal is proportional only to the: **(Q. 3.178)**
(a) Amplitude of the input i-f voltages.
(b) Amplitude of the audio modulation signals.
(c) Ratio of the input i-f voltages to the diodes.
(d) Ratio of the input audio voltages.
(e) None of the above.

III-54.   Fig. III-54 is an incomplete schematic diagram of an FM limiter stage. In order to make this circuit operate properly, it is necessary to: **(Q. 3.177)**

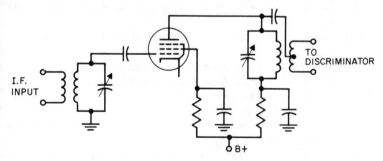

Incomplete schematic diagram of an FM limiter stage.

(a) Connect the suppressor grid to a low value of B+.
(b) Only ground the cathode.

(c) Connect the screen grid and plate to separate sources of B+.

(d) Short across the capacitor in series with the grid.

(e) Ground the cathode and connect a resistor from grid to ground.

III-55. A certain transmitter has an assigned frequency of 100.00 mc and a required tolerance of 0.0005 percent. The maximum and minimum allowed frequencies are: (Q. 3.176)

(a) 100,005,000 and 99,995,000 cycles.

(b) 100,000,500 and 99,999,500 cycles.

(c) 100,050,000 and 99,995,000 cycles.

(d) 100,000,500 and 99,999,950 cycles.

(e) None of the above.

III-56. The circuit of Fig. III-54 is able to operate as a limiter by virtue of its: (Q. 3.177)

(a) Grid-leak bias and low plate and screen grid voltages.

(b) Remote cut-off characteristics.

(c) Grid-leak bias and high values of plate and screen grid voltages.

(d) Low impedance plate circuit.

(e) Grounded condition of the supressor grid.

III-57. In a PNP, common-emitter transistor amplifier, the normal operating voltages are as follows: (Q. 3.184)

(a) Negative at the emitter and negative at the collector.

(b) Positive at the base and negative at the collector.

(c) Negative at the base and negative at the collector.

(d) Positive at the base and positive at the collector.

(e) Positive at the emitter and positive at the collector.

III-58. The alpha cut-off frequency of a transistor is defined as: (Q. 3.188)

(a) The low frequency at which the gain drops by 3 db.

(b) The high frequency of a compensated amplifier at which the gain rises by 3 db.

(c) The low frequency of a compensated amplifier at which the gain rises by 3 db.

(d) The high frequency at which the current gain drops by 3 db.

(e) The high frequency at which the current gain becomes unity.

III-59. Referring to the schematic diagram of Fig. 3.187(a) of the text, the purpose of R3 is: (Q. 3.187)

(a) To help compensate for emitter-to-base junction resistance changes with temperature.

(b) To compensate for emitter-to-collector junction resistance changes with temperature.

(c) To provide the forward bias for the transistor.

(d) To increase the overall gain of the amplifier.

(e) To provide reverse bias for the collector.

III-60. The transistor, common-base amplifier is similar to the vacuum tube: [Q. 3.192(J)]

  (a) Cathode-follower amplifier.

  (b) Video amplifier.

  (c) Grounded-grid amplifier.

  (d) Grounded-cathode amplifier.

  (e) Audio amplifier.

III-61. In comparing the common-collector transistor amplifier with the common-emitter amplifier, it is found that: [Q. 3.192(K)]

  (a) The common-emitter amplifier has lower voltage gain.

  (b) The common-collector amplifier has lower power gain.

  (c) The common-collector amplifier has a current gain of unity.

  (d) The common-emitter amplifier has a lower output resistance.

  (e) The common-collector amplifier has a signal inversion.

III-62. In a common-emitter transistor amplifier, a change in the base voltage of 0.02 volts produces a collector voltage change of 10 volts. The voltage gain of this amplifier (A_v) is: [Q. 3.192(L)]

  (a) 50

  (b) 200

  (c) 500

  (d) 50

  (e) 20

III-63. In Fig. III-63, the base current is approximately: [Q. 3.192(M)]

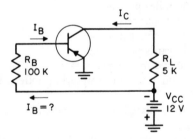

Common-emitter amplifier connected for "fixed" bias.

  (a) 12 ua.

  (b) 120 ua.

  (c) 0.0833 ma.

  (d) 83.3 ua.

  (e) 120 ma.

III-64. In a half-wave antenna, the center impedance is: (Q. 3.193)

  (a) 2500 ohms.

  (b) 73 ohms.

  (c) 730 ohms.

  (d) 250 ohms.

  (e) 36½ ohms.

III-65. In the case of a Marconi antenna, the actual length of the radiating element is: (Q. 3.193)

(a) One-quarter wavelength.

(b) One-half wavelength.

(c) Three-quarter wavelength.

(d) One wavelength.

(e) One-eighth wavelength.

III-66. In a horizontal-dipole antenna, the polarization is: (Q. 3.203)

(a) The same as the polarization of the magnetic field.

(b) In the vertical direction.

(c) In the horizontal direction.

(d) Circular.

(e) Measured at the center of the antenna.

III-67. If a sky wave meets a ground wave at a receiver and they are appreciably out of phase, this may cause: (Q. 3.201)

(a) Distortion of the modulation.

(b) Increased amplitude of the modulation.

(c) Increased amplitude of the received signal.

(d) Fading.

(e) Overloading of the r-f stage.

III-68. The velocity of propagation of radio waves in free space is: (Q. 3.208)

(a) 300,000,000 miles per second.

(b) 300,000 meters per second.

(c) 300,000,000 meters per second.

(d) 300,000,000 yards per second.

(e) 300,000,000,000 meters per second.

III-69. In a directional antenna employing both a director and a reflector: (Q. 3.210)

(a) The reflector is placed in front and the director at the rear of the antenna.

(b) Both of these elements are placed in front of the antenna.

(c) Both of these elements are placed at the rear of the antenna.

(d) The director is placed in front and the reflector at the rear of the antenna.

(e) The driven element is placed at the rear of these other two elements.

III-70. If a transmission line is terminated in a resistance equal to its characteristic impedance: (Q. 3.213)

(a) The line loss will be maximum.

(b) The standing-wave ratio will be maximum.

(c) The standing-wave ratio will be minimum.

(d) The input impedance will be twice the terminating resistance.

(e) None of the above.

III-71. Standing waves on a transmission line: (Q. 3.216)

(a) Increase the power fed to the antenna.

(b) Result in a cooler operating line.

(c) Decrease the power fed to the antenna.

(d) Appear only with coaxial lines.

(e) Prevent arcing along the line.

III-72. Some types of coaxial cables are filled with an inert gas, under pressure. The advantage of this is: (Q. 3.218)

(a) To increase the velocity of propagation.

(b) To prevent increased losses in the line.

(c) To reduce the internal breakdown voltage rating.

(d) To increase the characteristic impedance.

(e) To be able to use smaller diameter lines.

III-73. A grid-dip meter can be used to: (Q. 3.129)

(a) Measure the input-grid impedance of a tube.

(b) Measure the grid voltage of a vacuum-tube stage.

(c) Measure the amplitude of grid-circuit oscillations.

(d) Measure the gain of a vacuum-tube amplifier stage.

(e) Measure the resonant frequency of a tuned circuit.

III-74. The indication on an FM deviation meter is proportional to: (Q. 3.223)

(a) The peak amplitude of the a-f modulation.

(b) The RMS amplitude of the a-f modulation.

(c) The peak amplitude of the r-f wave.

(d) The frequency of the audio modulation.

(e) The instantaneous phase of the r-f wave.

III-75. Transmitter harmonics must be attenuated because: (Q. 3.225)

(a) They travel a shorter distance than the fundamental.

(b) They increase the power of the fundamental.

(c) They cause parasitic oscillations.

(d) They interfere with neutralization of r-f stages.

(e) They may cause interference with other stations.

III-76. In calibrating a secondary frequency standard against WWV, you should: (Q. 3.221)

(a) Be sure that the WWV transmission is being modulated.

(b) Zero beat a harmonic of the standard against WWV.

(c) Operate all equipment for a period of one minute to ensure stability.

(d) Modulate the standard.

(e) Connect a heterodyne frequency meter to the standard.

III-77. The operation of an absorption wavemeter depends primarily upon: (Q. 3.220)

(a) A calibrated oscillator and a meter.

(b) A calibrated, variable inductor.

    (c) A calibrated, tuned circuit and a vacuum-tube voltmeter.

    (d) A calibrated, vacuum-tube voltmeter.

    (e) The beat between two radio frequencies.

III-78. Fig. 3.222 of the text shows a block diagram of a typical heterodyne-frequency meter. The function of the 1.0 mc crystal oscillator is: (Q. 3.222)

    (a) To be zero beat against the unknown r-f input signal.

    (b) To verify the calibration of the variable-frequency oscillator.

    (c) To check harmonics of the 400 cycle oscillator.

    (d) To provide a harmonic which will beat against the unknown r-f input signal.

    (e) None of the above.

III-79. A primary advantage of a secondary cell as opposed to a primary cell is that a secondary cell: (Q. 3.226)

    (a) Has a higher temperature of operation.

    (b) Has a lower terminal voltage.

    (c) Can be recharged.

    (d) Has a paste-type of electrolyte.

    (e) Is sealed against the entrance of air.

III-80. The approximate, fully charged voltage of a lead-acid cell is: (Q. 3.232)

    (a) 2.1 volts.

    (b) 1.2 volts.

    (c) 1.5 volts.

    (d) 1.6 volts.

    (e) 6.0 volts.

III-81. A certain battery has a capacity of 160 ampere-hours. If this battery is discharged continuously for 16 hours, the maximum discharge current is: (Q. 3.232)

    (a) 16 amperes.

    (b) 1.6 amperes.

    (c) 10 amperes.

    (d) 1 ampere.

    (e) 10.6 amperes.

III-82. The chemical composition of the electrolyte of a lead-acid storage cell is: (Q. 3.227)

    (a) Lead-sulphate acid.

    (b) Hydrochloric acid.

    (c) Ammonium hydroxide acid.

    (d) Sulphuric acid.

    (e) Sulphur dioxide acid.

III-83. The specific gravity of a fully charged, lead-acid storage cell is: (Q. 3.227)

    (a) 3.100

    (b) 1.300

   (c) 13.000
   (d) 1.150
   (e) 0.1300

III-84. Under very low temperature conditions, a lead-acid battery: (Q. 3.228)
   (a) Will always freeze.
   (b) Will have an increased capacity.
   (c) Will discharge gases.
   (d) Will have a decreased capacity.
   (e) Should have a small quantity of anti-freeze mixed with the electrolyte.

III-85. Excessive sparking at the brushes of a d-c motor may be caused by· (Q. 3.239)
   (a) A short circuit in an armature coil.
   (b) An open circuit in the field coil.
   (c) Excessive spring tension on brushes.
   (d) Brushes too long.
   (e) Insufficient load on motor.

III-86. A d-c, shunt-wound motor has its field opened while it is running without a load. The motor will probably: (Q. 3.245)
   (a) Stop running.
   (b) Keep running at the same speed.
   (c) Have a very high value of field current.
   (d) Have a very low value of armature current.
   (e) Develop a very high value of armature current.

III-87. When cleaning the commutator of a motor or generator use: (Q. 3.244)
   (a) Very fine emery cloth.
   (b) A bias-cut file.
   (c) Commutator polishing paste.
   (d) Low-lead gasoline.
   (e) Dry cleaning fluid.

III-88. The purpose of a commutator on a d-c motor is: (Q. 3.242)
   (a) To maintain an alternating current in the armature.
   (b) To maintain a direct current in the armature.
   (c) To rectify the field current.
   (d) To reduce radio frequency interference.
   (e) To reduce brush sparking.

III-89. The speed of a d-c series motor is mostly determined by: (Q. 3.237)
   (a) The field current.
   (b) The load.
   (c) The armature current.
   (d) The brush tension.
   (e) The number of pairs of poles.

III-90. To find the true power of a circuit, multiply the apparent power (E × I), by: (Q. 3.235)

(a) The tangent of the phase angle.

(b) The sine of the phase angle.

(c) E/I

(d) I × R.

(e) The cosine of the phase angle.

III-91. The resonant frequency of a cavity resonator depends upon: (Q. 3.251)

(a) The excitation device dimensions.

(b) The mode of operation.

(c) Its physical dimensions.

(d) Its electrical dimensions.

(e) The capacitor which tunes it.

III-92. The main frequency determining element of a klystron is: (Q. 3.251)

(a) The repeller voltage.

(b) The accelerating voltage.

(c) Its mode of operation.

(d) Its resonant cavity.

(e) The inductance of the output probe.

III-93. Waveguides are not used extensively below about: (Q. 3.249)

(a) 3000 mc.

(b) 300 mc.

(c) 30,000 mc.

(d) 1000 mc.

(e) 750 mc.

III-94. A magnetron is operated at a duty cycle of .001. It has a peak power output of 100 kilowatts. Its average power is: (Q. 3.248)

(a) 1000 watts.

(b) 1,000,000 watts.

(c) 100 watts.

(d) 10,000 watts.

(e) None of the above.

III-95. A traveling-wave tube is used at frequencies in the order of: (Q. 3.247)

(a) 8000 mc.

(b) 30 mc.

(c) 300 mc.

(d) 100 mc.

(e) 500 mc.

III-96. The symbol for amplitude modulation, telephony, with double-sideband transmission is: (Q. 3.255)

(a) P3D.

(b) A3A.

(c) A3.

(d) A3B.

(e) A5C.

III-97.   The frequency range designated by the abbreviation HF is: (Q. 3.254)

(a) 3 to 30 mc.

(b) 30 to 300 mc.

(c) .3 to 30 Gc.

(d) 30 to 300 Gc.

(e) 3 to 30 kc.

III-98.   Figure III-98 is a schematic diagram of a transistor Colpitts crystal oscillator. If the resistor R_F were to become open, the effect would be: (Q. 3.286)

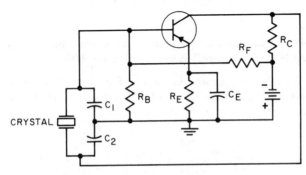

A transistor, Colpitts crystal oscillator.

(a) The amplitude of oscillations would increase.

(b) The amplitude of oscillations would drop slightly.

(c) The collector current will become excessive.

(d) The oscillations would cease.

(e) The forward-base bias would increase.

III-99.   Refer to Fig. 3.279 of the text. If capacitor C2 opened, the effect would be: (Q. 3.279)

(a) Amplitude of oscillations would increase.

(b) Meter M2 reading would increase.

(c) Meter M2 reading would decrease.

(d) Meter M1 reading would increase.

(e) Meter M1 reading would decrease, but would still register appreciable current.

III-100.   Refer to Fig. 3.288 of the text. An open C_k would result in: (Q. 3.288)

(a) Increased gain of the amplifier.

(b) Increased distortion.

(c) Decreased gain and decreased distortion.

(d) Excessive plate current.

(e) Decreased low- and high-frequency response.

ELEMENT IV

ADVANCED RADIOTELEPHONE

PART I: TECHNICAL

Q. 4.01. Show by a simple graph what is meant by: "the current in a circuit leads the voltage." What would cause this?

A. For the graph, see the figure, Fig. 4.01. This condition is caused by the current flowing in a purely capacitive circuit, causing the current to lead the voltage by 90 degrees.

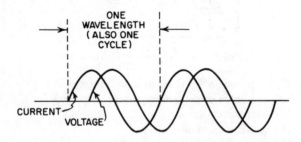

Fig. 4.01. Simple graph showing the current in a circuit, leading the voltage by 90 degrees.

D. The condition shown in the accompanying figure can only exist in a purely capacitive circuit (no resistance). As the amount of resistance in series with the capacitor is increased, the amount of current-lead angle decreases and becomes zero when the resistance is infinite. (Practically speaking, this occurs when the resistance exceeds ten times the capacitive reactance.) When the resistance and reactance are known, the phase angle may be found from the equation:

$$\theta = \tan^{-1} \frac{X_c}{R}$$

where: θ = phase angle between current and voltage.
         X_c = capacitive reactance in ohms.
         R = series resistance in ohms.
(See also Q. 3.09 and Q. 3.20.)

Q. 4.02. List the fundamental frequency and the first 10 harmonic frequencies of a broadcast station licensed to operate at 790 kc/s.

A. The fundamental frequency (or first harmonic) is 790 kilocycles. The other nine harmonics are as follows:
  (2) Second harmonic = 1580 kilocycles.
  (3) Third harmonic = 2370 kilocycles.
  (4) Fourth harmonic = 3160 kilocycles.
  (5) Fifth harmonic = 3950 kilocycles.
  (6) Sixth harmonic = 4740 kilocycles.
  (7) Seventh harmonic = 5530 kilocycles.
  (8) Eighth harmonic = 6320 kilocycles.
  (9) Ninth harmonic = 7110 kilocycles.
 (10) Tenth harmonic = 7900 kilocycles.

Q. 4.03. A series-parallel circuit is composed of a 5 ohm resistor in series with the parallel combination of a capacitor having a pure reactance of 20 ohms and an inductance having a pure reactance of 8 ohms. What is the total impedance of the circuit? Is the total reactance capacitive or inductive?

A. (a) The total impedance of the circuit is 14.2 ohms.
    (b) The total reactance is inductive.

D. Step 1: Solve the parallel impedance of the inductance and capacitance in parallel. Their pure reactances are given in the example, as X_L = 8 ohms and X_c = 20 ohms. To solve this impedance, assume a convenient voltage of 160 volts to appear across the parallel network only.

Step 2: Using the assumed voltage, solve for the branch currents or;

$$I_L = \frac{E_A}{X_L} = \frac{160}{8} = 20a$$

$$I_c = \frac{E_A}{X_c} = \frac{160}{20} = 8a$$

These currents are 180 degrees out of phase and so the net current for this branch is, $I_p = I_L - I_c = 20 - 8 = 12a$ (inductive).

Step 3: Find the impedance of this parallel branch,

$$Z_p = \frac{E_A}{I_p} = \frac{160}{12} = 13.3 \text{ ohms (inductive)}$$

Step 4:   Find the total series impedance of the entire circuit.

$$Z_T = \sqrt{R^2 + X_L^2} = \sqrt{5^2 + 13.3^2} = \sqrt{202} = 14.2 \text{ ohms (inductive)}$$

Q. 4.04.   The 10-kilohm cathode resistor of a certain amplifier is by-passed to ground with a capacitor. If it is desired to operate this amplifier at a minimum frequency of 5 kc/s what size capacitor should be used?

A.   The capacitor should be .032 ufd.

D.   The reactance of a cathode-bypass capacitor should be about one-tenth the value of the cathode resistor at the lowest frequency to be passed. From this basis, we have a simple formula to directly calculate the value of the capacitor in microfarads:

$$C_K = \frac{10^7}{2\pi f_1 R_K}$$

where: C_K = cathode capacitor in microfarads.

f_1 = lowest frequency to be passed, in cycles.

R_K = cathode bias resistance in ohms.

Therefore,

$$C_K = \frac{10^7}{6.28 \times 5 \times 10^3 \times 10 \times 10^3} = \frac{10^7}{6.28 \times 5 \times 10^7} = .032 \text{ ufd}$$

If no bypass capacitor were across the cathode resistor, the amplifier would, in general, have improved performance, but at a sacrifice in gain. Placing a capacitor of suitable value across the cathode resistor prevents degenerative effects due to instantaneous bias changes on the cathode, which are in phase with the applied signal. This is because the capacitor charges very little on increasing plate currents and discharges very little on decreasing plate currents. This condition requires that the time constant in the cathode circuit be long with respect to the time of the lowest audio frequency desired to be passed through the amplifier without degeneration.

Q. 4.05.   What effect does mutual inductance have on the total inductance of two coils connected in series?

A.   If the coils are connected so their fields are aiding, the total inductance is increased. If their fields are opposing, the total inductance is reduced.

D.   The total effective inductance of two mutually coupled coils may be found from the equation:

$$L_T = L_1 + L_2 \pm 2M$$

where: L_T = total effective inductance in henries.

L_1 = inductance of one coil in henries.
L_2 = inductance of second coil in henries.
M = mutual inductance in henries (+ if coil fields aid, or −
     if coil fields oppose).

(See Q. 3.26 for discussion of mutual inductance and Q. 3.27 for discussion of coefficient of coupling.)

Q. 4.06. 10 amps a.c. is flowing in a series circuit composed of 5-ohms resistance, 25-ohms capacitive reactance, and 12-ohms inductive reactance. What is the voltage across each component? What is the total voltage? Why is the total voltage not simply the sum of the individual voltages? Explain.

A. (a) The voltage across the resistor (E_R) = 50 volts.
(b) The voltage across the capacitor (E_c) = 250 volts.
(c) The voltage across the inductance (E_L) = 120 volts.
(d) The total voltage (E_T) = 139 volts.
(e) The total voltage cannot be the sum of the individual voltages, because it is made up of out-of-phase voltages which must be added vectorially.

D. (a) Find the voltage across the resistor (E_R).

$$E_R = I_T \times R = 10 \times 5 = 50 \text{ volts.}$$

(b) Find the voltage across the capacitor (E_c).

$$E_c = I_T \times X_c = 10 \times 25 = 250 \text{ volts.}$$

(c) Find the voltage across the coil (E_L).

$$E_L = I_T \times X_L = 10 \times 12 = 120 \text{ volts.}$$

(d) Find the total voltage (E_T) which is the vector sum of the above three voltages.

$E_T = I_T \times Z_T$ where Z_T equals the total series impedance of the circuit, or

$$Z_T = \sqrt{R^2 + (X_L - X_c)^2} = \sqrt{5^2 + (12-25)^2} = 13.9$$

Therefore,

$$E_T = 10 \times 13.9 = 139 \text{ volts.}$$

Q. 4.07. Show, by simple circuit diagrams at least two ways of obtaining a sawtooth wave. Explain how the waveshape is formed. Where, in television transmitters, are sawtooth waves employed? Why?

A. For three types of circuit diagrams, see the accompanying figures.

(a) When the circuit of Figure 4.07 (a) is originally energized, there is no charge in capacitor C_2 and the thyratron tube is held below cut-off by the bias developed across resistors R_4. Capacitor C_2 begins to charge

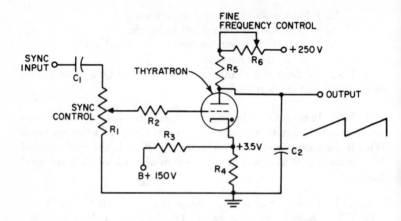

Fig. 4.07(a). A typical thyratron sawtooth-wave generator circuit.

toward +250 volts through resistors R_5 and R_6. C_2 continues to charge until a voltage is reached, at the plate of the thyratron, sufficient to ionize the tube. The exact value depends upon the bias and the particular tube. However, a practical value would be +30 volts. When the tube ionizes, the capacitor discharges rapidly through the tube until the de-ionization potential is reached (about +20 volts), at which time the capacitor begins to charge again. Thus, the capacitor charges slowly and discharges rapidly between +20 volts and +30 volts forming a sawtooth wave with an amplitude of 10 volts. Since only a small portion of the available charging voltage of +250 volts is used, the sawtooth is quite linear.

(b) The circuit of Figure 4.07(b) employs a *hard tube* (high-vacuum tube). In the absence of an input signal, the tube is held below cut-off by the fixed bias (−30 volts) on the grid. At this time capacitor charges toward +250 volts. When the positive-input pulse occurs, it overcomes

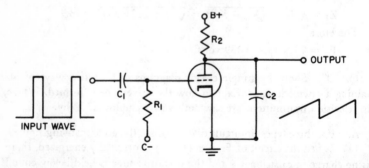

Fig. 4.07(b). A typical hard-tube sawtooth-wave generator circuit.

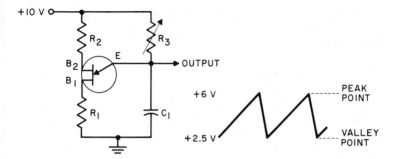

Fig. 4.07(c). Schematic diagram of a unijunction transistor (UJT) sawtooth generator, showing the output waveform (see text).

the bias and causes the tube to conduct heavily. This causes a rapid discharge of capacitor C_2. Following the positive pulse, the tube is again cut off and C_2 begins to charge again. The slow charge and rapid discharge action forms the sawtooth wave.

(c) The circuit of Fig. 4.07(c) shows a sawtooth generator incorporating a unijunction transistor (UJT). The unijunction transistor is able to function in this relaxation oscillator circuit as explained below. In order to help clarify the explanation of this circuit, refer also to the simplified equivalent circuit of Fig. 4.07(d).

Unlike the usual junction transistor, the unijunction transistor has no collector, but consists of a single crystal of N-type silicon mounted on a ceramic disc. The PN emitter junction is formed by alloying an aluminum wire to the top of the crystal nearest the base two contact. Base one and base two are simply defined by placing contacts at each end of the crystal.

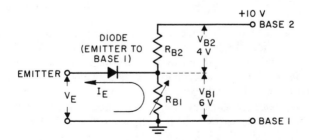

Fig. 4.07(d). Simplified equivalent circuit of a unijunction transistor (UJT) (see text).

Referring to the simplified equivalent circuit diagram of Fig. 4.07 (d), the emitter PN junction is shown as a separate diode connected between base one and base two. Since both bases are on a single crystal and the emitter is connected between the bases, an internal voltage divider is formed between base two and emitter, and between emitter and base one. (The total resistance between base two and base one is between 5,000 and 10,000 ohms.) With the emitter nonconducting, a typical voltage division is as shown, with $V_{B2} = 4V$; and $V_{B1} = 6V$ (assuming a base two supply voltage of +10V).

Note in the equivalent circuit diagram, that the resistance of base one (R_{B1}) is shown to be variable. This is true since in the absence of emitter current, R_{B1} has a fixed value, but when emitter current flows, the path is through R_{B1}, whose resistance varies inversely with the emitter current. (Typical values of R_{B1} are between 40 and 5,000 ohms, depending upon the amount of emitter current which may vary between 50 and 0 ma.)

The UJT circuit produces a continuous sawtooth output in the following manner. Assume that there is no charge in sawtooth capacitor C1 and that the system has just been turned on. C1 now begins to charge in the positive direction toward the +10V supply voltage. However, note in the simplified equivalent circuit that the normal voltage division between the two bases (no emitter current) is such that the voltage across base one (V_{B1}) is 6V.

In order for emitter current to flow (through base one), the emitter must be forward biased. This means that the emitter must go more positive than the 6V base one voltage. Thus, C1 charges through R3, toward +10V, in a fairly linear manner.

When the emitter voltage just exceeds +6V, emitter current begins to flow through base one. In the waveform shown in Fig. 4.07(c), this is designated as the "peak point." This is the point at which the capacitor stops charging (trace portion) and begins to discharge (retrace portion). As soon as emitter current begins to flow, C1 begins to discharge through the emitter to base one junction, through base one and R1.

Since current from the emitter is now passing through base one (in addition to the voltage divider current), the resistance of base one decreases (due to the physics of the base material), and the voltage appearing across base one is reduced, since the voltage divider has now changed to drop less voltage across R_{B1} and more across R_{B2}. (Note that an *increase* of current through R_{B1} has actually resulted in a *decrease* of voltage across it. This is the inverse of the Ohm's law condition and this situation is known as "negative resistance.")

As long as the decreasing voltage across C1 (during discharge) remains slightly higher than the voltage across base one (V_{B1}), emitter current will continue to flow and C1 will continue to discharge. C1 will continue to discharge until the end of the "negative resistance" portion of the UJT response curve is reached. At this point ["valley point," in Fig. 4.07(c)], any further increase in emitter current tends now to produce an *increase in voltage* across R_{B1} (positive resistance effect).

Thus, at the "valley point," V_{B1} suddenly becomes slightly higher than the emitter voltage (V_E), which is the voltage across capacitor C1. The emitter is now no longer forward biased and emitter current ceases. This is the end of the retrace portion of the sawtooth. Depending upon the particular type of UJT in use, this valley point will occur at about 2.5V. Since the "peak point" occurs at 6V, the sawtooth amplitude is 3.5V.

Now, with the emitter current cut off, C1 once again begins to charge toward the peak point to begin another cycle. The action is continuous and sawtooth waves will continue to be produced until the power is shut off. Note, in Fig. 4.07(c) that R3 has been made variable. Varying this resistor makes it possible to change the sawtooth repetition frequency. Of course, changing the value of C1 will also have the same effect on frequency.

(d) In television transmitters, sawtooth waves are employed in TV cameras, picture monitors and in oscilloscopes which are used to monitor the transmission of picture and synchronizing signals.

(e) Sawtooth waves are employed because they provide a relatively slow, linear motion of the electron beam across the screen during picture tracing and a very rapid retrace of the beam when no picture information is involved. This wave traces the beam horizontally at the rate of 15,750 cps. Simultaneously, a 60 cps sawtooth wave produces vertical deflection at a much slower rate, so that the picture is also traced out from top to bottom. In this manner, a linear, evenly-spaced picture is provided.

D. See Q. 4.73 for detailed discussion of TV scanning technique. See also Q. 4.74 and Q. 4.75.

Q. 4.08. What causes resistance noise in electrical conductors and shot-effect noise in diodes?

A. (a) So-called *resistance noise* in electrical conductors is caused by the random motion of molecules in the conductors.

(b) For *shot-effect* noise, see Q. 3.101.

D. (a) At any temperature above absolute zero, there is a certain amount of random molecular motion in all substances. This random motion in conductors, produces small voltages which are generally known as *thermal-agitation noise* voltages. The amplitude of this noise increases with temperature and the noise frequencies extend across the entire radio-frequency spectrum. In superheterodyne receivers, the noise generated in the antenna circuit, r–f amplifier and mixer stage is of the greatest importance. Only that noise occurring within the receiver i–f passband appears in the receiver output. Thus, narrowing the i–f passband is one way of reducing the effect of receiver noise.

Q. 4.09. **Find the gain of a triode amplifier with a plate resistance of 50,000 ohms and a load resistance of 75,000 ohms. The amplification factor is 25.**

A.   The gain equals 15.

D.   The gain of a triode amplifier may be found from the equation

$$A = \frac{\mu R_L}{R_L + R_p}$$

where: A = gain

μ = amplification factor

R_L = load resistance

R_p = tube plate resistance

Substituting the values given, we have,

$$A = \frac{25 \times 75,000}{50,000 + 75,000} = \frac{1875}{125} = 15$$

Q. 4.10. **List some precautions to be observed when soldering transistors and repairing printed circuits.**

A.   See Q 3.191.

Q. 4.11. **What is the gain factor of a transistor?**

A.   The current gain of a common-emitter transistor is the ratio of a small change of collector current to the small change of base current which causes it (generally, with a zero-resistance collector load). This ratio is defined by the Greek letter beta, or

$$\beta = \frac{\Delta I_c}{\Delta I_b} \bigg|_{V_c}$$

D.   A method of describing the "gain factor" of a common-base transistor is called the "current-amplification factor" (forward, short circuit) and is designated by the Greek letter alpha. Alpha is the ratio of a small change of collector current to the small change of emitter current causing it, or

$$\alpha = \frac{\Delta I_c}{\Delta I_e}\bigg|_{V_c}$$

Q. 4.12. What are the main disadvantages of using transistors in circuits rather than vacuum tubes assuming the cost is the same for both?

A.   Some disadvantages of using transistors rather than plug-in vacuum tubes are:

(a) Extreme variations of parameters due to temperature changes.
(b) Need for protective diodes in many circuits.
(c) Susceptible to switching-transient damage.
(d) Difficult to install and replace (except where transistor sockets are used).
(e) Can accept relatively low-voltage input signals.

D.   On the side of advantages, the transistor:
(a) Is smaller and lighter.
(b) Is more rugged.
(c) Has longer life.
(d) Has greater power efficiency.
(e) Requires no filament supply.
(f) Is especially adaptable to use in miniaturized circuits and printed circuit boards.
(g) Requires low voltage power supplies.

Q. 4.13. If a standard broadcast station is licensed to operate at a frequency of 1260 kc/s what are the minimum and maximum frequencies at which it may operate and still be within the proper limits established by the Commission's rules?

A.   The minimum frequency is 1,259,980 cycles. The maximum frequency is 1,260,020 cycles.

D.   The Commission's rules state that the carrier frequency shall be maintained within plus or minus 20 cycles of its assigned frequency.

Q. 4.14. Explain the operation of a resistance bridge. If the known resistances in such an instrument are 5 and 10 ohms, and if adjusting the third resistance to 50 ohms produces a perfect balance, what is the unknown resistance?

A.   (a) See the schematic of Fig. 4.14. The resistance bridge is used for accurate measurement of an unknown resistance. In the diagram, resistors R_1 and R_2 are fixed precision resistors of known value. R_3 is an accurately calibrated variable resistor and R_x is the unknown value of resistance to be measured. A fixed d–c voltage is applied to points A and B and a high resistance voltmeter is connected to points C and D. When

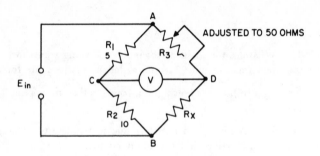

Fig. 4.14. Schematic diagram of a resistance bridge where R_x is the unknown value.

the ratio of $\dfrac{R_1}{R_2}$ equals $\dfrac{R_3}{R_x}$, the bridge is balanced as shown by a zero reading on the meter. The unknown value of resistance is then read from the calibration scale for R_3. The bridge achieves balance under these conditions because the voltage drops across R_1 and R_3 are equal and the voltage drops across R_2 and R_x are equal.

(b) The unknown resistance is found from the formula:

$$R_x = \frac{R_2}{R_1} \times R_3$$

$$R_x = \frac{10}{5} \times 50 = 100 \text{ ohms}$$

Q. 4.15. What is an audio frequency? What approximate band of frequencies is normally referred to as the audio-frequency range?

A. (a) An audio frequency is one which can be heard by the average person as a sound wave.

(b) The normal audio-frequency band is between 20 cycles and 20,000 cycles.

D. The actual audio range in use will vary with the equipment and its purpose. For example, in the case of "hi-fi" tape recorders and record players, the reproducible range may be from 20 cps to well in excess of 20,000 cps. For an AM broadcast station, the high frequency end may be cut off at about 5000 cps. In two-way voice communications, a range of about 200 cps to 2000 to 3000 cps may be adequate. On the other hand, an FM broadcast station may broadcast an audio range of 20 cps to 15,000 cps.

Q. 4.16.   What causes sound and how is it transmitted in air?

A.   (a) Sound is caused by a disturbance of air molecules which causes sound waves to be set up at an audio frequency (20 to 20,000 cps).

(b) Transmission of sound waves in the air occurs due to rarefraction and compression of air molecules (at audio frequencies) which cause the sound waves to move out from the originating point at about 1120 feet per second (sea level, at 20°C).

D.   Perception of sound is created by vibration of the ear drum responding to sound waves. The effect of such vibration is transmitted by nerves leading to the brain. Here it is translated into the effect known as sound.

Q. 4.17.   Sketch the physical construction of the following types of microphones and list their advantages and/or disadvantages: (a) dynamic, (b) ceramic, (c) crystal, (d) single button, (e) ribbon. Which types are normally used in the broadcast studio? Why?

A.   (a) For a sketch of a dynamic microphone, see Figure 4.17(a).
A "dynamic" or "moving coil" type of microphone is somewhat similar in construction to a small permanent magnet dynamic speaker.

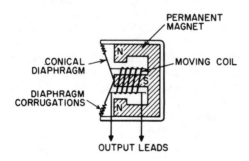

Fig. 4.17(a).   Cross section of a dynamic microphone.

The diaphragm is of the unstretched, non-rigid type and has a number of circular corrugations. These corrugations give the diaphragm a great amount of flexibility and excellent low frequency response. Attached to the diaphragm is a circular coil constructed of a large number of thin aluminum turns held together and insulated by a varnish. The coil, which moves with the diaphragm, passes between the poles of a strong permanent magnet, with very small clearance. When the diaphragm is actuated by sound waves, the coil moves in the magnetic field of the permanent magnet, and has induced into it a voltage corresponding to the sound variations.

The microphone has a low impedance output (25 to 50 ohms) and may be connected through long shielded cables to a distant amplifier. It is rugged, dependable, requires no power supply, and very little maintenance. The frequency response of those commonly available is approximately from 50 to 15,000 cycles.

Advantages of a dynamic microphone are:

(1) Rugged construction.

(2) High output level (−55db).

(3) Light weight.

(4) Wide frequency response (50–15,000 cycles).

(5) Low-hum pickup (−128 dbm).

(6) Low impedance (switchable for 30, 150 or 250 ohms in certain broadcast studio types).

(7) Relatively insensitive to temperature and humidity.

(8) Large dynamic operating range.

(9) Does not require power supply.

(b) The ceramic microphone is constructed in a similar manner to a crystal microphone and is shown in Figure 4.17(b). The basic difference is that the piezo-electric effect of certain ceramic materials replaces that of Rochelle-salt crystals. Ceramic is much less affected by temperature and humidity than Rochelle salt. However, the ceramic element like the crystal, is frequently enclosed in a moisture-proof case. The basic principle of operation is the same as for the crystal type (see part (c)). The output of ceramic microphones and their frequency response (for similar services) are very similar to the crystal type and they both feature high-impedance outputs. The output level for a good-quality microphone may be −55db and the frequency response from 50 to 12,000 cycles.

Advantages of a ceramic microphone are:

(1) Relatively inexpensive.

(2) High output level (−55db).

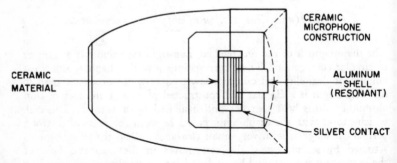

Fig. 4.17(b). Cross section of a ceramic microphone.
(Courtesy of RCA)

(3) Good frequency response.

(4) Does not require power supply.

Disadvantages of a ceramic microphone are:

(1) Tends to be susceptible to temperature and humidity (although less so than crystal type).

(2) May be susceptible to shock.

(3) Response may not be as smooth as the dynamic or ribbon type.

(4) Frequency response may not be as extensive as dynamic or ribbon type.

(5) High output impedance, makes it more susceptible to hum pickup and background noise.

(c) A diagram of a crystal microphone is shown in Figure 4.17 (c). Its operation is discussed in Q. 3.118, part (a).

The advantages and disadvantages of a crystal microphone are basically the same as for the ceramic microphone described in (b) above. The crystal microphone, however, is inferior to the ceramic type in regard to resistance to temperature extremes, humidity, and shock.

(d) For a diagram of a single-button (carbon) microphone, see Figure 4.17(d). A schematic of its normal connections is shown in Figure 3.116. A discussion of the construction and characteristics of this type of microphone, is given in Q. 3.116.

Advantages of a single-button carbon microphone are:

(1) High-output voltage.

(2) High sensitivity.

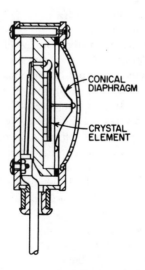

CONICAL
DIAPHRAGM

CRYSTAL
ELEMENT

Fig. 4.17(c). Crystal microphone assembly.

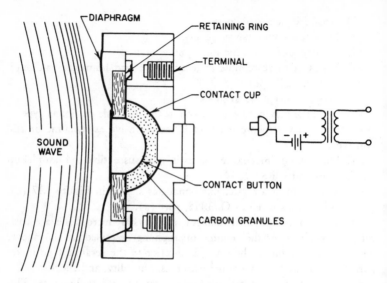

Fig. 4.17(d). Cross section of a single-button carbon microphone.

(3) Low cost.
(4) Relatively low impedance (50 to 100 ohms).
Disadvantages of a single-button carbon microphone are:
(1) High inherent noise level (hiss).
(2) Limited frequency response.
(3) Susceptible to moisture problems (packing of carbon granules).
(4) Requires d-c power supply.

(e) For sketch of a ribbon microphone, see Fig. 4.17(e). The ribbon (or velocity, or pressure gradient) microphone employs a very light ribbon of corrugated aluminum suspended to vibrate freely in a magnetic field. The ribbon is actually the diaphragm of the microphone and is exposed to the air on its two opposite faces. The ribbon vibrates in response to the velocity component of the sound wave and cuts magnetic lines of force causing proportional voltages to be induced into the ribbon. These voltages (at extremely low impedance) are fed to a transformer. The transformer raises the microphone impedance to be compatible with standard lines and facilities of the broadcast studio and also raises the microphone output voltage level to a practical value similar to a dynamic microphone.

Advantages of a ribbon microphone are:
(1) Wide frequency response (50–15,000 cycles).
(2) High output level (−55 dbm).
(3) Low output impedance (30-150-150 ohms, switchable).

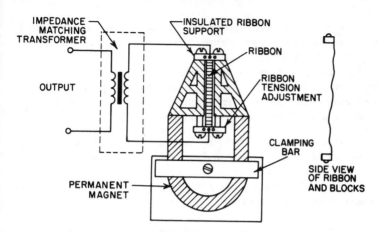

Fig. 4.17(e). Ribbon (velocity) microphone.

(4) Rugged construction.

(5) Light weight.

(6) Insensitive to heat and humidity.

(7) Large dynamic operating range.

(8) Does not require power supply.

(9) Low background noise.

Disadvantages of a ribbon microphone are:

(1) Ribbon is delicate and should not be subjected to sudden puffs of wind or blasting sounds.

(2) Ribbon should not be overstretched or it will lose its elasticity with a consequent reduction of overall performance.

(f) The microphones normally used in the broadcast studio are the dynamic and the ribbon types. The reasons for using these are:

(1) Light weight.

(2) Rugged construction.

(3) Low-hum pickup.

(4) Indefinite life.

(5) Wide and smooth frequency response characteristics.

(6) Relatively impervious to shock and vibration, temperature and humidity.

(7) Some types are built to have directional characteristics.

(8) Low background noise.

(9) Low impedance output.

(10) High-level output.

Q. 4.18. What is meant by the "phasing" of microphones? When is this necessary?

A. (a) "Phasing" of microphones indicates that each microphone will have the same output polarity for a given sound-pressure wave acting on the microphones.

(b) Phasing is necessary when two or more microphones are connected to a mixer. If this is not done the microphone outputs may oppose each other, causing a reduction of output. In addition, varying amounts of distortion may also be introduced.

D. Phasing may be particularly important when two similar microphones are placed in a symmetrical relationship to a performer. Also, for optimum operation of some amplitude-modulated transmitters, correct phasing may be important. This is true because of the unsymmetrical aspects of speech waveforms.

Q. 4.19. What is the difference between unidirectional, bidirectional, and omnidirectional mcrophones?

A. (a) A unidirectional microphone has its major lobe of pickup extending in only one direction.

(b) A bidirectional microphone has two major lobes of pickup which are separated by 180 degrees.

(c) An omnidirectional microphone picks up sounds with equal facility from all directions.

D. (a) A unidirectional microphone is used when it is desired to discriminate against sounds coming from all but one direction. An example is the use of such a microphone for a singer before a large audience.

(b) A bidirectional microphone may be used to pick up the voices of two people sitting across from one another, while discriminating against pickup from other directions.

(c) An omnidirectional microphone may be positioned in the center of activity when it is desired to pick up sound equally from all directions. For example, the microphone may be placed in the center of a round-table discussion.

Q. 4.20. What is a decibel?

A. Basically, the decibel is a unit used to express the *ratio* between two sound power levels, or two electrical power levels.

D. The formula for calculating decibels when the ratio of two powers is compared is $N = 10 \log_{10} \dfrac{P_2}{P_1}$. Here P_2 is always the larger power, and N is the ratio in db. The equation is true only when the two values of power are measured across equal impedances.

If an attenuation is indicated the answer will be in $-db$. If amplification is indicated the answer will be $+db$. Ex.: Find the number of db corresponding to a power ratio of 200:2.

Solution: $N = 10 \log_{10}\dfrac{P_2}{P_1} = 10 \ \log_{10}\dfrac{200}{2} = 10 \log_{10} 100 = 10 \times 2 = 20db$.

Db may also be used in expressing the ratio between two voltages or two currents as follows:

$$N = 20 \log_{10}\frac{E_2}{E_1} = 20 \log_{10}\frac{I_2}{I_1},$$ provided that the values of E and I

are measured at points of equal impedance.

The following will be found useful in treating db problems of power

1. An increase of 1 db ($+$) is an increase of power of 25%.
2. A decrease of 1db ($-$) is a decrease of power of 20%.
3. An increase of 3db ($+$) doubles the power.
4. A decrease of 3db ($-$) cuts the power in half.

To apply the above to voltage or current, merely double the number of db involved.

The decibel is often used as a value of power. For this application, it must express a ratio to some level taken as a standard reference level.

The standard reference used by the telephone company and by broadcast stations is the Volume Unit (V.U.), where 0 V.U. = 1 milliwatt, or .775 volts across 600 ohms. The standard broadcast studio reference of Volume Units (V.U.) is 0 V.U. = 1 milliwatt, or 0.775 volts in 600 ohms. V.U. is figured on the same basis as db: that is, it is based upon a logarithmic scale, but, using a highly damped meter, represents an average value.

It is interesting to note that a one-decibel change of a sinusoidal sound-wave level is barely distinguishable by the average human.

Q. 4.21. VU meters are normally placed across transmission lines of what characteristic impedance?

A.   600 ohms impedance.

D.   See Q. 4.20.

Q. 4.22. Show by a circuit diagram a method of desensitizing a VU meter to cause it to read lower than normal.

A. For the schematic diagram, see Fig. 4.22.

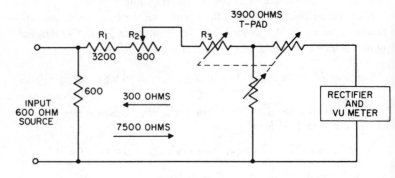

Fig. 4.22. VU meter bridging circuit.

D. For program monitoring, the VU meter input-circuit impedance is 7500 ohms, as seen by the program line. 3900 ohms in the meter is added to 3600 ohms supplied by R_1 and R_2. R_3 is a 3900 ohm T-pad and is used as the meter multiplier to adjust the sensitivity of the meter.

By adjustment of R_3, it is possible to set 0 VU to correspond to any desired incoming signal level. A good example is to make 0 VU correspond to the standard phoneline level of +4 dbm.

Q. 4.23. Why is it important to keep the contact points on attenuator pads used in a broadcast studio console clean? How are they cleaned?

A. (a) The contact points must be kept clean to insure reliable and noise-free operation of attenuator pads.

(b) Contact points may be cleaned with a clean, soft cloth and carbon tetrachloride. The leaves may also be cleaned the same way, being careful not to disturb their tension.

D. To help prevent wear of the contacts, lubricate them lightly using plain petroleum jelly applied with a clean cloth. The tension of the leaves should not be changed unless absolutely necessary. If this must be done, adjust the leaves using the sliding mounting screw until there is just adequate pressure to insure reliable contact.

Q. 4.24. What is a pre-amplifier? Where are they normally used in the broadcast station?

A. (a) A "pre-amplifier" is a high-gain audio amplifier used to increase the output signal level of a microphone, record player, or tape head.

(b) In a broadcast station they are normally used between the above three pick-up devices and the first mixer. They are located as close as possible to the pick-up devices.

D.   Pre-amplifiers are used ahead of mixing systems to improve their output signal-to-noise ratio. All mixers have certain inherent noise level and the output of most pick-up units is low, in the order of −55 VU (volume units). Therefore, pre-amplifiers are connected immediately following each pick-up unit and the output of each pre-amplifier is then fed to the mixer, thus raising the signal-to-noise ratio.

Some microphones have transistor pre-amplifiers built directly into the microphone housing. Such microphones are particularly valuable where a long line connects the microphone to the nearest available studio-type pre-amplifier, as is done in remote pick-up applications.

Q. 4.25.   Given the gain of an amplifier which amplifies feedback and the overall voltage gain of a circuit, how is it possible to determine the amount of feedback used? State the formula used and solve a sample problem.

A.   (a) The amount of feedback used can be determined by applying the formula for determining the gain of an amplifier with feedback in its transposed form.

(b) The formula for the gain of an amplifier with feedback is:

$$a' = \frac{a}{1 + Ba}$$

where: a' = gain with feedback

   a = gain without feedback

   B = fraction of output voltage fed back in opposition to input signal.

Transposing and solving for B, we have:

$$B = \frac{1}{a'} - \frac{1}{a}$$

We now assume that "a" equals 20, and "a'" equals 10. Solving for B we have

$$B = \frac{1}{10} - \frac{1}{20} = \frac{1}{20} = .05 = 5 \text{ percent}$$

D.   The gain of an amplifier with negative feedback may be determined from the formula, $a' = \dfrac{a}{1 + Ba}$, where a' is the gain with feedback, B is the fraction of the total output voltage fed back in opposition to the input signal voltage E_s, a is the gain without feedback. The low-

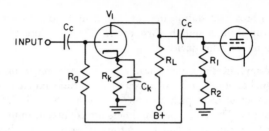

Fig. 4.26(a). An example of negative-voltage feedback.

frequency response will be affected according to the formula, $F'_1 = \dfrac{F_1}{1 + Ba}$, where F'_1 is the new low-frequency response without feedback. The high-frequency response will be affected according to the formula, $F'_2 = F_2(1 + Ba)$.

Q. 4.26. What is the technical requirement for negative feedback? Show by circuit diagrams how this is achieved for negative voltage feedback and negative current feedback.

A. (a) The basic requirements are to reduce distortion and improve amplifier stability.

(b) For the schematics, see the accompanying diagrams.

D. In Fig. 4.26(a), the percentage of feedback is determined by the division across R_1 and R_2. (See also Q. 4.25.) The phase of this voltage is in opposition to the input voltage.

In Fig. 4.26(b), the feedback voltage is developed across the unbypassed resistor R_K. Although the voltage across R_K is in phase with the input voltage, its effect on the cathode causes it (in the tube) to oppose the input voltage. Since the voltage across R_K is proportional to the tube current, this is a system of current feedback.

Q. 4.27. What is meant by the fidelity of an audio amplifier? Why is good fidelity an important consideration when replacing amplifiers in the broadcast station?

A. (a) The *fidelity* of an audio amplifier is its ability to reproduce in its output, a *true* (but amplified) version of the input signal. This refers not only to the frequency, but also to the phase characteristics of the input signal.

(b) Good fidelity is important when replacing amplifiers, in order that the station will continue to broadcast signals of very high quality, with a minimum of frequency and phase distortion.

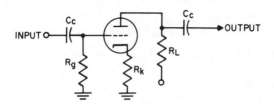

*Fig. 4.26(b). An example of negative-current feedback developed
across the unbypassed resistor, R_K.*

D.   In order that an amplifier shall provide high fidelity, it is vital
that the amplifier shall introduce a minimum of hum and noise components. In addition, the amplitude (dynamic) response shall be linear.
Harmonic and intermodulation distortion, introduced by the amplifier,
shall be kept to the lowest possible percentage. (See also Q. 3.104.)

**Q. 4.28.   What type of playback stylus is generally used in broadcast
station turntables? Why?**

A.   (a) A diamond stylus is generally used.

(b) A diamond stylus will provide the greatest number of playing
hours consistent with the allowable wear and distortion of the tip. Therefore, replacement is kept to the minimum.

D.   A stylus used to play stereophonic recordings will have a tip diameter of approximately 0.7 mil, while a monaural-playing stylus generally has a tip diameter of around 1 mil. A studio-quality stylus
generally employs hand-polished, "prime" diamonds that provide a great
many hours of first-quality reproduction. The tracking force for broad-
cast-type applications is approximately 1 to 2 grams; a magnetic-type
cartridge is usually preferred. Such a cartridge may have a relatively-flat
response ranging from 20 to 20,000 cps and an output of 2 to 7 mv (per
channel for a stereo type) at 1 kc/cm. Note that a stereo-type stylus is
essential for the reproduction of stereo records, but may also be used to
play monaural records. A monaural-type stylus, however, should never
be used to play stereo recordings, as it is likely to damage the recording,
and will not provide correct reproduction of the stereo record.

**Q. 4.29.   How does dirt on the playback head of a tape recorder af-
fect the audio output? How are such heads cleaned?**

A.   (a) Dirt or oxide on the playback head may cause a reduction
of audio-output amplitude, plus possible distortion. It may also reduce
high frequency response and cause *wow* or *flutter*. Dirt may also increase
head wear and increase the noise level.

(b) The playback head may be cleaned with alcohol, carbon-tetrachloride, or special commercial solvents made for this purpose.

D.   (b) There are also special cloth tapes which may be run through the tape recorder for the purpose of cleaning the tape heads. Such cloth tapes are impregnated with suitable solvents and do an efficient job of cleaning without the need for disassembly.

Q. 4.30.   What is wow and rumble as referred to turntables? How can they be prevented?

A.   (a) *Wow* is a low-frequency modulation of a record occurring once per record revolution.

(b) *Rumble* is caused by vibrations of the turntable. It is of low frequency and may either be a steady-state frequency or a series of random pulses.

(c) For prevention, see the discussion.

D.   (a) Wow is caused by record-groove velocity variations. It may occur in recording or in playback. According to NAB standards, such variations must not exceed ± 0.1 percent for recording and ± 0.3 percent for playback turntables. Wow is caused by small imperfections of the drive motor, drive mechanism, or by an eccentric disc or turntable. It can often be prevented by preventative-maintenance procedures. These include proper cleaning and lubrication of the drive mechanism and motor drive. A slightly oily, lint-free cloth should be used to wipe the hub and spindle. Use the same type of cloth to wipe bushings and thrust balls prior to lubrication. The same type of cloth dampened with naphtha (or similar solvent) can be used to clean such items as motor-drive pulleys and idlers, being certain not to leave oil on these items.

(b) Rumble is in general caused and cured by the same items mentioned in (a) above. In addition, check the inside surface of the turntable rim and wipe it clean. Defective shock mounts may also cause rumble and should be replaced. In the prevention of both wow and rumble, it is important that the turntable be perfectly leveled and balanced.

Q. 4.31.   What factors can cause a serious loss of high frequencies in tape recordings?

A.   The following can cause loss of high frequencies:

(a) A build-up of oxide (or dirt) on the tape head.

(b) Misalignment of the tape head, relative to the tape.

(c) Failure to maintain contact between the tape and the tape-head gap.

(d) Tape not passing squarely past the head.

(e) Nicks or cuts on the surface of the head, or a break-through of the head-gap due to wear.

(f) Uneven wear of the tape head.

(g) Incorrect bias current in tape head.

D. For correct high frequency reproduction, the tape-head gap should be exactly perpendicular to the tape. One way to check this is by means of a standard alignment tape, producing a steady, high-frequency signal. The head is rotated for maximum output and then secured in position.

For high frequencies, the contact between the tape head and tape should be firm. A separation of one-half mil, at these frequencies may cause the output to decrease by 20db or more. Therefore, the pressure pads should be checked for proper functioning. Any buildup of oxide or dirt on the tape head will separate the tape from the head and cause a loss of high frequencies. Cleaning of a tape head was discussed in Q. 4.29 above.

Q. 4.32. Explain the use of a stroboscope disc in checking turntable speed.

A. The stroboscope disc is placed on the turntable and illuminated by a light energized by the 60 cycle line. A neon or fluorescent light is excellent for this purpose. There are separate circles of bars for each speed. With the turntable running, observe the appropriate circle of bars for the particular speed being checked. If the speed is correct, the bars will appear to be stationary.

D. The speed most commonly used is $33\frac{1}{3}$ rpm and the stroboscopic disc has 216 bars for testing this speed. For 78 rpm, there are 92 bars in the ring. In checking speed, not more than 21 bars per minute should drift pass a chosen reference point in either direction. When the bars move in the direction of rotation, the speed is too high. If they move against the rotation, the speed is too low. To bring the turntable to the correct speed, simply adjust the vernier control of the turntable until the bars are stationary. For the most accurate speed setting, a record should be on the turntable and the pickup stylus in the record grooves.

Q. 4.33. Show how frequency response of a pickup unit of either a tape recorder or turntable is tested.

A. (a) The frequency response of a turntable pickup may be checked with the aid of a standard EIA frequency-test record. The output indicator on the associated amplifier is read for each test frequency and a curve obtained to show the overall frequency response.

(b) To check the frequency response of the pickup unit of a tape recorder, proceed as follows:

(1) Using a high quality audio oscillator, feed into the input of the tape recorder (while recording) sine waves at a number of frequencies

between 50 and 15,000 cycles. At each frequency used, the input must be maintained at a constant level.

(2) Play back the tape and record the playback response at each frequency, as read from a built-in or an external VU meter.

(3) Draw a graph plotting the various readings obtained during the playback, indicating frequency vs amplitude.

(4) In making this check, the frequency response of the amplifiers and equalizing circuits as well as the bias oscillators and tape head performance are checked. Also, the tape-head alignment is automatically checked. This is desirable since tape heads are not normally interchanged (unless damaged) and they should be tested in conjunction with their associated recording and reproducing devices.

D. Before testing the frequency response of a turntable pickup, it is essential to know the frequency response of its associated amplifier. If a frequency calibrated amplifier is available, this should be used. The response curve of the pickup-amplifier combination is plotted, as described above. Then the amplifier response curve is compared to the overall response, and a new frequency response curve of the pickup itself is made. This is done by removing the effect of the amplifier response from the overall response. If a frequency-calibrated amplifier is not available, the amplifier in use must be calibrated. This is done with a good audio oscillator. Various frequencies from 50 to 15,000 cycles at constant amplitude, are fed into the amplifier input and the output response is monitored to obtain a frequency-amplitude calibration curve.

If a tape head is to be tested independently of its companion amplifier, the same amplifier-calibration procedure as described above should be used. The tape-head frequency response is determined by monitoring the amplifier output in the same manner as given for a pickup. The overall response and the calibrated amplifier response are then compared to obtain the response of the tape head alone.

Q. 4.34. What is an STL system?

A. An STL (studio-to-transmitter-link) system is a system of relaying a program from a studio to its transmitter by means of radio transmission, rather than over wire facilities.

D. A typical example of STL use occurs in certain remote pickups, particularly where suitable wire transmission is not readily available. This is particularly true of some television remotes, because of the wide (4.5 mc) modulating frequency band required to be relayed to the transmitter. The transmitting and receiving antennas are generally half-wave dipoles in parabolic reflectors. Because of the UHF frequencies used, transmission must be strictly line-of sight. Present frequency assignments for STL stations are as follows:

(a) Aural broadcast STL station: 942-952 megacycles. (FM only.)

(b) Television STL station: 1900-2500 megacycles, 6875-7125 megacycles, 12,700-13,250 megacycles.

The frequencies listed above may be used for the simultaneous transmission of both picture and sound portions of TV programs. Multiplexing may be employed to provide additional communication channels for the transmission of aural program material and for operational communications.

Each broadcast STL or FM Intercity Relay station is required to employ a directional antenna. Considering one kilowatt of radiated power as a standard for comparative purposes, such antenna shall provide a free space field intensity at one mile of not less than 435 microvolts per meter in the main lobe of radiation toward the receiver and not more than 20 percent of the maximum value in any azimuth 30 degrees or more off the line to the receiver. Where more than one antenna is authorized for use with a single station, the radiation pattern of each shall be in accordance with the foregoing requirement.

Q. 4.35. What is a proof-of-performance? How does a proof-of-performance differ from annual equipment performance measurements required by the Commission's rules? What must be included in the annual equipment performance measurements?

A. (a) A *proof-of-performance* is a series of tests made on a broadcast installation. These tests cover the important characteristics of the installation to assure that no deterioration of station performance has occurred.

(b) A proof-of-performance test is made at reasonable intervals throughout the year to assure continuous compliance with the FCC rules and regulations. It may consist of the same test items as required by the annual equipment performance measurements or it may contain either a greater or lesser scope of testing as determined by the Chief Engineer of the station. The annual equipment performance measurements are required by the rules and specify certain definite tests which must be performed and recorded during a specific period of each year. The station is required to maintain compliance with the required station performance specifications at all times and the proper maintenance must be performed, whenever required, to assure compliance.

(c) The items included in the annual equipment performance tests are as follows:

1. AM Broadcast Stations.

   (a) The licensee of each standard broadcast station shall make the following equipment performance measurements at yearly intervals. One such set shall be made during the four-month period preceding the date of filing application for renewal of station license (normally every three years):

(1) Data and curves showing over-all audio frequency response from 30 to 7500 cps for approximately 25, 50, 85, and 100 (if obtainable) percent modulation. Family of curves should be plotted (one for each percentage above) with db above and below a reference frequency of 1000 cps as ordinate and audio frequency as abscissa.

(2) Data and curves showing audio frequency harmonic content for 25, 50, 85 and 100 percent modulation for fundamental frequencies of 50, 100, 400, 1000, 5000 and 7500 cps (either arithmetical or root sum square values up to the tenth harmonic or 16,000 cps). Plot family of curves (one for each percentage above) with percent distortion as ordinate and audio frequency as abscissa.

(3) Data showing percentage carrier shift for 25, 50, 85, and 100 percent modulation with 400 cps tone.

(4) Carrier hum and extraneous noise generated within the equipment and measured as the level below 100 percent modulation throughout the audio spectrum or by bands.

(5) Measurements or evidence showing that spurious radiations including radio frequency harmonics are suppressed or are not present to a degree capable of causing objectionable interference to other radio services. Field intensity measurements are preferred but observations made with a communications type receiver may be accepted. However, in particular cases involving interference or controversy, the Commission may require actual measurements. Measurements shall be made with the equipment adjusted for normal program operation and shall include all circuits between main studio amplifier input and antenna output including equalizer or correction circuits normally employed, but without compression if such amplifier is employed.

(b) The data required by paragraph (a) of this section together with a description of instruments and procedure, signed by the engineer making the measurements, shall be kept on file at the transmitter and retained for a period of two years, and on request shall be made available during that time to any duly authorized representative of the Federal Communications Commission.

2. FM Broadcast Stations.

(a) The construction, installation, operation and performance of the FM broadcast transmitting system shall be in accordance with R & R 73.317. (FCC Rules and Regulations.)

(b) The licensee of each FM broadcast station shall make the following equipment performance measurements at least at yearly intervals. One such set of measurements shall be made during the four-month period preceding the date of filing application for renewal of station license (normally, every three years).

   (1) Audio frequency response from 50 to 15,000 cycles for approximately 25, 50 and 100 percent modulation. Measurements shall be made on at least the following audio frequencies: 50, 100, 400, 1000, 5000, 10,000 and 15,000 cycles. The frequency response measurements should normally be made without deemphasis; however, standard 75 microsecond deemphasis may be employed in the measuring equipment or system provided the accuracy of the deemphasis circuit is sufficient to insure that the measured response is within the prescribed limits.

   (2) Audio frequency harmonic distortion for 25, 50 and 100 percent modulation for the fundamental frequencies of 50, 100, 400, 1000, and 5000 cycles. Audio frequency harmonics for 100 percent modulation for fundamental frequencies of 10,000 and 15,000 cycles. Measurements shall normally include harmonics to 30,000 cycles. The distortion measurements shall be made employing 75 microsecond deemphasis in the measuring equipment or system.

   (3) Output noise level (frequency modulation) in the band of 50 to 15,000 cycles in decibels below the audio frequency level representing a frequency of 75 kilocycles. The noise measurements shall be made employing 75 microsecond deemphasis in the measuring equipment or system.

   (4) Output noise level (amplitude modulation) in the band of 50 to 15,000 cycles in decibels below the level representing 100 percent amplitude modulation. The noise measurements shall be made employing 75-microsecond deemphasis in the measuring equipment or system. All measurements shall be made with the equipment adjusted for normal program operation and shall include all circuits between the main studio microphone terminals and the antenna output, including telephone lines, preemphasis circuits and any equalizers employed except for microphones, and without compression if a compression amplifier is installed.

(c) The data required by paragraph (b) together with a description of instruments and procedures signed by the engineer making the measurements shall be kept on file at the transmitter and retained for a period of two years and shall be made available during that time upon request to any duly authorized representative of the Federal Communications Commission.

D. (a) A "proof-of-performance" test represents the condition of the station which exists at the time of the test. The more frequently such tests are made and deficiencies corrected, the greater the guarantee that operating specifications are being met. It would be advantageous to perform certain minimum testing at frequent intervals to monitor the station performance. Among these latter tests are noise, distortion, frequency response, carrier shift, carrier hum and spurious radiation.

(b) The annual performance measurements must be made in the four-month period preceding the date of filing for license renewal. The date of filing for license renewal is three months before the expiration date of the license. Measurements can be taken by any qualified engineer and may be taken by the stations engineering personnel if adequate test equipment is available.

Q. 4.36. What are line equalizers? Why are they used? Where, in the transmission line are they normally placed?

A. (a) For a schematic diagram of a line equalizer, see Figure 4.36. A line equalizer is a high-pass filter which is inserted in a program audio-transmission line.

(b) The purpose of a line equalizer is to make the response characteristics of a transmission line independent of frequency within the desired range (transmission band), which is usually between 20 and 15,000 cycles.

(c) Many rented telephone lines are properly equalized by the telephone company to a specified high frequency. However, if equalization of an incoming line is required, it is performed where the line enters the studio (or studio-input equipment).

D. If a transmission line has appreciable length, the line capacitance will cause the high frequencies to be attenuated. The line, therefore, produces frequency distortion of programs passing through it. To eliminate frequency distortion, the line is equalized at the studio by means of a highpass filter, shown in Figure 4.36, which attenuates the low frequencies to the same degree that the line capacitance attenuates the high frequencies. The equalizer should have an attenuation characteristic curve which is exactly the same as the line response curve in order to produce a "flat" corrected response of line and equalizer. It is generally unnecessary to equalize a short line because of the relatively low line capacitance. The total shunting line

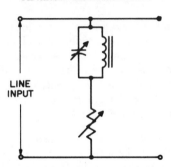

Fig. 4.36.   An equalizer circuit for a transmission line.

capacitance is proportional to the line length and if the line is short the capacity is relatively low. The high frequency response of a line may be improved if the line is terminated in an impedance which is low compared to the surge impedance of the line. Standing waves are produced due to the mismatch, but are not important in a short line due to the negligible phase shift which is introduced.

Q. 4.37.   What are limiting amplifiers? Why are they used in broadcast stations? Where are they normally placed in the program circuit?

A.   (a) A limiting amplifier, such as used in a broadcast station, is one which automatically reduces its gain when the peak program signal exceeds a predetermined value.

(b) Limiting amplifiers in broadcast stations are used to prevent overmodulation which would cause distortion and adjacent-channel interference.

(c) A limiting amplifier is normally connected to the audio input terminals of an AM transmitter, which is the input to the audio driver feeding the modulator.

D.   A broadcast station limiting amplifier is basically a protective device that prevents transmitter overmodulation on program peaks. This type of amplifier should not be used as a compression amplifier to reduce the dynamic range of program material (see Q. 4.41). Also, its purpose is not to increase the broadcast coverage area. In fact, if it's used for this, an excessive amount of compression will occur at all times, resulting in an *increase* of adjacent-channel interference. This effect defeats one of the main reasons for using a limiting amplifier. In practice, the amount of peak-gain reduction of a limiting amplifier is of the order of 3 to 5 db.

Q. 4.38.   Explain the operation of limiting amplifiers.

A. In peak limiting, the amplifier is controlled by rectifying a portion of the output signal to secure a component of direct-voltage which is proportional to the peaks. This direct component may then be used to control the bias of a remote cut-off pentode in a manner similar to AVC action. The gain of a peak limiter is quickly reduced on peaks and then smoothly restored, whenever the instantaneous peak amplitude of the signal exceeds a pre-determined value.

D. The use of an audio-peak limiter permits a higher average percentage of modulation to be achieved without the difficulties of over-modulation. Such limiters prevent the carrier from being put off the air following intensified peaks which might operate the overload relays. (See also Q. 4.37, Q. 4.40, and Q. 4.41.)

Q. 4.39. What are the uses of peak limiting amplifiers?

A. See Q. 4.37 and Q. 4.38.

D. See also Q. 4.40 and Q. 4.41.

Q. 4.40. What are AGC amplifiers and why are they used?

A. *Note: AGC amplifiers discussed in this question, refer to those used in broadcast studio equipment.*

(a) An AGC (automatic-gain control) amplifier is one which provides a relatively constant output-level signal for varying input-level signals.

(b) They are used to maintain a relatively constant transmitter input-level signal in spite of variations in signal level originating at the control room or remote pickup. They largely eliminate the need for manually *riding the gain* on the studio console. They also help to maintain a constant level when switching between different pickup facilities.

D. In addition to the characteristics disussed above, the AGC amplifier assists in maintaining a higher percentage of modulation than manual gain control. This is necessary to provide the widest and most reliable coverage of the broadcast station service area.

One use for the AGC amplifier is for automatic-announcer override of a musical program. In this case the announce portion may be fed in at a level about 15db higher than the musical program. The AGC amplifier will reduce its gain by approximately 15db so that the announcer will come through at normal level, but the music will be subdued by 15db and will appear as low-volume background.

Q. 4.41. Explain the operation and uses of compression amplifiers?

A. (a) A volume compressor is a circuit which reduces (compresses) the total dynamic range of speech or music. It reduces the amplifier gain when loud passages are present and increases the amplifier gain for very low passages. This device operates as follows: The signal to be compressed is rectified in such a manner as to produce a d–c voltage which varies in accordance with the envelope of the signal. This d–c voltage is then used to control the gain of an amplifier using a variable-mu tube. A more negative voltage is produced for loud passages and a less negative voltage for low passages. This voltage is used to bias the variable-mu amplifier and causes compression of the dynamic range of the input signal.

(b) Volume compressors are used in some broadcast stations to reduce the dynamic range it is required to transmit. On some types of programs the full dynamic range would tend to cause overmodulation of the transmitter. They also increase the signal-to-noise ratio by raising the volume of weak passages above the noise level.

D.   Another use of volume compression is during voice transmissions to maintain a high level of modulation. When speaking into a microphone, it is difficult to maintain a constant voice level. The compression circuit, which follows the *envelope* variations of the signal, automatically compensates for variations in speech amplitude.

Volume compression differs from limiting because it extends over substantially the entire operating (dynamic) range, instead of just a portion. Some broadcast transmitters employ both volume compression and limiting. These circuits are very common in long-distance short-wave radiotelephone transmitters.

Q. 4.42.   Draw the approximate equivalent circuit of a quartz crystal.

A.   For the equivalent circuit, see Fig. 4.42.

D.   In the equivalent circuit, the crystal proper is equivalent to a series-resonant circuit with the L, C and R being the electrical equivalent of the mechanical properties of the crystal. L is equivalent to the mass, C is equivalent to the elasticity and R is equivalent to the friction of the crystal. In practice, the L is extremely large and the R and C are extremely small. This accounts for the very high Q of a quartz crystal, which may be ten times or more as great as a good coil-capacitor tuned circuit. Coupling to the crystal is accomplished by sandwiching it between two metal plates (C_h). This forms a capacitor, with the crystal as the dielectric. However, C_h is very large compared to C and has a minor effect on the resonant frequency of the crystal.

The quartz crystal, its holder capacitance, and associated tube and stray capacitance actually form an equivalent tank circuit of very high Q. Etched crystals with plated electrodes, mounted in a vacuum, have been found to give Q's in the order of 500,000. This is exceptional, however,

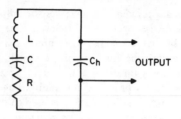

Fig. 4.42. Approximate equivalent circuit of a quartz crystal in its holder.

and the ordinary crystal installations have a Q (unloaded) in the order of 20,000 or more. Crystal oscillators are generally found in two forms. One is the tuned-plate variety, in which the crystal takes the place of the grid tank circuit (Q. 3.86(b)). The other type is the Pierce oscillator (equivalent to the "ultraudion"), in which the crystal is the sole tuned circuit in the oscillator (Q. 3.86(g)). In any event, the very high Q of the crystal makes for excellent oscillator stability, especially when a constant temperature is maintained.

Q. 4.43. What factors affect the resonant frequency of a crystal? Why are crystal heaters often left on all night even though the broadcast station is not on the air?

A. (a) The following factors affect the resonant frequency of a quartz crystal.

(1) The thickness and type of cut of the crystal.

(2) Temperature.

(3) Pressure of the crystal holder.

(4) Shunt reactance across the crystal.

(5) Capacitance of the crystal holder.

(b) Crystal heaters are left on all night to insure that upon turn-on the transmitter will immediately operate at the proper frequency. This procedure eliminates the necessity of turning on the oven several hours before morning "air-time."

D. Many crystal cuts have temperature coefficients in varying degrees. Thus, if a very close tolerance in output frequency is to be maintained, it is essential that the crystal temperature be kept absolutely constant. This is done by enclosing the crystal assembly within a constant temperature "oven." (See Q. 4.44 for operation of crystal ovens.) See also Q. 4.42.

Q. 4.44. Explain by the use of simple drawings the physical construction and the operation of mercury-thermometer and thermocouple types of crystal-heater controls.

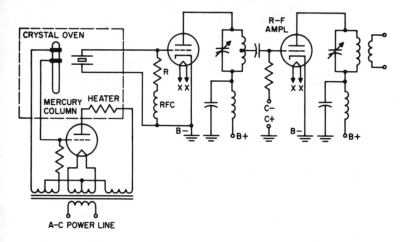

Fig. 4.44(a). A mercury-thermometer crystal heater.

A. (a) For diagram of a mercury-thermometer crystal heater, see Fig. 4.44(a). The mercury column can control a relatively small current and thus controls the grid circuit of the vacuum tube. The actual heater is a resistor which heats when plate current flows in the tube. When the oven reaches the desired temperature, the mercury column closes the contacts and the tube is turned off. As the oven cools, the mercury column drops and opens the contacts, causing the tube to conduct and the plate resistor to heat. This type of control is extremely sensitive to temperature changes.

When the oven is below operating temperature and the contacts are open the grid is connected to the right side of the grid winding through the resistor, while the cathode is always connected to the center tap (considered as a zero voltage reference point). When the grid is positive with respect to the cathode, the plate is also positive and plate current flows through the heater. When the oven reaches operating temperature and the contacts close, the grid is now directly connected to the left side of the grid transformer, which now controls the grid voltage. However, the left side polarity of the grid transformer is 180 degrees out of phase with the plate voltage and the tube will not conduct. No current flows through the heater and the oven begins its cooling cycle again. The crystal is enclosed in a specially designed heat filter which smooths out the temperature changes to maintain a virtually constant crystal temperature.

(b) For diagram of a thermocouple type of heater control, see Fig. 4.44(b). The thermocouple is not as sensitive as the mercury thermometer, but is simpler and cheaper. The basis of operation of this unit is the bimetallic element. This is composed of two thin strips

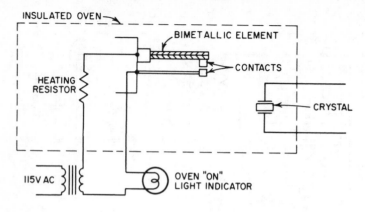

Fig. 4.44(b). Thermostat controlled crystal oven.

of different metals which are joined together. The metals are chosen so that the bottom strip has a greater coefficient of expansion than the upper strip. Thus, under heating conditions, the bimetallic strip will be forced upward breaking the contact. This system operates as follows: Assuming the oven to be below the correct operating temperature, the bimetallic strip will pull downward and close the contacts. This causes current to flow through the heating resistor and the oven temperature rises. When the temperature reaches a predetermined temperature, the bimetallic strip lifts and breaks the heating circuit and the cooling cycle begins again. As in (a) above, a heat filter may be used to smooth out temperature variations of the crystal. Some heating chambers are sealed and filled with an inert gas to prevent contact oxidation due to arcing when the contacts open and close.

Q. 4.45. Why are tubes used in linear R-F amplifiers not normally biased Class A?

A. Tubes used in linear R-F amplifiers are normally biased to operate as Class-B amplifiers rather than as Class-A because of the greater plate conversion efficiency obtained with the former. Ordinarily, a Class-A R-F linear amplifier realizes a carrier efficiency in the order of ten percent, whereas a Class-B R-F linear amplifier may easily achieve a carrier efficiency of from thirty to thirty-five percent. In the larger amplifiers a quite significant reduction in power and tube costs would thus result.

D. See Q. 3.59, Q. 3.143, and Q. 3.144.

Q. 4.46. Draw circuit diagrams of the following R-F amplifiers and explain their operations.
(a) Class-C R-F power amplifier with battery bias.
(b) Tetrode R-F power amplifier with grid-leak bias.

(c) R-F power amplifier with two tetrode tubes in parallel.

(d) R-F power amplifier with two tetrode tubes in push-pull.

(e) Plate-neutralized triode R-F amplifier.

(f) Grid-neutralized triode R-F amplifier.

(g) Triode frequency-doubler stage.

(h) Push-push frequency-doubler stage.

(i) Grounded-grid R-F amplifier.

A.   All the amplifiers to be described are operated as Class-C amplifiers even though each will differ from the others by some detail. In the Class-C amplifier, sufficient negative voltage is applied to the control grid to bias the tube appreciably beyond the plate current cut-off point. The exciting voltage applied to the grid is large enough to drive the grid positive during a portion of the excitation cycle and consequently appreciable grid current will flow at this time. The load, across which the output power is developed, is invariably a tuned or tank circuit resonant to the exciting frequency or some integral multiple thereof. The output voltage is sinusoidal and the circuit is arranged so that when maximum instantaneous plate current is flowing, the instantaneous voltage drop from plate to cathode is at its smallest value. Because the tube is biased beyond the cut-off point, the plate current flows for only a small portion of the exciting cycle and at the time when the plate-cathode voltage is at or near its minimum value. As a consequence, the plate dissipation, which is the product of the average instantaneous plate current and plate-cathode voltage during the time of the flow of plate current, is small as compared to other types of amplifiers. The Class-C amplifier is characterized by high power output and high plate-power conversion efficiency. Due to the non-linear characteristics of the plate current vs exciting voltage the amplifier is suitable only for the amplification of continuous wave signals.

(a) For the diagram see Fig. 4.46(a).

As shown, the grid of the amplifier has a negative voltage or bias applied to it with respect to the cathode. The bias, in this illustration, is

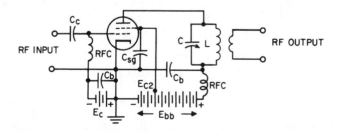

Fig. 4.46(a). Class-C R-F power amplifier with battery bias.

obtained from a battery, but in actual practice it may be obtained from a motor-generator or a rectifier-filter power supply as well as a battery.

(b) For the diagram see Fig. 4.46(b).

This amplifier is exactly like the amplifier of (a) above except that bias voltage for the tube is obtained by the voltage drop across the grid-leak resistor R_g. The circuit has been arranged to allow the rectified grid current, obtained when the grid is driven positive by the exciting voltage, to flow through the grid-leak and produce the required voltage drop and the required polarity for biasing. The coupling capacitor, C_c, also acts to keep the bias at a relatively constant level, instead of varying with the pulses of grid current. This method of obtaining bias has a decided advantage in its ability to minimize variation in output power with changes in the amplitude of the exciting voltage. For example, should the exciting voltage decrease, the grid will be driven somewhat less positive with a resulting decrease in grid current. The decreased grid current will result in less bias voltage being developed across R_g. The average plate power input will increase and the output power will remain relatively unchanged.

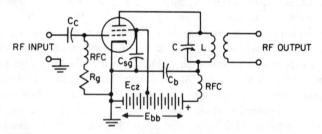

Fig. 4.46(b). Tetrode Class-C R-F power amplifier with grid-leak bias.

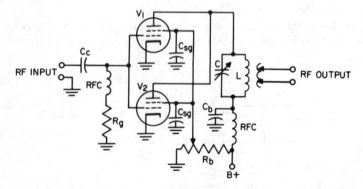

Fig. 4.46(c). Class-C R-F power amplifier with two tetrodes in parallel.

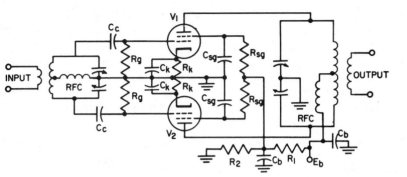

Fig. 4.46(d). Class-C R-F power amplifier with two tetrodes in push-pull.

(c) For the diagram see Fig. 4.46(c).

One method of obtaining more power from a given amplifier is to employ two tubes in parallel. The power thus obtained approximates twice the power obtainable from a single tube of the same type. Although the circuit may appear to be exactly the same, except for the additional tube, the voltage and current relations are different. For example, the tank circuit now must be proportioned to present approximately one-half of the original impedance to the plates of the tubes. Similarly, since the grids are effectively drawing twice as much rectified current, the driving or exciting source now will be looking at a load impedance approximately one-half of the original and will be required to deliver about twice as much exciting power as formerly.

(d) For the diagram see Fig. 4.46(d).

This circuit is essentially the same as for the amplifier described in (c) above, except that the tubes are arranged in series or push-pull. This arrangement has the advantage of reducing the even harmonic content in the output. This is obtained with added circuit complications to assure symmetry of drive, of load sharing and symmetry of output.

Of interest in this circuit is the manner in which bias is obtained from two sources—grid-leak and cathode bias. This has the advantage of restricting the flow of plate and screen currents to safe levels should the excitation voltage fail, with resulting loss of grid-leak bias.

(e) See Q. 3.125. (See also Q. 3.128.)
(f) See Q. 3.125. (See also Q. 3.128.)
(g) See Q. 3.131. (See also Q. 3.132.)
(h) See Q. 3.129. (See also Q. 3.130 and Q. 3.132.)
(i) See Q. 3.124.

Q. 4.47. Explain in a general way how radio signals are transmitted and received through the use of amplitude modulation.

A. In amplitude modulation, the instantaneous amplitude of a radio frequency wave is varied in direct proportion to the instantaneous amplitude of the intelligence to be transmitted. Such a wave, after being intercepted by the receiving antenna, is amplified and rectified by the radio receiver. The output of the rectifier, or detector, being directly proportional to the amplitude of the signal input, varies in amplitude in the same manner as the original intelligence and is therefore a true reproduction of such intelligence.

D. See Q. 3.138 through Q. 3.142. See also Q. 3.145, Q. 3.148, Q. 3.149, Q. 3.151, and Q. 4.89(a). For AM receiver operation, see Q. 3.155 through Q. 3.157, and Q. 3.161.

Q. 4.48. In amplitude modulation, what is the relationship of sideband power, output-carrier power and percent modulation? Give an example of a problem to determine sideband power if other necessary information is given.

A. The amount of power contained in the sidebands of an amplitude-modulated wave can be found with the aid of the following relationship:

$$P_{sb} = \frac{m^2}{2} P_c$$

where: P_{sb} = sideband power
P_c = carrier power
m = degree of modulation
= percent modulation/100

For example, a transmitter having a carrier output power of 10 kw is modulated 40%. Determine the amount of power in the sidebands. Using the above relation, we have:

$$P_{sb} = \frac{0.40^2}{2} \times 10 = \frac{0.16}{2} \times 10 = 0.08 \times 10 = 0.8 \text{ kw or } 800 \text{ watts}$$

D. See Q. 3.142, Q. 3.148, and Q. 3.149.

Q. 4.49. What is carrier shift? How is it measured? Show by a circuit diagram one method of measuring carrier shift.

A. (a) "Carrier shift" occurs when the relative amplitudes of the positive and negative modulation peaks are unsymmetrical. The shift is one of amplitude and not of carrier frequency.

(b) Carrier shift is measured by determining the average value of the unmodulated and modulated transmitted wave as explained in (b) of the discussion.

(c) For the diagram, see Fig. 4.49.

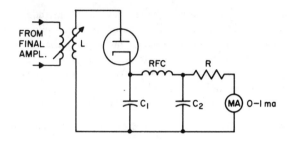

Fig. 4.49. Test equipment to detect carrier shift.

D.   (a) For a discussion of "carrier shift" see Q. 3.147(b).

(b) Refer to Fig. 4.49. The inductance of L is coupled to the transmitter stage it is desired to monitor and the degree of coupling is adjusted until $\frac{1}{2}$-scale reading is obtained on the 0–1 ma meter. The transmitter is now modulated and the meter observed. If no carrier shift or overmodulation exists, the needle will remain stationary. If the meter reading increases, there is positive carrier shift present, and if it decreases, there is negative carrier shift present.

(c) For a standard AM broadcast station, the carrier shift is normally measured at 25%, 50%, 75%, and 100% modulation. The measurement is performed with a 400 cycle tone for the audio modulation. The maximum permissible percentage of carrier shift at any of the above modulation percentages is 5%. This is determined by the degree of carrier-shift meter change (if any) between the unmodulated and the modulated conditions.

For example, if the meter reads 0.5 ma in the unmodulated condition and then reads 0.475 ma during modulation, this represents a 5% change and denotes a negative carrier shift of 5%.

Q. 4.50. Explain the direct and indirect methods of calculating operating power of broadcast stations. Give an example of each method.

A. With the direct method of calculating the operating power of a broadcast station, the r-f output current of the transmitter is squared and then multiplied by the effective resistance of the antenna system. That is, the output power is determined by the following relation:

$$P_{output} = I_{out}^{2} \times R_{ant}$$

For example, a transmitter delivers 10.0 r-f amperes to an antenna load of 500 ohms. The power output is:

$$P_{output} = 10^2 \times 500 = 50,000 \text{ watts or } 50 \text{ kw.}$$

Another method often used is called the indirect method in which the output power is determined by the product of plate volts, plate amperes and the plate efficiency of the final or output amplifier. For instance, a transmitter uses a Class-B r-f linear power amplifier as the final stage with a plate carrier efficiency of 31%. With an applied plate voltage of 20,000 volts, 8.2 amperes of d-c plate current are indicated by the total plate ammeter. The carrier power output of the transmitter is found by:

$$P_{output} = E_b \times I_b \times Eff = 20,000 \times 8.2 \times 0.31 = 50,000 \text{ watts or 50 kw}$$

D. See Q. 4.64, Q. 4.90(i), Q. 4.90(k), and Q. 4.102.

Q. 4.51. In relation to the safety of the radio operator, explain the function of:
(a) interlocks
(b) circuit breakers
(c) bleeder resistors

A. (a) Interlocks are switches applied to access doors, grilles, etc., of transmitting equipment. These interlocks are arranged to be mechanically operated and thus shut off the power supply to the transmitter if such doors, etc., are opened by the operator without first turning off the power. In this manner, the operator is protected against coming into contact with current carrying conductors and components.

(b) Primarily, circuit breakers are designed to protect electrical equipment from being damaged by excessive currents. The protection of the radio operator is only a very remote function of the breakers. Such protection as afforded the operator would be possibly the prevention of fire which could occur should excessive currents flow in equipment not protected by such breakers.

(c) The function of bleeder resistors is to remove or *bleed* the charge from filter capacitors when a transmitter is shut down. Such capacitors are rendered safe and the operator is protected from electric shock should he contact them in the performance of maintenance or repair on a shutdown transmitter.

It should be emphasized at this point that while the above facilities are for the protection of the operator, he should not depend on them. If maintenance or repair duties necessitate working on interior parts of the transmitter, the operator should safeguard himself by first grounding any part he must touch and thus render it harmless.

Q. 4.52. Explain the methods of cleaning relay contacts. Why is it necessary that the original contact shape is maintained?

A. If the relay contacts are not pitted, but merely oxidized or tarnished, it is best to clean them with a burnishing tool which removes only a very minute amount of contact material. Such a tool is in reality an extremely hard metal that has been sandblasted to produce microscopic roughness.

If the contact faces are pitted, it is then necessary to remove the roughness with a metal file that has been used for no other purpose. The contact faces should be restored to their original shape and condition with the removal of as little material as possible. Removing such small amounts of material assures the longest service life possible for the relay under the existing operating conditions. It is important that the original shape of the contact faces be preserved as this has been designed to give the best operation and the longest service life for the relay. For instance, a relay carrying heavy currents will have flat contact faces to obtain the greatest cross-sectional area and hence minimum resistance to current flow with attendant lowest heating of the contacts. Some relays have crowned or domed contacts to achieve maximum unit pressure between contacts. In any event, keeping the original contact shapes helps realize better operation from the relay.

Q. 4.53.   Explain the operation of the following relays:
(a) overload
(b) time-delay
(c) recycling

A. (a) The coil of an overload relay carries current under normal operating conditions, but the value of the current is insufficient to cause the relay to operate. Should the value of current exceed a pre-determined amount, the relay will operate and interrupt the source of current. Such relays are quite often used in the plate circuits of vacuum tubes and are adjusted to operate when the plate current exceeds a safe maximum value.

(b) In large vacuum tubes and in mercury-vapor rectifiers it is necessary that the filaments of such tubes have sufficient time to reach operating temperature and stability before the other electrode voltages are applied. Special relays, called time-delay relays, are activated at the moment of applying filament voltage, but through mechanical clockwork, hydraulic pistons or pneumatic bellows systems, do not actually close their contacts until after a definite time has elapsed. This delay time is normally adjustable to suit the desired operating conditions. After the contacts have closed, relays controlling the other electrode voltages may be operated. These latter relays usually have their coil currents routed through the time delay relay contacts.

(c) In some applications, overload relays will operate because of a transient or temporary overload. In such cases no harm will be done to the transmitter if the power is immediately re-supplied to the transmitter. To keep the *outage* time to a minimum, the overload relays are often arranged to automatically reclose or recycle. Such relays are normally arranged to recycle two or three times. If the overload continues, the relays are set to remain open until manually reset.

Q. 4.54. Draw a circuit diagram of a complete radiotelephone transmitter composed of the following stages:
(a) Microphone input connection
(b) Preamplifier
(c) Speech amplifier
(d) Class-B modulator
(e) Crystal oscillator
(f) Buffer amplifier
(g) Class-C modulated amplifier
(h) Antenna output connection
Insert meters in the circuit where necessary and explain, step-by-step, how the transmitter is tuned.

A.   For the diagram, see Fig. 4.54.
The transmitter may be tuned by the method outlined in the following steps:
1. Turn on all filaments and heaters in the transmitter.
2. Activate the bias supply for the modulator.
3. Apply plate voltage to the oscillator and adjust the oscillator plate inductor (L1) tap to a position giving minimum indication on M-1. Move the tap one position *closer* to the plate end of inductor.
4. After checking for a grid current indication in the buffer by M-2, apply plate, screen and suppressor voltages to the buffer and immediately adjust buffer tank inductor for a minimum reading on M-2, and maximum reading on power amplifier grid meter, M-3.
5. Measure frequency of transmitter. If not correct, make necessary adjustments by means of the trimmer capacitor across crystal (C_T).
6. Adjust the power amplifier tank inductor (L3) for a maximum indication of r-f current as shown by ammeter in the output. It is assumed that the transmitter is connected to its antenna system.
7. Adjust neutralizing inductor, L_N, for minimum r-f current.
8. Adjust the buffer tank inductor (L2) for maximum r-f current.
9. Repeat steps 6, 7 and 8 until the r-f current shown by the ammeter is zero or at a minimum.
10. Adjust the bias potentiometers (R1, R2) on the modulator for maximum bias to the modulator tubes.
11. Apply plate voltage to the power amplifier and immediately adjust its tank inductor (L3) for minimum plate current as shown on

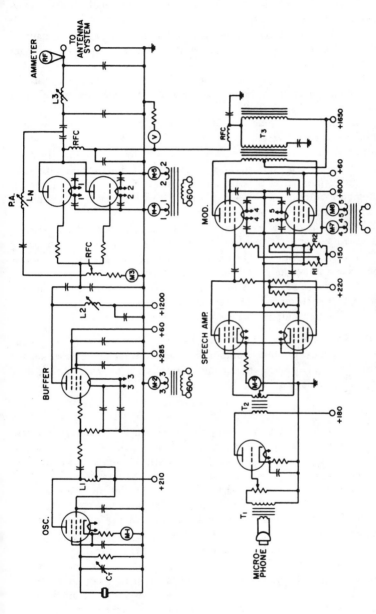

Fig. 4.54. Circuit diagram of a complete radiotelephone transmitter.

ammeters M-4 and M-5. R-f current at this point should be at a maximum and of normal expected value.

12. With input level control set to minimum, apply plate voltage to the preamplifier and speech amplifier and screen and suppressor voltages to the modulator.

13. Adjust the bias potentiometers in the modulator so that the modulator tubes draw normal and equal plate currents as indicated by ammeters M-7 and M-8.

14. Check the cathode current of the speech amplifier to see that it is within expected values.

15. Apply a 1000 cycle tone to the input of the preamplifier in place of the microphone and increase the input level slowly while observing the modulation envelope with an oscilloscope. Observe all ammeters in the power amplifier and modulator to see that they stay within expected values while modulation is increased to 100%.

16. Note modulation envelope and see if troughs of modulation reach the zero axis at 100% modulation. If not, slightly readjust neutralizing inductor (L_N) until troughs reach zero. At each change of L_N, readjust buffer and power amplifier tank inductors for resonance.

17. Check to see if both modulator tubes are drawing equal cathode currents. If not, readjust bias potentiometers until they do.

18. The transmitter may now be considered tuned.

Q. 4.55. Show by a circuit diagram two methods of coupling a standard broadcast transmitter output to an antenna. Include a provision for impedance matching, attenuating harmonics, and guarding against lightning damage.

A.   For the diagrams, see Fig. 4.55.

D.   (a) The T-type network, shown in Fig. 4.55(a), is a low-pass type. As in any low-pass filter, it discriminates against frequencies above its desired pass band. Therefore, this network discriminates against harmonic frequencies. The T-network is adjusted to provide a correct impedance match between the coaxial transmission line and the broadcast antenna. See also Q. 4.56 for the adjustment procedure.

(b) Fig. 4.55 (b) illustrates an L-type of coupling network with an adjustable inductance (L1) for impedance matching. Since L1 and C2 constitute a low-pass filter, harmonics are discriminated against. The static-drain choke (RFC 2) is used to bleed off static-atmospheric charges from the antenna tower as well as from the induced energy from nearby lightning discharges. Its presence also prevents false operation of the arc-suppression relay, whose operation is now explained.

High-voltage flashovers may take place in a transmission line or coupling network in the presence of lighting flashes. While not too important in themselves, such flashovers may result in an r-f arc being

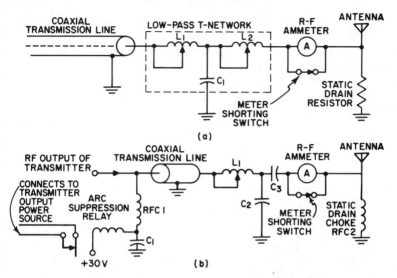

Fig. 4.55. (a) Simple schematic of a low-pass T-type coupling network between a coaxial line and a broadcast antenna; (b) schematic of an L-type coupling network to a broadcast antenna, including provision for arc suppression.

formed which will be of a sustained nature because of the power being supplied by the transmitter. Considerable damage may occur to the transmission line, or coupling network, by continuous arcing and it is the function of the relay circuit to prevent this. Note that +30 volts is applied to one end of the relay coil, the other end of which connects through RFC 1 to the inner conductor of the transmission line. Capacitor C3 prevents a d-c path to ground for this voltage. If a flashover occurs, the arc will form a return path to ground for the +30 volts through the relay. The relay will become energized opening the contacts and interrupting the transmitter output power. At this time the arc is rapidly extinguished and the relay again de-energized. Actually, the program interruption is of such short duration as to be unnoticeable. The voltage drop in the arc is about 15 volts; the balance, or 15 volts is available to operate the relay.

Q. 4.56. Explain the method of adjusting a "T" network of two tunable coils and a fixed capacitor in order that a standard broadcast station operating at 1340 kc will be properly coupled to its antenna.

A. See Fig. 4.55(a). This T-coupling network may be adjusted as follows:

(a) The input impedance of the antenna is measured at the exact operating frequency. This may be done with a shielded r-f bridge normally used to make antenna measurements.

(b) Connect the T-coupling network to the antenna, but do not connect the transmission line to the network.

(c) Assume the input impedance of the antenna to be 30 ohms of resistance and 30 ohms of capacitive reactance. Assume the transmission line to have 70 ohms impedance.

(d) The reactance of L1 (X_{L1}) and L2 (X_{L2}) may be found from the following:

$$X_{L1} = + \sqrt{R1R2}$$
$$X_{L2} = + \sqrt{R1R2}$$

where: R1 = transmission line impedance
  R2 = antenna resistance

Therefore

$$X_{L1} = X_{L2} = \sqrt{30 \times 70} = \sqrt{2100} = +45.9$$

(e) Since the antenna has a capacitive reactance of -30 ohms, this must be added to the reactance of L2 which tunes with the antenna reactance. Therefore, using the bridge, adjust L2 for a reactance at 1340 kc of $45.9 + 30$, or 75.9 ohms. This cancels the effect of the antenna's capacitive reactance which otherwise would cause a high VSWR and poor efficiency.

(f) Adjust L1 for a reactance at 1340 kc of $+45.9$ ohms.

(g) If the common shunt capacitor, C1, is variable, it should be adjusted to -45.9 ohms at 1340 kc.

(h) With the transmission line disconnected, connect the bridge to the input of the T-coupling network. An impedance of 70 ohms should be read. Minor touch-up adjustments may be made to achieve this.

(i) Connect the transmission line and make a final low-power check as described in the discussion. If this is normal, full power may be applied.

D. The T-network provides two primary functions:

(1) To match the impedance of the transmission line to the antenna.

(2) To tune the antenna to the required resonant frequency (in this case 1340 kc).

The use of two series inductances permits one (L1) to be used to terminate the transmission line and the other (L2) to be used to match the antenna circuit. The shunt capacitor (C1) is common to both circuits and its value is determined solely by the operating frequency. In tuning the antenna, L2 is made to resonate with the antenna reactance. L1 is adjusted afterward to match the resistance of the transmission line to the resistance of the antenna.

A check of the matching condition may be made with the aid of two low-range r-f thermocouple ammeters. One meter is inserted at each end of the ungrounded coaxial conductor. Low r-f power is fed to the line, sufficient to cause the meters to provide good readings. If the tuning is proper, the meter readings will be within approximately 15 percent of each other.

Q. 4.57. Define field intensity. Explain how it is measured.

A. (a) Field intensity is a measure of the strength of a radio wave at any given point.

(b) Field intensity is measured in millivolts or microvolts per meter.

A common method of measuring field intensity utilizes a sensitive receiver, a standard signal generator and a loop antenna. The loop is connected to the receiver and oriented to give maximum reception. The receiver gain is adjusted to give a convenient reading on a microammeter which is inserted in the second detector circuit. The loop is now rotated so that no signal is received and a voltage from the signal generator is introduced in series with the loop. The signal generator is adjusted to the same frequency as the incoming signal and the generator output is varied until the receiver output indication is the same as it was when receiving the incoming signal. The signal generator output voltage is now measured with a suitable vacuum tube voltmeter and this reading, in conjunction with the effective antenna height (given in calibration data with the receiver), is the equivalent field strength indication.

D. (a) See Discussion (a) of Q. 3.203.

(b) See Discussion (b) of Q. 3.203.

Q. 4.58. Cathode-ray oscilloscopes are frequently used to register percentage modulation. Sketch the visual displays of

(a) 0% modulation.

(b) 50% modulation.

(c) 100% modulation.

(d) 120% modulation.

A. See Fig. 4.58(a).

D. Additional trapezoidal waveforms illustrating modulation percentage indications on an oscilloscope are shown in Fig. 4.58(b).

The percentage of modulation may be calculated from:

$$\% = \frac{B - A}{B + A} \times 100.$$

Q. 4.59. Explain, in a general way, how radio signals are transmitted and received through the use of frequency modulation.

404   *Radio Operator's License Q and A*

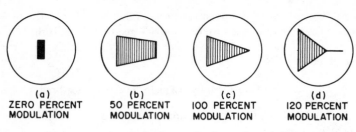

Fig. 4.58(a).   Cathode-ray displays of modulation.

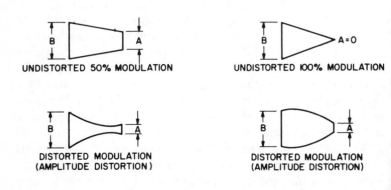

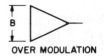

Fig. 4.58(b).   Trapezoidal patterns of modulation.

A.   In a frequency-modulation system, the frequency of the carrier wave is varied in proportion to the strength of the modulating signals. The rate of frequency deviation is at the frequency of the modulating wave. In an FM broadcast station, the amount of frequency deviation is limited to $\pm$ 75 kilocycles and the modulating frequency to approximately 15,000 cycles. The FM signals are received by a resonant antenna and conveyed to the receiver. The receiver is normally a superheterodyne, which is in many respects similar to an AM receiver. Major differences are found in the limiter, which reduces noise interference, and the detector, which must respond to frequency variations rather than amplitude variations. The FM detector reproduces the original modulating wave from the frequency variations of the carrier wave.

D.   (a) See Q. 3.162 through Q. 3.169.
(b) For receiver operation, see Q. 3.177 and Q. 3.178.

Q. 4.60   Draw a circuit diagram of a reactance-tube modulator and explain its operation.

A.   For diagrams and complete discussion, see Q. 3.162.

D.   A simplified block diagram of a reactance tube modulated FM transmitter is shown in Fig. 4.60. Frequency multipliers are needed in this system since the reactance tube is not capable of providing sufficient modulation directly. Another benefit derived from the use of frequency multiplication is the operation of the master oscillator at a comparatively low frequency. This makes it possible to obtain better frequency stability.

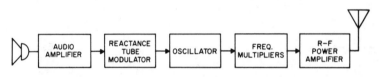

Fig. 4.60.   A simplified block diagram of a reactance tube modulated FM transmitter.

Q. 4.61.   What is the difference between frequency and phase modulation?

A.   (a) In frequency modulation (FM), the instantaneous *frequency* of the carrier wave is caused to deviate in proportion to the amplitude of the modulating wave.

(b) In phase modulation (PM), the instantaneous *phase* of the carrier wave is shifted in proportion to the amplitude of the modulating wave.

D.   In actuality, the difference between FM and PM is not as sharply defined as might be imagined. In the process of directly varying the carrier frequency, the phase is indirectly changed. Conversely, when directly varying the phase of the carrier, the frequency is indirectly changed. Because of this interrelation, both FM and PM are referred to as frequency modulation. In fact, the original Armstrong "FM" system was actually one of phase modulation (see Q. 4.62, following). An FM receiver is unable to differentiate between FM and PM and reproduces both equally well.

Q. 4.62.   Describe briefly the operation of the Armstrong and phasitron methods of obtaining phase modulation.

A.   A block diagram of the Armstrong method of obtaining phase modulation is shown in Fig. 4.62(a). Figure 4.62(b) gives a vectorial representation of the relationships of the recombined carrier and sidebands. In this system, the output of a balanced modulator, which consists of two sidebands and no carrier, is recombined with the carrier

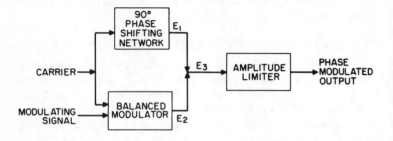

Fig. 4.62. (a) Block diagram of the Armstrong method of
obtaining phase modulation.

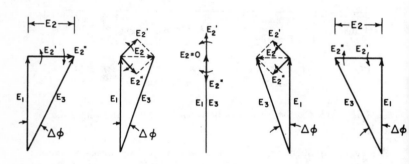

Fig. 4.62. (b) Vectorial representation of Armstrong-phase
modulation.

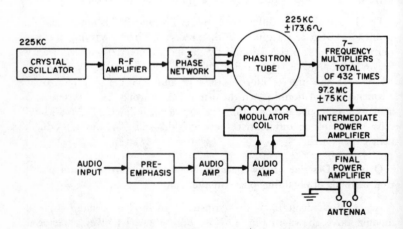

Fig. 4.62 (c). Block diagram of an FM broadcast transmitter.

which has had its phase shifted by 90°. The wave resulting from this recombining, as shown by the vector diagrams, has its instantaneous phase shifted in accordance with the modulating signal's amplitude.

A block diagram of a transmitter employing the phasitron method of obtaining frequency modulation is shown in Fig. 4.62(c). In this system, a special tube called a phasitron, employs within its envelope three beam-deflecting anodes in addition to the usual control, screen and suppressor grids. These deflecting anodes are energized by a three phase carrier as shown in the diagram. Surrounding the complete envelope of the tube and co-axial with it, is an inductance coil energized with the modulating signal.

As a result of the field formed within the tube by the inductor and the three-phase carrier both acting on the electron stream, a frequency modulated output is obtained. To achieve phase modulation rather than frequency modulation, the audio input to the modulating section may be routed through a network whose response is *directly* proportional to frequency.

D. See Q. 4.59 through Q. 4.61.

Q. 4.63. What is the purpose of pre-emphasis in an FM transmitter? Of de-emphasis in an FM receiver? Draw a circuit diagram of a method of obtaining pre-emphasis.

A. (a) For pre-emphasis, see Q. 3.163, Discussion (b).
(b) For de-emphasis, see Q. 3.163, Discussion (c).
(c) For pre-emphasis circuit diagram, see Fig. 3.163(a).

Q. 4.64. What is effective radiated power? Given transmitter power output, antenna resistance, antenna transmission line loss, transmitter efficiency and antenna power gain, show how ERP is calculated.

A. (a) Effective radiated power is the power actually delivered to the antenna, multiplied by the power gain of the antenna in the direction of interest.

The power delivered to the antenna is the transmitter-output power less the power lost by the transmission line connecting the transmitter to the antenna. The power gain of the antenna and the transmission line losses are usually expressed in decibels (db). The power gain of the antenna system includes the transmission line; the transmission-line losses in db are subtracted from the antenna-power gain in db.

The simplest method of calculating the ERP is to convert the db power gain of the antenna system into a power ratio and multiply the transmitter power output by this ratio to find the ERP.

(b) For example, assume a transmitter with a power output of 10.1 kw feeds an antenna with a power gain of 24.6 db via a transmission line with a loss of 1.6 db.

The power gain of the antenna system is 24.6–1.6 or 23.0 db. Using the relationship, $db = 10 \log \dfrac{P_1}{P_2}$, we can find that the transmitter's power output will be multiplied by 200 times. The ERP is 10.1×200 or 2020 kw.

D. See Q. 4.50.

Q. 4.65. What type of antenna site is technically best for an AM broadcast station? For an FM broadcast station? For a VHF television station? For a UHF station?

A. Since the ground or earth plays an important part in the operation of the Marconi type of antenna normally used for AM broadcast stations, it is best to choose an antenna site that is reasonably level and that has very good ground conduction (low resistance). These requirements are best met by salt meadows or swamps. See also Q. 4.70.

For VHF television, FM broadcast and UHF television stations, propagation of radio waves are effective for not much greater distances than line of sight. Because of such characteristics, the best location for antennas for these services is the highest point in the area to be served. This will give maximum area of coverage.

D. See Q. 4.70.

Q. 4.66. How does a directional antenna array at an AM broadcast station reduce radiation in some directions and increase it in other directions?

A. The following example is given for two vertical antennas spaced 180 degrees and having equal currents in phase.

Refer to Fig. 4.66. The two vertical antennas are spaced 180 degrees apart. This is also equivalent in time to one half cycle of the exciting r.f., or in distance, one half wavelength. That is to say, in the interval of time required for a radio wave to traverse the distance from antenna *A* to antenna *B*, the sine wave will have completed one half or 180 degrees of a cycle. As shown in the diagram, the currents to each antenna are of equal magnitude and are in phase. Let us assume first that the wave has left antenna *A* and is proceeding toward antenna *B*. This motion takes place along a straight line. By the time this wave arrives at antenna *B*, 180 degrees later, the exciting current for antenna *B* has changed by 180 degrees and the wave now radiated by antenna *B* is exactly 180 degrees out of phase with the wave that has just arrived from antenna *A*. Thus the two waves completely cancel in the direction leading away from antenna *B*. A similar action takes place in the direction from antenna *B* to antenna *A*. That is, by the time the original wave from antenna *B* arrives at antenna *A*, the exciting current of antenna *A* has changed by 180 degrees and again the two radiated waves will cancel out in the direction leading away from an-

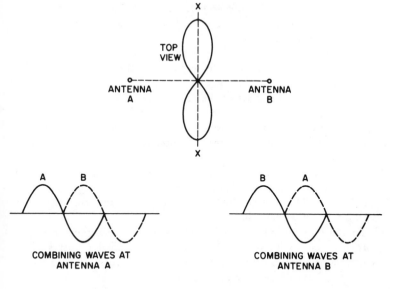

*Fig. 4.66. The combining action of two waves coming from
vertical antennas spaced 180 degrees apart.*

tenna *A*. Thus it is seen that the radiation along a line connecting the
two antennas will always be zero. On the other hand, if we take two
points such as *X* and *Y*, it may be seen that the two radiated waves
must always arrive together at these points in phase and so are additive.
This causes maximum radiation to take place in the direction *XY*.

**Q. 4.67.   What factors can cause the directional antenna pattern of an
AM station to change?**

A.   The erection of structures containing significant amounts of metal
within the induction field of an AM antenna or antenna array is very
likely to cause a change in the directional pattern of the array, especially
if the metallic members of the structure have lengths that are not
negligible in comparison with the wavelength of the station's radiation.

In antenna arrays, where the directional pattern depends upon the
current and phase relations in the several elements, the directional pattern is affected by changes in temperature and humidity. Both of these
cause changes in element tuning and the phase-shifting networks and
lines feeding the elements. It is a design object to make the system sufficiently stable and noncritical to reduce these effects to a minimum.

D.   See Q. 4.66 and Q. 4.70.

**Q. 4.68.   What adjustable controls are normally provided at an AM
broadcast station, to maintain the directional pattern?**

A. The controls normally provided at an AM broadcast station for pattern maintenance can logically be divided into two categories—current and phasing.

The control of current to the individual antenna elements is very often managed by adjustable tapping points on the tank inductor of the transmitter.

The control of the phase of the currents being fed to the individual elements is usually accomplished by variable inductors in the phase-shifting networks in the individual element feeds. In the cases where the phase-shifting is done before the currents enter the transmission lines, the adjustments can be accomplished by manual means. Very often, these networks may be located in small structures at the base of the towers that are used as antenna elements. In this case, the adjusting of the variable inductors is generally accomplished by motors controlled from within the transmitter building.

To assist in the adjustment of the pattern, metering provisions are normally made with pick-up loops at the individual elements. These meters indicate the magnitude and phase of the currents in the transmitter building fed by these pick-up loops.

D. See also Q. 4.65 through Q. 4.67.

Q. 4.69.   Define polarization as it refers to broadcast antennas.

A. See Q. 3.203, part (e) of the answer and discussion.

Q. 4.70.   What is the importance of the ground radials associated with standard broadcast antennas? What is likely to be the result of a large number of such radials becoming broken or seriously corroded?

A. (a) The ground radials act as a good conducting ground and reduce possible ground-resistance losses to a minimum.

(b) In general, broken ground conductors will decrease the efficiency of the antenna system; the antenna resistance may be varied and the radiation pattern changed.

D. The most important losses in an antenna system occur in the conductors, insulation, antenna tuning inductance and in the ground. The largest of these losses usually occurs in the ground. The ground acts as the second plate of a capacitor with the antenna acting as the other plate and the air as the dielectric. The charging currents for this capacitor must return through the earth to the ground point at the transmitter proper. Since the earth is generally a poor conductor, other means must be found to return these currents to the transmitter ground point. One method often used is to bury wires near the surface of the earth to provide a good conducting path to the transmitter ground point. The system usually consists of a large number of radial wires with a good earth termination for each wire. Such wires are generally more than a half-wavelength long. It has been determined that the longer such wires are made, the stronger the ground signals will be for a given power input.

Q. 4.71. Explain the operation of the image-orthicon camera tube. Include in your explanation a schematic diagram of the tube which shows focusing and scanning details.

A.   For a sketch of the image-orthicon tube, see the diagram of Fig. 4.71. The operation of this tube follows. In analyzing the operation of this tube, it is convenient to divide it into three sections; the image section, the scanning section and the electron multiplier section.

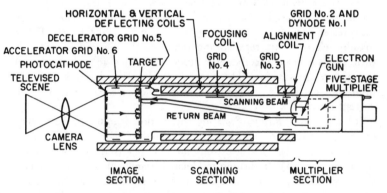

Fig. 4.71. Sketch of the Image-Orthicon television camera tube.

(a) *Image Section*: The illumination from the televised scene is focused by the camera-lens system upon the semi-transparent photocathode surface, which is mounted just inside of the tube face. The photocathode emits electrons whose intensity is a function of the intensity of the light impinging on each portion of its surface. Thus, in effect an "electron picture" is emitted from the inner surface of the photocathode. Behind the photocathode, is an electron-accelerator grid (No. 6) and a thin-glass target, in front of which is mounted a very fine wire-mesh screen. The photocathode is at a high negative potential with respect to the glass target. The screen, on the other hand, is slightly positive with respect to the glass target. The "electron picture" is accelerated through the screen and strikes the glass target, causing secondary emission from the target. This secondary emission is collected by the screen, leaving a positive charge pattern on the face of the glass which corresponds to the picture-light pattern. The brighter the original light, the more positive is the charge. Because the glass is very thin, the charge pattern is easily transmitted to the rear of the target. The electron focus in the image section is maintained by the ring grid (No. 6) and the field of the focusing coil.

(b) *Scanning Section*: The electron gun (near the rear of the tube) produces a low-velocity electron beam which is focused by the focusing coil and grid No. 4. The beam is aligned along the axis of the tube by the alignment coil (located just forward of the electron gun). Horizontal and vertical beam deflection in the standard scanning pattern is produced by the horizontal and vertical deflection coils. As the beam approaches the rear of the glass target, the potential of grid No. 5 causes it to decelerate to a very low velocity. As the beam scans the target, it encounters areas of negative, zero and positive charges. When the beam encounters areas of negative or zero charge, it is repelled and returns to the electron gun. If the beam encounters areas of positive charge, enough electrons are removed from the beam to neutralize the charge. Thus, the brighter the original scene, the more positive will be the charge and the greater the number of electrons given up by the beam. The remaining electrons are repelled and return to the electron gun. The return electron beam becomes amplitude modulated in accordance with the picture information. The nature of the return beam is such that minimum current is returned for bright picture areas and maximum current for dark picture areas.

(c) *Electron Multiplier Section*: This section operates on the principle of secondary emission and consists of a multiplier-focus grid (No. 3), five multiplier dynodes (electron-multiplier electrodes) and a signal-collecting plate. The returning modulated beam strikes the first dynode, which is actually grid No. 2 and releases secondary electrons several times as intense as the original beam. In similar fashion, the electron beam strikes each of the other dynodes, each time obtaining an electron multiplication caused by secondary emission. The total electron multiplication is several hundred times. As a result, the output-signal level is in the order of several microamperes and is well above the noise level of the first-video amplifier. Because of this, the amplifier noise is not a limiting factor in picture reproduction and a high quality, high definition picture is obtained.

D.   See Q. 4.72.

Q. 4.72.   What are the advantages and the disadvantages of the Vidicon TV camera tube in comparison to the Image-Orthicon tube?

A.   Figure 4.72 shows a cross section of the Vidicon-television camera tube.

(a) Advantages of the Vidicon compared to the Image-Orthicon are:

(1) Small size.

(2) Less weight.

(3) Simpler tube construction.

(4) Fewer tube accessories and simpler circuits (for some models).

(5) Ruggedized (some models) to withstand severe shock, vibration and humidity.

(6) Low power input (some models).

(7) Adapted for use with transistorized cameras.

(8) Excellent for industrial use and closed-circuit TV, because of above.

(9) Presently preferred for studio, color and black and white TV cameras.

(b) Advantages of the Image-Orthicon compared to the Vidicon are:

(1) Greater amplitude response at the operating-light level.

(2) Requires less "on the scene" illumination.

(3) Requires considerably less "on the tube face" illumination.

(4) Excellent signal-to-noise ratio characteristics.

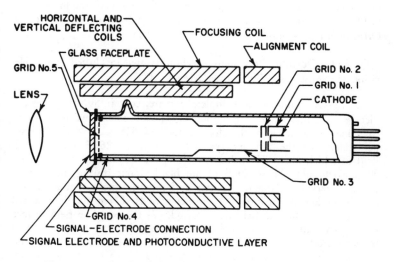

Fig. 4.72. Sketch of the Vidicon television camera tube.

D. It is difficult to make a direct comparison between the Vidicon and Image Orthicon-camera tubes. Each type has a number of models having different characteristics for particular applications. Image Orthicons vary in dimensions from 3 inches to 4.6 inches in diameter and from 15.5 to 19.7 inches in length. Vidicons have diameters of 0.58 to 1.6 inches, and lengths from 3.40 to 8 inches. Although the Image Orthicon had been the preferred studio-camera tube, improved Vidicon tubes have now made this tube the preferred one. For example, an RCA Vidicon (type 8051) having a 1.6 inch diameter and an 8 inch length (among other types) is recommended for new studio equipment. This tube has higher resolution (1200 lines) than most Image Orthicons, but is lower in sensitivity. Its amplitude response is equal to most Image Orthicons. Another type of RCA Vidicon (C74016) has both electrostatic focusing and deflection, thus reducing the size, weight and complexity of the camera. This tube has a low power (0.6 watt) heater, high sensitivity and a resolution capability of about 500 lines.

For ultra-compact cameras, for use in industrial applications the RCA-type 4427 may be used. This tube is only 0.6 inch in diameter and 3.4 inches long. It provides 400 line resolution and will produce satisfactory pictures with illumination of only 0.2 foot candle on the tube face.

Some idea of the relative sensitivities of a typical Image Orthicon and a Vidicon may be obtained from the following example. With a standard illumination of 0.01 foot-candle, the signal output of the Image Orthicon is about 10 microamperes, while the Vidicon output is about 0.008 microampere. From this example, the advantage of the Image Orthicon in overcoming circuit noise is evident.

Q. 4.73. Describe the scanning technique used in United States television transmissions. Why is interlacing used?

A. (a) A frame is a complete picture containing all necessary picture elements. There are a total of 525 horizontal sweep cycles or *lines* in one frame and, therefore, a total of 525 × 30 = 15,750 lines per second. Of the 525 lines per frame there are 262.5 lines in each field of which about 242.5 lines contain picture information and about 20 lines do not. These 20 lines are blanked out during the vertical retrace interval. At the transmitter and receiver, the scanning process may be broken down into four distinct periods. These may be referred to as (1) the odd line field trace period, (2) the odd line field retrace period, (3) the even line field trace period, (4) the even line field retrace period during which no picture information is transmitted, about retrace period. The permissible time allowed for each operation is approximately as follows: (1) For the even line field trace period during which picture information is being transmitted, about 15,417 microseconds or 242.5 horizontal sweep cycles, (2) for the even line field 1250 microseconds or 20 horizontal sweep cycles. This period is also known as the vertical blanking interval. The even line field trace and retrace periods have the same time allowances and the same number of horizontal sweep cycles as the odd line field trace and retrace periods. Each trace and retrace period constitutes a complete field. There are 60 of these fields (odd and even) per second. An odd line field plus an even line field equals one *frame* of which there are 30 per second.

(b) Interlaced scanning is used in order to eliminate flicker from the television picture.

D. (a) The scanning process takes place as follows: A narrow beam of electrons is produced and directed upon an image plate in a camera tube or a fluorescent screen in a kinescope (receiving) cathode ray tube. Due to the presence of various synchronizing pulses, the beam at the camera tube and the beam at the kinescope tube are locked in step with each other and may be considered to be covering the same basic areas of the picture in question, simultaneously. The electron beam is acted upon by electromagnetic coils or electrostatic plates in such a manner that it is caused to move relatively slowly from left to right (trace), during which time picture information is present, and then moves quickly from right to left (retrace) in which time no picture information is present, as the beam is blanked out. During the left to right movement (in 53.34 microseconds) the beam also is moving slightly downwards so that when the retrace takes place (in 10.16 microseconds) the beam returns at the left hand side of the screen slightly below its original starting position. The distance below is equal to the width of two lines, since every other line is skipped in interlaced scanning. In a similar manner the beam moves across horizontally and downward until the entire picture area has been covered in about 242.5 lines. At this point (beginning of vertical blanking interval) the screen is blanked out and the beam returns horizontally and upwards in about 3 to 5 lines until it reaches the top of the picture, This completes one field. The downward scanning process is now resumed but the beam is now so positioned that it falls into the empty line spaces previously left in the preceding field. About 242.5 lines are again completed in the downward direction until the beam reaches the bottom of the picture. At this time the picture is again blanked out and the beam moves horizontally and upwards in about 3 to 5 lines until it reaches the top. This completes another field and one *frame*. This sequence of events is repeated at the frame repetition rate of 30 cycles per second.

(b) One of the very important factors in transmitting a television signal is the number of complete pictures sent each second. In motion picture practice it is common to show 24 frames or pictures per second to give the illusion of smooth and continuous motion. However, due to the action of a shutter, each frame is shown twice; being blanked out for a short period of time and then shown again. Thus to the eye it appears that there are 48 pictures per second while in reality there are only 24. This optical illusion is necessary in order to eliminate flicker from the picture. Flicker refers to a change of light intensity and not to motion. Reference is made to electric light bulbs operated from a 25 cycle power source. A very noticeable and objectionable flicker may be readily observed by watching the bulbs. On the other hand, bulbs operating from a 60 cycle source apparently have no flicker at all. To eliminate flicker, the repetition rate should be in excess of 40 pictures per second. A system similar to motion picture practice is used in television and this is called interlaced scanning. The frame or picture repetition rate in television has been standardized at 30 per second. This rate is not sufficient to eliminate flicker. Each frame, therefore, has been split into two parts called fields. Thus there are 60 fields per second. Instead of scanning all of the lines which make up a picture, in sequence, every other line is scanned first. This makes up one field. Then, the alternate lines are scanned completing the second field and one frame. In this way, the illusion of 60 pictures per second is gained and the appearance of flicker is eliminated.

Q. 4.74. Make a sketch showing equalizing, blanking, and synchronizing pulses of a standard U.S. television transmission.

A.   For the sketch, see Fig. 4.74.

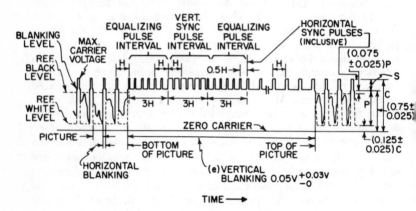

Fig. 4.74. Sketch showing equalizing, blanking, and synchronizing pulses of a standard U.S. television transmission.

D.   (a) As shown in the figure, six equalizing pulses are present on each side of the serrated vertical synchronizing pulses. These equalizing pulses serve two important functions: One is to maintain correct interlacing of the odd and even fields of each frame. This will enable the scanning lines of one field to fit perfectly between the scanning lines of the following (or preceding) field. Basically, the equalizing pulses permit the vertical synchronizing pulse to begin at the correct time at the end of either odd or even fields. The second function is to maintain a continuous string of horizontal synchronizing pulses to the horizontal scanning circuit. In Figure 4.74, "H" equals the time from one horizontal line to the next horizontal line, or 63.5 microseconds. "V" equals the time from the start of one field until the start of the next field, or 262½ "H" periods, or 16,667 microseconds.

(b) In general, the purpose of synchronizing pulses is to maintain the correct scanning pattern and to synchronize or lock-in the action of the receiving tube (Kinescope) scanning beam with that of the camera tube scanning beam.

There are two types of synchronizing pulses, the amplitude of each type being confined to the region between 75% and 100% of maximum carrier amplitude. The upper tip of the synchronizing pulses is at an amplitude corresponding to 100% and the base of the pulses is at an an amplitude corresponding to 75%. The horizontal pulses are rectangular in shape and extend above the top of the horizontal blanking pulses (see the figure). They have a width equal to about 5.08 microseconds. There is one horizontal synchronizing pulse for each horizontal line, or 525 per frame and 15,750 per second. The horizontal synchronizing pulse normally occurs at the time when the electron beam has progressed to the extreme right hand edge of the picture. The pulse acts upon a horizontal multivibrator or blocking oscillator type of sweep generator in such a way as to initiate the start of the horizontal retrace.

The vertical synchronizing pulse is somewhat more complicated being formed from 6 vertical serrated pulses which are electronically added in an integrating circuit to form a single pulse. There is one complete vertical synchronizing pulse for every field, or 2 per frame and 60 per second. The vertical pulse acts upon a vertical multivibrator or blocking oscillator type of sweep generator in such a way as to initiate the starting of the electron beam to return to the top of the picture from the extreme lower part.

(c) Blanking pulses are rectangular pulses of short duration used to extinguish the electron beam during the retrace, and are of negative polarity when applied to the intensity grid of the electron gun at both the transmitting and receiving cathode ray equipment. At the end of each horizontal line just before the retrace is initiated, the horizontal blanking pulse extinguishes the electron beam so that it returns to the left side of the picture unnoticed. The horizontal blanking pulse width is 10.16 microseconds, and there are 525 per frame or one for each horizontal synchronizing pulse. When the scanning beam reaches the extreme bottom of the picture and just prior to the vertical retracing, the vertical blanking interval pulse causes the electron beam to be extinguished so that the lines moving upward will not be seen. The duration of the vertical blanking interval pulse is about 1250 microseconds and there are 60 per second.

(d) See also Q. 4.73.

Q. 4.75. Make a sketch which shows the difference between blanking and synchronizing pulses used for color and those used for monochrome.

A. The monochrome synchronizing and blanking pulses are shown in Figure 4.74. The blanking and synchronizing pulses used for color are shown in Figure 4.75.

D. The synchronizing and blanking pulses used for color transmission are identical with those used for monochrome television with the exception of the addition of the "color burst" synchronizing signal. This consists of a short "burst" of the chrominance sub-carrier frequency of 3.579545 megacycles. This sub-carrier is superimposed on the "back porch" of the horizontal blanking pulses. This "color burst" signal is separated at the receiver and is used, in conjunction with an AFC system, to synchronize the receiver's chrominance-subcarrier oscillator to the same frequency and phase as the equivalent oscillator at the transmitter. In this manner the reproduction of colors at the receiver is synchronized with those produced at the transmitter.

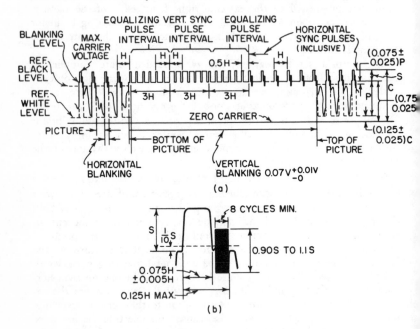

Fig. 4.75. (a) *Sketch showing equalizing, blanking and synchronizing pulses used for color-television transmission;* (b) *details of the "color burst" signal on the "back porch" of the horizontal-blanking pulse.*

Q. 4.76. Sketch the amplitude characteristics of an idealized picture transmission of a television station in the United States.

A. For the sketch, see Figure 4.76.

D. Referring to the accompanying figure, it is seen that a standard television channel is six megacycles wide. Unlike conventional double-sideband amplitude modulation as used for AM-broadcast stations, television picture transmission is accomplished by "vestigial" (partial) sideband transmission. Note that while the upper sideband drops to zero,

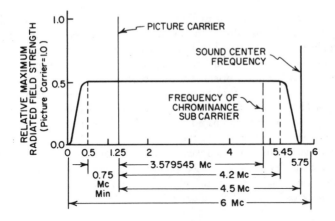

Fig. 4.76. Idealized picture transmission amplitude characteristic.

4.5 megacycles above the picture carrier, the lower sideband extends to only 1.25 megacycles. This system permits a greater number of TV channels in the allotted frequency spectrum. Since all of the picture information is contained in a single sideband, no loss of information takes place.

Both sidebands are normally produced by the modulation process and the undesired portion of the lower sideband is eliminated at the transmitter by a vestigial side-band filter. It is not feasible to eliminate the entire lower sideband because of undesirable phase shifts which would occur to signals adjacent to the cut-off frequency. At the receiver, the i-f response at the picture carrier is at the 50-percent amplitude point to compensate for the unequal sidebands. In a color transmission, the chrominance subcarrier and its sidebands are caused to modulate the picture carrier. The chrominance subcarrier has a frequency of 3.579545 megacycles and is so indicated in the figure. The aural portion of the program is transmitted by FM on a separate carrier which is located 4.5 megacycles above the picture carrier.

Q. 4.77. For what purpose are reflectometers or directional couplers used in TV transmission systems?

A. Reflectometers are used to:
(a) Measure standing-wave ratio on the transmission line.
(b) Measure the relative power output of the transmitter.

(c) Protect the transmission line against high-voltage surge damage, such as a lightning strike on the antenna.

D. The reflectometer is used in both the aural and visual transmitter output circuits, generally at the input to the transmission line. The reflectometer may consist of special peak-reading vacuum-tube voltmeter circuits. Two signal pick-up coils are used to feed energy to the vacuum-tube voltmeter. One is oriented to intercept the incident wave going to the antenna and the other to intercept the reflected wave from the antenna. (The incident and reflected currents are 180 degrees out of phase.) The two waves are compared to provide a standing-wave ratio. To measure the power going to the antenna, the incident-wave circuit is used alone. In addition, the reflected-wave circuit may be used to actuate a protective device. This device protects the transmission line against damage due to high-surge currents and is actuated whenever the return current exceeds a specified value.

Q. 4.78. Explain the operation of a turnstile TV antenna.

A. A simplified sketch of a turnstile antenna is shown in Fig. 4.78(a). The antenna as used in practice actually consists of two antennas at right angles to each other, thus giving the appearance of a turnstile. A single section of a turnstile antenna provides a radiation pattern which is very similar to two vertically-stacked horizontal dipoles. That is; it provides a bi-directional pattern (figure 8 pattern) with reduced radiation in the vertical plane. The single section is sometimes called a "batwing" antenna and is shown in simplified form in Fig. 4.78(b). In order to provide an omnidirectional pattern for uniform-area coverage, two antennas are mounted at right angles and are fed 90 degrees out of phase with each other. For greater gain and lower angles of radiation, several turnstile antennas may be stacked vertically on a pole. A six layer antenna provides a gain over a single layer type of about seven times. The turnstile antenna radiates a horizontally polarized wave for both picture and sound transmissions. (Receiving antennas are of course horizontally polarized.)

D. A complete discussion of the operation of this antenna is not feasible in this book. However, a simplified explanation follows. The "bat-wing" antenna is derived from a "slot" antenna and its operation is briefly as follows: (See Fig. 4.78(c).) The figure shows a solid conducting sheet, one-half wavelength high with a slot in its middle section. The antenna is fed at the center points as indicated (with a coaxial line). When this antenna is excited, voltage and current patterns are set up as shown. Because the currents flow horizontally, radiation takes place from both the front and rear of the sheet. At about one-quarter wavelength from the slot, the current decreases to a negligible amount.

The impedance characteristics and vertical and horizontal-radiation patterns are similar to those of a conventional dipole. By reducing the width of the antenna at the center (see Fig. 4.78(a), above) the vertical radiation is decreased. To reduce wind resistance, a framework construction may be used to replace the sheet without changing the antenna characteristics, providing the spaces are a small portion of a wavelength. The antenna is fed with a coaxial line. The inner conductor is connected to one center point of the slot and the outer conductor to the opposite center point. The impedance of the antenna is about 72 ohms at the center-feed points.

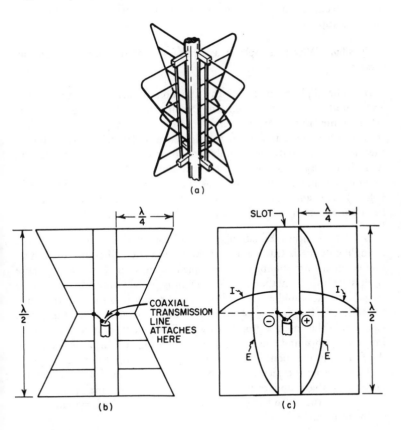

Fig. 4.78. (a) Sketch of a single-layer turnstile antenna; (b) sketch of a single "bat-wing" section used for a turnstile antenna; (c) solid sheet "slot" antenna used in developing the "bat-wing" section of a turnstile antenna (see text).

Q. 4.79.   What type of polarization is generally used in the transmission of the aural portion of television signals?

A.   Horizontal polarization is used for both the picture and sound signals.

D.   Horizontal polarization was chosen as a result of field trials and of theoretical analyses. The field trial showed stronger signals were obtained using horizontal polarization than using vertical polarization. Horizontal polarization also reduces the "ghost" problem due to reflected signals. In addition, most man-made noise is vertically polarized and horizontally polarized receiving antennas are less susceptible to noise pickup.

Q. 4.80.   Why is a diplexer a necessary stage of most TV transmitters?

A.   The diplexer performs the function of combining the picture and sound-transmitter outputs and feeding them to a single antenna. At the same time, it prevents cross-feed of either output into the other. It also may be used to convert the single-ended (unbalanced) output of the picture transmitter to a double-ended or balanced-to-ground output. This is necessary to properly feed the antenna load presented to the picture transmitter, which is a balanced load. (See also Figure 4.81 below.) The antenna load presented to the sound transmitter is unbalanced and so matches the output of the sound transmitter.

D.   Simultaneous radiation of the picture and sound signals from a single antenna is feasible only if the transmission lines and the radiating elements are completely decoupled with respect to the opposite signals. If this is not done, cross-coupling may introduce the picture signal into the sound signal and the sound signal into the picture signal. In addition, the tuning of each transmitter would affect the other. Isolation in the antenna proper is accomplished by separating the antenna into two groups and connecting these in a bridge circuit as explained in the following question. The two antenna groups are series-fed, in push-pull fashion by the picture transmitter and are shunt-fed, in push-push fashion by the sound transmitter. The transmission line system is decoupled by the introduction of reactances in the feed system of the sound transmitter.

Q. 4.81.   Draw a circuit diagram of a typical bridge-type diplexer used in a television transmitter for the purpose of transmitting both video and audio from a turnstile antenna.

A.   For the diagram, see Figure 4.81.

D. The feed line from the vestigial-sideband filter of the picture transmitter is normally single ended. However, this transmitter (as shown in the figure) is connected to the two sets of turnstile antenna elements in a balanced fashion. To accomplish this conversion, a "balun" (balanced-to-unbalanced) transformer is used. This consists of a quarter-wavelength sleeve shorted to the outer conductor of the coaxial line at

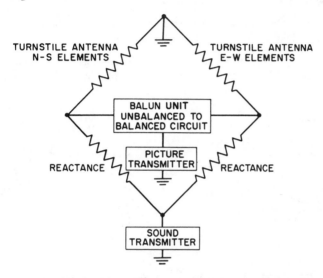

Fig. 4.81. Schematic diagram of a bridge diplexer for a television transmitter.

one end and open at the output end of the line. A balanced output is taken from the coaxial line at the open end of the sleeve. In practice a symmetrical balanced output is obtained by connecting two baluns back-to-back to form a bridge circuit. The circuit will operate either from balanced-to-unbalanced loads or vice versa merely by interchanging the generator and load connections. The two reactances shown in the figure may consist of two, one-quarter wavelength segments of coaxial line, measured for the band-center frequency. Although not shown in the simplified diagram of Fig. 4.81, the N-S and E-W antenna elements are fed 90° out of phase with each other to produce a non-directional antenna pattern.

The turnstile antenna elements represent equal impedances. Also the two line reactances are equal. Therefore, the bridge is balanced and signals appearing across the feed of one transmitter cannot appear across the feed of the other. In addition the turnstile elements are physically at right angles and this prevents magnetic coupling between them. Thus, the picture and the sound signals are fed simultaneously to a common antenna without cross coupling. For additional discussion, see the previous question.

Note: In some installations an FM-broadcast transmitter may also be fed to a TV antenna by an extension of the diplexer, which is called a "triplexer." In this case, no interference to the TV signals (or vice versa) is caused by the FM broadcast signal.

Q. 4.82.   Describe how to tune a broadcast antenna by (1) the RF-bridge method and (2) the substitution method.

A.   (a) The bridge method of tuning is described in Q. 4.56.

(b) The "substitution" method of tuning follows. Refer to the schematic of Fig. 4.82. The "substitution" method may be used if a

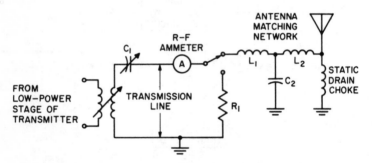

Fig. 4.82.   Circuit for tuning a broadcast antenna by the "substitution" method.

shielded r-f bridge is not available. The substitution resistance, R_1, has a resistance equal to the transmission line impedance, commonly 70 ohms.

(1)   Connect the antenna-matching network unit to the antenna.

(2)   As shown in the diagram, the transmission line is connected between the T_1-C_1 circuit and the substitution-resistor circuit.

(3)   With S_1 at the R_1 position, adjust T_1 for an adequate reading on the R-F ammeter.

(4)   Adjust C_1 for maximum meter reading.

(5)   Switch to L_1 and readjust C_1 for maximum current. Observe whether an increase or decrease of capacitance is required. If an increase is required, the matching network load is capacitive. If a decrease is required, the matching network load is inductive. If no change is required the load is resistive.

(6)   A "cut and try" procedure is required to adjust the matching network. When the matching network is correctly adjusted, there will be no change in the meter reading when switching from the tuner to R_1.

D.   A non-reactive resistor (R_1) must be used and necessarily has a relatively low-voltage rating. Therefore, full power cannot be applied to the circuit. If desired, tuning may be accomplished with the use of a very accurately calibrated R-F signal generator. The generator is set to the exact transmitter frequency and connected to the input of the coupling circuit. The tuning then proceeds as described in the answer above. The use of a signal generator makes it unnecessary to hook up to a low-power stage of the transmitter. Whether the "substitution" or the bridge method is use, a final check, as described in Q. 4.56, should be performed before full power is applied to the antenna circuit.

Q. 4.83.   In relation to a-c circuits what is the relationship between (1) rms values, (2) maximum and minimum values, (3) peak values, and (4) peak-to-peak values.

A.   (a) The rms (or effective value) of a current or voltage is equal to 0.707 of the peak value of the wave. The peak value equals 1.414 times the rms value.

(b) Maximum and minimum values are the highest and lowest values of a portion of a waveform, or of a train of waveforms.

(c) The peak value is equal to 1.414 times the effective (rms) value. The peak value is also equal to 1.57 times the average value; or, the average value equals 0.636 times the peak value.

(d) The peak-to-peak value equals twice the peak value. Also, it equals 2.828 times the rms value.

D.   (a) The conventional type of a-c ammeter is calibrated to indicate effective (rms) values of current. Effective value is equal to 0.707 of peak value, in the case of sine-wave currents.

The meter itself responds to the average torque. For pure sine-wave currents, the indicated reading is dependent upon the scale calibration, which usually gives the rms value. What a meter does, relatively, on non-sine-wave currents depends on the meter, but in the usual case, the meter indicates the effective value of current.

An a-c voltmeter has a scale which is calibrated to read the rms value or 0.707 of peak. The average value equals 0.636 of peak and the ratio of the two equals $\dfrac{0.636}{0.707} = 0.9$. The scale reading must therefore be multiplied by 0.9 to obtain the *average* value. It is understood that this is the average value over one-half cycle; the average value of a sine wave over a full cycle is of course zero.

Q. 4.84.   Show by diagrams the delta method and the wye method of connecting transformer secondaries in a power distribution system. Show also how various output voltages might be obtained from each.

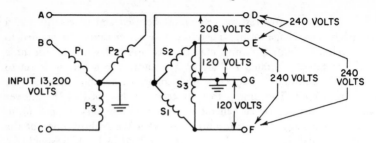

Fig. 4.84. (a) Schematic of a delta-connected secondary in a three-phase power system.

A. For the diagrams, see the accompanying figures.

D. (1) The diagram of Figure 4.84(a) is the system most commonly used for power distribution in this country. A typical input voltage would be 13,200 volts. The input line is fed into a wye-connected primary. The secondary is delta-connected and feeds 240 volts to three-phase loads through wires D, E and F. As shown, secondary S3 is center tapped and the center tap is grounded. This is shown as wire G. This is called a "split-phase" connection and supplies single phase 120 volts between E and G and also between F and G. This power is used to supply lighting, wall receptacles and small motors. Wire D is called the "high leg" of the system. Note in the figure that 208 volts appears between D and G. In some cases single-phase loads requiring 220 to 230 volts are connected between D and G. This is particularly true if the split phase is heavily loaded by 120-volt loads and the three-phase loading is light. By so doing, the currents in wires E and F may be reduced. 240 volt, single-phase loads may be connected at D-E, D-F and E-F. 240 volt, three-phase loads are connected to wires D-E-F. In practice, the installation is often made with three, single-phase transformers. The

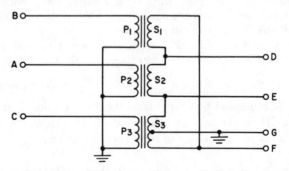

Fig. 4.84. (b) A wye-delta three-phase connection using three single-phase transformers and an equivalent of Fig. 4.84(a).

connections for this scheme are shown in Figure 4.84(b). The letters for the various leads and the voltages between the various wires correspond to those in Fig. 4.84(a).

(2) A distribution system employing a wye primary and wye secondary is shown in Fig. 4.84(c). This scheme is preferred wherever the major power requirements are to be single-phase, 120-volt loads, such as in office buildings. The voltage between wire G and each of D, E and F will be 120 volt, single phase. By proper load distribution, the three circuits can be maintained in a substantially balanced condition for three-phase use. Three-phase equipment requiring 220–230 volt power may be connected to wires D, E and F.

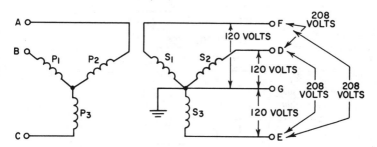

Fig. 4.84 (c) Schematic of a wye-connected secondary in a three-phase power system.

(3) Fairly high-power radio stations frequently use three-phase power at 480 volts for greater efficiency. In cases of transmitters operating at 50,000 watts of output r-f power, the plate transformers for the main rectifiers may have a primary-excitation three-phase voltage as high as 4,160 volts. However, in such a case, a 240 volt, three-phase supply is provided to operate filament transformers, blowers, water pumps and all other auxiliary equipment. The 240 volt supply can also be used, as described in (1) above, to provide the necessary 120 volt single-phase power.

Q. 4.85. Draw circuit diagrams of:

(a) A triode Class-C amplifier properly coupled to a push-pull power amplifier (modulator).

(b) A beam power Class-C amplifier coupled to a push-pull Class-B power amplifier (modulator).

For both cases, show the modulating signal input, the R-F exciting voltage input and the modulated output. Include neutralization for the triode case. Explain the operation of both the above types of Class-C plate modulated amplifiers.

A. (a) For the diagram see Fig. 4.85(a).

For an explanation of the operation of this stage as a Class-C amplifier, see Q. 4.46(a) and Q. 3.125. For a description of the modulation process see Q. 3.143.

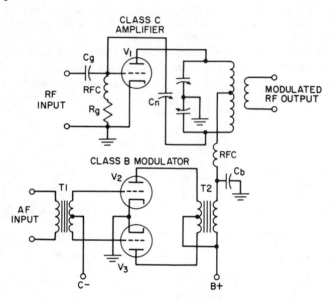

Fig. 4.85. (a) Schematic diagram of a triode Class-C amplifier coupled to a Class-B amplifier (modulator).

(b) For the diagram see Fig. 4.85(b).

For an explanation of the operation of this stage as a Class-C amplifier, see Q. 4.46(b). For a description of the modulation process see Q. 3.143.

Q. 4.86. Why is plate modulation more desirable than grid modulation for use in standard broadcast transmitters? Why is grid modulation more desirable in television video transmitters?

A. (a) Plate modulation may only be more desirable in the case of high-power transmitters. (See discussion 3.)

(b) Most video transmitters use grid modulation. This is necessary because the wide band width required (about 5.25 megacycles) makes it necessary to use very low values of plate load impedances. To produce enough power in these low impedances for plate modulatiton, would require extremely high currents which would be impractical. Grid modulation requires much less driving power and is, therefore, more practical.

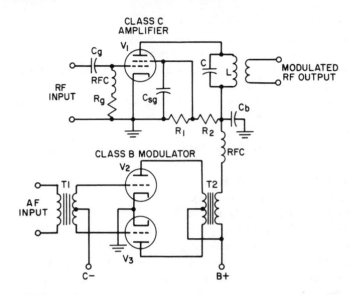

Fig. 4.85. (b)   Schematic diagram of a beam power Class-C amplifier coupled to a Class-B push-pull modulator.

D.   (a) A comparison between grid and plate modulation is given in Q. 3.145.

(b) A comparison between the characteristics of plate and grid modulation follows.

The characteristics of plate modulation are as follows:

(1) Audio power for 100% modulation equals 50% of d-c input power to r-f modulated amplifier.

(2) Plate voltage of modulated amplifier varies in proportion to audio modulating signal.

(3) Load presented to the modulator tube consists of the d-c plate impedance of the modulated amplifier.

(4) The r-f output voltage of the modulated amplifier is a linear function of the applied plate voltage.

(5) Modulated amplifier operates class C.

(6) Grid bias should be obtained partly from a fixed source and partly from grid-leak bias.

(7) The d-c plate current of the modulated amplifier is constant with or without modulation.

(8) High class C efficiency of the modulated amplifier.

(9) Easy to adjust.

(10) Constant grid excitation voltage.

(11) Very low distortion.

The characteristics of grid modulation are:

(1) Modulation power required is comparatively small. (Just enough to overcome grid circuit losses.)

(2) Grid bias varies in proportion to the audio modulating signal.

(3) D-c plate voltage kept constant.

(4) R-f stage operated class C.

(5) Carrier output is only about ¼ of power obtained using same tube modulated.

(6) Relatively poor efficiency.

(7) Constant grid excitation carrier signal.

(8) Carrier efficiency about 35 to 40%.

(9) Bias source must have good regulation. (No grid-leak bias.)

(10) Driver regulation must be good.

(c) Plate modulation is generally only more desirable in *high-power* broadcast transmitters. In low-power broadcast transmitters (1 to 5 kw), grid modulation is often used for the advantage of its circuit simplicity. For an AM station with an r-f output power of 1.125 kw, modulated 100 percent, the d-c input power to the plate modulator will be about 700 watts. For grid modulation and the same r-f power output, only about 10 watts of audio power is required.

From the consideration of a high-power transmitter (above approximately 10-20 kw) the greater carrier-output efficiency of a plate-modulation system, makes the choice of this system necessary. Whereas a grid-modulated amplifier may operate at a carrier efficiency of about 37.5 percent, the plate-modulated amplifier may provide a carrier efficiency of 75 percent. In addition, plate-modulation systems are easier to adjust and offer relatively low plate dissipation requirements of the tubes.

Q. 4.87. Explain why dry air or inert gases are often used in R-F transmission lines which link broadcast transmitters and antennas.

A. This is done to prevent arcing within the cables.

D. See Q. 3.218, Discussion.

Q. 4.88. Describe the procedure of installing transmission lines between broadcast transmitters and antennas. Include information as to characteristic impedance, bends, kinks, cutting and connections. Discuss both the solid dielectric and the gas-filled lines.

A. Coaxial-transmission lines, both solid dielectric and gas-filled, connecting broadcast transmitters to antennas are usually installed by:

supporting them on wooden frames two or three feet above the ground, supporting them by messenger wires hung on poles as in telephone cable practice, or underground in concrete lined trenches with suitable covers for protection. It is poor practice to use direct burial as it is difficult to repair the lines should a fault occur. In the case of solid dielectric lines, which are normally flexible to a good degree, it is good practice to suspend them from messenger wires even when they are supported by low wooden frames to prevent undue tension on the lines.

To prevent undesirable radiation from the outer conductors of both types of lines, they should be well grounded to earth at forty- or fifty-foot intervals. This will reduce the existence of any voltage differences between the outer conductors and ground.

The lines should be installed, insofar as practicable, with a minimum of bends. Where bends are mandatory, such bends should be made with as large a radius as possible. The reason for this is that any bending results in a change of the circular cross-section to one that is more or less elliptical, depending on the severity of the bend. Such a change in cross-section results in a change of characteristic impedance at that point and will result in a standing wave being produced between that point and the input to the line. The ability of the line to withstand voltage stress between the conductors is reduced.

Should too sharp a bend in the line be attempted, the line will kink, and the foregoing disadvantages will be manifested to even a more severe degree.

In cutting a solid dielectric line to fit it for a connection to another length or to prepare it for termination at equipment, it is very important to avoid nicking the central conductor when baring it of the dielectric. This not only physically weakens the conductor but also introduces an electrical discontinuity which may introduce standing waves on the line. In gas-filled lines, such cutting must be done so that both conductors, inner and outer, are square across the ends and both must be smooth and free from burrs so that gas-tight connections can easily be made. It is imperative to take precautions to prevent any metal chips from lodging inside the line as these will not only result in electrical discontinuities but will decrease the amount of voltage the line can withstand.

Connections in solid dielectric lines should only be made with coaxial fittings especially designed for such lines as only these fittings will produce a satisfactory electrical and mechanical connection. In the case of gas-filled lines, connections are made by gasketed fittings or by solder sweating. In the case of sweating, a minimum of flux and solder should be used to prevent any excess from oozing inside the line and causing an electrical discontinuity and reduced voltage flashover ability. Such connections in the gas-filled line, both gasketed and sweated, should be tested for gas leaks by the use of a soap and water solution upon completion of the line and after it has been charged with its nitrogen or dry air to its operating pressure.

D. In the case of gas-filled lines, which are usually of rigid copper pipe, it is very important to make provisions to allow the line to expand and contract with variations in temperature.

For coaxial lines using air or gas dielectric, the optimum inner diameter of the outer conductor is about 3.6 times the diameter of the inner conductor. With these proportions, the attenuation of such a line is at a minimum. Such a ratio of diameters results in the lines having characteristic impedances of approximately 77 ohms.

For solid-dielectric lines, the same conductor proportions are generally used as well. However, because of the increased line capacitance resulting from the higher dielectric constant of the insulating material, the characteristic impedance of these lines is in the order of 50 ohms.

Q. 4.89. Draw a block diagram for each of the following broadcast transmitters complete from the microphone (and/or camera) inputs to the antenna outputs. State the purpose of each stage and explain briefly the overall operation of the transmitters.

  (a) Standard (AM) Broadcast
  (b) FM Broadcast
  (c) Multiplex FM Broadcast
  (d) TV Broadcast
  (e) Color TV Broadcast

A. (a) For block diagram of a standard AM broadcast transmitter, see Fig. 4.89(a).

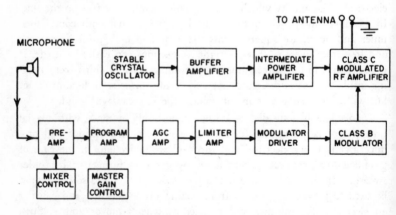

Fig. 4.89. (a) Block diagram of an AM broadcast transmitter.

(1) The crystal oscillator produces a stable-carrier frequency at low power. Depending upon the inherent crystal stability, it may or may not require oven-temperature control. (See Q. 4.43 and 4.44, above.)

(2) The buffer amplifier isolates the crystal oscillator to improve its stability. (See Q. 3.98.)

(3) The intermediate-power amplifier raises the output r-f power of the buffer to a level sufficient to drive the modulated r-f amplifier.

(4) The Class-C modulated r-f amplifier supplies the energy which is required to drive the antenna system at the rated r-f power. This stage may be operated as a parallel or a push-pull amplifier. (See Q. 4.85.)

(5) The pre-amplifier improves the signal-to-noise ratio before mixing. (See Q. 4.24 above.)

(6) The program amplifier (and line amplifier) raises the signal level to an amount adequate to drive the AGC and limiter amplifiers.

(7) For AGC amplifier, see Q. 4.40 above.

(8) For limiter amplifier, see Q. 4.38 above.

(9) The modulator driver supplies the necessary audio power to drive the Class-B modulator.

(10) The Class-B modulator varies the plate voltage of the Class-C r-f amplifier in accordance with the frequency and amplitude of the audio signal. This, in turn, varies the amplitude of the r-f-output wave to the antenna, producing an amplitude-modulated wave. (See Q. 4.85.)

(b) For block diagram of an FM broadcast transmitter (phase-modulated), see Fig. 4.62(c).

(1) The crystal oscillator produces a highly stable low-frequency CW carrier at 225 kc.

(2) The r-f amplifier increases the oscillator amplitude sufficient to drive the three-phase network.

(3) The three-phase network has a three-phase output at 225 kc which is used as one input to the phasitron tube. (For phasitron operation, see Q. 4.62 above.) The action of the modulator coil on the phasitron produces an *equivalent* FM signal with a deviation of plus and minus 173.6 cps.

(4) The above frequency-modulated signal is passed through a seven-stage multiplier giving a total frequency (and deviation) multiplication of 432 times. The output of the multipliers is 97.2 mc, plus and minus 75 kc.

(5) The intermediate-power amplifier supplies adequate power to drive the final amplifier.

(6) The final power amplifier provides the rated power output to drive the FM-transmitting antenna.

(7) From the microphone to the input of the pre-emphasis network the functions of the blocks are the same as described in part (a) of this question.

(8) The ·pre-emphasis network provides a high-frequency audio boost. (See Q. 3.163 and Q. 4.63.)

(9) The two audio amplifiers increase the audio amplitude and power to a level sufficient to drive the modulator coil. (See Q. 4.62 above.)

(c) For block diagram of an FM multiplex-broadcast transmitter, see Fig. 4.89(c). This shows a simplified block diagram of a direct FM system.

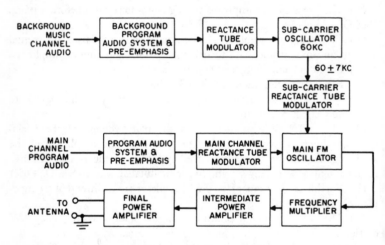

Fig. 4.89. (c) Block diagram of an FM multiplex-broadcast transmitter (direct FM system).

(1) The "Program Audio System and Pre-Emphasis" block includes (for simplicity) all the blocks preceding the audio amplifiers in Fig. 4.62(c).

(2) The main-program channel is discussed first. The main program audio is fed into its reactance-tube modulator, which produces direct frequency modulation at a relatively low carrier frequency and also at a relatively low-frequency deviation.

(3) The output of the main FM oscillator is passed through frequency multipliers. The output of these is at the final desired carrier frequency and deviation. (In a typical case the output of the master oscillator may be at an r-f frequency of 5.394 mc, with a deviation of ± 4.167 kc. After passing through multiplying stages totaling 18 times,

the final carrier output will be 97.1 mc with a deviation of ± 75 kc.)

(4) The functions of the intermediate power amplifier and final power amplifier are as discussed in parts (a) and (b) above.

(5) The multiplex channel is frequently used to provide background music for stores and factories. It functions by providing a sub-carrier (here taken as 60 kc) which is modulated (FM) by the background music. In turn, the FM sub-carrier then frequency modulates the main FM oscillator. At the background-music receiver, the 60 kc sub-carrier is filtered out and detected in the usual FM manner. For transmission standards of FM multiplex operation, see Q. 4.118, following.

(6) See (c)(1) above (audio block in background-music channel).

(7) From the background-program audio block, the audio is fed to a reactance-tube modulator.

(8) The reactance-tube modulator directly frequency modulates the 60 kc sub-carrier to an assumed ± 7 kc for 100 percent modulation.

(9) The 60 kc ± 7 kc signal is then used to drive the sub-carrier, reactance-tube modulator. This modulator frequency modulates the main FM oscillator with the 60 kc ± 7 kc signal. (Modulation limits and standards are given in Q. 4.118.)

(d) For block diagram of a TV broadcast transmitter, see Fig. 4.89(d).

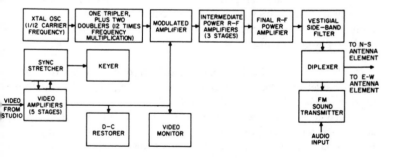

Fig. 4.89 (d). Block diagram of a typical monochrome TV transmitter using low-level modulation.

(1) The block diagram shown is of a low-level modulated monochrome visual TV transmitter. Although not shown here, visual transmitters also may employ medium-level or high-level modulation.

(2) The first block in the figure is a crystal oscillator operating at one-twelfth of the desired picture carrier frequency. For example, the picture carrier for channel 2 is 55.25 megacycles. In this case the crystal

oscillator would operate at one-twelfth of this frequency, or 4.6 (approximately) megacycles. This is done to insure good crystal oscillator stability. Following the crystal oscillator is a series of frequency multipliers consisting of one tripler and two doublers providing a total frequency multiplication of 12 times. Thus, the output of the multipliers is at actual picture carrier frequency and is then applied to the modulated amplifier stage. The modulated amplifier also receives an input consisting of the composite video signal including sync and blanking pulses. The video signal is provided at about 25 volts peak-to-peak level by a five-stage video amplifier. This amplifier receives its input from the studio cameras, relay equipment, or from a line amplifier. D-c restorers are provided to reinsert the d-c component of the signal before application to the modulated amplifier.

(3) In addition, a video monitor is used to afford continuous monitoring of the composite video signal. Such factors as proper sync level, and white and black levels may be observed on the monitor. Synchronizing and blanking pulses as well as equalizing pulses are generated and keyed in at the appropriate times by the Keyer unit. The sync stretcher controls the amplitude of the sync pulses to compensate for compression or variations in amplitude.

(4) The modulated amplifier output is a low-level r-f monochrome TV signal. This is brought up to the desired transmitting strength by three stages of intermediate r-f power amplification and then by the final r-f power amplifier.

(5) Note that the final r-f power amplifier output is fed through a vestigial sideband filter and a diplexer before being applied to the transmitting antenna. The use of the vestigial (partial) filter assures that the undesired portion of the *lower picture sidebands* will be attenuated in accordance with the FCC requirements. This attenuation must be at least 20 db at a point 1.25 megacycles below the visual carrier to prevent interference with the next lower TV channel.

(6) The diplexer is a device used for the purpose of supplying both the visual and aural modulated carriers to the same transmitting antenna without crosstalk. Electrically, the diplexer is a circuit with the aural and visual transmitters connected across opposite arms of the bridge, thus preventing crosstalk from occurring between the two sources.

(e) For block diagram of a color TV transmitter, see Fig. 4.89(e).
(1) The "Color Camera" contains three separate camera tubes. Filters are employed with each tube so that one tube responds to green, one to

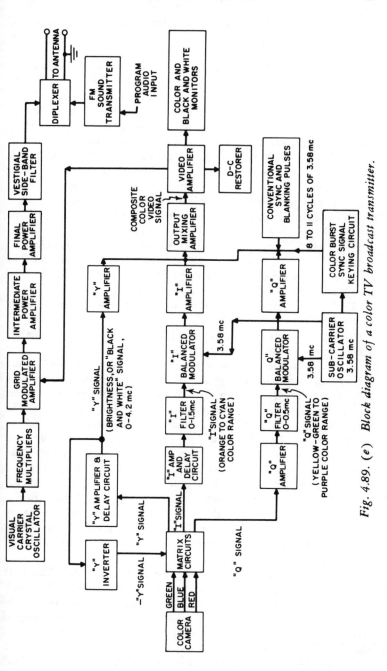

Fig. 4.89. (e) Block diagram of a color TV broadcast transmitter.

blue and one to red. As indicated in the block, amplitude-varying signals corresponding to the green, blue and red picture components are sent separately to the "Matrix Circuits."

(2) The "Matrix Circuits" are lumped into one block but actually contain amplifier circuits and resistive networks. The purpose of the "Matrix Circuits" is to produce certain combinations of the green, blue and red camera inputs and to produce three entirely different signals, known as the "Y," "I" and "Q" signals. These signals are produced by addition, subtraction and inversion of the three camera signals.

The "Y" (or brightness) signal has a bandwidth of 0 to 4.2 mc. It is produced in the matrix by combining the outputs of the three camera tubes in the proportions: 59 percent green, 11 percent blue and 30 percent red. This is the signal viewed on a conventional black and white set. On a color set it supplies fine detail information (above 1.5 mc bandwidth) which is sent only in black and white.

(3) The "Y" signal is sent to the "Y Amplifier and Delay Circuit." Here the "Y" signal is amplified and delayed about 1 microsecond. The delay is necessary to match the delay normally imposed by the "Q" filter and by the "I" filter plus its delay circuit.

(4) The "Y" inverter is necessary for the operation of the "Matrix Circuits."

(5) The "Y" signal is further amplified by a second "Y" amplifier and is then passed to the "Output Mixing Amplifier."

(6) The two other outputs of the "Matrix Circuit" are the "I" and "Q" signals (chrominance signals). Each of these signals represents a certain range of colors, which in combination can produce green, blue, red, or any other desired mixture color on the receiver-color tube. The "Q" signal alone is capable of producing colors ranging from yellow-green to purple. The "I" signal alone can produce colors ranging from cyan (bluish-green) to orange. The two signals acting together can produce a very-wide range of colors to produce a full-color picture.

(7) The "I" signal is fed to the "I Amplifier and Delay Circuit." This delay is necessary to match the delay of the "Q" signal. There is no delay circuit required in the "Q" channel. This is because the inherent delay of the "Q" filter introduces the greatest signal delay (about 1 microsecond) and is the reference time to which the "I" and "Y" signals must be matched.

(8) The "I" signal is then passed through the "I" filter. This filter restricts the "I" signal bandwidth to 0 to 1.5 megacycles. This bandwidth restriction is required to fit the color information within the conventional TV transmission channel and also to reduce the possibility of creating an interference pattern on the color tube due to the mixing of the "I" and "Q" signals.

(9) The "Q" signal coming from the matrix is fed into the "Q" amplifier and the "Q" filter. The "Q" filter restricts the "Q" signal

bandwidth to a range of 0 to 0.5 megacyles. This bandwidth is adequate for reproducing sufficient detail for the colors represented by the "Q" signal. (Fine detail in a color picture is supplied by the black and white, or "Y" signal.)

(10) The "I" and "Q" signal outputs from their respective filters are applied to the "I" and "Q" balanced modulators. Each balanced modulator also receives an input voltage from the 3.58 mc sub-carrier. The sub-carrier input to the "Q" (quadrature) balanced modulator is shifted in phase by 90 degrees relative to the sub-carrier fed to the "I" (in-phase) balanced modulator.

(11) In the "I"-balanced modulator, orange-to-cyan range color signals (0 to 1.5 mc.) are heterodyned with the sub-carrier. The sub-carrier is suppressed by the balanced modulator and its output is a set of sidebands ranging from 2.08 to 5.08 megacycles (3.58 mc $\pm$ 1.5 mc). Frequencies above 4.2 megacycles are later suppressed by the transmitter. The sub-carrier is suppressed to prevent the formation of a fine dot structure on black and white TV receivers. At the color receiver, the sub-carrier is reinserted in synchronous detectors which have as their output, the "I" and "Q" signals, reproduced.

(12) In the "Q"-balanced modulator, the yellow-green to purple range color signals (0 to 0.5 mc) are heterodyned with the 90 degree phase-shifted sub-carrier. Again, the sub-carrier is suppressed and the output is a set of sidebands ranging from 3.08 to 4.08 megacycles (3.58 $\pm$ 0.5 mc). Because of the 90 degree sub-carrier phase shift, the sidebands for the "Q" and "I" signals are 90 degrees out of phase with one another and can be transmitted together without interference. They can then be individually recovered by the receiver synchronous detectors, by using two reinserted sub-carriers, 90 degrees out of phase with one another.

(13) The outputs of "I" and "Q" balanced modulators are fed through the "I" and "Q" amplifiers and combined with the "Y" signal in the "Output Mixing Amplifier."

(14) To reproduce color accurately at the receiver, the receiver sub-carrier oscillator must be locked in frequency and phase with the transmitter sub-carrier oscillator. This is done by the use of a *color burst sync signal*. This signal consists of a burst of 8 to 11 cycles of 3.58 mc sub-carrier oscillator signal, which is keyed to be added to the *back porch* of the horizontal blanking pulses. (See Q. 4.75 above.) The keying is accomplished by the block labled, "Color Burst Sync Signal Keying Circuit." This signal is fed to the "Output Mixing Amplifier."

(15) The conventional monochrome TV, horizontal and vertical sync and blanking pulses (see Q. 4.74 above) are generated in the block so marked and are also fed to the "Output Mixing Amplifier."

(16) The output of the "Output Mixing Amplifier" is a composite color-video signal consisting of the following signal voltages:

(a) Color burst sync signal.
(b) "Q" signal.
(c) "I" signal.
(d) "Y" signal.
(e) Conventional sync and blanking pulses.

(17) The composite-color signal is fed through video amplifiers to the grid-modulated amplifier, d-c restorer and to color and black and white monitors.

(18) For discussion of the remainder of the blocks in Figure 4.89(e), see part (d) of this question.

PART II: RULES AND REGULATIONS

Note: The following questions and answers all pertain to FCC Rules and Regulations. This information is based on Parts 73, 74, and 17 of these Rules and Regulations. With each question, the appropriate Part and Section number is given to enable the student to look up additional reference material if desired. However, the answer to each question, as given, is complete in itself.

STANDARD AM BROADCAST

Q. 4.90. Define the following terms as they relate to standard broadcast stations. (R & R 73.1 to 73.14)

(a) Standard broadcast station
(b) Standard broadcast band
(c) Standard broadcast channel
(d) Daytime
(e) Nighttime
(f) Sunrise and sunset
(g) Broadcast day
(h) Experimental period
(i) Operating power
(j) Plate input power
(k) Antenna power
(l) Antenna current
(m) Antenna resistance
(n) Modulator stage
(o) Modulated stage
(p) Last radio stage

(q) Percentage modulation (amplitude)
(r) High level modulation
(s) Low level modulation
(t) Plate modulation
(u) Grid modulation

A. (a) The term "standard broadcast station" means a broadcasting station licensed for the transmission of radiotelephone emissions primarily intended to be received by the general public and operated on a channel in the band 535–1605 kilocycles.

(b) The term "standard broadcast band" means the band of frequencies extending from 535 to 1605 kilocycles.

(c) The term "standard broadcast channel" means the band of frequencies occupied by the carrier and two sidebands of a broadcast signal with the carrier frequency at the center. Channels shall be designated by their assigned carrier frequencies. The 107 carrier frequencies assigned to standard broadcast stations shall begin at 540 kilocycles and be in successive steps of 10 kilocycles.

(d) The term "daytime" means that period of time between local sunrise and local sunset.

(e) The term "nighttime" means that period of time between local sunset and 12 midnight local standard time.

(f) The terms "sunrise and sunset" mean, for each particular location and during any particular month, the time of sunrise and sunset as specified in the instrument of authorization.

(g) The term "broadcast day" means that period of time between local sunrise and 12 midnight local standard time.

(h) The term "experimental period" means that time between 12 midnight and local sunrise. This period may be used for experimental purposes in testing and maintaining apparatus by the licensee of any standard broadcast station on its assigned frequency and with its authorized power, provided no interference is caused to other stations maintaining a regular operating schedule within such period. No station licensed for "daytime" or "specified hours" of operation may broadcast any regular or scheduled program during this period.

(i) "Operating power" depends upon the context within which it is employed and may be synonomous with "normal power" or "antenna power."

(j) "Plate input power" means the product of the direct plate voltage applied to the tubes in the last radio stage and the total direct current flowing to the plates of these tubes, measured without modulation.

(k) "Antenna input power" or "antenna power" means the product of the square of the antenna current and the antenna resistance at the point where the current is measured.

(l) "Antenna current" means the radio-frequency current in the antenna with no modulation.

(m) "Antenna resistance" means the total resistance of the transmitting antenna system at the operating frequency and at the point at which the antenna current is measured.

(n) "Modulator stage" means the last amplifier stage of the modulating wave which modulates a radio-frequency stage.

(o) "Modulated stage" means the radio-frequency stage to which the modulator is coupled and in which the continuous wave (carrier wave) is modulated in accordance with the system of modulation and the characteristics of the modulating wave.

(p) "Last radio stage" means the oscillator or radio-frequency-power amplifier stage which supplies power to the antenna.

(q) "Percentage modulation" with respect to an amplitude modulated wave means the ratio of half the difference between the maximum and minimum amplitudes of the amplitude modulated wave to the average amplitude expressed in percentage.

(r) "High level modulation" is modulation produced in the plate circuit of the last radio stage of the system.

(s) "Low level modulation" is modulation produced in an earlier stage than the final.

(t) "Plate modulation" is modulation produced by introduction of the modulating wave into the plate circuit of any tube in which the carrier frequency wave is present.

(u) "Grid modulation" is modulation produced by introduction of the modulating wave into any of the grid circuits of any tube in which the carrier frequency wave is present.

Q. 4.91. What are the specifications of a plate-current meter in the last radio stage of a transmitter? (R & R 73.39)

A. Instruments indicating the plate current or plate voltage of the last radio stage (linear scale instruments) shall meet the following specifications:

(a) Length of scale shall be not less than $2\frac{3}{10}$ inches.

(b) Accuracy shall be at least 2 percent of the full scale reading.

(c) The maximum rating of the meter shall be such that it does not read off scale during modulation.

(d) Scale shall have at least 40 divisions.

(e) Full scale reading shall not be greater than five times the minimum normal indication.

D. Instruments indicating antenna current, common point current, and base currents shall meet the following specifications:

(a) Instruments having logarithmic or square law scales.

(1) Shall meet the same requirements as paragraphs (a), (b) and (c) in the answer above for linear scale instruments.

(2) Full scale reading shall not be greater than three times the minimum normal indication.

(3) No scale division above one-third full scale reading (in amperes) shall be greater than one-thirtieth of the full scale reading. (Example: An ammeter meeting requirement (1) having full scale reading of 6 amperes is acceptable for reading currents from 2 to 6 amperes, provided no scale division between 2 and 6 amperes is greater than one-thirtieth of 6 amperes, or 0.2 ampere.)

Q. 4.92. Under what conditions may remote-reading antenna ammeters be used to indicate antenna current? (R & R 73.39)

A. Remote-reading antenna ammeters may be used provided that the indicating instruments are capable of being connected directly into the antenna circuit at the same point as, but below (transmitter side), the antenna ammeter. The meter(s) in the remote control equipment may utilize an arbitrary scale division provided a calibration curve showing the relationship between the arbitrary scale and the scale of the antenna ammeter is maintained at the remote control point. The meter(s) in the remote control equipment must be calibrated once a week against the regular meter and the results thereof entered in the operating log.

D. (a) All remote meters shall meet the same requirements as the regular antenna ammeter and their calibration shall be checked against the regular meter at least once a week. In addition, remote meters shall be provided with shielding or filters as necessary to eliminate any feedback from the antenna to the transmitter. In shunt-fed antennas, the transmission-line current meter at the transmitter may be used as a remote antenna ammeter, provided the transmission line is terminated directly into the excitation-circuit feed line, which must employ series tuning only.

(b) The specifications for an antenna ammeter are given in Q. 4.91 above.

Q. 4.93. What is the maximum temperature variation at the crystal from the normal operating temperature when using X or Y cut crystals? When using low temperature coefficient crystals? (R & R 73.40)

A. The maximum temperature variation at the crystal from the normal operating temperature shall not be greater than,

(a) Plus or minus $0.1°$ C when an X or Y cut crystal is employed.

(b) Plus or minus $1.0°$ C when low temperature coefficient crystal is employed.

D. Unless otherwise authorized, a thermometer shall be installed in such manner that the temperature at the crystal can be accurately measured within 0.05° C for *X* or *Y* cut crystal or 0.5° C for low temperature coefficient crystal. It is preferable that the tank circuit of the oscillator tube be installed in the temperature controlled chamber.

Q. 4.94. Who keeps the keys to the fence which surrounds the antenna base at a standard broadcast station? Where are the keys usually kept? (R & R 73.40)

A. The keys are kept in the possession of the operator on duty at the transmitter.

D. It is not necessary to protect the equipment in the antenna tuning house and the base of the antenna with screens and interlocks, provided the doors to the tuning house and antenna base are fenced and locked at all times, with the keys in the possession of the operator on duty at the transmitter. Ungrounded fencing or wires should be effectively grounded, either directly or through proper static leaks. Lightning protection for the antenna system is not specifically required but should be installed.

Q. 4.95. Changes to the broadcast transmitter of what general nature require Commission approval? What type of changes or alterations do not require approval? (R & R 73.43, 73.44)

A. (a) No licensee or permittee shall change, in the last radio stage, the number of vacuum tubes, nor change to vacuum tubes of different power rating or class of operation, nor change the system of modulation, without authority of the Commission.

(b) Other changes which do not affect the maximum power rating or operating power of the transmitter or the operation or precision of the frequency control equipment may be made at any time without authority of the Commission, but in the next succeeding application for renewal of license such changes which affect the information already on file shall be shown in full.

Q. 4.96. What is the Commission's requirement regarding maintenance of operating power (antenna input power)? (R & R 73.52)

A. The authorized antenna input power for each station shall be equal to the nominal power for such station, with the following exceptions:

(1) For stations with nominal powers of 5 kilowatts, or less, the authorized antenna input power to directional antennas shall exceed the nominal power by 8 percent.

(2) For stations with nominal powers in excess of 5 kilowatts, the authorized antenna input power to directional antennas shall exceed the nominal power by 5.3 percent.

D. Where the authorized antenna input power is less than the nominal power, the transmitter may be operated at the reduced level necessary to supply the authorized antenna input power. Applications for authority to operate with antenna input power which is less than nominal power and/or to employ a dissipative network in the antenna system shall be made on FCC Form 302. The technical information supplied on section II-A of this form shall be that applying to the proposed conditions of operation.

Q. 4.97. What is the frequency tolerance at standard broadcast stations? (R & R 73.59)

A. The operating frequency of each station shall be maintained within 20 cycles of the assigned frequency.

Q. 4.98 What are the Commission's requirements concerning stations which operate their transmitters by remote control? (R & R 73.67)

A. (a) Operation by remote control shall be subject to the following conditions:

(1) The equipment at the operating and transmitting positions shall be so installed and protected that it is not accessible to or capable of operation by persons other than those duly authorized by the licensee.

(2) The control circuits from the operating positions to the transmitter shall provide positive on and off control and shall be such that open circuits, short circuits, grounds or other line faults will not actuate the transmitter and any fault causing loss of such control will automatically place the transmitter in an inoperative position.

(3) A malfunction of any part of the remote control equipment and associated line circuits resulting in improper control or inaccurate meter readings shall be cause for the immediate cessation of operation by remote control.

(4) Control and monitoring equipment shall be installed so as to allow the licensed operator at the remote control point to perform all the functions in a manner required by the Commission's rules.

(5) The indications at the remote control point of the antenna current meter or, for directional antennas, the common point current meter and remote base current meters, shall be read and entered in the operating log each half hour.

(6) The indications at the transmitter, if a directional antenna station, of the common point current, base currents, phase monitor sample loop currents and phase indications shall be read and entered in the operating log once each day for each pattern. These readings must be made within two hours after the commencement of operation for each pattern.

(b) All stations, whether operating by remote control or direct control, shall be equipped so as to be able to follow the Emergency Action Notification procedures described in R & R 73.911.

Q. 4.99. At what place must the station license be posted? **Where must the licenses of the operators be posted? (R & R 73.92)**

A. (a) The station license and any other instrument of station authorization shall be posted in a conspicuous place and in such manner that all terms are visible, at the place the licensee considers to be the principal control point of the transmitter. At all other control points listed on the station authorization, a photocopy of the station license and other instruments of station authorization shall be posted.

(b) The original operator license, or FCC Form 759, of each station operator shall be posted at the place where he is on duty as an operator.

Q. 4.100. What are the operator requirements at a non-directional 5 kw standard broadcast station? At a directional 5 kw standard broadcast station where the ratio of antenna currents must be within 5°, or the phases within three degrees? At a directional 5 kw standard broadcast station which is not required to maintain closer tolerances than the immediately preceding case? At a non-directional 20 kw standard broadcast station? (R & R 73.93)

A. (a) In cases where a station is authorized for non-directional operation with power not in excess of 10 kilowatts, the routine operation of the transmitter may be performed by an operator holding a valid first-class or second-class radiotelephone or radiotelegraph operator license or a radiotelephone third-class operator permit which has been endorsed for broadcast station operation.

(b) A station using a directional antenna system, which is required by the station authorization to maintain the ratio of the currents in the elements of the system within a tolerance which is less than 5% or the relative phases of those currents within a tolerance which is less than 3° shall, without exception, employ first-class radiotelephone operators who shall be on duty and in actual charge of the transmitting system during hours of operation with a directional radiation pattern.

(c) A station whose authorization does not specifically require therein the maintenance of phase and current relationships within closer tolerances than above specified shall employ first-class radiotelephone operators for routine operation of the transmitting system during periods of directional operation: *Provided, however,* That holders of second-class licenses or third-class permits endorsed for broadcast station operation, may be employed for routine operation of the transmitting system if the following conditions are met:

(1) The station must have in full-time employment at least one first-class radiotelephone operator.

(2) The station shall be equipped with a type-approved phase (antenna) monitor fed by a sampling system installed and maintained pursuant to accepted standards of good engineering practice.

(3) At least once each day, 5 days each week, unless required more frequently by the terms of the station authorization, or rules governing

operation by remote control, a first-class radiotelephone operator shall record the following observations in the station maintenance log for each directional radiation pattern used:

(i) Common point current.

(ii) Antenna base currents.

(iii) Sample loop currents or remote antenna base currents and phase monitor indications.

(iv) Antenna base current ratios, and remote antenna or sample loop current ratios, and the deviations in these ratios, in percent, from the licensed values. A station authorized to use the same directional radiation pattern during all hours of operation shall record these observations with successive readings not less than 12 hours apart.

(d) A station using a nondirectional antenna, during periods of operation with authorized power in excess of 10 kilowatts, may employ first-class radiotelephone operators, second-class operators, or operators with the third-class permits endorsed for broadcast station operation for routine operation of the transmitting system if the station has in full-time employment at least one first-class radiotelephone operator and complies with the provisions of paragraphs (f) and (g) of this section. (See Discussion.)

D.   With regard to all four types of broadcast stations designated in the question and answer, the routine operation of the transmitting system may be performed by an operator holding a second-class license or third-class permit endorsed for broadcast station operation. Unless, however, performed under the immediate and personal supervision of an operator holding a first-class radiotelephone license, an operator holding a second-class license or third-class permit endorsed for broadcast station operation, may make adjustments only of external controls, as follows:

(1) Those necessary to turn the transmitter on and off;

(2) Those necessary to compensate for voltage fluctuations in the primary power supply;

(3) Those necessary to maintain modulations levels of the transmitter within prescribed limits;

(4) Those necessary to effect routine changes in operating power which are required by the station authorization;

(5) Those necessary to change between nondirectional and directional or between differing radiation patterns, provided that such changes require only activation of switches and do not involve the manual tuning of the transmitter final amplifier or antenna phasor equipment. The switching equipment shall be so arranged that the failure of any relay in the directional antenna system to activate properly will cause the emissions of the station to terminate.

A station using a nondirectional antenna and with authorized power of 10 kilowatts or less shall have at least one first-class radiotelephone operator, readily available at all times, either in full-time employment, or, in the alternative, the licensee may contract in writing for the services on a part-time basis of one or more such operators. Signed contracts with part-time operators shall be kept in the files of the station and shall be made available for inspection upon request by an authorized representative of the Commission. A signed copy of contracts shall be forwarded to the Engineer in Charge of the radio district in which the station is located within three (3) days after the contract is signed.

Q. 4.101. What specific equipment performance measurements must be made at all standard broadcast stations on an annual basis? During what period of time preceding the date of filing for a renewal of the station license should such measurements be made? (R & R 73.47)

A. See Q. 4.35 for complete answers and discussion.

Q. 4.102. Explain how operating power is computed using direct measurement? Using indirect measurement? Under what conditions at a standard broadcast station may the indirect method be used?

A. (a) *Direct Measurement*: The antenna-input power determined by direct measurement is the square of the antenna current times the antenna resistance at the point where the current is measured and at the operating frequency.

(b) *Indirect Measurement*: The operating power determined by indirect measurement from the plate input power of the last radio stage is the product of the plate voltage (E_p), the total plate current of the last radio stage (I_p), and the proper factor (F) given in paragraph (b) of this section: That is,

$$\text{Operating power} = E_p \times I_p \times F$$

Factor to be used.

Factor (F)	Method of modulation	Maximum rated carrier power	Class of amplifier
0.70	Plate	0.25-1.0 kw	
.80	Plate	5 kw and over	
.35	Low Level	0.25 kw and over	B
.65	Low Level	0.25 kw and over	BC[1]
.35	Grid	0.25 kw and over	

[1] All linear amplifier operation where efficiency approaches that of Class C operation.

Note: When the factor F is obtained from the table, this value shall be used even though the antenna input power may be less than the maximum rated carrier power of the transmitter.

(c) Operating power shall be determined on a temporary basis by the indirect method: (1) In case of an emergency where the licensed antenna system has been damaged by causes beyond the control of the licensee (see R & R 73.45), or (2) Pending completion of authorized changes in the antenna system, or (3) If any change is made in the antenna system or any other change is made which may affect the antenna system.

D.   The operating power is normally measured by the direct method, except as discussed in part (c) of the answer, above. The following discussion pertains to measuring the antenna resistance for use with the direct method.

(a) The resistance variation method, substitution method and bridge method are acceptable methods of measuring the total antenna resistance.

(b) A determination of the resistance of an omni-directional antenna shall be made by taking a series of measurements at 5, 10, 15, and 20 kc/s on each side of the operating frequency. The values measured should be plotted with frequency as abscissa and resistance in ohms as ordinate and a smooth curve drawn. The point on the ordinate where this curve intersects the operating frequency gives the value of the antenna resistance.

(c) Antenna resistance for a directional antenna system shall be measured at the point of common radio frequency input to the directional antenna system. The following conditions shall obtain:

(1) The antenna shall be finally adjusted for the required pattern.

(2) The reactance at the operating frequency and at the point of measurement shall be adjusted to zero or as near thereto as practical.

(3) Suitable radio-frequency bridge or other method shall be employed to determine the resistance and reactance at the point of common radio-frequency input.

(4) Resistance and reactance measurements at approximately 5, 10, 15, and 20 kc/s on each side of the operating frequency shall be made. The values measured shall·be plotted and the resistance at the operating frequency determined in the same manner as set forth in paragraph (c) of this section.

(5) A permanently installed antenna ammeter shall be placed in each element of the system as well as at the point of measurement of resistance.

(d) The license for a station of power of 5 kw or under which employs a directional antenna will specify the antenna resistance as 92.5 per cent of that determined at the point of common input. The resistance specified for stations of a power over 5 kw will be 95 percent of that determined at the point of common input.

Q. 4.103.   What is the Commission's requirement as to maintenance of percentage of modulation? (R & R 73.55)

A.   The percentage of modulation shall be maintained at as high a level as is consistent with good quality of transmission and good broadcast service. In no case shall it exceed 100 percent on negative peaks of frequent recurrence, or 125 percent on positive peaks at any time. Generally, modulation should not be less than 85 percent on peaks of frequent recurrence, but where such action may be required to avoid objectionable loudness, the degree of modulation may be reduced to whatever level is necessary for this purpose, even though, under such circumstances, the level may be substantially less than that which produces peaks of frequent recurrence at a level of 85 percent.

Q. 4.104. What should be done if the station's modulation monitor becomes defective? If the frequency monitor becomes defective? (R & R 73.56, 73.60)

A. (a) In the event that the modulation monitor becomes defective, the station may be operated without the monitor pending its repair or replacement for a period not in excess of 60 days without further authority of the Commission.

(b) In the event that the frequency monitor becomes defective, the station may be operated without the monitor pending its repair or replacement for a period not in excess of 60 days without further authority of the Commission.

D. (a) The station may be operated without a modulation monitor, provided:

(1) Appropriate entries shall be made in the maintenance log of the station showing the date and time the monitor was removed from and restored to service.

(2) The Engineer in Charge of the radio district in which the station is located shall be notified both immediately after the monitor is found to be defective and immediately after the repaired or replacement monitor has been installed and is functioning properly.

(3) The degree of modulation of the station shall be monitored with a cathode ray oscilloscope or other acceptable means.

(4) If conditions beyond the control of the licensee prevent the restoration of the monitor to service within the above allowed period, informal request in accordance with R & R 1.549 of the FCC may be filed with the Engineer in Charge of the radio district in which the station is operating for such additional time as may be required to complete repairs of the defective instrument.

(5) Each station operated by remote control shall continuously, except when other readings are being taken, monitor percent of modulation or shall be equipped with an automatic device to limit percent of modulation on negative peaks to 100.

(b) The station may be operated without a frequency monitor, provided:

(1) Appropriate entries shall be made in the maintenance log of the station showing the date and time the monitor was removed from and restored to service.

(2) The Engineer in Charge of the radio district in which the station is located shall be notified both immediately after the monitor is found to be defective and immediately after the repaired or replacement monitor has been installed and is functioning properly.

(3) The frequency of the station shall be measured by an external source at least once each 7 days and the results entered in the station log.

(4) If conditions beyond the control of the licensee prevent the restoration of the monitor to service within the above allowed period, informal request in accordance with R & R 1.549 of the FCC may be filed with the Engineer in Charge of the radio district in which the station is located for such additional time as may be required to complete repairs of the defective instrument.

Q. 4.105. Under what conditions may a standard broadcast station use its facilities for communications directly with individuals or other stations? What notice shall be given when a station is operating during a local emergency? (R & R 73.98)

A. (a) A standard broadcast station may communicate directly with individuals or other stations during a period of emergency or imminent emergency in the area in which the station is located.

(b) A licensee or permittee operating under the provisions of this section shall as soon as possible after the beginning of such emergency use, send notice to the Commission at Washington, D.C., and to the Engineer in Charge of the district in which the station is located stating the nature of the emergency and the use to which the station is being put.

D. The licensee of a standard broadcast station or permittee of such a station operating under program test authority is authorized only to disseminate radio communications intended to be received by the public. However, during a period of emergency or imminent emergency in the area in which the station is located such a licensee or permittee may also (during the hours, at the frequency, and with the facilities specified in its instrument of authorization) utilize such station for transmitting communications directly related to the emergency which are intended to be received by specific individuals for the purpose of dispatching aid, assisting in rescue operations, or otherwise promoting the safety of life and property or alleviating hardship. In the course of such operation or any other operation permitted under the provisions of this section, a station may communicate with stations of other classes and in other services. For the purposes of this section, an emergency shall mean a situation that would generally and seriously endanger life and property or cause substantial hardship as a result of events such as hurricane or other severe weather conditions, flood, earthquake or wide-area forest fire. The term shall not include situations resulting from frosts, or localized fires which are not a source of general danger.

Q. 4.106. How many times and when must the station's operating log be signed by an operator who goes on duty at 10 a.m. and off duty at 6 p.m.? (R & R 73.111)

A.   The operator shall sign the log twice each day. Once when starting duty at 10 a.m. and once when going off duty at 6 p.m.

Q. 4.107. What entries shall be made in the station's operating log? In the station's maintenance log? (R & R 73.113, 73.114)

A.   (a) The following entries shall be made in the operating log:

(1) An entry of the time the station begins to supply power to the antenna and the time it stops.

(2) An entry of each interruption of the carrier wave, where restoration is not automatic, its cause and duration followed by the signature of the person restoring operation (if licensed operator other than the licensed operator on duty).

(3) An entry, at the beginning of operation and at intervals not exceeding one-half hour, of the following (actual readings observed prior to making any adjustments to the equipment) and, when appropriate, an indication of corrections made to restore parameters to normal operating values:

(i) Operating constants of last radio stage (total plate voltage and plate current).

(ii) Antenna current or common point current (if directional) without modulation, or with modulation if the meter reading is not affected by modulation.

(iii) Frequency monitor reading.

(4) An entry each day of the following where applicable:

(i) Antenna base current(s) without modulation, or with modulation if the meter reading is not affected by modulation, for each mode of operation:

(*a*) Where remote antenna meters or a remote common point meter are normally employed but are defective.

(*b*) Where required by the station license for directional antenna operation.

(ii) Where there is remote control operation of a directional antenna station, readings for each pattern taken at the transmitter (within 2 hours of commencement of operation with each pattern) of:

(*a*) Common point current without modulation, or with modulation if the meter reading is not affected by modulation.

(*b*) Base current(s) without modulation, or with modulation if the meter reading is not affected by modulation.

(*c*) Phase monitor sample loop current(s) without modulation, or with modulation if the meter reading is not affected by modulation.

(*d*) Phase indications.

(b) The following entries shall be made in the maintenance log:

(1) An entry, each week, of the following where applicable:

(i) A notation indicating the readings of the tower base current ammeter(s) and the associated remote antenna ammeter(s) (actual readings observed prior to remote antenna ammeter recalibration) and indicating calibration of the remote ammeter(s) against the tower base ammeter(s).

(ii) Time and result of test of auxiliary transmitter.

(iii) A notation of all frequency checks and measurements made independently of the frequency monitor and of the correlation of these measurements with frequency monitor indications.

(iv) A notation of the calibration check of automatic recording devices as required by R & R 73.113(b) (3).

(2) An entry of the date and time of removal from and restoration to service of any of the following equipment in the event it becomes defective:

(i) Modulation monitor.

(ii) Frequency monitor.

(iii) Final stage plate voltmeter.

(iv) Final stage plate ammeter.

(v) Base current ammeter(s).

(vi) Common point ammeter.

(3) Record of tower light inspections where required.

(4) Entries made so as to describe fully any experimental operation during the experimental period.

D. (a) Automatic devices accurately calibrated and with appropriate time, date and circuit functions may be utilized to record the entries in the operating log, provided that:

(1) They do not affect the operation of circuits or accuracy of indicating instruments of the equipment being recorded;

(2) The recording devices have an accuracy equivalent to the accuracy of the indicating instruments;

(3) The calibration is checked against the original indicators at least once a week and the results noted in the maintenance log;

(4) Provision is made to actuate automatically an aural alarm circuit located near the operator on duty if any of the automatic log readings

are not within the tolerances or other requirements specified in the rules or instrument of authorization;

(5) Unless the alarm circuit operates continuously, devices which record each parameter in sequence must read each parameter at least once during each 10-minute period and clearly indicate the parameter being recorded;

(6) The automatic logging equipment is located at the remote control point if the transmitter is remotely controlled, or at the transmitter location if the transmitter is manually controlled;

(7) The automatic logging equipment is located in the near vicinity of the operator on duty and is inspected by him periodically during the broadcast day; and

(8) The indicating equipment conforms with the requirements of R & R 73.39 except that the scales need not exceed 2 inches in length and arbitrary scales may not be used.

(b) Upon completion of the inspection required by R & R 73.93 (j), the inspecting operator shall enter a signed statement that the required inspection has been made, noting in detail the tests, adjustments, and repairs which were accomplished in order to insure operation in accordance with the provisions of this subpart and the current instrument of authorization of the station. The statement shall also specify the amount of time, exclusive of travel time to and from the transmitter, which was devoted to such inspection duties. If complete repair could not be effected, the statement shall set forth in detail the items of equipment concerned, the manner and degree in which they are defective, and the reasons for failure to make satisfactory repairs.

R & R 73.93 (j) reads as follows:

At all standard broadcast stations, a complete inspection of all transmitting and monitoring equipment in use shall be made by an operator holding a valid radiotelephone first-class operator license at least once each day, 5 days each week, with an interval of no less than 12 hours between successive inspections. This inspection shall include such tests, adjustments, and repairs as may be necessary to insure operation in conformance with the provisions of this subpart and the current instrument of authorization for the station.

Q. 4.108. How long must the station's operating logs be kept? (R & R 73.115)

A. Logs of standard broadcast stations shall be retained by the licensee or permittee for a period of two years.

D. Logs involving communications incident to a disaster or which include communications incident to or involved in an investigation by the Commission and concerning which the licensee or permittee has been notified, shall be retained by the licensee or permittee until he is specifically authorized in writing by the Commission to destroy them. Logs incident to or involved in any claim or complaint of which the licensee or permittee has notice shall be retained by the licensee or permittee until such claim or complaint has been fully satisfied or until the same has been barred by statute limiting the time for the filing of suits upon such claims.

Q. 4.109. What information (logs and records) must be made available to an authorized Commission employee? **(R & R 73.116)**

A.   The following shall be made available upon request by an authorized representative of the Commission:

(a) Program, operating and maintenance logs.

(b) Equipment performance measurements.

(c) Copy of most recent antenna resistance or common-point impedance measurements submitted to the Commission.

(d) Copy of most recent field intensity measurements to establish performance of directional antennas.

FM BROADCAST

Q. 4.110. What specific equipment performance measurements must be made at all FM broadcast stations on an annual basis? **(R & R 73. 254)**

A.   See Q. 4.35 above.

Q. 4.111. During what time period may an FM broadcast station transmit signals for testing and maintenance purposes? **(R & R 73.262)**

A.   The period between 12 midnight and 6:00 a.m., local standard time, may be used for experimental purposes in testing and maintaining apparatus by the licenses of any FM broadcast station on its assigned frequency and not in excess of its authorized power, without specific authorization by the Commission.

Q. 4.112. What are the operator license requirements for FM broadcast stations? **(R & R 73.265)**

A.   (a) A station with authorized transmitter output power of 25 kilowatts or less shall have at least one first-class radiotelephone operator readily available at all times, either in full-time employment, or in the alternative, the licensee may contract in writing for the services on a part-time basis of one or more such operators.

(b) A station with authorized transmitter output power in excess of 25 kilowatts may employ first-class radiotelephone operators, second-class operators, or operators with the third-class permits endorsed for broadcast station operation for routine operation of the transmitting system if the station has in full-time employment at least one first-class radiotelephone operator.

(c) Routine operation of the transmitting system may be performed by an operator holding a second-class license or third-class permit endorsed for broadcast station operation. Unless, however, performed under the immediate and personal supervision of an operator holding a first-class radiotelephone license, an operator holding a second-class license or third-class permit endorsed for broadcast station operation may make adjustments only of external controls, as follows:

(1) Those necessary to turn the transmitter on and off:

(2) Those necessary to compensate for voltage fluctuations in the primary power supply;

(3) Those necessary to maintain modulation levels of the transmitter within the prescribed limits.

D.   (a) With the exceptions set forth in paragraph (c), above, adjustments of the transmitting system and inspection, maintenance, and required equipment performance measurements shall be performed only by a first-class radiotelephone operator.

(b) At all FM broadcast stations, a complete inspection of the transmitting system and required monitoring equipment in use shall be made by an operator holding a first-class radiotelephone license at least once each day, 5 days a week, with an interval of not less than 12 hours between successive inspections. This inspection shall include such tests, adjustments, and repairs as may be necessary to insure operation in conformance with the provisions of this subpart and the current station authorization.

Q. 4.113.   By what methods may operating power at FM broadcast stations be computed?   (R & R 73.267)

A.   The operating power of each station shall be determined by either the direct or indirect method.

D.   (a) Using the direct method, the power shall be measured at the output terminals of the transmitter while operating into a dummy load of substantially zero reactance and a resistance equal to the transmission line characteristic impedance. The transmitter shall be unmodulated during this measurement. If electrical devices are used to determine the power output, such devices shall permit determination of this power to within an accuracy of ±5 percent of the power indicated by the full scale reading of the electrical indicating instrument of the device. If temperature and coolant flow indicating devices are used to determine the power output, such devices shall permit determination of this power to within an accuracy of 4 percent of measured average power output. During this measurement the direct plate voltage and current of the last radio stage and the transmission line meter shall be read and compared with similar readings taken with the dummy load replaced by the antenna. These readings shall be in substantial agreement.

(b) Using the indirect method, the operating power is the product of the plate voltage (E_p) and the plate current (I_p) of the last radio stage, and an efficiency factor, F, as follows:

$$\text{Operating power} = E_p \times I_p \times F$$

(c) The efficiency factor, F, shall be established by the transmitter manufacturer for each type of transmitter for which he submits data to the Commission, over the entire operating range of powers for which the transmitter is designed, and shall be shown in the instruction books supplied to the customer with each transmitter. In the case of composite equipment, the factor F shall be furnished to the Commission with a statement of the basis used in determining such factor.

Q. 4.114.   What is the allowable frequency tolerance at FM broadcast stations? (R & R 73.269)

A.   The center frequency of each FM broadcast station shall be maintained within 2000 cycles of the assigned center frequency.

Q. 4.115.   What is SCA? What are some possible uses of SCA? (R & R 73.293)

A.   (a) SCA stands for Subsidiary Communications Authorization. It is used to authorize limited types of subsidiary services on a multiplex basis.

(b) Some possible uses are:

(1) Transmission of programs which are of a broadcast nature, but which are of interest primarily to limited segments of the public wishing to subscribe thereto. Illustrative services include: background music; storecasting; detailed weather forecasting; special time signals; and other material of a broadcast nature expressly designed and intended for business, professional, educational, religious, trade, labor, agricultural or other groups engaged in any lawful activity.

(2) Transmission of signals which are directly related to the operation of FM broadcast stations; for example: relaying of broadcast material to other FM and standard broadcast stations; remote cueing and order circuits; remote control telemetering functions associated with authorized STL operation, and similar uses.

D.   (a) Applications for Subsidiary Communications Authorizations shall be submitted on FCC Form 318. An applicant for SCA shall specify the particular nature or purpose of the proposed use.

(b) SCA operations may be conducted without restriction as to time so long as the main channel is programmed simultaneously.

Q. 4.116. What items must be included in an SCA operating log? (R & R 73.295)

A. Each licensee or permittee shall maintain a daily operating log of SCA operation in which the following entries shall be made (excluding subcarrier interruptions of five minutes or less) :

(1) Time subcarrier generator is turned on.

(2) Time modulation is applied to subcarrier.

(3) Time modulation is removed from subcarrier.

(4) Time subcarrier generator is turned off.

(5) An entry describing the results obtained in determining the frequency of each SCA subcarrier.

Program and operating logs for SCA operation may be kept on special columns provided on the station's regular program and operating log sheets.

D. To the extent that SCA circuits are used for the transmission of program material, each licensee or permittee shall maintain a daily program log in which a general description of the material transmitted shall be entered once during each broadcast day: *Provided, however,* That in the event of a change in the general description of the material transmitted, an entry shall be made in the SCA program log indicating the time of each such change and a description thereof.

Q. 4.117. Define the following terms as they apply to FM broadcast stations: (R & R 73.310)

(a) Antenna power gain.

(b) Center frequency.

(c) Effective radiated power.

(d) FM broadcast band.

(e) FM broadcast channel.

(f) FM broadcast station.

(g) Field strength.

(h) Frequency modulation.

(i) Frequency swing.

(j) Multiplex transmission.

(k) Percentage modulation.

(l) Cross-talk.

(m) Left signal.

(n) Left stereophonic channel.

(o) Main channel.

(p) Pilot subcarrier.

(q) Stereophonic separation.

(r) Stereophonic subcarrier.

(s) Stereophonic subchannel.

A. (a) Antenna power gain: The square of the ratio of the root-mean-square free space field strength produced at 1 mile in the horizontal plane, in millivolts per meter for 1 kilowatt antenna input power to 137.6 mv/m. This ratio should be expressed in decibels (db). (If specified for a particular direction, antenna power gain is based on the field strength in that direction only.)

(b) Center frequency: The term "center frequency" means:

(1) The average frequency of the emitted wave when modulated by a sinusoidal signal.

(2) The frequency of the emitted wave without modulation.

(c) Effective radiated power: The term "effective radiated power" means the product of the antenna power (transmitter output power less transmission line loss) times (1) the antenna power gain, or (2) the antenna field gain squared. Where circular or elliptical polarization is employed, the term effective radiated power is applied separately to the horizontal and vertical components of radiation. For allocation purposes, the effective radiated power authorized is the horizontally polarized component of radiation only.

(d) FM broadcast band: The band of frequencies extending from 88 to 108 megacycles per second, which includes those assigned to non-commercial educational broadcasting.

(e) FM broadcast channel: A band of frequencies 200 kc/s wide and designated by its center frequency. Channels for FM broadcast stations begin at 88.1 mc/s and continue in successive steps of 200 kc/s to and including 107.9 mc/s.

(f) FM broadcast station: A station employing frequency modulation in the FM broadcast band and licensed primarily for the transmission of radiotelephone emissions intended to be received by the general public.

(g) Field strength: The electric field strength in the horizontal plane.

(h) Frequency modulation: A system of modulation where the instantaneous radio frequency varies in proportion to the instantaneous amplitude of the modulating signal (amplitude of modulating signal to be measured after pre-emphasis, if used) and the instantaneous radio frequency is independent of the frequency of the modulating signal.

(i) Frequency swing: The instantaneous departure of the frequency of the emitted wave from the center frequency resulting from modulation.

(j) Multiplex transmission: The term "multiplex transmission" means the simultaneous transmission of two or more signals within a single channel. Multiplex transmission as applied to FM broadcast stations means the transmission of facsimile or other signals in addition to the regular broadcast signals.

(k) Percentage modulation: The ratio of the actual frequency swing to the frequency swing defined as 100 percent modulation, expressed in percentage. For FM broadcast stations, a frequency swing of ±75 kilocycles is defined as 100 percent modulation.

(l) Cross-talk: An undesired signal occurring in one channel caused by an electrical signal in another channel.

(m) Left (or right) signal: The electrical output of a microphone or combination of microphones placed so as to convey the intensity, time, and location of sounds originating predominately to the listener's left (or right) of the center of the performing area.

(n) Left (or right) stereophonic channel: The left (or right) signal as electrically reproduced in reception of FM stereophonic broadcasts.

(o) Main channel: The band of frequencies from 50 to 15,000 cycles per second which frequency-modulate the main carrier.

(p) Pilot subcarrier: A subcarrier serving as a control signal for use in the reception of FM stereophonic broadcasts.

(q) Stereophonic separation: The ratio of the electrical signal caused in the right (or left) stereophonic channel to the electrical signal caused in the left (or right) stereophonic channel by the transmission of only a right (or left) signal.

(r) Stereophonic subcarrier: A subcarrier having a frequency which is the second harmonic of the pilot subcarrier frequency and which is employed in FM stereophonic broadcasting.

(s) Stereophonic subchannel: The band of frequencies from 23 to 53 kilocycles per second containing the stereophonic subcarrier and its associated sidebands.

Q. 4.118. What are the transmission standards of subsidiary communications multiplex operations? (R & R 73.319)

A. (a) Frequency modulation of SCA subcarriers shall be used.

(b) The instantaneous frequency of SCA subcarriers shall at all times be within the range 20 to 75 kilocycles: Provided, however, That when the station is engaged in stereophonic broadcasting, the instantaneous frequency of SCA subcarriers shall at all times be within the range 53 to 75 kilocycles.

(c) The arithmetic sum of the modulation of the main carrier by SCA subcarriers shall not exceed 30 percent: Provided, however, That when the station is engaged in stereophonic broadcasting, the arithmetic sum of the modulation of the main carrier by the SCA subcarriers shall not exceed 10 percent.

Note: Inasmuch as presently approved FM modulation monitors have been designed to meet requirements for modulation frequencies of from 50 to 15,000 cycles, the use of such monitors for reading the modulation percentages during SCA multiplex operation may not be appropriate since the subcarriers utilized are above 20,000 cycles.

(d) The total modulation of the main carrier, including SCA subcarriers, shall meet the requirements of 85 to 100 percent.

D.   Frequency modulation of the main carrier caused by the SCA subcarrier operation shall, in the frequency range 50 to 15,000 cycles, be at least 60 db below 100 percent modulation: Provided, however, that when the station is engaged in stereophonic broadcasting, frequency modulation of the main carrier by the SCA subcarrier operation shall, in the frequency range 50 to 53,000 cycles, be at least 60 db below 100 percent modulation.

Q. 4.119.   What are the stereophonic transmission standards provided by the Commission's Rules? (R & R 73.322)

A.   (a) The modulating signal for the main channel shall consist of the sum of the left and right signals.

(b) A pilot subcarrier at 19,000 cycles plus or minus 2 cycles shall be transmitted that shall frequency modulate the main carrier between the limits of 8 and 10 percent.

(c) The stereophonic subcarrier shall be the second harmonic of the pilot subcarrier and shall cross the time axis with a positive slope simultaneously with each crossing of the time axis by the pilot subcarrier.

(d) Amplitude modulation of the stereophonic subcarrier shall be used.

(e) The stereophonic subcarrier shall be suppressed to a level less than one percent modulation of the main carrier.

(f) The stereophonic subcarrier shall be capable of accepting audio frequencies from 50 to 15,000 cycles.

(g) The modulating signal for the stereophonic subcarrier shall be equal to the difference of the left and right signals.

D.   (a) The pre-emphasis characteristics of the stereophonic subchannel shall be identical with those of the main channel with respect to phase and amplitude at all frequencies.

(b) The sum of the side bands resulting from amplitude modulation of the stereophonic subcarrier shall not cause a peak deviation of the main carrier in excess of 45 percent of total modulation (excluding SCA subcarriers) when only a left (or right) signal exists; simultaneously in the main channel, the deviation when only a left (or right) signal exists shall not exceed 45 percent of total modulation (excluding SCA subcarriers).

(c) Total modulation of the main carrier including pilot subcarrier and SCA subcarriers shall meet the requirements of 85 to 100 percent modulation, with maximum modulation of the main carrier by all SCA subcarriers limited to 10 percent.

(d) At the instant when only a positive left signal is applied, the main channel modulation shall cause an upward deviation of the main carrier frequency; and the stereophonic subcarrier and its sidebands signal shall cross the time axis simultaneously and in the same direction.

TELEVISION BROADCAST

Q. 4.120.   What are the operator requirements for television stations? (R & R 73.661)

A.   One or more operators holding a valid radiotelephone first-class operator license shall be on duty at the place where the transmitting apparatus is located or at a remote control point and in actual charge thereof whenever the transmitter is delivering power to the transmitting antenna.

D.   The original license (or FCC Form 759) of each station operator shall be posted at the place where he is on duty. The licensed operator on duty and in charge of a television broadcast transmitter may, at the discretion of the licensee, be employed for other duties or for the operation of another station or stations in accordance with the class of license which he holds and the rules and regulations governing such other stations. However, such other duties shall in no way impair or impede the required supervision of the television broadcast transmitter.

Q. 4.121.   What is the frequencey tolerance for television stations? (R & R 73.668)

A.   (a) The carrier frequency of the visual transmitter shall be maintained within ±1000 cycles of the authorized carrier frequency.

(b) The center frequency of the aural transmitter shall be maintained 4.5 megacyles, ±1000 cycles, above the visual carrier frequency.

Q. 4.122.   What items must be included in a television station's operating log? In its maintenance log? (R & R 73.671, 73.672)

A.   (a) The following entries shall be made in the operating log by the properly licensed operator in actual charge of the transmitting apparatus oniy.

(1) An entry of the time the station begins to supply power to the antenna and the time it stops.

(2) An entry of each interruption of the carrier wave, where restoration is not automatic, its cause and duration followed by the signature of the person restoring operation (if licensed operator other than the licensed operator on duty).

(3) An entry, at the beginning of operation and at intervals not exceeding one-half hour, of the following (actual reading observed prior to making any adjustments to the equipment) and, when appropriate, an indication of corrections made to restore parameters to normal operating values:

(i) Operating constants of last radio stage of aural transmitter (total plate voltage and plate current).

(ii) Transmission line meter readings for both transmitters.

(iii) For remote control operation, the results of observations of vertical interval test signal transmissions.

(4) Any other entries required by the instrument of authorization or the provisions of this part.

(5) The entries required by R & R 17.49 (a), (b), and (c) concerning daily observations of tower lights.

(b) The following entries shall be made in the maintenance log:

(1) An entry each week of the time and result of test of auxiliary transmitters.

(2) A notation each week of the calibration check of automatic recording devices.

(3) An entry describing the method used and the results obtained in determining the operating frequency of the transmitter:

(i) Whenever the frequency check is made.

(ii) Whenever the frequency measurement is made.

(4) An entry of the date and time of removal from and restoration to service of any of the following equipment in the event it becomes defective:

(i) Visual modulation monitoring equipment or aural modulation monitor.

(ii) Final stage plate voltmeters of aural and visual transmitters.

(iii) Final stage plate ammeters of aural and visual transmitters.

(iv) Visual and aural transmitter transmission line radio frequency voltage, current, or power meter.

(5) The entries required by R & R 17.49(d) concerning quarterly inspections of the condition of tower lights and associated control equipment and an entry when towers are cleaned or repainted.

(6) Entries shall be made so as to describe fully any operation for testing and maintenance purposes.

(7) Whenever the calibration of the output power meter is made as required by R & R 73.689(b) (1) and (2) with a brief description of the method and results.

(8) Any other entries required by the instrument of authorization or the provisions of this part.

D. For automatic logging devices, see discussion for Q. 4.107(a), above.

Q. 4.123. Define the following terms as they apply to television broadcast stations: (R & R 73.681)

(a) Aspect ratio.

(b) Aural transmitter.

(c) Aural center frequency.

(d) Blanking level.
(e) Chrominance.
(f) Chrominance subcarrier.
(g) Color transmission.
(h) Effective radiated power.
(i) Field.
(j) Frame.
(k) Free space field intensity.
(l) Frequency swing.
(m) Interlaced scanning.
(n) Luminance.
(o) Monochrome transmission.
(p) Negative transmission.
(q) Peak power.
(r) Reference black level.
(s) Reference white level.
(t) Scanning.
(u) Scanning line.
(v) Standard television signal.
(w) Synchronization.
(x) Television broadcast band.
(y) Television channel.
(z) Television transmission standards.
(aa) Vestigial sideband transmission.
(bb) Visual transmission power.

A. (a) Aspect ratio: The ratio of picture width to picture height as transmitted.

(b) Aural transmitter: The radio equipment for the transmission of the aural signal only.

(c) Aural center frequency: (1) The average frequency of the emitted wave when modulated by a sinusoidal signal; (2) the frequency of the emitted wave without modulation.

(d) Blanking level: The level of the signal during the blanking interval, except the interval during the scanning synchronizing pulse and the chrominance subcarrier synchronizing burst.

(e) Chrominance: The colorimetric difference between any color and a reference color of equal luminance, the reference color having a specific chromaticity.

(f) Chrominance subcarrier: The carrier which is modulated by the chrominance information.

(g) Color transmission: The transmission of color television signals which can be reproduced with different values of hue, saturation, and luminance.

(h) Effective radiated power: The product of the antenna input power and the antenna power gain. This product should be expressed in kilowatts and in decibels above one kilowatt (dbk). (If specified for a particular direction, effective radiated power is based on the antenna power gain in that direction only. The licensed effective radiated power is based on the average antenna power gain for each horizontal plane direction.)

(i) Field: Scanning through the picture area once in the chosen scanning pattern. In the line interlaced scanning pattern of two to one, the scanning of the alternate lines of the picture area once.

(j) Frame: Scanning all of the picture area once. In the line interlaced scanning pattern of two to one, a frame consists of two fields.

(k) Free space field intensity: The field intensity that would exist at a point in the absence of waves reflected from the earth or other reflecting objects.

(l) Frequency swing: The instantaneous departure of the frequency of the emitted wave from the center frequency resulting from modulation.

(m) Interlaced scanning: A scanning process in which successively scanned lines are spaced an integral number of line widths, and in which the adjacent lines are scanned during successive cycles of the field frequency.

(n) Luminance: Luminous flux emitted, reflected, or transmitted per unit solid angle per unit projected area of the source.

(o) Monochrome transmission: The transmission of television signals which can be reproduced in gradations of a single color only.

(p) Negative transmission: Where a decrease in initial light intensity causes an increase in the transmitted power.

(q) Peak power: The power over a radio-frequency cycle corresponding in amplitude to synchronizing peaks.

(r) Reference black level: The level corresponding to the specified maximum excursion of the luminance signal in the black direction.

(s) Reference white level of the luminance signal: The level corresponding to the specified maximum excursion of the luminance signal in the white direction.

(t) Scanning: The process of analyzing successively, according to a predetermined method, the light values of picture elements constituting the total picture area.

(u) Scanning line: A single continuous narrow strip of the picture area containing highlights, shadows, and half-tones, determined by the process of scanning.

(v) Standard television signal: A signal which conforms to the television transmission standards.

(w) Synchronization: The maintenance of one operation in step with another.

(x) Television broadcast band: The frequencies in the band extending from 54 to 890 megacycles which are assignable to television broadcast stations. These frequencies are 54 to 72 megacycles (channels 2 through 4), 76 to 88 megacycles (channels 5 and 6), 174 to 216 megacycles (channels 7 through 13), and 470 to 890 megacycles (channels 14 through 83).

(y) Television channel: A band of frequencies 6 megacycles wide in the television broadcast band and designated either by number or by the extreme lower and upper frequencies.

(z) Television transmission standards: The standards which determine the characteristics of a television signal as radiated by a television broadcast station.

(aa) Vestigial sideband transmission: A system of transmission wherein one of the generated sidebands is partially attenuated at the transmitter and radiated only in part.

(bb) Visual transmitter power: The peak power output when transmitting a standard television signal.

Q. 4.124. How is operating power determined for the visual transmitter at a television broadcast station? For the aural transmitter? (R & R 73.689)

A. (a) Visual transmitter: The operating power of the visual transmitter shall be determined at the output terminals of the transmitter, which includes any vestigial sideband and harmonic filters which may be used during normal operation. For this determination the average power output shall be measured while operating into a dummy load of substantially zero reactance and a resistance equal to the transmission line characteristic impedance. During this measurement the transmitter shall be modulated only by a standard synchronizing signal with blanking level set at 75 percent of peak amplitude as observed in an output monitor, and with this blanking level amplitude maintained throughout the time interval between synchronizing pulses.

(b) Aural transmitter: The operating power of the aural transmitter shall be determined by either the direct or indirect method.

(1) Using the direct method, the power shall be measured at the output terminals of the transmitter while operating into a dummy load of substantially zero reactance and a resistance equal to the transmission line characteristic impedance. The transmitter shall be unmodulated during this measurement. If electrical devices are used to determine the output power, such devices shall permit determination of this power to within an accuracy of ±5 percent of the power indicated by the full scale reading of the electrical indicating instrument of the device. If temperature and coolant flow indicating devices are used to determine the power output, such devices shall permit determination of this power to within an accuracy of 4 percent of measured average power output.

During this measurement the direct plate voltage and current of the last radio stage and the transmission line meter shall be read and compared with similar readings taken with the dummy load replaced by the antenna. These readings shall be in substantial agreement.

(2) Using the indirect method, the operating power is the product of the plate voltage (E_p) and the plate current (I_p) of the last radio stage, and an efficiency factor, F, as follows:

$$\text{Operating power} = E_p \times I_p \times F$$

(3) The efficiency factor, F, shall originally be established by the transmitter manufacturer for each type of transmitter for which he submits data to the Commission, and shall be shown in the instruction books supplied to the customer with each transmitter. In the case of composite equipment, the factor F shall be furnished to the Commission by the applicant along with a statement of the basis used in determining such factor.

D. If electrical devices are used to determine the output power, such devices shall permit determination of this power to within an accuracy of ± 5 percent of the power indicated by the full scale reading of the electrical indicating instrument of the device. If temperature and coolant flow indicating devices are used to determine the power output, such devices shall permit determination of this power to within an accuracy of 4 percent of measured average power output. The peak power output shall be the power so measured in the dummy load multiplied by the factor 1.68. During this measurement the direct plate voltage and current of the last radio stage and the transmission line meter shall be read and compared with similar readings taken with the dummy load replaced by the antenna. These readings shall be in substantial agreement.

Q. 4.125. Sketch the amplitude characteristic of an idealized picture transmission (R & R 73.699)

A. For sketch and discussion, see Q. 4.76.

Q. 4.126. Draw the synchronizing waveform for television transmissions (monochrome). Be certain to show the white level, black level, blanking level, line writing and vertical blanking interval. Where on the synchronizing waveform would the "color burst" for color transmissions appear? (R & R 73.699)

A. (a) For monochrome synchronizing waveform, see Q. 4.74.
(b) For "color burst" sketch and discussion, see Q. 4.75.

EMERGENCY BROADCAST SERVICE

Q. 4.127. Define the following terms which apply to the Emergency Broadcast System: **(R & R 73.903, 73.907–73.916)**
(a) Emergency Broadcast System (EBS).
(b) Emergency Broadcast System (EBS) Authorization.
(c) Emergency Action Notification.
(d) Emergency Action Condition Termination.
(e) Emergency Action Condition.
(f) Basic Emergency Broadcast System (EBS) Plan.

A. (a) The Emergency Broadcast System consists of broadcast stations and interconnecting facilities which have been authorized by the Commission to operate in a controlled manner during a war, threat of war, state of public peril or disaster, or other national emergency.

(b) An Emergency Broadcast System Authorization is an authorization issued by the Commission only to licensees of Broadcast stations, to permit operation of such stations during a National-level Emergency Action Condition.

(c) The Emergency Action Notification is the notice to all licensees, participating non-government entities, and the general public of the existence of an Emergency Action Condition.

(d) The Emergency Action Condition Termination is the notice to all licensees, participating non-government entities, and the general public of the termination of an Emergency Action Condition.

(e) The Emergency Action Condition is an emergency situation, covering the period of time between the transmission of an Emergency Action Notification and an Emergency Action Condition Termination.

(f) The Basic Emergency Broadcast System Plan is the document containing the detailed description of how stations operating in the Radio Broadcast Services will be notified and operated in the Emergency Broadcast System.

Q. 4.128. Describe the Emergency Action Notification Attention Signal. **(R & R 73.933)**

A. The Emergency Action Notification Attention Signal is as follows:
(a) Cut the transmitter carrier for 5 seconds. (Sound carrier only for TV stations.)
(b) Return carrier to the air for 5 seconds.
(c) Cut transmitter carrier for 5 seconds. (Sound carrier only for TV stations.)
(d) Return carrier to the air.

(e) Broadcast 1000 cycle steady state tone for 15 seconds.

(f) Broadcast the Emergency Action Notification Message.

Q. 4.129. Under normal conditions all standard, FM, and TV broadcast stations must make what provisions for receiving Emergency Action Notifications and Terminations? (R & R 73.932)

A. All broadcast station licensees must install, unless specifically exempt, the necessary equipment to receive Emergency Action Notifications by means of reception of radio broadcast messages, and must maintain this equipment in a state of readiness for reception, including arrangements for human listening watch or automatic alarm devices, or both. Such equipment shall have its termination at the transmitter control point.

Q. 4.130. What type of station identification shall be given during an Emergency Action Condition? (R & R 73.933)

A. The station identification shall be the call letters of the station and the operational area name of the particular area the station is serving.

Q. 4.131. Must stations operate in accordance with Section 73.52 of the Commission's Rules during an Emergency Action Condition? (R & R 73.933)

A. Broadcast stations are exempt from complying with R & R 73.52 during an Emergency Action Condition.

D. R & R 73.52 discusses the maintenance of operating power for a broadcast station and is fully presented in Q. 4.96.

Q. 4.132. How often and at what times must EBS tests be sent? (R & R 73.961)

A. Tests involving transmission of the Emergency Action Notification Attention Signal and test message by Standard, FM, and television broadcast stations, shall be made once each week on an unscheduled basis between the hours of 8:30 a.m. and local sunset. Results of these tests shall be forwarded to the Commission by the licensees concerned, in accordance with detailed instructions.

SPECIAL BROADCAST SERVICES

Q. 4.133. What is the uppermost power limitation imposed on remote pickup broadcast stations? STL stations? Intercity Relay broadcast stations? (R & R 74.435, 74.534)

A. STL Intercity Relay and remote pickup broadcast stations will be licensed with a power output not in excess of that necessary to render satisfactory service. The license for these stations will specify the maximum authorized power. The operating power shall not be greater than necessary to carry on the service and in no event more than 5 percent above the maximum power specified. Engineering standards have not been established for these stations. The efficiency factor for the last radio stage of transmitters employed will be subject to individual determination but shall be in general agreement with values normally employed for similar equipment operated within the frequency range authorized.

Q. 4.134. What records of operation must be maintained for each licensed remote pickup broadcast station? (R & R 74.481)

A.   (a) The licensee of a remote pickup broadcast base or mobile station shall maintain an operating log to show when and for what purpose the station is operated. The following basic data shall be recorded.

(1) The date and time of operation.

(2) The purpose of the operation.

(3) The location of the transmitter, if a mobile or portable station.

(4) The station with which it communicates.

(5) Frequency check, if made.

(6) Entries concerning daily observations of tower lights and quarterly inspections of the condition of the tower lights and associated control equipment and an entry when towers are cleaned or repainted.

(7) Any pertinent remarks concerning the transmissions or equipment deemed desirable or necessary by the operator.

(b) An entry shall be made of any frequency check made pursuant to the requirements of R & R 74.462.

(c) If the station instrument of authorization requires painting and the lighting of the antenna structure, the log entries concerning lighting shall be made daily whether or not the transmitter is used.

(d) Station records shall be kept in such manner as to be available for inspection by a duly authorized representative of the Commission upon request. The records shall be retained for a period of 2 years.

Q. 4.135. What is the basic difference between STL and Intercity Relay broadcast stations? (R & R 74.501)

A.   (a) An STL station is used to transmit aural program material from a studio to the transmitter of a broadcast station.

(b) An Intercity Relay station is used to transmit aural program material between broadcast stations.

D.   See Q. 4.34.

Q. 4.136. What type of antenna must be used with STL and Inter-city Relay broadcast stations? (R & R 74.536)

A.   Each aural broadcast STL and Intercity Relay station is required to employ a directional antenna. Considering one kilowatt of radiated power as a standard for comparative purposes, such antenna shall provide a free space field intensity at one mile of not less than 435 mv/m in the main lobe of radiation toward the receiver and not more than 20 percent of the maximum value in any azimuth 30 degrees or more off the line to the receiver. Where more than one antenna is authorized for use with a single station, the radiation pattern of each shall be in accordance with the foregoing requirement.

Q. 4.137. What is the frequency tolerance provided by the Commission's Rules for an STL and an Intercity Relay broadcast station? (R & R 74.561)

A.   The licensee of each aural broadcast STL and Intercity Relay station shall maintain the operating frequency of the station within plus or minus 0.005 percent of the assigned frequency.

D.   The frequency band 947–952 mc/s is divided into nine 500 kc/s channels for assignment to aural broadcast STL and intercity relay stations. Each of the following frequencies is the center frequency of a channel:

Mc/s	Mc/s	Mc/s	Mc/s
942.5	945.0	947.5	950.0
943.0	945.5	948.0	950.5
943.5	946.0	948.5	951.0
944.0	946.5	949.0	951.5
944.5	947.0	949.5	

A single broadcast station licensee will normally be limited to the assignment of one 500 kc/s channel between the same point of origin and destination. If the circuit carries only one aural program channel, the center frequency of the channel will be assigned. If a single licensee requires more than one aural program channel between the same point of origin and destination, more than one transmitter may be authorized to operate within a single 500 kc/s channel, employing carrier frequencies above and below the center frequency listed in this paragraph.

ANTENNAS

Q. 4.138. Under what two general conditions must antenna structures be painted and lighted? (R & R 17.21)

A. Antenna structures shall be painted and lighted when:

(a) They require special aeronautical study; or

(b) They exceed 170 feet in height above the ground.

(c) The Commission may modify the above requirement for painting and/or lighting of antenna structures, when it is shown by the applicant that the absence of such marking would not impair the safety of air navigation, or that a lesser marking requirement would insure the safety thereof.

Q. 4.139.   What color(s) should antenna structures be painted? Where can paint samples be obtained? (R & R 17.23)

A. (a) Antenna structures shall be painted throughout their height with alternate bands of aviation surface orange and white, terminating with aviation-surface orange bands at both top and bottom. The width of the bands shall be equal and approximately one-seventh the height of the structure, provided however, that the bands shall not be more than 40 feet nor less than 1½ feet in width.

(b) Paint samples may be obtained from paint manufacturers who make paint in accordance with the specifications set forth by the FCC for aviation-surface orange and white.

Q. 4.140.   If a tower is required to be lighted and the lights are controlled by a light-sensitive device and the device malfunctions, when should the tower lights be on? (R & R 17.25)

A. The lights shall burn simultaneously from sunset to sunrise and shall be positioned so as to insure unobstructed visibility of at least one of the lights from aircraft at any angle of approach.

Q. 4.141.   As a general rule, a light-sensitive device used to control tower lights should face which direction? (R & R 17.25)

A. The light-sensitive device should face North.

D. A light-sensitive control device or an astronomic-dial clock and time switch may be used to control the obstruction lighting in lieu of manual control. When a light-sensitive device is used, it should be adjusted so that the lights will be turned on at a north sky light-intensity level of about 35 foot-candles and turned off at a north sky light-intensity level of about 58 foot-candles.

Q. 4.142.   If the operation of a station's tower lights are not continuously monitored by an alarm device, how often should the lights be visually checked? (R & R 17.47)

A. The lights should be visually checked at least once each 24 hours.

Q. 4.143. How often should automatic-control devices and alarm circuits associated with antenna-tower lights be checked for proper operation? (R & R 17.47)

A. Such devices should be checked at intervals not to exceed 3 months.

Q. 4.144. What items regarding the operation of antenna-tower lighting should be included in the station's maintenance log? (R & R 17.49)

A. The licensee of any radio station which has an antenna structure requiring illumination shall make the following entries in the station record of the inspections required by R & R 17.47: **(a)** The time the tower lights are turned on and off each day if manually controlled; **(b)** The time the daily check of proper operation of the tower lights was made, if automatic alarm system is not provided; (c) In the event of any observed or otherwise known failure of a tower light: (1) Nature of such failure. (2) Date and time the failure was observed, or otherwise noted. (3) Date, time, and nature of the adjustments, repairs, or replacements made. (4) Identification of Air Traffic Communication Station (Federal Aviation Agency) notified of the failure of any code or rotating-beacon light or top light not corrected within 30 minutes, and the date and time such notice was given. (5) Date and time notice was given to the Air Traffic Communication Station (Federal Aviation Agency) that the required illumination was resumed. (d) Upon completion of the periodic inspection required at least once each three months: (1) The date of the inspection and the condition of all tower lights and associated lighting-control devices, indicators and alarm systems. (2) Any adjustments, replacements, or repairs made to insure compliance with the lighting requirements and the date such adjustments, replacements, or repairs were made.

Q. 4.145. Generally speaking, how often should the antenna tower be painted?

A. All towers shall be cleaned or repainted as often as necessary to maintain good visibility.

Q. 4.146. Is it necessary to have available, replacements lamps for the station's antenna tower lights?

A. A sufficient supply of spare lamps shall be maintained for immediate replacement purposes at all times.

Q. 4.147. Generally speaking, how soon after a defect in the antenna-tower lights is noted, should the defect be corrected?

A. Replacing or repairing of lights, automatic indicators or automatic alarm systems shall be accomplished as soon as practicable.

Q. 4.148. What action should be taken if the tower lights at a station malfunction and cannot be immediately repaired.

A. The licensee shall report immediately by telephone or telegraph to the nearest Airways Communication Station or office of the FAA any observed or otherwise-known failure of a tower light not corrected within thirty minutes.

FCC-TYPE SAMPLE TEST FOR ELEMENT IV

IV-1. Figure IV-1 shows a series a-c circuit in which 10 amperes is flowing. Find the applied voltage, E_T. (Q. 4.06)

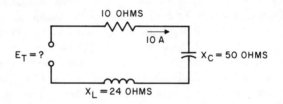

An a-c series circuit, consisting of a resistance, a capacitance, and an inductance.

    (a) 27.85 volts.
    (b) 278.5 volts.
    (c) 139 volts.
    (d) 2785 volts.
    (e) 2.785 volts.

IV-2. The 1000 ohm cathode resistor of a vacuum-tube amplifier is bypassed with a capacitor. It is desired to operate the amplifier at a minimum frequency of 100 cycles. The required size of the capacitor is: (Q. 4.04)
    (a) 15.92 μF.
    (b) 1.592 μF.
    (c) 0.032 μF.
    (d) 8.0 μF.
    (e) 25.0 μF.

IV-3. If a transmitter is licensed to operate at 1020 kilocycles, its 7th harmonic is: (Q. 4.02)
  (a) 7140 mc.
  (b) 7140 kc.
  (c) 2040 mc.
  (d) 2040 kc.
  (e) None of the above.

IV-4. Sawtooth waves are employed in the operation of an oscilloscope because: (Q. 4.07)
  (a) Of their high repetition rate.
  (b) They can reproduce Lissajous figures.
  (c) They represent all harmonic frequencies.
  (d) They make possible a linear reproduction of a waveform.
  (e) They provide the vertical deflection for the scope.

IV-5. Resistance noise in electrical conductors is caused by: (Q. 4.08)
  (a) Low temperatures.
  (b) Low resistances.
  (c) Random molecular motion.
  (d) Random temperature changes.
  (e) Excessive mechanical flexing.

IV-6. A certain triode amplifier has a plate resistance of 25,000 ohms, an amplification factor of 20 and a plate load resistance of 50,000 ohms. The gain of this amplifier is: (Q. 4.09)
  (a) 133
  (b) 100
  (c) 50
  (d) 13.3
  (e) 133.3

IV-7. A standard broadcast station is licensed to operate at 910 kilocycles. What are the maximum and minimum frequencies at which it is permitted to operate? (Q. 4.13)
  (a) 910,020 and 909,980 cycles.
  (b) 910,200 and 909,800 cycles.
  (c) 910,002 and 909,800 cycles
  (d) 912,000 and 909,800 cycles.
  (e) None of the above.

IV-8. The normal audio frequency band is considered to be: (Q. 4.15)
  (a) 10 to 10,000 cycles.
  (b) 300 to 3000 cycles.
  (c) 30 to 30,000 cycles.
  (d) 50 to 5000 cycles.
  (e) 20 to 20,000 cycles.

IV-9.   If the phasing of two or more microphones is not correct, the results may be: (Q. 4.18)

(a) Reduced frequency response.

(b) Reduced output and distortion.

(c) Excessive high-frequency response.

(d) A stereophonic effect.

(e) Non-directional pickup.

IV-10.   The standard reference for volume units is: (Q. 4.20)

(a) 0 V. U. = 1 milliwatt in 5000 ohms.

(b) 0 V. U. = 10 milliwatts in 600 ohms.

(c) 0 V. U. = 1 milliwatt in 500 ohms.

(d) 0 V. U. = .0775 volts in 500 ohms.

(e) 0 V. U. = 1 milliwatt in 600 ohms.

IV-11.   A pre-amplifier in a broadcast station is used to: (Q. 4.24)

(a) Provide pre-emphasis.

(b) Improve the signal-to-noise ratio of the mixer.

(c) Provide de-emphasis just prior to the mixer.

(d) Increase the overall percentage of modulation.

(e) Prevent overmodulation by automatic control.

IV-12.   An amplifier has a gain without feedback of 50 and a feedback of 10%. The gain with feedback is: (Q. 4.25)

(a) 8.33

(b) 0.833

(c) 45

(d) 5.0

(e) 37.5

IV-13.   An important loss of high frequencies in tape recordings may be caused by: (Q. 4.31)

(a) No gap between the tape and the tape head.

(b) Tape head gap being exactly perpendicular to the tape.

(c) An air gap between the tape and the tape head.

(d) Direct contact between the tape and the tape head.

(e) A lack of magnetic oxide on the tape head.

IV-14.   An STL system is: (Q. 4.34)

(a) An aircraft-to-ground communications system.

(b) A ship-to-shore radio communications system.

(c) A satellite-to-land radio communications system.

(d) A studio-to-transmitter link, radio communications system.

(e) An SHF radio, two-way communications system.

IV-15.   In a "proof-of-performance" test for an AM Broadcast Station, a required test is to measure: (Q. 4.35)

(a) The deviation ratio.

(b) The modulation index.

(c) The percent carrier shift.

(d) The audio frequency amplitude.

  (e) The amplitude of parasitic oscillations.

IV-16. If equalization of an incoming telephone line to a broadcast studio is required, the line equalizer equipment is generally placed: (Q. 4.36)

  (a) At the telephone company station.

  (b) Where the line connects to the studio-input equipment.

  (c) After the studio mixer panel.

  (d) At the sending end of the line.

  (e) About 50% down the total length of the line.

IV-17. Limiting amplifiers in broadcast stations are used to: (Q. 4.37)

  (a) Smooth out all amplitude variations.

  (b) Prevent overmodulation of the transmitter.

  (c) Maintain the modulation at a constant percentage at all times.

  (d) Limit the high frequency response to 15,000 cycles.

  (e) Limit any possible excessive amplitudes of low frequencies between 30 and 500 cycles.

IV-18. A resonant quartz crystal (ordinary) in its holder forms a tuned circuit with a Q in the order of: (Q. 4.42)

  (a) 250

  (b) 10

  (c) 100

  (d) 10,000,000

  (e) 20,000

IV-19. In a mercury-thermometer type crystal heater, the mercury column serves to: (Q. 4.44)

  (a) Control the grid circuit of a vacuum tube.

  (b) Directly switch current on and off to a heater.

  (c) Indicate the temperature of the crystal operation on a calibrated scale.

  (d) Warn the operator of possible overheating conditions.

  (e) Provide the actual heat for the crystal.

IV-20. A class B linear R-F amplifier is preferred over a class A type because: (Q. 4.45)

  (a) It operates at the extended cut-off point.

  (b) It has an efficiency in the order of 10%.

  (c) It has an efficiency in the order of 35%.

  (d) It requires more power input for a given power output.

  (e) It cancels all odd harmonics.

IV-21. A significant advantage of using grid-leak bias in a class C R-F power amplifier is that: (Q. 4.46)

  (a) It protects the tube in the event that the input signal is lost.

  (b) It permits a lower amplitude of driving signal to be used.

  (c) It increases the average plate current.

  (d) The output power remains relatively constant with changes of input signal.

(e) The input signal amplitude is regulated.

IV-22. An amplitude-modulated transmitter has a carrier output power of 50 kw and is modulated 50%. The amount of power in the sidebands is: (Q. 4.48)

(a) 6.25 kw.

(b) 6.25 watts.

(c) 31.25 kw.

(d) 62.5 watts.

(e) 0.6.25 watts.

IV-23. "Carrier shift" occurs when: (Q. 4.49)

(a) The carrier frequency changes upward.

(b) The carrier frequency changes downward.

(c) The positive and negative modulation peaks become equal.

(d) The positive and negative modulation peaks are unsymmetrical.

(e) The carrier is frequency modulated.

IV-24. The operating power of a broadcast station is calculated with the direct method by: (Q. 4.50)

(a) The product of the antenna current squared, and the effective antenna resistance.

(b) The product of the plate volts, the plate current, and the plate efficiency of the final amplifier.

(c) The product of the final amplifier plate current squared and the effective antenna resistance.

(d) The use of a VSWR meter.

(e) The product of the total input current squared and the highest power supply voltage.

IV-25. Recycling relays are normally tripped when: (Q. 4.53)

(a) A continuous overload exists.

(b) A temporary or transient overload exists.

(c) Insufficient current is drawn, which is less than the relay rating.

(d) Battery charging current is excessive.

(e) The highest B+ power supply voltage is too low.

IV-26. In transmitters, bleeder resistors are used primarily to: (Q. 4.51)

(a) Ensure excellent power supply regulation.

(b) Discharge filter capacitors when the transmitter is shut down.

(c) Bleed off a portion of the power-supply ripple.

(d) Provide negative feedback in the modulator.

(e) Provide bias for the modulator, final amplifier.

IV-27. In an AM transmitter, the R-F amplifier plate-circuit ammeters: (Q. 4.54)

(a) Are used to calculate the output R-F power.

(b) Are used to indicate correct plate-circuit tuning, by tuning for a dip in the reading.

(c) Are used to indicate correct plate-circuit tuning, by tuning for a maximum reading.

(d) Are used to detect parasitic oscillations.

(e) Are used only during neutralization.

IV-28.   A "T" network used with a broadcast station antenna system: (Q. 4.56)

(a) Is used basically to prevent harmonic radiation.

(b) Is used to adjust the directional pattern.

(c) Is used in measuring the antenna current.

(d) Is used to match the impedance of the transmission line to the antenna.

(e) Is used for lightning suppression.

IV-29.   The field intensity of a 10 kw transmitter measured two miles from the transmitter is 500 μV/meter. At a distance of eight miles from the transmitter, the field intensity is: (Q. 3.203)

(a) 62.5 μV.

(b) 125 μV.

(c) 12.5 μV.

(d) 6.25 μV.

(e) 1.25 μV.

IV-30.   Figure IV-30 is a representation of a cathode-ray oscilloscope display of amplitude modulation. The approximate percentage of modulation shown is: (Q. 4.58)

Trapezoidal pattern of modulation.

(a) 25%.

(b) 10%.

(c) 50%.

(d) 75%.

(e) 100%.

IV-31.   A reactance tube functions by virtue of the fact that the tube is made: (Q. 4.60)

(a) To operate at saturation plate current.

(b) To operate at cut-off bias.

(c) To operate as a pure resistance.

(d) To function as an inductive or capacitive reactance.

(e) To function as a varactor.

IV-32.   In frequency modulation, the instantaneous: (Q. 4.61)
   (a) Carrier phase follows the amplitude of the modulation.
   (b) Carrier frequency follows the amplitude of the modulation.
   (c) Carrier amplitude follows the phase of the modulation.
   (d) Modulation amplitude determines the output power.
   (e) Modulation frequency determines the deviation.

IV-33.   In an FM receiver, de-emphasis: (Q. 4.63)
   (a) Is a method of FM demodulation.
   (b) Is used for FM demodulation.
   (c) Is necessary to demodulate single-sideband transmission.
   (d) Is a method of demodulating narrow-band FM.
   (e) Occurs immediately following the FM detector.

IV-34.   A transmitter with an output power of 10 kW feeds an antenna with a power gain of 11.6 db via a transmission line having a power loss of 1.6 db. The effective radiated power (ERP) is: (Q. 4.64)
   (a) 100 kW.
   (b) 1000 kW.
   (c) 10 kW.
   (d) 32.2 kW.
   (e) None of the above.

IV-35.   The directional antenna pattern of an AM station may change if: (Q. 4.68)
   (a) The transmitter power is increased.
   (b) The transmitter power is reduced.
   (c) A slight change in transmitter frequency occurs.
   (d) The phase of currents fed to individual elements is changed.
   (e) The transmission-line loss increases.

IV-36.   In the Image-Orthicon camera tube, the function of the multiplier section is to: (Q. 4.71)
   (a) Improve the signal-to-noise ratio of the output signal.
   (b) Improve the gamma of the camera tube.
   (c) Increase the definition of the camera tube.
   (d) Discharge the thin-glass target in the image section.
   (e) Improve the focus of the scanning beam.

IV-37.   In a television field, there are 262.5 scanning lines. Of these, the number of lines which actually produce picture information is: (Q. 4.73)
   (a) 181.25
   (b) 242.5
   (c) 200.0
   (d) 262.5
   (e) 142.5

IV-38.   In a television transmission, the function of the equalizing pulses is to: (Q. 4.74)
   (a) Equalize the time of each field.

   (b) Equalize the time of each frame.

   (c) Ensure correct interlacing of odd and even fields.

   (d) Prevent vertical roll of the picture.

   (e) Equalize the centering of the picture.

IV-39.   In a TV color transmission, the frequency of the color sub-carrier is: (Q. 4.76)

   (a) 4 mc.

   (b) 3.58 mc.

   (c) 1.25 mc.

   (d) 4.5 mc.

   (e) 5.45 mc.

IV-40.   In TV transmission systems, a reflectometer is used to: (Q. 4.77)

   (a) Produce a controlled standing-wave ratio.

   (b) Eliminate standing waves on the transmission line.

   (c) Measure the transmission line, standing-wave ratio.

   (d) Reflect the incident waves on the transmission line.

   (e) Absorb the reflected waves on the transmission line.

IV-41.   In a TV transmission system, the function of a diplexer is to: (Q. 4.80)

   (a) Modulate the picture transmitter.

   (b) Modulate the sound transmitter.

   (c) Mix the color subcarrier with the picture carrier.

   (d) Mix the picture and sound transmitter outputs and feed them to a single antenna.

   (e) Mix the monochrome and color transmitter outputs and feed them to a single antenna.

IV-42.   The average value of a sine wave is related to its peak value by the figure: (Q. 4.83)

   (a) 0.636

   (b) 1.414

   (c) 0.9

   (d) 0.707

   (e) 1.636

IV-43.   The conventional type of a-c voltmeter or ammeter is calibrated to read the: (Q. 4.83)

   (a) Peak value.

   (b) RMS value.

   (c) Average value.

   (d) Peak-to-peak value.

   (e) Actual value.

IV-44.   Refer to the schematic diagram of a class C amplifier shown in Fig. 4.85(a). In the absence of an R-F input signal the R-F amplifier's: (Q. 4.85)

   (a) Grid current will be maximum.

(b) Plate current will be minimum.

(c) Cathode bias will be maximum.

(d) Plate current will be maximum.

(e) Grid bias will be maximum.

IV-45. Most television video transmitters use grid modulation because: (Q. 4.86)

(a) Of the high values of load impedance required.

(b) Of the wide bandwidth required.

(c) Plate modulation will be too distorted.

(d) The video carrier is frequency modulated.

(e) It requires greater driving power.

IV-46. In the block diagram of a monochrome TV transmitter shown in Fig. 4.89(d), the purpose of the sync stretcher is to: (Q. 4.89)

(a) Increase the width of the sync pulses.

(b) Decrease the frequency of the sync pulses.

(c) Control the amplitude of the sync pulses.

(d) Stretch (or decrease) the time of the vertical retrace interval.

(e) None of the above.

IV-47. In a standard AM broadcast station employing X- or Y-cut crystals, the maximum permissible temperature variation is: (Q. 4.93)

(a) Plus or minus 0.1 degree C.

(b) Plus or minus 1.0 degree C.

(c) Plus or minus 0.5 degree C.

(d) Plus or minus 0.05 degree C.

(e) Plus or minus 0.15 degree C.

IV-48. The allowable frequency tolerance at FM broadcast stations is: (Q. 4.114)

(a) Plus or minus 20 cycles.

(b) Plus or minus 200 cycles.

(c) Plus or minus 0.05 percent.

(d) Plus or minus 2000 cycles.

(e) Plus or minus 0.01 percent.

IV-49. In the system of television, vestigial sideband transmission: (Q. 4.123)

(a) Both sidebands are reduced in amplitude.

(b) Only one of the sidebands is reduced in amplitude.

(c) The frequency bandwidth of one sideband is reduced.

(d) The frequency bandwidth of both sidebands is reduced.

(e) The carrier is suppressed and only one sideband is transmitted.

IV-50. An Intercity Relay station normally transmits: (Q. 4.135)

(a) Aural programs between broadcast stations.

(b) Video programs between broadcast stations.

(c) Emergency broadcasts only.

(d) Telephone messages between cities.

(e) Only programs handled by satellites.

ELEMENT VIII

SHIP RADAR TECHNIQUES

Question 8.01. What are the FCC license requirements for the operator who is responsible for the installation, servicing, and maintenance of ship radar equipment? (R & R 83.155)

Answer. Such an operator must have a first or second-class radiotelephone or radiotelegraph license plus a ship radar endorsement (Element 8).

Discussion. Replacements of fuses and receiving-type tubes may be made by unlicensed persons.

Q. 8.02. Who may operate radar equipment in the Ship Service? (R & R 83.155)

A. The Master, or any person designated by the Master may operate a ship radar station during the course of normal rendition of service.

D. Only properly licensed personnel may supervise or be responsible for the performance of any adjustments or tests during or coincident with the installation, servicing, or maintenance of ship radar equipment while it is radiating energy.

Q. 8.03. Under what conditions may a person who does not hold a radio operator license operate a radar station in the Ship Service? (R & R 83.155)

A. The following conditions apply:

1. The radar equipment shall employ as its frequency-determining element a nontunable, pulse-type magnetron.

2. The radar equipment shall be capable of being operated during the course of normal rendition of service in accordance with the radio law and the rules and regulations of the Commission by means of exclusively external controls. See also preceding question.

Q. 8.04. Who may make entries in the installation and maintenance record of a ship radar station? (R & R 83.405)

A. Entries shall be made by or under the personal supervision of the responsible installation, service, or maintenance operator concerned in each case. The station licensee is also jointly responsible for the faithful and accurate making of such entries.

Q. 8.05. What entries are required in the installation and maintenance record of a ship radar station? (R & R 83.405)

A. The following entries are required:
1. The date and place of initial installation.
2. Any necessary steps taken to remedy any interference found to exist at the time of such installation.
3. The nature of any complaint (including interference to radio communication) arising subsequent to initial installation and the date thereof.
4. The reason for the trouble leading to the complaint, including the name of any component or component part which failed or was misadjusted.
5. Remedial measures taken, and the date thereof.
6. The name, license number, and date of the ship radar operator endorsement on the first- or second-class radio operator license of the responsible operator performing or immediately supervising the installation, servicing, or maintenance.

Q. 8.06. Who has the responsibility for making entries in the installation and maintenance record of a ship radar station? (R & R 83.405)

A. See Question 8.04.

Q. 8.07. Within what frequency bands do ship radar transmitters operate? (R & R 83.404)

A. The following frequency bands are authorized: 2900 to 3100 mc; 5460 to 5650 mc; 9300 to 9500 mc.

Q. 8.08. May fuses and receiving type tubes be replaced in ship radar equipment by a person whose operator license does not contain a ship radar endorsement? (R & R 83.155)

A. Yes. No license is required for such replacement.

D. See Q. 8.01.

Q. 8.09. Explain briefly why radar interference to a radiotelephone receiver is frequently characterized by a steady tone in the radio loud-speaker.

A. A steady tone is often heard. This is the pulse repetition rate of keying the radar transmitter (or a harmonic) which is detected in the receiver and heard as an audio tone.

D. Radar transmitters are *pulse* modulated; that is, the carrier is turned on and off (or pulsed) at regular intervals. The pulse repetition rate is determined by the timing unit and is usually within audio range. It is possible for the timing signal to reach receivers directly through power lines, etc., or by being radiated and then detected in the receiver, where it is heard as a steady tone signal. This interference cannot generally be "tuned out" of the receiver because of the harmonics present in each pulse which cause many heterodyning frequencies to be generated. Also, some of the interference is due to detection of the radar carrier signal by the communications receiver and it is not possible to tune out such interference.

Q. 8.10 Describe how various types of interference from a radar installation may be apparent to a person when listening to a communications receiver.

A. Radar interference in a communications receiver will generally take either or both of the two following forms:
1. A steady tone due to the pulsed rate. This will have a musical sound.
2. Noise or "hash." This is usually caused by such items as:
(a) Radar motor generator, or
(b) Improper grounding, bonding, and shielding.

D. See Q. 8.09, Q. 3.240 and also Q. 3.181.

Q. 8.11. How are the various types of radar interference recognized in (a) auto-alarm equipment, (b) direction-finding equipment?

A. (a) Radar interference in auto-alarm equipment may be detected by plugging the earphones into the jack provided on the auto alarm for listening purposes and listening for hash or a steady tone. The radar may be shut down temporarily to determine if it is causing the interference detected.
(b) The same procedure as in (a) above may be used to detect radar interference in direction-finding equipment. It may also be advantageous to rotate the D/F loop in trying to find the source of in-

terference, although radar interference from the same ship the D/F is on, may not have directional properties.

D. See Questions 8.09, 8.10, and 8.13.

Q. 8.12. On what frequencies should the radar serviceman look for radar interference to communication receivers on ships equipped with radar?

A. It is possible to find radar interference on practically any communication frequency because of the many harmonics produced by pulsing.

D. See Question 8.09.

Q. 8.13. In checking a direction finder for interference caused by radar equipment, would it be a good policy to check for interference while the D/F loop is being rotated?

A. It would be a good policy, although not necessarily effective as the interference may not show directional properties especially if it is coming from the power line or timer.

D. See Questions 8.11 (b) and 8.15.

Q. 8.14. List at least two types of indications on a loran scope that signifies that a radar installation is causing interference to the loran.

A. Two types of indications on a loran scope signifying radar interference are:
1. Narrow vertical pulses or "spikes" moving across the scope screen.
2. Hash or "grass" in the vicinity of the scanning lines.

D. The "spikes" on a loran scope are caused by the radar *pulse*s originating in the timing unit. Since there is no synchronization between the loran sweep and the radar pulsing, the spikes cannot remain stationary but will move across the screen. "Grass" interference would correspond to hash or noise if heard on a headset. It may originate in the motor generator set or be caused by poor grounding and bonding.

Q. 8.15. Is there any likelihood of a radar installation causing interference to radio receivers if long connecting lines are used between the radar transmitter and the radar modulator?

A. There is, if such lines are not shielded and terminated properly.

D. The pulses produced by the timing unit to trigger the radar transmitter (magnetron) are of extremely short duration and so contain many harmonic frequencies. Thus a pulse with a *repetition* rate of 1,000 cps and a pulse width of 1 microsecond could easily contain harmonic frequencies of appreciable amplitude up to and beyond 30 mc. If long connecting lines which are shielded improperly are used, the radiation of these harmonic frequencies may cause interference in any and all communications and other receivers which may tune to such harmonics.

Q. 8.16. What steps might be taken by a radar serviceman to eliminate a steady-tone of interference to radio communication receivers, or interference to loran receivers evidenced by "spikes?"

A. First check the grounding, bonding, and shielding of all units. If there are built-in filters in the radar set, check these. If not present, such filters may have to be installed.

D. The surest way to eliminate this type of interference is to prevent its *radiation*. Low-pass filters should be installed in all power lines to prevent interference from spreading through this path to other equipment. All grounding, bonding, and shielding should be thorough and well done.

It would be extremely difficult to try and filter out the radar pulses from receiving equipment. The reason for this is that the pulses are very steep and of short duration (1 microsecond or less). This means that such pulses contain *many* harmonics of the fundamental repetition rate. A radar with a pulse repetition rate of say 1,000 cps, could have harmonics of this rate, every 1,000 cps up to many megacycles. Thus, effective filtering is extremely difficult for either the radar transmitter or outside receiving equipment.

If, in this case, you tried to filter out (at the radar) all modulation frequencies above 1,000 cps, you would completely destroy the shape of the radar pulse by removing its harmonics. Under this condition, the radar could not function usefully.

Q. 8.17. What steps might be taken by a radar serviceman to reduce "grass" on a loran scope or motor-generator noise in communication receivers?

A. Make sure that the commutators, slip rings, and brushes are all in good condition. If filters are present at the motor-generator set, check these and also bonding and grounding as well as power connections for tightness and good contact. See also Questions 8.10 and 8.14.

D. See Q. 3.240 and also Q. 3.181.

Q. 8.18. Name at least four pieces of radio or electronic equipment aboard ship that might suffer interference from the radar installation.

A. Some pieces of equipment which may suffer from radar interference are:
1. Communications receivers
2. Loran
3. Auto-alarm
4. Direction finder
5. Public-address system.

D. See Questions 8.09 through 8.17 and 8.19.

Q. 8.19. Why is it important that all units of a radar installation be thoroughly bonded to the ship's electrical ground?

A. There are two important reasons for this.
1. To place all external metal components at ship's ground and thus prevent the possibility of shock to operators and others.
2. To reduce interference caused by the radar to other pieces of electronic equipment on shipboard.

D. See Questions 8.14 and 8.17.

Q. 8.20. What may cause bright flashing pie sections to appear on a radar PPI scope?

A. This may be caused by a defective crystal in the afc section of the radar receiver.

D. Any other defect in an afc system which would cause "unlocking" and "sweeping" of the afc could also cause bright flashing to appear. A somewhat similar-appearing defect may be caused by "spoking." Generally, this refers to an irregular rotation of the deflection coil about the neck of the PPI tube. Such irregular rotation may result from a defective servo amplifier, or from mechanical binding of the deflection-coil assembly. It may also result from poor synchro slip-ring contacts or a defective deflection-coil drive motor.

Q. 8.21. What symptoms on a radar scope would indicate that the radar receiver mixer crystal is defective?

A. Any or all of the following symptoms may be present:
1. "Targets" (or echoes) will be unusually weak or will not be seen at all.

2. An excessive noise level ("grass") may be present on the scope.

3. The crystal current meter on the radar receiver will read abnormally low, or zero.

D. Great care should be taken in testing or replacing crystals as static charges may ruin them (see Question 8.49). The front-to-back resistance ratio is a measure of the condition of the crystal and may be checked as indicated in Question 8.22.

Q. 8.22 What tests may a radar serviceman make to determine whether or not the radar receiver mixer crystal is defective?

A. The serviceman may make a quick check by observing the reading on the crystal current meter of the radar receiver. Also, the front-to-back ratio of the crystal may be checked roughly by reading the forward and backward resistance on an ohmmeter.

D. One method of determining the condition of a crystal is to determine its front-to-back resistance ratio. This should be done with a high-impedance or electronic-type voltmeter. First measure the resistance across the crystal with the meter leads in either position. Then reverse the meter leads and measure it again. The larger reading, divided by the smaller reading, gives you the front-to-back ratio. In a normal crystal, this should be in the order of 20 to 1 or so. This may vary with different types, and you should find out the normal front-to-back ratios for the particular crystals in your radar. As a guide in measuring, the 1N23E crystals should read about 250 to 500 ohms for one polarity and about 10,000 ohms for the reverse polarity.

Q. 8.23. In a radar set, what are indications of (a) a defective magnetron, (b) a weak magnet in the magnetron, (c) defective crystal in the receiver converter stage?

A. (a) Defective Magnetron:
1. Sweep, noise, and range marks appear, but no targets.
2. Arcing in modulator tube.
3. Low magnetron current indication.
4. Arcing in magnetron.
5. Weak signals on PPI.
6. Targets appear "fuzzy" with "spokes" present.
7. Magnetron undercurrent relay drops out.
8. Poor afc action.
(b) Weak Magnet of Magnetron:
1. Magnetron current meter will show an increase.
2. Oscillation may stop under extreme cases of weakening.

3. Oscillation frequency will probably change.

4. Afc action may be poor.

(c) Defective Crystal: See Question 8.21.

D. The magnetron should never be operated without the magnet in position. To do so, may destroy the tube in a short time. To prevent this from happening, an overload relay is generally provided to protect the magnetron from damage. These relays are normally an integral part of a modulator. For example, one overload relay may appear in the modulator high-voltage d-c supply to protect the supply against defects in the modulator and in the pulse-forming network. Another may be in series with the inverse-protective diode. This relay protects the modulator against defects in the magnetron or magnetron-pulse transformer, which may cause a mismatch between the pulse-forming network and the magnetron. A mismatch tends to cause reflections in the pulse-forming network. Each reflection doubles the voltage on the network and may, if unprotected by the inverse diode and its overload relay, cause a breakdown of the network or its associated components.

The inverse-diode circuit is connected to the input of the pulse-forming network in such a way as to discharge to ground any undesired reflections on the network.

Q. 8.24. What precautions should a radar serviceman take when working with or handling a magnetron to prevent weakening or damage to the magnetron?

A. The following precautions should be taken to protect the *magnet* unit of the magnetron.

1. Do not subject the magnet to extreme heat.

2. Do not subject the magnet to shocks or blows.

3. Keep all magnetic materials, such as tools, away from the immediate vicinity of the magnet.

The magnetron tube proper should be treated as any other delicate electron tube.

Q. 8.25. What precaution should a radar serviceman observe when making repairs or adjustments to a radar set to prevent personal injury to himself or other persons?

A. First shut off all power. Then be sure to *discharge* all high-voltage capacitors *fully* by means of a suitable grounding stick or cable. Always handle cathode-ray tubes with great care. (If possible, wear **gloves and goggles.**)

D.   If adjustments or repairs must be made with power on, always have a second person at the site who can shut off the power and render immediate assistance, if required.

Q. 8.26.   Is there any danger in testing or operating radar equipment aboard ship when explosive or inflammable cargo is being handled?

A.   There would be some danger due to the possibility of arcing occurring in various parts of the radar equipment. It would be best to take no chances and shut off the radar when inflammable or explosive cargo is being handled.

D.   In addition to the danger caused by arcing, a further possible source of ignition is the radar beam itself. This is especially true of a high-power focused beam. The energy in such a beam may be sufficient to ignite certain highly flammable material, or it may cause r-f arcing between metallic surfaces, thereby creating a hazard. If any danger of flame or explosion exists, do not operate the radar set (or any other radio transmitter).

Q. 8.27.   What considerations should be taken into account when selecting the location of the radar antenna assembly aboard ship?

A.   There are two prime considerations:
1.   The antenna proper should be located so that it will encounter a minimum number of obstructions while scanning the area around the ship. This is particularly important in the directions forward and off the bows.
2.   The length of waveguide run from the antenna to the radar transmitter should be kept to the minimum practical run.

D.   1.   Because of the very high frequencies and the parabolic reflector used in radar transmission, the beam is concentrated into very narrow angles. Thus, any obstruction which is in the path of the beam blocks it almost as effectively as if it were a searchlight beam. This may produce areas in which no target pickup is possible and make the radar "blind" in certain directions. This is particularly undesirable in areas directly ahead or behind the ship because of possible collision conditions.
2.   The waveguide from the antenna to the radar transmitter is a form of transmission line. There are some rather difficult mechanical considerations to be met in installing waveguides and these, in general, increase as the length of run becomes greater. In addition to the installation problem, the losses of the waveguide increase with greater lengths and there is also a greater possible accumulation of moisture due to condensation, in longer lengths of waveguide.

Q. 8.28. Describe briefly the construction of a waveguide. Why should the interior of the waveguide be clean, smooth, and dry?

A.   A waveguide is a form of transmission line and consists of a hollow rectangular or circular pipe. The waves are carried *inside* of the pipe. Waveguides are frequently made of copper or brass and are often plated on the interior with silver to assure a smooth and highly conducting interior surface. The interior should be kept clean, smooth, and dry in order to assure minimum losses and prevent interior arcing.

D.   See Q. 3.249, Q. 3.250, Q. 8.30, Q. 8.31, and Q. 8.33 through Q. 8.35.

Q. 8.29. When installing waveguides, why should long, perfectly level sections of waveguides be avoided? Why is a small hole about ⅛ inch in diameter sometimes drilled on the underside of an elbow in a waveguide near the point where it enters the radar transmitter?

A.   Long, level runs are undesirable because of the possibility of accumulating condensed moisture inside of the waveguide. A small hole at the lowest point of the waveguide may be drilled to drain out condensed moisture in the waveguide.

D.   See Q. 3.250 and Q. 8.28.

Q. 8.30. Why are waveguides used in preference to coaxial lines for the transmission of microwave energy in most shipboard radar installations?

A.   Waveguides are preferred over coaxial lines for transmitting microwave energy because their losses are considerably less and also because for a given size they can transmit more power than a coaxial line.

D.   A simple comparison between a circular waveguide and a coaxial line of similar dimensions is made here to illustrate the two advantages mentioned above. Refer to Fig. 8.30. A coaxial line has an inner conductor which must be insulated from the outer conductor. Frequently, this is done by means of insulating beads. At microwave frequencies, the dielectric loss in the beads is considerable. A waveguide, as generally used, has only air as a dielectric. However, air has a negligible dielectric loss at practically any frequency which makes the dielectric losses in a hollow waveguide less than that of a coaxial line. The high-frequency current losses in a waveguide are also less than for

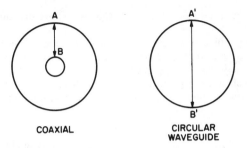

A
B

COAXIAL

A'
B'

CIRCULAR
WAVEGUIDE

Fig. 8.30. Comparison between coaxial line and circular waveguide.

a coaxial line. This is due to the elimination of the thin inner conductor in which most of the "copper losses" occur.

A waveguide can carry more power than a coaxial line of the same diameter. Referring again to the figure, we can see that the distance *A'-B'* is greater than *A-B* in the coaxial line. Since the maximum voltage appears between points *A'-B'* in a round waveguide, it is evident that a greater air space appears in the waveguide than in the coaxial line between maximum voltage points. This means a greater breakdown voltage rating for the waveguide, which, in turn, indicates a greater power handling capacity for a given outside diameter of line.

Q. 8.31. Why are rectangular cross-sectional waveguides generally used in preference to circular cross-sectional waveguides?

A. Circular waveguides are generally not used in radar because their electric field has a tendency to change direction at bends and thus change the polarization of the wave. Rectangular waveguides, on the other hand, can be made to maintain the desired polarization.

D. An exception to the above is to be found in a *rotating* joint which permits the antenna to move with respect to the fixed waveguide. This rotating joint must be circular for mechanical reasons, while the waveguide leading up to the rotating joint is usually rectangular. By means of special devices, the desired polarization is passed on to the antenna regardless of the rotation of the circular joint.

Q. 8.32. Describe how waveguides are terminated at the radar antenna reflectors.

A. There are a number of ways in which a waveguide may be terminated at the radar antenna reflector. Two methods are shown in Fig. 8.32. In part (a) are shown three variations of "horn" radiators. These horns point into the parabolic reflector, which forms the energy into a narrow beam. In part (b) of the figure, the wavelength is terminated in a polystyrene window placed at the focal point of the parabolic reflector.

D. A brief discussion of each of the two above-mentioned systems follows:

(a) Horn radiators are frequently used to obtain directive radiation in the microwave region. Their physical dimensions must be large when compared with the operating wavelength, but this becomes entirely practical at microwave frequencies. The operation of an electromagnetic horn radiator is similar to that of acoustic horns used with

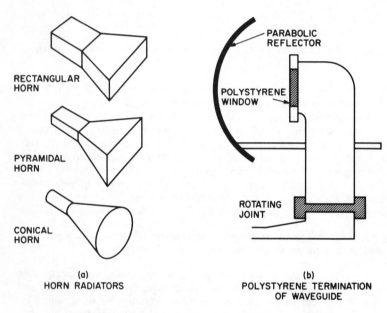

| (a) | (b) |
| HORN RADIATORS | POLYSTYRENE TERMINATION OF WAVEGUIDE |

Fig. 8.32. Two methods of terminating waveguides.

certain loudspeaker systems, that is, the horn serves to match the impedance of the waveguide to the impedance of external space. Horns are frequently directed toward a parabolic reflector, which then serves to concentrate the energy into a narrow beam suitable for accurate tracking purposes.

(b) Another method of terminating a waveguide at the antenna reflector is by means of a polystyrene window, as shown in part (b) of the figure. The polystyrene window is placed at the focal point of the parabolic reflector. The "window" acts as an impedance-matching device between the waveguide and the parabolic reflector, and free space. The correct impedance match is obtained by selecting the correct physical dimensions of the window.

Q. 8.33. What precautions should be taken when installing vertical sections of waveguides with choke-coupling flanges to prevent moisture from entering the waveguide?

A. Moisture may be prevented from entering by inserting a suitable gasket at each choke-coupling flange and making certain that the flanges are joined tightly.

D. See Q. 3.250, Q. 3.252, and Q. 8.29.

Q. 8.34. Why are choke joints often used in preference to flange joints to join sections of waveguides together?

A. Choke joints are often used in preference to simple flange joints because they prevent loss of energy when used as expansion or rotating joints and also because they will tolerate a moderate degree of misalignment of the waveguide sections without excessive losses.

D. See next question for sketches and discussion of choke joints.

Q. 8.35. Draw a longitudinal section of a waveguide choke joint and explain briefly its principle of operation.

A. See Fig. 8.35. The choke joint includes a circular groove (or "slot") which has a depth of one-quarter wavelength. This means that the input impedance of the slot (across *A-B*) will be infinite. The

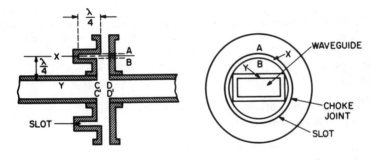

Fig. 8.35. Cross section of choke joint.

distance from the center of the slot to the waveguide (*X-Y*) is also a quarter wave. The infinite impedance of *A-B* is effectively transformed through the quarter-wave section *X-Y*, into a short circuit across *C-D*. Thus, *C* and *D* are effectively connected *electrically* even though they may not be mechanically.

D. Choke joints are commonly used to connect portions of a waveguide together. Such joints are used to fulfill one or more of these functions:

(a) To provide low-loss electrical connection between two parts of the system, such as the waveguide and the magnetron itself.

(b) To provide mechanical isolation between two parts of the system so that vibration from one part will not damage another, for example, the antenna vibrations should not be transmitted to the magnetron.

(c) To permit the removal of certain sections of the waveguides to facilitate repairs and replacements.

The choke joint usually consists of two flanges. These are fixed to the waveguide at their center and face each other. The right-hand flange (in the figure) is machined flat while the left-hand flange contains the slot (described above).

In practice, the two flanges may be separated mechanically by as much as several millimeters. (One millimeter equals about 1/25 of an inch.) The separation must not, in general, exceed this distance to prevent excessive losses and reflections.

Q. 8.36. Describe how a radar beam is formed by a paraboloidal reflector.

A. A narrow beam of r-f energy is formed by a parabolic reflector in a manner which is analogous to the reflection of light from a parabolic *light* reflector as used in a searchlight.

D. The r-f energy is fed into the reflector at its focal point as shown in the figures of Question 8.32. Because of the paraboloidal shape of the reflector, practically all of the r-f energy which reaches the reflector will be effectively focused into a narrow beam and reflected. The parabolic reflector (or "dish") must be large in comparison with the wavelength. In general, the larger the reflector (diameter), the narrower will be the beam.

Q. 8.37. What effect, if any, does the accumulation of soot or dirt on the antenna reflector have on the operation of a ship radar?

A. A thin layer of soot or dirt has little or no effect upon the operation of a ship radar since the microwave energy is apparently able to penetrate a normal accumulation with only small losses.

D. An excessive amount of "crust" on the surface of the reflector may decrease the performance of the set, especially for weak targets and, in such cases, the reflecting surface should be wiped clean. It is more important to keep the plastic window at the end of the waveguide clean. An accumulation of soot or dirt here can introduce considerable loss.

Q. 8.38. What is the purpose of an echo box in a radar system? Explain the principle of operation of the echo box. What indications may be expected on a radar scope when using an echo box and the radar set is operating properly? When the radar set is not operating properly?

A. (a) The purpose of an echo box is to provide an artificial target which may be used to tune the receiver and also give an indication of the over-all radar system performance.

(b) An echo box is a very high Q resonant cavity which is shock-excited by the transmitted pulse. In turn, its oscillations are returned to the receiver and appear as an artificial target on the radar scope.

(c) Ship radars generally use a PPI scope. When the echo box is motor-tuned (see discussion), the indication consists of a series of spokes extending radially outward from the center of the PPI scope as shown in part (a) of Fig. 8.38. The spoke length is maximum

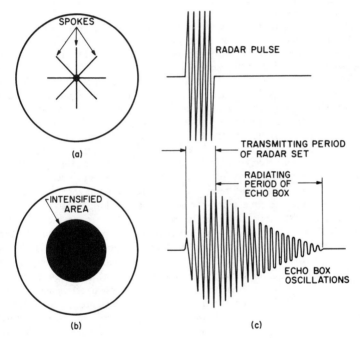

Fig. 8.38. (a) Indication on PPI due to motor-driven echo box, (b) indication on PPI due to echo box set at resonance, (c) relation between transmitted-pulse and echo-box oscillations.

when the radar is operating normally. When the echo box is simply left at resonance, the central portion of the PPI scope will be intensified, as shown in part (b) of the figure.

(d) When the radar is not operating properly, the length of the spokes (or radius of intensified area) will be less than under normal operation.

D. Normal radar target signals do not, in general, furnish a satisfactory means of checking radar system performance. Variations in atmospheric conditions, the difference in the character of various signals, and also the lack of proper reference signals make it difficult for the operator to check the performance of the radar. This is particularly true of a ship radar where the geographical location of the radar may be constantly changing. To overcome these difficulties, a so-called "echo box" has been designed to furnish a standard reference signal so that the operation of the radar can be checked periodically against the reference in any geographical location. This echo box consists of a high Q resonant cavity with means provided for coupling some transmitter energy into and out of the box. In addition, a plunger arrangement is provided to change the length of the cavity and thus vary its resonant frequency. In some cases, this plunger is driven by a motor through a reciprocating device so that the cavity is periodically tuned through resonance for a short period of time. As previously described, this action results in a series of spokes being produced due to the sweep rotation of the PPI scope.

The action of the echo box in providing a reference signal is briefly as follows: During the short transmitting pulse, some of the transmitted energy is fed into the echo box and shock excites it into oscillations which increase in amplitude during the pulse time. This is shown in part (c) of the figure. At the end of the transmitting pulse, the echo box continues to oscillate at a decaying amplitude and reradiates energy back to the radar receiver. A short time after the end of the transmitted pulse, the amplitude of oscillations in the echo box will decrease below the sensitivity level of the receiver. The time from the end of the transmitter pulse to the time when the oscillations no longer produce an indication on the scope through the receiver is known as the "ringing time." This ringing time is a function of the power output of the transmitter and the sensitivity of the receiver and manifests itself on the PPI in the form of spokes or as an intensified area with a certain radius. The length of these spokes (or the radius) is measured when the radar system is known to be operating at good efficiency. Using this as a standard reference, periodic measurements are made with the echo box and any radical decrease in the ringing time means that either the transmitting or receiving components of the radar may be defective and repairs are in order.

Q. 8.39. Draw a block diagram of a radar system, labeling the antenna, duplexer, transmitter, receiver, modulator, timer, and the indicator.

A. See Fig. 8.39.

D. A general discussion of the radar system is presented below for the benefit of students.

Radar (radio direction and ranging) is a specialized application of the principles of radio which makes it possible to detect the presence of near or distant objects regardless of visual or atmospheric conditions; to determine their exact direction and range (distance) and to a limited extent to identify the nature of their character. Basically, a radar set consists of a transmitter and receiver located at the same point, a highly directional antenna system and an indicator (generally a cathode ray tube) to show the presence of reradiated waves and thus of objects. Detection of an object is accomplished by causing a narrow beam of r-f energy to "search" a given area. Whenever the beam strikes a conducting object, it causes waves to be reradiated in many directions from the object. A very small fraction of the original radiated energy is returned to the radar set where it is picked up by the same antenna that focused the original radiation upon the object. A receiver of great sensitivity amplifies the received signal (echo) and applies it to a cathode ray tube to provide a visual indication of the presence of the object. The direction of the object will be the same as the direction of the antenna.

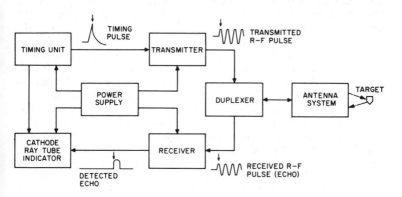

Fig. 8.39. Block diagram of a radar system.

The range can be determined with great accuracy based upon the fact that radio-frequency energy travels at the velocity of light (300,000,000 meters per second, or about 186,000 statute miles per second). Most radar transmitters employ the pulse modulation method. A radio-frequency pulse of short duration (about 1 microsecond on the average) and high peak power is transmitted at regular intervals. Between transmitted pulses, the receiver is permitted to operate and to detect the reradiated waves. The receiver output is connected to the indicator where the difference in time between the transmitted and received waves can be measured and the range determined. As an example, assume that a pulse is transmitted to an object 18.6 miles away. In one microsecond the pulse can travel .186 miles (328 yards). Therefore, it will require 100 microseconds for the pulse to reach the object. When it strikes the object, it is reradiated without loss of time and returns to the radar set in an additional 100 microseconds, or a total elapsed time of 200 microseconds. Note that the wave actually has to travel twice the distance to the object. Because the range thus provided is twice the actual range, an allowance must be made in the indicator to measure only one-half of the elapsed time, or the true range.

The Indicator: (Discussion of the indicator is here restricted to that type directly applicable to marine radar sets.) The indicator must be a device which can accurately measure the elapsed time between transmitted and received pulses and convert it directly into range. It must also be capable of discriminating against objects with different ranges and the same bearing, and between objects with different bearings and the same range. The P.P.I. (plan-position-indicator) cathode-ray tube admirably fulfills all of the above requirements by providing a polar chart of the immediate area surrounding the ship from a minimum range of about 80 yards to approximately 40 miles. The P.P.I. scope provides a continuous plot of both moving and fixed objects. The sweep (time base) starts at the center of the tube at a time which is directly related to the originating time of the transmitting pulse. It travels radially out to the circumference (like the spoke of a wheel). This sweep line is divided into equal distances by means of range markers which provide indications about a half-mile apart on low ranges, thus affording instantaneous visual checks of the range of objects. Objects are indicated (as well as range markers) by a bright spot upon the P.P.I. tube at a distance from the center corresponding to the range of the object. The radial sweep is caused to rotate (as a wheel spoke would rotate) in exact synchronism with the antenna, so that the object indication upon the P.P.I. tube will be of the same bearing as the antenna. The P.P.I. tube has a relatively long persistence screen, so that as the sweep rotates, a continuous picture of the surrounding area appears on the screen.

The Timer: The timer unit (or synchronizer or keyer) is generally the most complicated part of the radar and has a number of important functions to perform. A detailed discussion is beyond the scope of this book, but a general list of its functions is as follows:

1. Determines pulse repetition rate.
2. Determines range markers.
3. Provides range markers.
4. Coordinates all operations in the system.
5. Provides sweep, with blanking and unblanking.
6. Specialized functions such as "heading flash" in marine systems.

The Transmitter: The transmitter usually consists of the following units:

1. A pulse shaping circuit, to determine the length of the transmitted pulse.

2. A modulator, which applies the pulse (about 1 microsecond, 10,000 to 15,000 volts) to the magnetron, and

3. The magnetron, which is the actual r-f oscillator. (There are no r-f amplifiers.)

The antenna system: In order to obtain accurate bearings, it is quite necessary that the radiation pattern of the antenna be extremely narrow. Such a pattern can be most conveniently obtained by the use of a parabolic reflector of suitable dimensions, which at these frequencies is fed by means of waveguide radiators (Q. 8.27 and Q. 8.32). The parabolic reflector focuses the r-f energy into a narrow beam, just as a searchlight reflector provides a narrow light beam from a light source. For the r-f beam to be sufficiently narrow, the dimensions of the parabolic reflector must be in the order of many wavelengths. To accomplish this and yet restrict the overall dimensions of the antenna to a reasonably small size, it is necessary that the operating wavelength be short (3 centimeters; there are 2.54 centimeters per inch). A marine radar antenna has a radiation pattern which is extremely narrow with respect to azimuth (compass) directions, but is relatively broad with respect to vertical directions.

The Receiver: Radar receivers are almost always of the superheterodyne type. The receiver must have great sensitivity in order to receive and amplify the very weak reradiated r-f pulses to a value suitable for use by the P.P.I. scope. Since the input signal may be in the order of one microvolt, the i-f amplifier must have a gain in the order of one or two million to provide sufficient input signal to the second detector (1 or 2 volts). In order to pass the very steep and short-duration pulses, the i-f amplifier must be capable of passing a band of frequencies in the order of 5 to 10 megacycles. The wide band-pass reduces the gain of the individual stages so that the number of stages in the i-f amplifier is often more than six to eight.

There are no r-f amplifiers in the receiver. The input signal is applied directly to a crystal mixer, and the local oscillator is generally of the reflex klystron type. (See Q. 3.246 and Q. 8.70.)

The intermediate frequencies are in the order of 30 megacycles. Automatic frequency control is often employed, to compensate for frequency drift of the magnetron or local oscillator (reflex klystron), in order to maintain the proper difference frequency of 30 megacycles, and thus provide the maximum indicated response upon the P.P.I. tube at all times.

For a discussion of a duplexer, see Q. 8.41.

Q. 8.40. Explan briefly the principle of operation of a radar system.

A. Very briefly, radar operates to detect an object at a distance by directing a narrow beam of r-f energy at the object and then detecting a portion of the reflected beam when it arrives back at the radar.

D. For a more complete discussion of radar, see Q. 8.39.

Q. 8.41. Draw a simple block diagram of a radar duplexer system, labeling the waveguide, the TR box, the anti-TR box, the receiver, and the transmitter.

A. See Fig. 8.41.

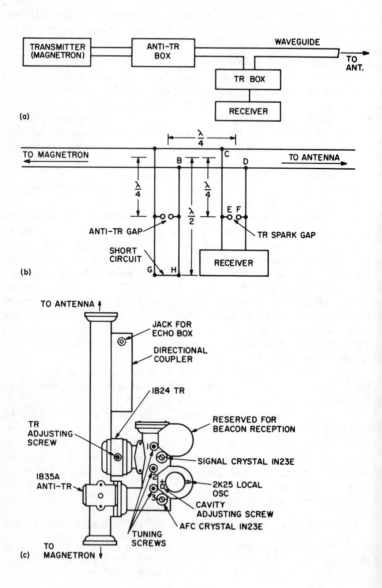

Fig. 8.41. (a) *Block diagram of duplexer;* (b) *simplified diagram of duplexer;* (c) *duplexer assembly.*

D. Ship radars use a common antenna system for transmitting and receiving. In such a system, it is necessary to protect the receiver from damage due to the high-power transmitter pulse and also to prevent the transmitter from absorbing too much power from the reflected echo between transmitting pulses. It is, therefore, necessary to provide some form of "switch" to disconnect the receiver effectively from the waveguide during the transmitter pulse and to disconnect the transmitter from the waveguide the rest of the time. Such a switch is often called a *duplexer*. This is not a simple switch, but is made up of certain measured lengths of waveguide and two special spark-gap tubes. How this switch operates may be seen with the aid of the simplified drawing shown in part (b) of the figure.

When the transmitter pulses, both of the spark gaps are fired and represent practically a short circuit across the gap terminals. The anti-TR connects into the waveguide a quarter-wavelength from its gap and thus reflects an open circuit across points *A* and *B*. The transmitter sees a very high impedance at *A-B* and does not "pour" any appreciable power into the anti-TR. The TR gap also fires at this time producing a short across *E-F*. This prevents all but a small amount of power from entering the receiver. A high impedance appears at *C-D*, one-quarter wavelength away, and permits the transmitter power to proceed to the antenna almost without loss. Thus while the transmitter is pulsing, the receiver is protected and the full power is delivered to the antenna. After the transmitter pulse, both gaps become open circuits. The shorting bar of the anti-TR line is a half-wavelength from *A-B* and reflects a *short* across these points (*A-B*). This short is, in turn, reflected to points *C-D,* one-quarter wavelength away, as an *open* circuit and effectively blocks received signals from passing this point toward the transmitter. Instead, the received power is effectively all shunted into the receiver. In part (c) of the figure is shown a complete drawing of a typical duplexer.

Q. 8.42. Draw a simple block diagram of a radar receiver, labeling the signal crystal, the local oscillator, the afc crystal stage, the i-f amplifier, and the discriminator.

A. See Fig. 8.42.

D. For general discussion of a radar receiver, see Question 8.39. A brief discussion of the afc system follows. Two signals are fed into the afc crystal detector. One is from the magnetron (greatly attenuated), the other from the local oscillator (reflex klystron). The difference frequency between these two is detected, amplified, and fed into the discriminator. The discriminator is reasonated at 30 mc, the normal i-f frequency of the signal circuits. If the magnetron and local oscillator are operating at their correct frequencies 30 mc apart (to produce 30 mc i.f.) there will be no output from the discriminator. If, however, either the magnetron or klystron (or both) should drift in frequency, the output of the afc crystal will be greater or less than 30

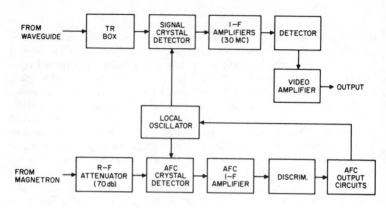

Fig. 8.42. Simplified diagram of radar receiver.

mc. This will cause an output voltage from the discriminator whose sign and magnitude is proportional to the drift. This control voltage is amplified and fed back to the reflector plate of the klystron in such a way as to cause the frequency of the klystron to change to a value needed to produce again a 30 mc i.f.

Q. 8.43. Draw a simple cross-sectional diagram of a magnetron showing the anode, cathode, and the direction of electronic movement under the influence of a strong magnetic field.

A. See Fig. 8.43.

D. See Q. 3.248 and Q. 8.70.

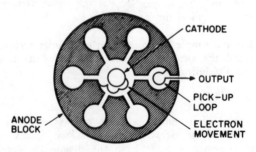

Fig. 8.43. Cross-section of magnetron showing electron movement.

Q. 8.44. Explain briefly the principle of operation of the magnetron.

A. See Q. 3.248.

D. See also Fig. 8.43 and Q. 8.70.

Q. 8.45. Why is the anode in a magnetron in a radar transmitter normally maintained at ground potential?

A. This is done to protect personnel from high-voltage shocks and to reduce the problem of insulating the magnetron from the chassis.

D. The anode (containing the resonant cavities) comprises the metal shell of the magnetron. This is mechanically coupled to the wave-guide. If the high-voltage pulse were to be applied to the anode, it would be as a highly positive pulse. This would necessitate the insulation of the anode from the chassis as well as the insulaton of the wave-guide from the anode. This is difficult to do and expensive. In addition, even if the insulation were present, there would be great danger to personnel encountering the magnetron or even the waveguide. To overcome this, the metal shell of the magnetron (and waveguide) is *grounded* and a *negative* high-voltage pulse fed into the *cathode* of the magnetron. This makes construction much simpler and also is much safer for handling by personnel.

Q. 8.46. Draw a simple frequency-converter circuit (mixer) as frequently used in radar superheterodyne receivers and indicate which is the crystal stage.

A. See Fig. 8.46. (See also Fig. 8.41.)

D. See Q. 8.39.

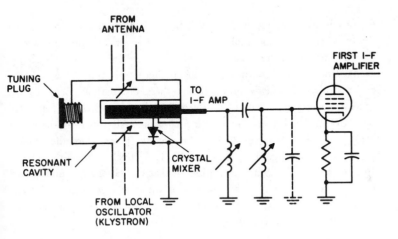

Fig. 8.46. Mixer circuit of radar receiver.

Q. 8.47. What is the purpose of the klystron tube in a radar set?

A. The klystron tube is the local oscillator of the radar **receiver**. It is coupled to the mixer crystal to produce the i.f. as shown in Question 8.46.

Q. 8.48. Explain briefly the principle of operation of the reflex klystron.

A. A schematic of a reflex klystron is shown in Fig. 8.48. The klystron is a resonant-cavity device which is energized by the action of "bunches" of electrons. Briefly, it operates as follows: Electrons are

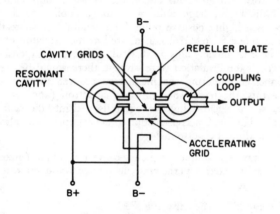

Fig. 8.48. Reflex klystron.

emitted by the cathode in a steady stream and accelerated toward the cavity grids by the potential on the accelerating grid. When the stream of electrons first enters the cavity grids, the resonant cavity is shock-excited into oscillation thus producing alternating voltages across the cavity grids. The fields produced by these alternating potentials act upon the electron stream to produce "bunches" of electrons separated by spaces in which there are very few electrons. After passing the cavity grids, the *bunches* are repelled by the negative potential of the repeller plate and return again to these grids. The bunches have the proper *spacing* and *timing* when returning so that oscillations are maintained in the resonant cavity. The volume of the cavity is varied to make large changes of frequency. Small changes of frequency are made by varying the repeller voltage over a narrow range.

D. See Q. 3.246 and Q. 8.70.

Q. 8.49. What care should be taken when handling silicon crystal rectifier cartridges for replacement in radar superheterodyne receivers?

A. The technician should discharge any static charge in his body by touching a convenient ground with his hands. The crystal should be handled very carefully as it may be damaged mechanically by applying excessive pressures.

D. The silicon crystals which are used as mixers (and afc crystals) have a *low*, safe current rating. They may be damaged by static charges accumulated on the body of the person handling them. Such persons should first "discharge" themselves by touching a suitable grounding point. The crystals are wrapped in lead foil when stored, to protect them against stray charges. This foil should not be removed, until the crystal is placed in use. The unit into which the crystal is inserted should also be grounded before installation.

Q. 8.50. What nominal intermediate frequencies are commonly found in radar receivers?

A. Radar receivers commonly use i.f.'s of 30 or 60 mc.

D. See Q. 8.39 and Q. 8.42.

Q. 8.51. Describe briefly the construction and operation of radar TR and anti-TR boxes. What is the purpose of a "keep alive" voltage?

A. The operation of TR and anti-TR boxes is fully described in Question 8.41. The construction of a TR box is shown in Fig. 8.51. This consists of a TR tube mounted in a resonant cavity. The high Q of the cavity reduces the power needed to maintain the spark gap. The TR tube contains two metal electrodes which act as a spark gap. The tube itself is partially evacuated and has a small amount of water vapor inside to reduce the time of deionization.

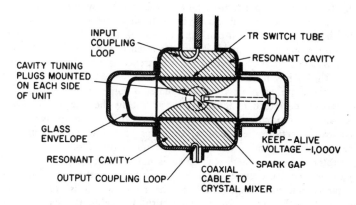

Fig. 8.51. Cross section of TR switch.

A third electrode is placed inside of one of the main electrodes. This is known as a "keep-alive" electrode. It has a "keep-alive" voltage applied to it. This is a constant negative potential (about 1,000 volts) which keeps the gas and vapor in the tube slightly ionized at all times and accelerates the breakdown of the main gap. A TR box is similar to an anti-TR box, but may not have a "keep-alive" electrode in the TR tube.

D. See Question 8.41.

Q. 8.52. What is the purpose of the discriminator stage in a radar superheterodyne?

A. The discriminator is part of the afc system. Its function is to generate a corrective voltage which is sent to the local oscillator (klystron) to maintain the correct intermediate-frequency difference output from the mixer.

D. See Q. 8.42 for a discussion of the afc system. See also Q. 3.177(d).

Q. 8.53. What type of detector is used frequently in radar receivers?

A. A silicon crystal detector (mixer) is commonly used.

D. See Questions 8.40, 8.42, 8.46, and 8.49.

Q. 8.54. What is "sea return" on a radar scope?

A. "Sea return" is the reflection, or "echo," of radar signals bouncing off the waves of the sea and returning to the radar set.

D. Sea return response in a radar set is caused by the transmitted pulses striking the tops of waves at such an angle that they are reflected back to the radar antenna and appear on the PPI (Plan Position Indicator) scope as a solid block of interference. Due to the reflection angles involved in sea return, such interference is usually confined to areas within a few miles of the radar set.

It is, therefore, possible to discriminate to some extent against the reception of sea return in favor of targets within the interference area. This can be automatically accomplished by causing the receiver gain to be lower at times representing distances of a few miles from the radar, and automatically restoring the normal gain at times representing greater distances where sea return is not troublesome. A reduction of gain at relatively close distances is effective in this case, since a ship target reflects a signal back to the radar which is considerably stronger than the signal due to sea return. Reducing the gain in sea return areas, reduces the intensity of the PPI display due to sea return to a greater extent than it reduces the display due to target return, and thus the target often can be observed through sea return interference.

(See also Q. 8.39 for basic discussion of radar set.)

Q. 8.55. Explain briefly the purpose of the sensitivity time control circuit in a radar set.

A. The sensitivity time control automatically reduces the gain of the radar receiver for nearby targets, to reduce interference from such effects as sea return.

D. In order to reduce sea return response in a radar set, the operator should manually adjust the "Suppressor" control (or sensitivity time control, STC) until the solid pattern of sea return is thinned out and stronger ship targets which may be present close to the radar set are more easily observed. See also Q. 8.54.

Q. 8.56. What is the distance in nautical miles to a target if it takes 123 microseconds for a radar pulse to travel from the radar antenna to the target, back to the antenna and be displayed on the PPI scope?

A. The distance to the target is 10 nautical miles.

D. A radar pulse will go out 1 nautical mile *and return* in about 12.3 microseconds. Therefore, in 123 microseconds, the distance to the target is, $123/12.3 = 10$ nautical miles.

Q. 8.57. What is the purpose of an "artificial transmission line" in a radar set?

A. An "artificial transmission line" determines the shape and duration of the transmitted pulse.

D. (See also Question 8.58.) Ship radar transmitters generally have output r-f pulses varying in length from $\frac{1}{4}$ to 1 microsecond. This output r-f pulse is obtained by triggering the magnetron with a high-voltage d-c pulse. The pulse must have a fixed duration and a square top for good magnetron frequency stability. In order to obtain a suitable driving pulse, a "line-controlled" blocking oscillator is frequently employed. This consists of a high-voltage blocking oscillator whose pulse output duration is controlled by an artificial transmission line in its grid circuit. Briefly, the operation is as follows: A driving pulse from the synchronizer is applied to the blocking oscillator (one-shot) and forces it into conduction, thus starting the output pulse. This pulse also travels down the artificial line and is reflected when it reaches its open end. This reflected pulse comes back to the grid of the blocking oscillator with negative polarity cutting it off and terminating the output pulse. By suitable selection of the constants of the line, the time of travel up and back can be determined to a very close degree, thus controlling the length of the output pulse. The pulse from the blocking oscillator triggers a modulator tube, which actually pulses the magnetron at high voltage (10 to 15 kv). The construction of an artificial transmission line is described in Question 8.58.

Q. 8.58. Draw a simple diagram of an artificial transmission line showing inductance and capacitance, source of power, the load, and the electronic switch.

A.   See Fig. 8.58 and also Question 8.57.

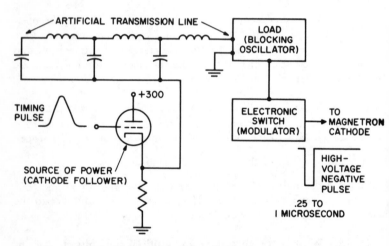

Fig. 8.58. Artificial transmission line and associated circuits.

D.   A convenient means of producing a very short duration rectangular pulse is to use an artificial transmission line. This is a device, which by lumped constants of capacitance and inductance, simulates an actual line with a certain characteristic impedance and wavelength. An actual line is not used because its physical length would be prohibitive. The required pulse duration is controlled by designing the line to have a certain equivalent "length." Thus, it takes an impulse a definite time to travel to the end of the line (open) and be reflected back to the load, in this case, the grid circuit of a blocking oscillator. The operation of this circuit is described in Question 8.57. See also Question 8.61.

Q. 8.59. What component in a radar set determines the pulse repetition rate?

A.   The pulse repetition rate is determined by the timer (or synchronizer) unit.

D.   See Q. 8.39 and Q. 8.40. Typical repetition rates (depending upon transmitted pulse width) are 100, 200, 500, 750, 1000, 2000 and 3000 cps. The higher the repetition rate, the narrower the transmitted pulse width must be in order not to overload the magnetron and modulator. The duty cycle (see Q. 8.62) remains fairly constant over the range of repetition rates.

Q. 8.60.   What circuit element determines the operating frequency of the self-blocking oscillator?

A.   (See Fig. 8.60 (a) for a tube-type, free-running, blocking oscillator and Fig. 8.60 (b) for a transistor type.)

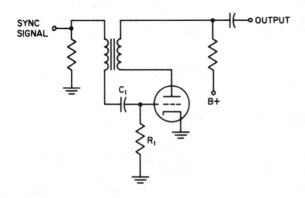

Fig. 8.60(a).   Circuit of synchronized blocking oscillator (tube-type).

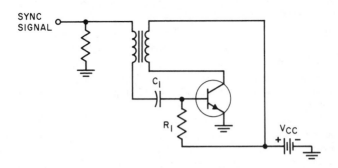

Fig. 8.60(b).   Circuit diagram of synchronized blocking oscillator (transistor type).

D.   The question is a little indefinite since there is no *single* circuit element which determines the repetition frequency. All of the circuit elements, including the tube and transformer as well as the operating potentials, affect the frequency. However, it is true that R_1 and C_1 have the greatest effect on frequency.

Note in the transistor version that R1 is returned to $+V_{CC}$, rather than to ground. This is essential for the oscillator to be self-starting, as a transistor with zero bias is biased at class C operation. Connecting R1 to $+V_{CC}$ provides the required forward bias to cause the transistor to be conducting before the start of oscillations.

In marine radar sets, a synchronized blocking oscillator is used to produce the trigger pulse for the transmitter. This will oscillate for only one cycle for each synchronizing pulse applied to the grid. In this case, the repetition frequency is determined solely by the synchronizing pulses. This would require a "one-shot" blocking oscillator, which simply means that the oscillator is biased off, in the absence of a synchronizing pulse.

Q. 8.61. What is the purpose of the rotary spark gap used in some radar sets?

A. The rotary spark gap is a mechanical system for modulating a magnetron directly at high level.

D. When an *electronic* modulator tube is used, it is frequently connected in a manner shown in the simplified drawing which is part (a) of Fig. 8.61. This operates briefly as follows:

Between triggering pulses, the modulator tube V_1 is held below cutoff by a fixed bias. During this interval, the high-voltage capacitor, C_1, charges through the charging diode, V_2, as shown by the dotted arrows, to about 12,000 volts (for example). When the triggering pulse appears, it overcomes the modulator bias, the modulator tube conducts heavily, and the high voltage of C_1 is applied to the magnetron with negative polarity. This is shown by the solid arrows. C_1 only discharges a relatively small amount, thus maintaining almost a constant voltage.

Some radar units use a spark gap and pulse-forming line instead of the blocking-oscillator modulator system. This has the advantage of generating the magnetron high-voltage d-c pulse directly at high level instead of having to amplify it in several tubes. No modulator tubes are required and the efficiency is very high (80 to 90 per cent). It has, however, the disadvantages of being a *mechanical* rather than an electronic device, of generating radio-frequency interference which must be filtered, and offering no opportunities for accurate pulse shaping. A simplified drawing of such a system is shown in part (b) of the figure. The true operation of this circuit is quite complicated, but a simplified explanation follows. The rotary gap makes contacts at a very high rate, commonly at 400, 800, or 1,600 times per second. When the gap is open, the pulse-forming line charges through V_1, L_1 and V_2. This

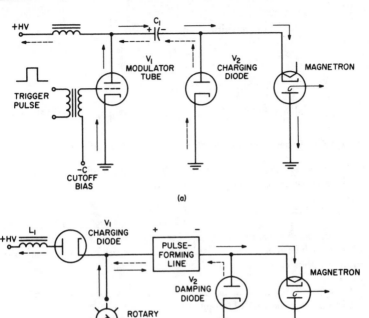

Fig. 8.61. (a) Electronic modulator for magnetron; (b) rotary spark-gap modulator.

produces shock excitation of a resonant circuit consisting of L_1 and the capacitance of the pulse-forming line. Because of the diodes, the oscillation causes the line to charge to a voltage about 1.8 times the applied voltage and remain at the value. When the gap fires, the voltage at point A becomes zero and the now negative pulse-forming line voltage is applied to the magnetron for the duration of the arc. The cycle then repeats.

Q. 8.62. What is the peak power of a radar pulse if the pulse width is 1.0 microsecond, pulse repetition rate is 900 and the average power is 18 watts? What is the duty cycle?

A. The peak power is 20,000 watts. The duty cycle is 0.0009.

D. Step 1: The duty cycle must *first* be found.

$$\text{Duty cycle} = \frac{\text{Pulse width}}{\text{Pulse repetition time}}$$

$$\text{Pulse repetition time} = \frac{1}{F} = \frac{1}{900}$$

$$\text{Duty cycle} = \frac{0.000001}{1/900} = 0.0009.$$

Step 2: Find the peak power.

$$\text{Peak power} = \frac{\text{Average power}}{\text{Duty cycle}} = \frac{18}{0.0009} = 20,000 \text{ watts.}$$

Q. 8.63. What is meant by "bearing resolution" of a radar set?

A. Bearing resolution may be defined as the ability of a radar set to distinguish between targets at the same range but different azimuth directions.

D. Bearing resolution is mainly determined by the *width* of the radar beam. A narrow beam is better able to separate targets at the same radial distance than a wide beam. The resolution is also influenced by the receiving circuits and the PPI scope.

Q. 8.64. Explain how heading flash and range-marker circles are produced on a radar PPI scope.

A. (a) Heading flash is produced whenever the radar beam points dead ahead. This is accomplished by closing a switch in the antenna which causes an intensifier pulse of short duration to intensify a radial line of the PPI scope representing the heading.

(b) Range-marker circles are produced on a radar PPI scope as follows: A range-marker oscillator, in conjunction with suitable squaring and peaking circuits, produces "pips" (or short positive pulses). There is a definite spacing between these pips, corresponding to range in miles (or yards), which is a function of the range-marker oscillator frequency. These pips are produced in synchronism with sweep and are applied at intensified pulses to the grid of the PPI. Each time the sweep causes the beam to go out from the center to the edge, a series of accurately spaced intensified pips appears. Since the sweep rotates, these pips then form range-marker circles. (See Fig. 8.67.)

D. (a) The radar operator must know exactly when the radar beam is dead ahead so that he can accurately indicate the relative bearing of all targets. The PPI sweep line is normally blanked out as it rotates with only the targets intensifying the screen. To provide heading flash (or dead-ahead indication), it is necessary to intensify the sweep line momentarily each time the antenna points dead ahead. Briefly, this is accomplished by the momentary closing of a cam-actuated microswitch located in the antenna assembly. This microswitch is closed only when the antenna points dead ahead. When the switch is closed, it actuates a circuit that produces an intensifier pulse of the desired duration. This pulse (positive) is fed to the grid of the PPI scope where it causes a bright sweep line to appear on the PPI in an azimuth indication corresponding to the dead-ahead position of the antenna.

(b) A block diagram of a range-marker generating system from a typical marine radar [2] is shown in Fig. 8.64. This operates as follows:

1. The negative input pulse to V_1 shock excites an L-C tank circuit in the cathode into sine-wave oscillation. The frequency depends on the range in use and the *number* of range rings desired on that particular range. On the $1\frac{1}{2}$ mile range, three rings will be seen on one model.

2. The sine waves from the L-C tank are then shaped by the three following stages to form *square* pulses with extremely sharp leading edges.

3. The positive output of these amplifiers is used to trigger a "one-shot" (or single-swing) blocking oscillator which generates a short duration ($\frac{1}{3}$ microsecond) pulse in synchronization with the leading edge of each squared-up pulse. These are the range-marker pulses.

4. The range-marker pulses are then fed through a cathode follower and limiter into a two-stage video amplifier. The output of the video amplifier then feeds directly into the grid of the PPI where each pip produces an intensification of the sweep.

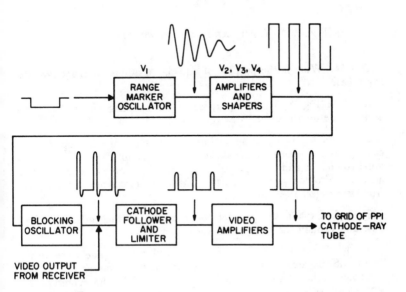

Fig. 8.64. Block diagram of a range-marker system.

---

[2] Radiomarine Corp. of America.

Q. 8.65. Draw a diagram of a cathode-ray tube as used in radar showing the principal electrodes in the tube and the path of the electron beam.

A. See Fig. 8.65.

D. See Questions 8.66, 8.67, and 8.68.

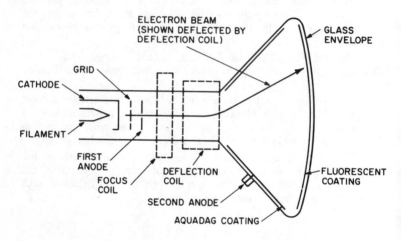

Fig. 8.65. Cross section of a cathode-ray tube.

Q. 8.66. What is the purpose of aquadag coatings on radar cathode-ray tubes?

A. (See Fig. 8.65.) The purpose of the aquadag coating is to act as an anode for the cathode-ray tube.

D. Aquadag is a graphite solution in water which is applied as a coating to the inside of cathode-ray tubes (as in Fig. 8.65). It is a good conductor and is employed in radar cathode-ray tubes as a second anode. It also acts as an electrostatic shield to protect the electron beam from stray electric fields.

Q. 8.67. Explain the principle of operation of the cathode-ray PPI tube and explain the function of each electrode.

A. 1. PRINCIPLE OF OPERATION. A PPI tube is one on which a "map" of the area being scanned is presented insofar as targets and fixed land echoes are concerned. (See Fig. 8.67.) The center of the PPI screen represents the position of the radar antenna. The electron beam moves out radially from the center to the outer edge and is *rotated* in synchronism with the radar antenna. In practice, the scanning beam proper is blanked out and only the target indications and range rings are *intensified* on the screen. The distance from the center

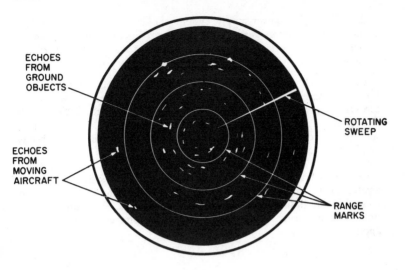

ECHOES
FROM
GROUND
OBJECTS

ECHOES
FROM
MOVING
AIRCRAFT

ROTATING
SWEEP

RANGE
MARKS

Fig. 8.67.   A PPI presentation. (Courtesy FAA)

of the screen to the target is a measure of the *range*, while the radial *direction* indicates the target's azimuth bearing (relative).

2. FUNCTION OF ELECTRODES. (See Fig. 8.65.) The PPI tube has a filament similar to that used in receiving tubes. This filament heats up and, in turn, heats a coated cathode, causing electrons to be emitted from the cathode. These electrons first encounter a grid which functions in a manner similar to the grid in a conventional triode. That is, it controls the amount of electrons passing it and, thus, the *intensity* of the spot produced on the PPI screen. After passing the grid, the electrons (now restricted to a fairly narrow stream) are acted upon by the first anode, which produces some acceleration of the electron stream toward the screen. Further and final acceleration is provided by the second anode (aquadag coating).

D. PPI tubes frequently employ *magnetic* focusing accomplished by a focus coil, which is located as indicated in Fig. 8.65. Deflection is usually accomplished by a magnetic deflection coil which moves the beam radially out from the center to the outer edge of the screen. The rotating effect of the sweep may be accomplished by *rotating* the deflection coil mechanically in synchronism with the antenna. (See Question 8.69.)

Another method of rotating the sweep, employs fixed deflection coils. This system employs a *rotating magnetic field*, which is synchronized with the movement of the radar antenna.

Q. 8.68. What precautions should the service and maintenance operator observe when replacing the cathode-ray tube in a radar set?

A. The radar power-supply system should be turned off and *all* high-voltage capacitors *completely discharged* by a well-insulated screwdriver or other device. Care must be taken to avoid breakage of a cathode-ray tube which may result in serious injury to the serviceman.

D. It has been demonstrated recently that cuts resulting from broken cathode-ray tubes (or other fluorescent devices) may result in serious poisoning of the bloodstream. This is due to the action of the fluorescent material. Therefore, be especially careful in disposing of such broken devices to avoid cutting the hands, arms, or face. The use of gloves is to be recommended in such cases.

Q. 8.69. Draw a simple diagram showing how a synchro generator located in the radar antenna assembly is connected to a synchro motor located in the indicator to drive the deflection coils. Show proper designation of all leads, designating where a-c voltages (if needed) are applied.

A. See Fig. 8.69.

D. Ship radars employ one or more PPI indicators (see Q. 8.39 and Q. 8.65). In this type of indicator, it is necessary to synchronize the rotation of the sweep line on the PPI tube with the rotation of the radar antenna. This is usually accomplished by a servo system, as illustrated in Fig. 8.69.

A synchro-control transformer has its rotor geared to the rotation of the antenna. The rotor (R_1, R_2) of this synchro is supplied with 115 volt, 400 cps excitation. As the rotor turns, varying voltages are induced in the three-winding stator (S_1, S_2, S_3). These varying voltages are fed directly to the stator of the indicator synchro-control transformer. (Note that the rotor of the indicator synchro is mechanically coupled to the deflection coil and to the indicator-servo motor.) As a result, an "error" voltage is induced in the indicator-synchro rotor. This "error" voltage is fed to the grid of the first stage of the servo amplifier. The output of the servo amplifier is a push-pull amplifier that feeds one winding of a two-phase servo motor. The second phase (displaced by 90 degrees) is excited directly from the 115 volt, 400 cps line. As a result of the servo-amplifier output, the servo motor is caused to rotate.

The phase of the "error" voltage is such that the servo motor rotates to drive the deflection coil in the same direction as the antenna. Further, the amplitude of the "error" voltage is high when the antenna and deflection coil are greatly out of synchronization (in azimuth) and decreases to a very low amplitude when the two are in synchronization. In order to continuously drive the deflection coil, a small "error" voltage must always be present. This means that a very small *lag* angle always exists between the antenna and deflection coil.

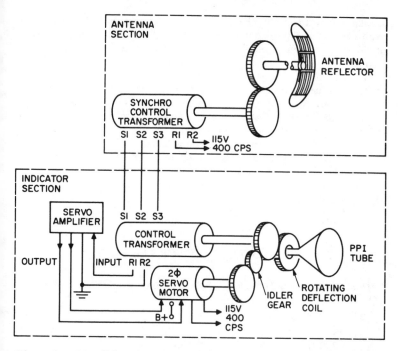

Fig. 8.69. Simplified diagram of radar servo system driving rotating indicator-deflection coil.

Since the indicator synchro is directly geared to the deflection coil, it "senses" when the deflection coil and antenna are approaching synchronization and automatically reduces its error voltage (to the servo amplifier) to the value just necessary to achieve and maintain synchronization.

Q. 8.70. In what range of frequencies do magnetron and klystron oscillators find application?

A. Magnetron oscillators are most generally used in the frequency range between 600 and 30,000 megacycles. Klystron oscillators are most generally used in the frequency range between 3000 and 30,000 megacycles.

D. A magnetron oscillator derives its name by virtue of a magnetic field which is set up perpendicular to the electric field existing between cathode and plate (or plates). In a multi-anode type of magnetron, the plate segments are made up of cavity resonators. These cavity resonators receive their operating energy from the circular movement of electrons just outside of the opening to each cavity. If an electron is accelerated by the cavity fields, energy is taken from the cavity, but if an electron is slowed down by the cavity fields then energy is given up to the cavity and oscillations are thereby maintained. Magnetron oscillators are widely used in radar sets as pulsed power oscillators of high peak power. A klystron oscillator is a "velocity modulated" type of high frequency oscillator, that is, the relative velocities of the electron beam are made to vary in such a way that "bunches" of electrons are formed. These "bunches" pass through cavity resonator grids in the proper phase relationship to maintain oscillation in the cavity resonator. Klystrons are used for local oscillators and low power transmitters. Klystron tubes are also available in the form of amplifiers. The "reflex" klystron is most widely used as a receiver local oscillator, and is also used in one type of video sweep generator. (See also Q. 3.246 and Q. 3.248.)

FCC-TYPE SAMPLE TEST FOR ELEMENT VIII

VIII-1.   One of the frequency bands on which ship radars operate is: (Q. 8.07)
  (a) 5000 to 5200 mc.
  (b) 5460 to 5650 mc.
  (c) 9000 to 9250 mc.
  (d) 3200 to 3450 mc.
  (e) 4460 to 4650 mc.

VIII-2.   Radar interference heard on a receiver frequently appears as: (Q. 8.10)
  (a) Intermittent pulses.
  (b) Constantly varying tone frequencies.
  (c) A steady tone, always at 400 cps.
  (d) A hissing noise.
  (e) A steady tone at the radar repetition rate.

VIII-3.   Radar interference to communications receivers occurs: (Q. 8.12)
  (a) Only at the radar transmitting R-F frequency.
  (b) Only at the basic radar repetition rate.
  (c) On practically any communication frequency.
  (d) Only below 10 mc.
  (e) Only above 300 mc.

VIII-4.   To be responsible for the installation, maintenance, and servicing of ship radar equipment, an operator must have: (Q. 8.01)
  (a) A first- or second-class radiotelephone or radiotelegraph license, plus a ship-radar endorsement.
  (b) A third-class operator's license, plus a ship radar endorsement.
  (c) A first- or second-class radiotelephone or radiotelegraph license.

(d) A third-class operator's license, plus a broadcast endorsement.

(e) A first-class radiotelegraph license, plus a receiver endorsement.

VIII-5. Persons who are permitted to operate a ship's radar are: (Q. 8.02)

(a) Only properly licensed individuals.

(b) Any person holding an engineer's license.

(c) Any person designated by any officer on the ship.

(d) The Master, or any person designated by him.

(e) The First Mate, or any person designated by him.

VIII-6. In joining sections of waveguide together, choke joints are often used: (Q. 8.34)

(a) To prevent moisture from entering the waveguide.

(b) To maintain the pressure of inert gas.

(c) To reduce losses caused by misalignment of waveguide sections.

(d) To permit the escape of entrapped moisture without causing excessive losses.

(e) To maintain the correct bandwidth of the waveguide.

VIII-7. When used in conjunction with a radar set, the purpose of an echo box is to: (Q. 8.38)

(a) Listen to the tone of the pulse repetition rate.

(b) Tune the magnetron to the correct frequency.

(c) Provide a second or echo pulse, which is transmitted from the radar antenna, to increase the range.

(d) Provide an artificial target, which may be used to tune the radar receiver.

(e) Provide an artificial target, which may be used to tune the radar synchronizer.

VIII-8. A radar pulse is transmitted to an object 37.2 miles away. The time required for the pulse to be returned to the radar receiver is: (Q. 8.39)

(a) 400 microseconds.

(b) 200 microseconds.

(c) 800 microseconds.

(d) 600 microseconds.

(e) 1000 microseconds.

VIII-9. A PPI cathode-ray tube as used on a radar set: (Q. 8.39)

(a) Is used to check the percentage of modulation.

(b) Indicates only the range of a target.

(c) Indicates both the range and azimuth of a target.

(d) Indicates the range, azimuth, and altitude of a target.

(e) Is used for receiver alignment.

VIII-10. Oscillations of a klystron tube are maintained: (Q. 8.48)

(a) By plate-to-cathode feedback.

(b) By bunches of electrons passing the cavity grids.

(c) By feedback between the accelerating grid and the repeller plate.

(d) By circulating bunches of electrons within the cavities.

(e) By variations in the repeller-plate potential.

VIII-11.   A radar set has a pulse width of 0.05 microsecond, a pulse repetition rate of 2000 cycles per second, and a peak power of 100 kw. The duty cycle is: (Q. 8.62)

(a) 0.0001

(b) 0.0009

(c) 0.005

(d) 0.00005

(e) 0.009

VIII-12.   Klystron oscillators are most often used in the frequency range of: (Q. 8.70)

(a) 300 to 3000 mc.

(b) 30 to 30,000 mc.

(c) 100 to 10,000 mc.

(d) 3000 to 30,000 mc.

(e) 3000 to 300,000 mc.

VIII-13.   The oscillators of a magnetron oscillator are maintained if: (Q. 8.70)

(a) Electrons are slowed down by the cavity fields.

(b) The magnet has sufficient strength.

(c) The electrostatic field matches the electromagnetic field in strength.

(d) Electrons are speeded up by the cavity fields.

(e) Electrons are formed into bunches having the proper timing.

VIII-14.   A synchro generator in a radar set is used to: (Q. 8.69)

(a) Generate the synchronizing pulses.

(b) Synchronize the sweep starting time of the PPI with the synchronizer.

(c) Supply position information of an antenna, to a servo system.

(d) Supply range information to the PPI.

(e) Generate range markers for the PPI.

VIII-15.   The heading flash on a radar PPI is produced: (Q. 8.64)

(a) By an oscillator in the radar synchronizer.

(b) By a flash circuit in the PPI scope.

(c) By a time-delay circuit triggered by the magnetron.

(d) By a cam-operated switch in the antenna.

(e) By a cam-operated switch in the PPI scope.

VIII-16.   The function of an artificial transmission line in a radar set is to: (Q. 8.58)

(a) Conduct the R-F to the radar antenna.

(b) Determine the shape and duration of the radar pulse.

(c) Determine the pulse repetition rate of the radar pulse.

(d) Connect the magnetron to the waveguide.

(e) Measure the power output of the magnetron.

VIII-17.   The pulse repetition rate of a radar set is determined by: (Q. 8.59)
   (a) A self-pulsing magnetron.
   (b) The modulator, which triggers the magnetron.
   (c) The synchronizer, or timer unit.
   (d) The servo unit.
   (e) The range-mark generator oscillator.
VIII-18.   The radar set, sensitivity-time control circuit: (Q. 8.55)
   (a) Can reduce sea-return response.
   (b) Make it possible to discriminate between targets that are very close together.
   (c) Controls the width of the magnetron pulse.
   (d) Is used to increase sea return.
   (e) Is a circuit in the synchronizer that permits fine control of the radar-repetition rate.
VIII-19.   Radar receivers commonly use intermediate frequencies of: (Q. 8.50)
   (a) 455 kc.
   (b) 10.7 mc.
   (c) 43.0 mc.
   (d) 30 or 60 mc.
   (e) 4.5 mc.
VIII-20.   The function of the TR box in a radar system is to: (Q. 8.41)
   (a) Protect the magnetron from overload.
   (b) Protect the waveguide against arcing due to moisture.
   (c) Protect the receiver while the magnetron is firing.
   (d) Protect the antenna while the magnetron is firing.
   (e) Increase the sensitivity of the receiver.
VIII-21.   If the duration of the radar transmitted pulse, on a particular range of operation, is increased, the required bandwidth of the receiver's I-F amplifiers: (Q. 8.39)
   (a) May be decreased.
   (b) Must remain as before.
   (c) Must be increased.
   (d) Must be doubled.
   (e) None of the above.
VIII-22.   In a radar set, the local oscillator klystron tube is constantly kept on the correct frequency by: (Q. 8.48)
   (a) A spectrum analyzer.
   (b) Frequent manual adjustments.
   (c) Reference to the PPI tube.
   (d) An AFC system.
   (e) Feedback from the range-marker oscillator.
VIII-23.   In the usual radar set, the receiver R-F amplifier: (Q. 8.42)
   (a) Must be solid-state.

(b) Does not exist.

(c) Has a high signal-to-noise ratio.

(d) Has a low signal-to-noise ratio.

(e) Is located at the antenna, to reduce losses.

VIII-24. The maximum usable range of the usual radar set (on any particular range setting) is determined by: (Q. 8.39)

(a) The interval between transmitted pulses.

(b) The width of the transmitted pulses.

(c) The bandwidth of the receiver I-F stages.

(d) The duty cycle.

(e) The horizontal resolution on the PPI tube.

VIII-25. A thin layer of dirt and grime covers the reflecting surface of the parabolic dish of a radar set. The practical effect on the performance of the radar will be: (Q. 8.37)

(a) A decrease in range.

(b) A reduction in horizontal resolution.

(c) No noticeable effect.

(d) A slightly smeary picture on the PPI.

(e) None of the above.

VIII-26. The purpose of using waveguide-choke joints is to: (Q. 8.34, 8.35)

(a) Lengthen the waveguide run.

(b) Eliminate moisture from the waveguide.

(c) Present a correct terminating impedance for the waveguide.

(d) Join two sections of waveguide with minimum losses.

(e) Pressurize the waveguide.

VIII-27. A typical value for the receiver I-F of a radar set is: (Q. 8.39)

(a) 30 mc.

(b) 130 mc.

(c) 10.7 mc.

(d) 455 kc.

(e) 90 mc.

VIII-28. In a radar set, the function of the magnetron is to: (Q. 8.43)

(a) Act as the receiver local oscillator.

(b) Produce the transmitter R-F power.

(c) Modulate the transmitter.

(d) Determine the transmitted pulse width.

(e) Help determine the antenna beam shape.

VIII-29. Some waveguides are pressurized with dry air. This is done in order to: (Q. 8.28)

(a) Increase the velocity of propagation.

(b) Maintain the correct mode of operation.

(c) Keep the thin walls from bending inward.

(d) Reduce the possibility of internal arcing.

(e) Maintain pressure in the choke joints and thus ensure a better match to the magnetron.

VIII-30.   When operating a magnetron in a radar set, the following precaution should be taken: (Q. 8.23, 8.24)

(a) Allow a 15-minute warm-up before applying the high voltage.

(b) Check all pulse widths before operating each time.

(c) Make certain there are no magnetic materials in the vicinity of the magnet.

(d) Bring the high voltage up very slowly to maximum.

(e) Realign the magnet each day to ensure correct operation.

VIII-31.   Fuses and receiving-type tubes may be replaced: (Q. 8.08)

(a) Only by a person holding a first-class operator's license.

(b) Only by an operator who has previously obtained the permission of the master of the ship.

(c) Only by the Radio Officer in charge.

(d) Only by a person holding a ship radar endorsement.

(e) By an unlicensed person under the supervision of the licensed operator in charge of maintenance.

VIII-32.   In a radar set receiver, an AFC system may be used to: (Q. 8.42)

(a) Automatically maintain the correct magnetron frequency.

(b) Maintain the desired klystron frequency.

(c) Keep the I-F stages on frequency.

(d) Provide automatic control of receiver gain.

(e) Detect the radar pulse after it returns from the target.

VIII-33.   In the usual PPI tube, a "map" of the scanned area is seen by virtue of: (Q. 8.67)

(a) The short persistence of the tube's phosphor.

(b) Applying the "heading flash" to the cathode.

(c) The long persistence characteristic of the phosphor of the tube.

(d) The signal applied to the second anode.

(e) None of the above.

VIII-34.   The PPI tubes have an aquadag coating on the inside of the tube. The purpose of this coating is: (Q. 8.66)

(a) To prevent the escape of light.

(b) To act as the second anode.

(c) To shield the tube magnetically.

(d) To decelerate the electron beam.

(e) To deflect the electron beam.

VIII-35.   A radar set has a pulse repetition rate of 2000 cycles per second. The pulse repetition time is: (Q. 8.62)

(a) 500 μsec.

(b) 5000 μsec.

(c) 2000 μsec.

(d) 200 μsec.

(e) 1000 μsec.

VIII-36.   The transmitted pulse length of a radar set is 0.5 micro-second. For good PPI reproduction of the received pulse, the receiver and video amplifier bandwidth should be approximately: (Q. 8.39)

(a) 10 mc.

(b) 4 mc.

(c) 0.5 mc.

(d) 1.0 mc.

(e) 455 kc.

Hint: To reproduce sufficient harmonics so as not to distort the pulse shape, use the equation: $F = 2/T$

VIII-37.   A certain radar set has a transmitted pulse width of 1.0 microsecond, a pulse repetition rate of 1000 cycles per second and a peak power output of 100 kw. The average power output is: (Q. 8.62)

(a) 100 W.

(b) 1 kW.

(c) 100 kW.

(d) 10 W.

(e) None of the above.

VIII-38.   A radar set uses no R-F amplifier and a crystal detector as the first stage of the receiver because: (Q. 8.39)

(a) An R-F amplifier would produce a better signal-to-noise ratio.

(b) There are no suitable tubes or transistors available at the microwave frequencies involved.

(c) An R-F amplifier would distort the incoming pulse shape.

(d) An R-F amplifier would decrease the maximum range.

(e) An R-F amplifier could not be matched to the waveguide output impedance.

VIII-39.   In a radar system, the reciprocal of the pulse repetition time interval is the: (Q. 8.62)

(a) Pulse width.

(b) Duty cycle.

(c) Reciprocal of the duty cycle.

(d) Radar maximum range.

(e) Pulse repetition frequency.

VIII-40.   The coarse frequency adjustment of a reflex klystron is accomplished by: (Q. 8.48)

(a) The AFC system.

(b) An adjustment in the synchronizer.

(c) Adjusting the flexible wall of the resonant cavity.

(d) Varying the repeller voltage.

(e) Varying the accelerator voltage.

VIII-41. In a radar AFC system, designed to keep the local oscillator frequency correct, the AFC discriminator compares the frequencies of the: (Q. 8.42)

(a) Klystron and repetition-rate generator.
(b) Klystron and magnetron.
(c) Magnetron and repetition-rate generator.
(d) Range-mark generator and the magnetron.
(e) None of the above.

VIII-42. A radar set has several switchable ranges. The following is true at the lowest switchable range: (Q. 8.39)

(a) The repetition rate is lowest and the pulse width is highest.
(b) The repetition rate is highest and the pulse width is lowest.
(c) Short-range targets cannot be resolved.
(d) Long-range targets will be seen most clearly.
(e) The repetition rate is highest and the pulse width is highest.

VIII-43. On the PPI scope of a marine radar set, it is possible to determine: (Q. 8.67)

(a) Altitude and range of the target.
(b) The instantaneous speed of the target.
(c) True North.
(d) The range and bearing of a target.
(e) The location of navigational beacons.

VIII-44. A radar PPI scope displays bright, flashing pie sections. This may be caused by: (Q. 8.20)

(a) A defect in the AFC system.
(b) Excessive gain of the receiver.
(c) Insufficient gain of the receiver.
(d) Normal rotation of the radar antenna.
(e) Interference from a Loran receiver.

VIII-45. The display on the PPI scope of a radar set will have greater intensity under the following conditions: (Q. 8.39)

(a) Higher antenna rotation speeds.
(b) Lower antenna rotation speeds.
(c) Lower pulse repetition rate.
(d) Higher pulse repetition rates.
(e) Both (b) and (d) are true.

VIII-46. The repetition rate of a pulsed-radar set refers to the: (Q. 8.62)

(a) Receiver AFC sweeping rate.
(b) Antenna rotation speed.
(c) Reciprocal of the duty cycle.
(d) Magnetron pulse rate.
(e) Klystron pulse rate.

VIII-47. In a radar-set receiver, the usual mixer stage is: (Q. 8.39)

(a) An FET.

(b) A tunnel diode.

(c) A silicon crystal.

(d) A Rochelle Salts crystal.

(e) A multi-grid vacuum tube designed for microwave frequencies.

VIII-48.   In order to match the output impedance of the radar receiver to the input impedance of a coaxial line, the circuit generally used is: (Q. 8.39)

(a) A step-down, video transformer.

(b) A cathode (or emitter) follower.

(c) A quarter-wave transmission line section.

(d) A common-emitter stage.

(e) A grounded grid stage.

VIII-49.   When it is desired that short-range targets be clearly seen on a pulsed-radar set, it is important that the receiver and display system have: (Q. 8.39)

(a) The shortest possible recovery time.

(b) A long time constant.

(c) A restricted high-frequency response.

(d) Low-pass filters.

(e) Both (b) and (d) are correct.

VIII-50.   To achieve good bearing resolution when using a pulsed-radar set, an important requirement is: (Q. 8.63)

(a) A narrow, antenna-beam width in the horizontal plane.

(b) A narrow, antenna-beam width in the vertical plane.

(c) A very narrow transmitted pulse.

(d) A low repetition rate.

(e) A high duty cycle.

ELEMENT IX

BASIC BROADCAST

Q. 9.01. Define the following words or phrases: standard broadcast station (R & R 73.1); standard broadcast band (R & R 73.2); standard broadcast channel (R & R 73.3); FM station (R & R 73.310); FM band (R & R 73.310); daytime (R & R 73.6); nighttime (R & R 73.7); broadcast day (R & R 73.9); and EBS (R & R 73.912).

A. The following are the required definitions:

1. Standard broadcast station: A broadcasting station licensed for the transmission of radiotelephone emissions, primarily intended to be received by the general public and operated on a channel in the 535-1605 kilocycle band.

2. Standard broadcast band: The band of frequencies extending from 535 to 1605 kilocycles.

3. Standard broadcast channel: The term "standard broadcast channel" means the band of frequencies occupied by the carrier and two side bands of a broadcast signal with the carrier frequency at the center. Channels shall be designated by their assigned carrier frequencies. The 107 carrier frequencies assigned to standard broadcast stations shall begin at 540 kilocycles and be in successive steps of 10 kilocycles.

4. FM station: A broadcasting station licensed for the transmission of radiotelephone emissions primarily intended to be received by the general public and operated on a channel in the band of 88 to 108 megacycles.

5. FM band: The band of frequencies extending from 88 to 108 megacycles.

6. Daytime: That period of time between local sunrise and local sunset.

7. Nighttime: that period of time between local sunset and local sunrise.

8. Broadcast day: That period of time between local sunrise and 12 o'clock midnight, local time.

9. Emergency Broadcast System (EBS): The Emergency Broadcast System (EBS) is a system of facilities and personnel of nongovernment broadcast stations and other authorized facilities licensed or regulated by the Federal Communications Commission, including approved and authorized integral facilities or systems, arrangements, procedures, and interconnecting facilities, which have been authorized by the Commission to operate in a controlled manner during a grave national crisis or war.

Q. 9.02. Make the following transformations: kilocycles to cycles; kilovolts to volts; and milliamperes to amperes.

A. (a) One kilocycle equals 1000 cycles.

(b) One kilovolt equals 1000 volts.

(c) One milliampere equals one thousandth of an ampere.

D. The prefix "kilo" means to multiply by 1000 times whatever quantity follows.

The prefix "milli" means to take one-thousandth of whatever quantity follows.

Q. 9.03. Draw the face of the following meters and know how to read each one: ammeter; voltmeter; frequency monitor meter; VU meter (for percent modulation); and arbitrary scale meter.

A. The ammeter face is shown in Fig. 9.03(a).

The voltmeter face is shown in Fig. 9.03(b).

The frequency monitor meter face is shown in Fig. 9.03(c).

The VU meter face is shown in Fig. 9.03(d).

The arbitrary scale meter is shown in Fig 9.03.(e).

D. (a) An ammeter usually consists of a rotatable coil mounted between the poles of a permanent magnet. The current to be measured passes through the coil and produces an opposing flux that causes the coil to rotate. The amount of rotation is proportional to the magnitude of the current. A needle attached to the coil indicates values of current on a calibrated scale. In radio work, milliammeters and microammeters are more commonly used. These measure thousandths and millionths of amperes, respectively. See also Q. 3.84.

(b) See Q. 3.79, Q. 3.81 and Q. 3.84.

(c) The frequency monitor meter registers deviations of -30 to $+30$ cps from the AM broadcast station's operating frequency. The FCC requirements limit AM frequency deviation to ± 20 cps. See also Q. 4.97.

(d) See Q. 4.20, Q. 4.21 and Q. 4.22.

(e) An arbitrary scale meter with a scale from 0 to 100 is shown in part (e) of the figure. Such a meter might be used when only a

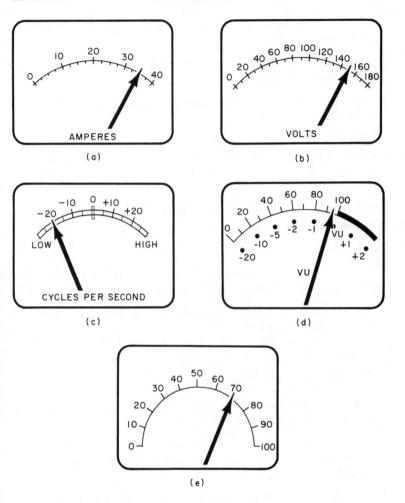

*Fig. 9.03. Faces of meters: (a) ammeter; (b) voltmeter;
(c) frequency monitor meter; (d) VU meter; and
(e) arbitrary scale meter.*

relative indication of voltage or current is desired, rather than exact values of these parameters.

Q. 9.04. What should an operator do if the remote antenna ammeter becomes defective? (R & R 73.58)

A. If no specified substitute meter is available, the station may be operated without the defective meter for a period not to exceed 60 days without further authority of the FCC. In order to operate the station, the meter may be shorted out.

D.   See R & R in Appendix I for further information regarding related action to be taken.

Q. 9.05.   What should an operator do if the remote control devices at a station so equipped malfunction? (R & R 73.67)

A.   A malfunction of any part of the remote control equipment and associated line circuits resulting in improper control or inaccurate meter readings shall be cause for immediate cessation of operation by remote control.

Q. 9.06.   What is the permissible percentage of modulation for AM stations? (R & R 73.55.)

A.   See Q. 4.103.

Q. 9.07.   What is the permissible frequency tolerance of standard broadcast (AM) stations? Of FM stations? (R & R 73.59, 73.269)

A.   For standard broadcast (AM) stations, the tolerance is ± 20 cycles from the assigned frequency.

For FM stations, the tolerance is ± 2000 cycles from the assigned frequency.

D.   See Q. 4.97 and Q. 4.114.

Q. 9.08.   What stations may be operated by a Third-Class Broadcast Operator? (R & R 73.93, 73.265)

A.   A person holding a Radiotelephone Third-Class Operator Permit with Broadcast Endorsement may *routinely* operate all types of AM and FM broadcast stations.

D.   In all cases, it is required that a First-Class Operator be employed by the station on either a part-time or a full-time basis, depending upon the type of station involved. (See Addendum to Element IX for further information on this matter.)

Note that a Third-Class Broadcast Operator may only *routinely* operate broadcast stations. His duties are strictly defined and unless he is under the immediate supervision of a First-Class Operator, he may make adjustments only of external controls, as follows:

(1) Those necessary to turn the transmitter on and off.
(2) Those necessary to compensate for voltage fluctuations in the primary power supply.
(3) Those necessary to maintain modulation levels of the transmitter within prescribed limits.

(4) Those necessary to effect routine changes in operating power which are required by the station authorization.

(5) Those necessary to change between non-directional and directional or between differing radiation patterns, provided that such changes require only activation of switches and do not involve the manual tuning of the transmitter final amplifier or antenna phasor equipment. The switching equipment shall be so arranged that the failure of any relay in the directional antenna system to activate properly will cause the emissions of the station to terminate.

Q. 9.09.   What are the power limitations on broadcast stations? (R & R 73.52)

A.   See Q. 4.96.

D.   For additional details see R & R 73.52 in Appendix I.

Q. 9.10.   What logs must be kept by broadcast stations, according to the Rules and Regulations of the FCC? (R & R 73.111)

A. The licensee or permittee of each standard broadcast station shall maintain Program, Operating, and Maintenance Logs.

D.   See R & R 73.111 in Appendix I. See also, Q. 4.106 through Q. 4.109 and Q. 4.116.

Q. 9.11.   Who keeps the station logs? (R & R 73.111)

A. Each log shall be kept by the person or persons competent to do so, having actual knowledge of the facts required. Such person(s) shall sign the appropriate log when starting duty and again when going off duty.

Q. 9.12.   What entries are made in the Program Log? In the Operating Log? (R & R 73.112 and R & R 73.113)

A.   The following entries shall be made in the Program Log:

1. An entry of the time each station identification announcement (call letters and location) is made.

2. An entry briefly describing each program broadcast, such as, "music," "drama," "speech," together with the name or title thereof, and the sponsor's name, with the beginning time and ending time of the program.

3. An entry showing that each sponsored program has been announced as sponsored, paid for, or furnished by the sponsor.

4. An entry showing the name of the network originating the program for each program of network origin.

The following entries shall be made in the Operating Log:

1. An entry of the time the station begins to supply power to the antenna and the time it stops.

2. An entry of each interruption of the carrier wave where restoration is not automatic and its cause and duration, followed by the signature of the person restoring operation (if licensed operator is other than the licensed operator on duty).

3. An entry, at the beginning of operation and at intervals not exceeding one-half hour, of the following:

(a) Operating constants of last r-f stage (total plate current and plate voltage).

(b) Antenna current (or common point current, if directional) without modulation.

(c) Frequency monitor reading.

4. An entry each day of the following, where applicable:

(a) Antenna base current(s) without modulation for each mode of operation:

    (1) Where remote antenna meters or a remote common point meter are normally employed, but are defective.

    (2) Where required by the station license for directional antenna operation.

(b) Where there is remote control operation of a directional antenna station, readings for each pattern taken at the transmitter (within two hours of commencement of operation with each pattern) of:

    (1) Common point current without modulation.

    (2) Base current(s) without modulation.

    (3) Phase monitor sample loop current(s) without modulation.

    (4) Phase indications.

5. Any other entries required by the instrument of authorization or the provisions of Part 73 of the FCC Rules and Regulations.

D.   See, also, R & R 73.113 in Appendix I for certain additional comments on the above requirements. See also Q. 4.107.

Q. 9.13.   When may abbreviations be used in the station logs? (R & R 73.111)

A.   Abbreviations may be used if the proper meaning or explanation is contained elsewhere in the log.

Q. 9.14.   How and by whom may station logs be corrected? (R & R 73.111)

A. Any necessary correction may be made only by the person originating the entry who shall strike out the erroneous portion, initial the correction made, and indicate the date of correction.

Q. 9.15.   According to the Rules and Regulations of the FCC, how long must station logs be retained? (R & R 73.115)

A. See Q. 4.108.

Q. 9.16. What information must be given an FCC inspector at any reasonable hour? (R & R 73.116)

A. The following shall be made available upon request:
1. Program, Operating, and Maintenance logs.
2. Equipment performance measurements (see R & R 73.47).
3. A copy of the most recent antenna resistance or common-point impedance measurements submitted to the Commission.
4. A copy of the most recent field intensity measurements to establish performance of directional antennas (see R & R 73.151).

Q. 9.17. What is included in a station identification and how often is it given? (R & R 73.117)

A. The call letters and location are given in a station identification. It is given at the beginning and ending of each time of operation and during operation (1) on the hour and (2) hourly, as close to the hour as feasible, at a natural break in program offerings.

D. See R & R 73.117 for exceptions to above.

Q. 9.18. What should an operator do if the modulation monitor becomes defective? (R & R 73.56)

A. See Q. 4.104.

Q. 9.19. What should an operator do if the frequency monitor meter becomes defective? (R & R 73.252)

A. See Q. 4.104.

Q. 9.20. When should minor corrections to the transmitter be made —before or after logging the meter readings? (R & R 73.113)

A. Minor corrections to the transmitter should be made after logging the meter readings.

D. The readings in the log represent the actual readings at the time made and entered. Corrections to the transmitters should follow.

Q. 9.21. Should the sponsor's name ever be omitted when reading commercials on the air? (R & R 73.119)

A. Ordinarily, the sponsor's name is never omitted when reading commercials on the air.

D. See R & R 73.119 in Appendix I for additional details.

Q. 9.22. When should an operator announce a program as "recorded"? (R & R 73.118)

A. The operator should announce a program as "recorded" when the element of time associated with the program is significant and the impression may· be created that the broadcast is occurring simultaneously with the event.

D. See R & R 73.118 in Appendix I for additional details.

Q. 9.23. How often should tower lights be checked for proper operations? (R & R 17.47)

A. At least once every 24 hours.

D. See Q. 4.138 through Q. 4.148, and R & R 17.37 in Appendix I.

Q. 9.24. What record is kept of tower light operation? (R & R 17.49

A. A record is kept in the station log of the following:

1. The time the tower lights are turned on and off each day, if manually controlled.

2. The time the daily check of proper operation of the tower lights was made, if automatic alarm system is not provided.

3. Details regarding any failure of tower lights.

D. See Q. 4.144, and R & R 17.38 in Appendix I.

Q. 9.25. What should an operator do if the tower lights fail? (R & R 17.48)

A. The operator shall report immediately by telephone or telegraph to the nearest Flight Service Station or office of the Federal Aviation Agency any observed or otherwise known failure of a code or rotating beacon light or top light not corrected within 30 minutes, regardless of the cause of such failure. Further notification by telephone or telegraph shall be given immediately upon resumption of the required illumination.

D. See Q. 4.146 through Q. 4.148.

Q. 9.26. What is EBS? (R & R 73.912)

A. The Emergency Broadcast System (EBS) consists of broadcast stations and interconnecting facilities that have been authorized by the Commission (FCC) to operate in a controlled manner during a war, threat of war, state of public peril or disaster, or other national emergency.

D. See Q. 4.127 through Q. 4.132.

Q. 9.27. What is an Emergency Action Condition (R & R 73.908)

A. The condition which exists after the transmission of an Emergency Action Notification and before the transmission of the Emergency Action Termination.

D. See Q. 4.127.

Q. 9.28. What equipment must be installed in broadcast stations in regard to reception of an Emergency Action Notification? (R & R 73.932)

A. The necessary equipment to receive Emergency Action Notifications (or Terminations) by means of reception of radio broadcast messages.

D. See Q. 4.129, and R & R 73.932 in Appendix I.

Q. 9.29. How often should EBS test transmissions be sent? During what time period are they sent? (R & R 73.961(e))

A. Test transmissions shall be made once each week on an unscheduled basis between the hours of 8:30 a.m. and local sunset.

D. See Q. 4.132, and R & R 73.961(e) in Appendix I.

Q. 9.30. During a period of an Emergency Action Condition, what should all nonparticipating stations do? (R & R 73.933(a))

A. All nonparticipating stations will observe radio silence in accordance with the Emergency Broadcast System Plan.

D. See R & R 73.933(a) in Appendix I for additional details.

Q. 9.31. If the tower lights of a station are required to be controlled by a light-sensitive device, and this device malfunctions, when should the tower lights be "on"? (R & R 17.25(a) (3))

A. All lights shall burn continuously or shall be controlled by a light sensitive device adjusted so that the lights will be turned on at a north sky light intensity level of about 35 foot-candles and turned off at a north sky light intensity level of about 58 foot-candles.

ADDENDUM TO ELEMENT IX

The information which follows is based upon an FCC Information Bulletin and an FCC Study Guide and describes certain aspects of operator duties and station operation as they apply to a Third-Class Radiotelephone Operator who also has a broadcast endorsement. For the purposes of this section only, such an operator is referred to simply as a "third-class operator."

Note that much of the following information does not appear as answers to questions for Element IX and thus is of particular importance to the student. This material is condensed and paraphrased from the FCC Rules and Regulations. Therefore, for a more complete understanding of the specific points, it is suggested that the student refer to the appropriate sections of the FCC Rules and Regulations as given in the various paragraphs below.

LICENSE REQUIRED

The permissible duties of a third-class operator have been expanded to include all types of AM and FM broadcast stations, with regard to *routine* station operation. Note that the duties of such operators are strictly defined and that in all cases it is required that a first-class operator be employed by the station on either a full-time or a part-time basis. For further details about this most important point, see Q. 4.100 and Q. 9.08. Also, see R & R 73.93 in Appendix I. [Students are also referred to R & R 73.265 (FM Broadcast Stations) and R & R 73.565 (Non-Commercial Educational FM Broadcast Stations), not included in this text because of lack of space.]

ADDITIONAL DEFINITIONS

FM Stereophonic Broadcast—The transmission of a stereophonic program by an FM broadcast station utilizing the main channel and a stereophonic subchannel (R&R 73.310)

FM Subsidiary Communications Authorization (SCA)—An authorization granted to an FM station for the simultaneous transmission of one or more signals on assigned subcarrier frequencies within the station's assigned channel. Special decoding equipment is required to receive program material furnished on the SCA subchannel. Such material, although broadcast related, is normally intended for paying subscribers. (R&R 73.293)

Sunrise and Sunset—For each particular location and during any particular month, the times of sunrise and sunset are specified on most AM broadcast station licenses. This is necessary because not all standard (AM) broadcast stations are permitted to operate at night. In order to control objectionable skywave interference, stations which are permitted to operate at night are frequently required to change their modes of operation. These changes may involve the use of directional antenna systems, a reduction in operating power, or both, and normally occur at the sunrise and sunset times listed in the station license. (R&R 73.8)

Broadcast Day—That period of time between local sunrise and 12 midnight local time. (R&R 73.9)

Nominal Power—The power of a standard broadcast station as specified in a system of classification which includes the following values: 50 kW, 25 kW, 10 kW, 5 kW, 1 kW, .5 kW, 0.25 kW. (R&R 73.14)

EQUIPMENT ADJUSTMENTS PERMITTED

Transmitter operators are responsible for proper operation of the equipment. A first-class operator may repair a transmitter, maintain it, and make major adjustments. A third-class operator may only make minor adjustments. At AM and FM broadcast stations, a third-class operator may make adjustments only of external controls necessary to turn the transmitter on and off, to compensate for voltage fluctuations in the primary power supply, and to maintain modulation levels of the transmitter within prescribed limits.

Third-class operators at standard (AM) broadcast stations may also make adjustments of external controls necessary to carry out routine changes in operating power required by the station authorization, and to change between non-directional and directional or between differing radiation patterns, provided that such changes require only activation of switches and do not involve the manual tuning of the transmitter final amplifier or antenna phasor equipment. The switching equipment shall be so arranged that the failure of any relay in the directional antenna system to activate properly will cause the emissions of the station to terminate

It is extremely important that transmitter operators know how to read and evaluate the required meters and monitors, and to know when adjustments are to be made or when the station's first-class operator should be notified of impending problems. The operator must also know when the transmitter should be turned off because of serious malfunction. Detailed charts or instructions should be available to the operator so that he can readily determine that the transmitter is operating correctly and within the terms of FCC Rules and station license. (R&R 73.93, 73.265, and 73.565)

NORMAL OPERATING POSITION

The normal operating position is to be located so that the transmitter, required monitors, and other required metering equipment are readily accessible, and sufficiently close to the operator so that deviation from normal indications of required instruments can be observed in a 360° arc. However, if operation by remote control is authorized, the normal operating position must be placed so that the required controls and instruments are readily accessible and located sufficiently close to the operator so that deviations from normal indications of required instruments can be observed in a 360° arc. See Sections 73.93, 73.265, and 73.565 of the Commission's Rules.

MODULATION AND MODULATION MONITORS

The percentage of modulation at AM and FM broadcast stations should be maintained at as high a level as possible consistent with good quality of transmission. Generally, the modulation should not be less than 85 percent on peaks of frequent recurrence. However, it may be less than 85 percent when necessary to avoid objectionable loudness. At AM broadcast stations, modulation must not exceed 100 percent on negative peaks and 125 percent on any positive peak. At FM broadcast stations, modulation must not exceed 100 percent on either positive or negative peaks. (R&R 73.55, 73.268, and 73.568)

Each station must have in operation a modulation monitor which the operator uses to determine whether the modulation is at the proper level. The modulation monitor consists of a meter and a peak flasher. The meter does not indicate the peak modulation, but indicates a value somewhat less than the peak modulation. The "peak flasher" indicates modulation peaks. Generally the peak flasher is set so that when it flashes, it is an indication that the modulation is excessive and that corrective action must be taken by the operator. (R&R 73.50, 73.56, 73.253, 73.268, 73.553, and 73.568)

OPERATING POWER

Each AM and FM broadcast station is authorized to operate at a specified operating power as indicated on the station license. Operating power for AM stations is normally the antenna input power and for FM stations it is the transmitter output power. The operating power must be maintained as near as possible to the value specified by the station license and shall be not more than 105 percent or less than 90 percent of this level. Noncommercial educational FM broadcast stations licensed to operate with transmitter output power of 10 watts or less may be operated at less than the authorized power, but not more than 105 percent of the authorized power.

Non-directional AM broadcast stations employ only a single antenna tower. Power determined by the *direct* method is equal to the product of the antenna resistance and the square of the antenna current. Directional AM broadcast stations employ multiple radiating elements. Power determined by the direct method for these stations is equal to the product of the resistance common to all antenna towers (common point resistance) and the square of the current common to all antenna towers (common point current). At FM broadcast stations, if power is determined by the direct method, it is read directly from the RF transmission line meter. This meter must be calibrated each six months to give a direct indication of the power supplied to the antenna.

Generally, AM broadcast stations must determine the operating power by the direct method. FM broadcast stations may determine the operating power by either method, but most use the indirect method.

For both AM and FM broadcast stations, operating power determined by the indirect method is equal to the product of the plate voltage (Ep) and the plate current (Ip) of the last radio stage, and an efficiency factor F: Operating Power = Ep × Ip × F. When the power of an AM station is determined by the indirect method, the calculated value of Ep × Ip or Ep × Ip × F is to be entered in the operating log when required transmitter meter readings are taken. (R&R 73.51, 73.52, 73.267, and 73.567)

INDICATING INSTRUMENTS

Each transmitter is equipped with meters to indicate plate voltage and plate current. These meters indicate the operating constants of the transmitter amplifier. Each transmitter has normal operating levels of plate voltage and plate current and the operator should know what corrective actions should be taken when the meters indicate abnormal values.

At the place in the circuit where the antenna resistance or common point resistance is measured, an antenna ammeter is inserted to measure current into the antenna system. This meter is a direct indication as to whether the station is operating at, above, or below the licensed power. This meter indication should be maintained as close as possible to the licensed operating current and the operator should know what actions are necessary when the meter indications deviate from that value. Usually the antenna ammeter is located at the base of the tower and not easily accessible to the operator on duty. For this reason most stations use a remote antenna ammeter which is located at the normal operating position of the person on duty. The remote antenna ammeter indication may be entered in the operating log in lieu of the base current meter indication provided the remote meter is calibrated once weekly. (R&R 73.39, 73.58, 73.258, and 73.558)

ELECTRICAL TERMS

Three common electrical terms are volts, amperes, and watts. One thousand volts is a kilovolt (kV) and 1000 watts is a kilowatt (kW). One one-thousandth (1/1000) of an ampere is a milliampere (mA). The operator should know how to use these terms interchangeably. For instance:

> 2000 volts is the same as 2 kilovolts
> .5 kilovolts is the same as 500 volts
> 200 watts is the same as .2 kilowatts
> 20 kilowatts is the same as 20,000 watts
> .5 amperes is the same as 500 milliamperes
> 250 milliamperes is the same as .25 amperes

DIRECTIONAL ANTENNA MONITORS AND ANTENNA CURRENT RATIOS

Non-directional AM stations use a single antenna tower and transmit the radio signal with equal strength in all directions from the station. Directional AM stations utilize more than one antenna tower. By establishing the position of each tower, the power radiated by each tower, and the phase of the signal in each tower, different signal strengths can be radiated in various directions. Directional antenna systems are used to improve the signal over desired areas and to reduce the signal in the direction of other stations to prevent interference.

To determine if a directional antenna system is radiating the signal according to a specified radiation pattern, an instrument called an antenna monitor is installed at the station. The antenna monitor enables the operator to determine if the radio frequency (R-F) current in each tower is of the correct value and if the phase of the signal radiated by each tower is also correct. Some antenna monitors indicate the ratio of current in each tower to the current in one tower called the reference tower.

If the signal arrives at each tower at the same time, the current in each tower is said to be "in phase." In most directional antenna systems, the time the radio frequency signal reaches each tower from the transmitter is not the same. The time difference or phase is measured in degrees. For each directional antenna tower, the station license contains a list of the required signal phases and antenna base current ratios. The antenna base current ratio for a tower is calculated by dividing the current meter reading for that tower by the current meter reading of the designated reference tower. The ratio, either calculated or read on the antenna monitor, must not deviate more than 5 percent from the value on the station license. Operators on duty at AM stations using directional antenna systems should know how to read the antenna monitor meters, and should know how to use charts, tables, or other instructions to determine if the station is operating correctly, if attention by the station's first-class operator is required, or if the station must terminate operation. (R&R 73.69, and 73.95)

REMOTE CONTROL EQUIPMENT AND OPERATION

Some broadcast stations have the main studio at one location and the transmitter and associated equipment at another location. Rather than have an operator on duty at the transmitter, the controls and metering functions of the transmitter may be located at the studio or other location and the operator on duty at this control point. A remote control authorization must be obtained by the licensee from the Commission. Equipment must be installed at the control point that will permit the operator to perform all monitoring and operating functions required by the Commission's rules. If any part of the remote control equipment, meters, or the associated control circuits have a malfunction which results in improper control or meter readings, operation of the transmitter by remote control must cease and an operator placed on duty at the transmitter until the malfunction has been corrected. (R&R 73.67, 73.274, and 73.575)

POSTING OF OPERATOR PERMITS

The operator must post his permit or posting statement at the place where he is on duty at the transmitter control point. FCC Form 759 is a posting statement used by operators employed at more than one station. The permit is posted at one station and FCC Forms 759 are posted at other stations where the operator is employed. The station license and other operating authorizations must be posted at the transmitter control point with all terms visible. (R&R 73.92, 73.264 and 73.564)

STATION INSPECTION AND AVAILABILITY OF RECORDS

The licensee of any radio station shall make the station available for inspection by representatives of the Commission at any reasonable hour. Proofs of performance, logs, measurement records, and other documents required to be maintained must also be available for inspection. (R&R 73.97, 73.263, 73.63, 73.116, 73.286, 73.586)

FM STEREO AND SUBSIDIARY COMMUNICATIONS AUTHORIZATIONS

In addition to monaural operation, FM stations may elect to broadcast stereo programming. This is accomplished by inserting a subchannel within the main FM channel assignment. In addition to the stereophonic subchannel, an entirely different subchannel may also be used. Stations using this subchannel operate under a Subsidiary Communications Authorization (SCA). Programs transmitted by way of the Subsidiary Communications Authorization cannot be received without a special multiplex receiver. Most SCA subcarriers are used for the transmission of subscription background music. Other SCA uses are for detailed weather forecasting, special time signals, and other material of a broadcast nature expressly designed and intended for business, professional, educational, religious, trade, labor, agriculture, or other groups engaged in any lawful activity. (R&R 73.293, 73.295, 73.297, 73.593, 73.595, and 73.596)

GENERAL LOG REQUIREMENTS

Broadcast stations are required to keep several kinds of logs. The transmitter operator on duty is required to keep the operating (transmitter) log and frequently is responsible for keeping the program log. All logs must be kept by a station employee who is competent to do so having actual knowledge of the facts. Operating and Program logs must be signed by the person keeping the logs both at the beginning and end of his period of duty. The logs must be orderly and legible and in such detail that data required is readily available. Each log page must be numbered and dated and times shown in local time. If the area observes "advanced time" during summer months, the log should so indicate.

No log or preprinted log or schedule which becomes a log may be erased or obliterated during the period of required retention. Corrections must be made by striking out the erroneous portion or by a corrective explanation on the log or attached to it. Any corrections or changes, no matter by whom made, must be initiated by the person keeping the log prior to his signing off duty. If changes must be made after the operator has signed off duty, an explanation must be made on the log or an attachment, dated and signed by the person who kept the log or other officials of the station depending on whether the log was a program or operating log. (R&R 73.111, 73.112, 73.113, 73.281, 73.282, 73.283, 73.581, 73.582 and 73.583)

PROGRAM LOG

Stations are required to keep program logs of the material broadcast each day. The transmitter operator often must complete the program log in addition to his duties of keeping the transmitter operating log. The program log contains entries identifying each program by name or title and the time the program began and ended. Each program must be identified in the log as to its type and source.

Program log entries for commercial matter must indicate the amount of time devoted to commercial matter during an hourly segment (beginning on the hour) or the duration of each commercial message during the hourly segment. Each sponsored program or announcement must be identified as such during its broadcast, and an indication is required in the log to show this was done. Log entries for each public service announcement must include the name of the organization or interest on whose behalf it was broadcast.

Entries must be made of the time each required station identification was broadcast.

An entry for each announcement of or in behalf of a political candidate is required and must include the name and political affiliation of the candidate.

FM broadcast stations utilizing a subsidiary communications authorization must also describe the material transmitted on the SCA subchannel. This information may be kept on a special column of the station's regular program log. In the event of a change in the general description of the material transmitted, an entry must be made indicating the time of each such change and a description thereof. (R&R 73.112, 73.282, 73.295, 73.582, and 73.595)

OPERATING LOG

The operator in actual charge of the transmitter at AM and FM broadcasting stations must record certain meter readings in the operating log at the beginning of operation in each mode and at intervals not exceeding three hours. These entries must be the readings observed prior to making any adjustments of the transmitter, and if adjustments are made to restore parameters to their proper operating values, the corrected indications are to be logged. If any parameter deviation is beyond a prescribed tolerance, a notation describing the nature of the corrective action to return the parameter to the proper operating value must be entered. Indications of all parameters whose value is affected by modulation of the carrier should be read without modulation. The operator signs the log when he begins duty and again when going off duty to indicate the time period when he was in charge of the transmitting equipment. An entry is required for the daily check of the tower lighting system to ensure proper illumination of the tower. The time the transmitter begins to supply power to the antenna and the time it ceases are also recorded.

At all standard (AM) broadcast stations, the following entries shall be made in the operating log:

1. Last stage plate voltage meter reading.
2. Last stage plate current meter reading.
3. Antenna current or common point current reading.

At AM broadcast stations employing directional antenna systems, additional operating log entries may include:

1. Remote antenna base current meter readings, or antenna monitor sample current meter readings.
2. Antenna monitor phase readings, if operation is by direct control.

At FM broadcast stations operating with a transmitter power output above 10 watts, the following entries shall be made in the operating log:

1. Last stage transmitter plate voltage meter reading.
2. Last stage transmitter plate current meter reading.
3. R-F transmission line meter reading (only FM stations determining the operating power by the direct method need log this).

An FM station operating under a Subsidiary Communications Authorization must keep a log of its operation. The log may be included as part of the operating log for the main channel or may be kept separately. Entries are required of the time the subcarrier generator is turned on and when it is turned off (excluding subcarrier interruptions of 5 minutes or less). An entry is also required for the time modulation is applied to the subcarrier and the time the modulation is removed from the subcarrier.

FM broadcast stations with an operating power of 10 watts or less are required to log only the time the station begins to supply power to the antenna, the time it stops, and entries concerning the daily observations of tower lights. (R&R 73.113, 73.283, 73.295, 73.583, and 73.595)

ORDER OF SUSPENSION

Upon receipt by the Commission of application for hearing, the order of suspension shall be held in abeyance until the conclusion of the hearing which shall be conducted under such rules as the Commission may prescribe. Upon the conclusion of the hearing the Commission may affirm, modify, or revoke its order of suspension. (See also Q. 1.18, Section 303(m)(2), and R&R 1.85)

SPONSOR IDENTIFICATION

When a broadcast station transmits matter for which it receives or expects to receive any compensation such as money, services, or other consideration, the station must announce that the matter is sponsored or furnished and also announce the name of the sponsor. However, when a commercial product or service is advertised, use of the sponsor's corporate name, trade name, or name of the product or service will suffice if it is clear that the product name identifies the sponsor. Broadcast station licensees are responsible to ensure that their employees or others connected with program material are fully aware that accurate sponsor identification must be obtained and broadcast. Sponsored programs and announcements that do not promote a specific commercial service or product must also be identified by the name of the actual sponsor. Operators keeping program logs must be alert to ensure that sponsored matter is announced at the time of the broadcast and the sponsor is correctly identified in the program log. (R&R 73.119 and 73.289)

LOTTERIES

Broadcast stations are prohibited from transmitting announcements or programs promoting or containing other information that would promote lotteries. A lottery is any scheme in which money or a prize of value is awarded to a person selected by lot or chance, if a condition of winning is that a person must have furnished any money, purchased a particular product or service, or have in his possession a product sold by the sponsor. For example, a door prize given away to a person selected from tickets purchased to gain entry to a particular event is considered a lottery, and the door prize drawing cannot be promoted by radio announcements. Prizes given away to winners selected by lot when "no purchase is necessary" to enter the drawing would not be considered lottery prizes and announcements promoting these "free entry" drawings may be broadcast. Broadcast station operators who are monitoring program material should be aware of the prohibition of broadcasting any type of lottery promotion. (R&R 73. 122 and 73.292)

BROADCAST OF TELEPHONE CONVERSATIONS

Before broadcasting a telephone conversation or recording a telephone conversation for later broadcast, the parties to the conversation must be informed of the intention to broadcast the conversation. However, station employees who may be presumed to be aware that their telephone conversations are intended for broadcast are not required to be advised of the broadcasting of their calls. Also, no notice of broadcast is required for persons originating calls to programs which normally broadcast telephone conversations coming into the program. (R&R 73.1206)

EMERGENCY BROADCAST SYSTEM AND SYSTEM TEST TRANSMISSIONS

The Emergency Action Notification as it applies to broadcast stations is the notice of the existence of an Emergency Action Condition. An Emergency Action Condition is a national, state, or local area emergency situation posing a threat to the safety of life or property. The FCC provides each broadcast station with a checklist, in summary form, of actions to be taken by the station's operators upon receipt of an Emergency Action Notification, Emergency Action Termination, or test transmission received.

Each station must have in operation at the control point a monitor receiver for receiving the Emergency Action Notification or termination announcements transmitted by a designated control station. During National level emergency conditions certain stations will continue operating. Other stations not participating in the National level emergency plan must discontinue operations for the duration of the National Level Emergency Action Condition.

Each station is required to transmit at least once each week an EBS test transmission announcement and signal. All station operators must be thoroughly familiar with the procedures for transmitting the EBS signals and be prepared to take appropriate action in the event of an actual alert. The operator must also be familiar with the operation of the EBS monitor receiver and procedures to follow upon receipt of a test or alert signal from another station. (See Q. 9.26 through Q. 9.30.)

BROADCAST OF TAPED, FILMED, OR RECORDED MATERIAL

Any taped, filmed, or recorded program material in which time is of special significance, or where an attempt is made to create the impression that an event is occurring at the time of the broadcast, shall be identified at the beginning as taped, filmed, or recorded. The language of the announcement shall be clear and in terms commonly understood by the public. See Section 73.1208 of the Commission's Rules.

REBROADCAST

The term "rebroadcast" means reception by radio of the programs of a radio station, and the simultaneous or subsequent retransmission of such programs by a broadcast station. No broadcasting station shall rebroadcast a program, or part of a program, of another broadcasting station without the express authority of the originating station. A copy of the written consent of the licensee originating the program shall be kept by the licensee of the station rebroadcasting such program. See Section 73.1207 of the Commission's Rules.

CYCLES TO HERTZ

In past years it was common to refer to frequency in units of cycles per second or "cycles." Multiple prefixes of kilo or mega were frequently used to indicate radio frequency. In recent years the term "hertz" was substituted by international agreement for "cycles per second." For example, a broadcast station may be assigned a frequency of 760 kilohertz (abbreviated 760 kHz) or 92.1 megahertz (abbreviated 92.1 MHz).

STATION IDENTIFICATION

Broadcast station identification announcements shall be made: at the beginning and ending of each period of operation and hourly, as close to the hour as feasible, at a natural break in program offerings. Official station identification shall consist of the station's call letters immediately followed by the name of the community or communities specified on the license as the station's location. See Section 73.1201 of the Commission's Rules.

BROADCAST STATION METERS

Some types of broadcast station meters are given in Q. 9.03, and their uses are there described. Additional types of meters which may be commonly found in many broadcast stations are shown in Fig. 9-A.

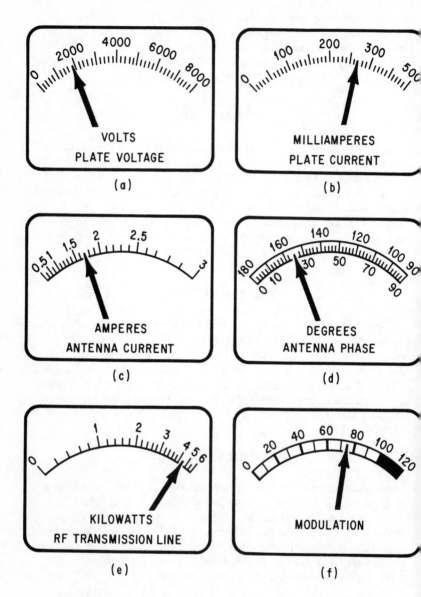

Fig. 9-A. The meters shown are similar to the ones an operator may use in the operation of broadcast stations. The operator should be familiar with these meters, know how to read them, and know what they are used for (see Addendum text).

Plate-Voltage Meter: The type shown in the figure is similar to one which might be used to measure the plate voltage of the final R-F stage of a transmitter. The product of plate voltage and plate current indicates the input (d-c) power to the final amplifier. See also in this addendum under OPERATING POWER and INDICATING INSTRUMENTS.

Plate-Current Meter: The type shown in the figure is similar to one which might be used to indicate the plate current of the final R-F stage of a transmitter. The product of plate voltage and plate current indicates the input (d-c) power to the final amplifier. See also in this addendum under OPERATING POWER and INDICATING INSTRUMENTS.

Antenna-Current Meter: As the name implies, this meter measures the amount of R-F antenna current being fed to the feed point of the antenna. One of the important uses of the reading on this meter is the calculation of transmitter operating power, as described in this addendum under OPERATING POWER, INDICATING INSTRUMENTS, and DIRECTIONAL ANTENNA MONITORS AND ANTENNA CURRENT RATIOS.

Antenna-Phase Meter: When a broadcast station employs a directional antenna, the correct directivity pattern depends upon the phase at which each antenna element is fed (and the ratio of each antenna current to the others). This meter provides the operator with a direct phase reading of each antenna. See also in this addendum under EQUIPMENT ADJUSTMENTS PERMITTED, INDICATING INSTRUMENTS, and DIRECTIONAL ANTENNA MONITORS AND ANTENNA CURRENT RATIOS.

R-F Transmission-Line Meter: This type of meter may be used in an FM transmitter, to give a direct indication of the operating power. See also OPERATING POWER and INDICATING INSTRUMENTS.

Modulation Meter: The permissible percentage of modulation for each class of station is specified by the FCC. This figure is given directly on the face of a modulation meter. See also Q. 9.06 and, in this addendum, EQUIPMENT ADJUSTMENTS PERMITTED, and MODULATION AND MODULATION MONITORS.

Note: It is usually required that the reading of the above-described meters be entered in the station log. See in this addendum under OPERATING LOG and see also Q. 9.12.

SAMPLE TEST QUESTIONS

For each Element in this book, an FCC-type sample examination is provided herein. This is of course also true for Element IX. However, to assist the student to be better prepared to pass the examination for Element IX, the following additional five sample examination questions and answers, as provided by the FCC, are presented. Note that the asterisk (*) denotes the correct answer.

1. Station identification must be given:
   *a. On the hour.
   b. On the half hour.
   c. At 30-minute intervals.
   d. After a commercial.
   e. After each newscast.

2. The plate voltmeter reads 2 kilovolts. This is the same as:
   a. .002 volts.
   b. 2 volts.
   c. 20 volts.
   d. 200 volts.
   *e. 2000 volts.

3. The plate voltmeter at an FM broadcast station reads 2 kilovolts and the plate current meter reads 500 milliamperes. With an efficiency of 70 percent, the operating power as determined by the indirect method is:
   a. 140 watts.
   b. 350 watts.
   *c. 700 watts.
   d. 1000 watts.
   e. 1400 watts.

4. The antenna resistance at a standard broadcast station is 40 ohms and the antenna current is 5 amperes. The power calculated by the direct method is:
   a. 8 watts.
   b. 200 watts.
   c. 900 watts.
   *d. 1000 watts.
   e. 8000 watts.

5. Tower one of a three tower directional antenna array is the reference tower. The antenna current for tower one is 6 amperes. The antenna current for tower two is 2 amperes, and the antenna current for tower three is 3 amperes. The antenna base current ratio of tower two is:
   *a. .33
   b. .5
   c. 1
   d. 2
   e. 3

FCC-TYPE SAMPLE TEST FOR ELEMENT IX

IX-1.   Abbreviations may be used in the station logs when: (Q. 9.13)
- (a) An emergency exists and at no other time.
- (b) The person in charge of the station is not present.
- (c) Permission is granted by the FCC for individual cases.
- (d) The proper meaning is contained elsewhere in the log.
- (e) Only the night shift is on duty.

IX-2.   The power limitations on broadcast stations are: (Q. 9.09)
- (a) 5 percent above or 10 percent below the licensed power.
- (b) 10 percent above or 5 percent below the licensed power.
- (c) Maximum licensed power required at all times.
- (d) Not more than 15 percent above the licensed power.
- (e) 10 percent above or 10 percent below the licensed power.

IX-3.   The FM band (entertainment) extends from: (Q. 9.01)
- (a) 535 to 1605 kc.
- (b) 88 to 108 kc.
- (c) 88 to 108 mc.
- (d) 54 to 60 mc.
- (e) 60 to 66 mc.

IX-4.   One milliampere equals: (Q. 9.02)
- (a) One thousand amperes.
- (b) One-thousandth of an ampere.
- (c) One-thousandth of a volt.
- (d) One ten-thousandth of an ampere.
- (e) One-millionth of an ampere.

IX-5.   The permissible percentage of modulation for AM broadcast stations is: (Q. 9.06)
- (a) Not more than 100% or less than 85%.
- (b) Not less than 100% for all program material.
- (c) 50% for voice and 100% for music programs.
- (d) Not more than 85% or less than 75%.
- (e) None of the above.

IX-6.   If the antenna tower lights of a broadcast station fail for more than 30 minutes, the operator should: (Q. 9.25)
- (a) Shut down the station and notify the FCC.
- (b) Periodically broadcast this information at least once every half hour.
- (c) Report this fact immediately to the nearest office of the FAA.
- (d) Report this fact immediately to the nearest office of the State Aviation Authority.
- (e) Report this fact immediately to the nearest office of the FCC.

IX-7.   EBS test transmissions should be sent during the hours of: (Q. 9.29)

    (a) Midnight and 8:30 a.m.
    (b) 8:30 a.m. and local sunset.
    (c) 8:30 a.m. and midnight.
    (d) Midnight and 3 a.m.
    (e) 12 noon and midnight.

IX-8. Antenna lights should be checked for proper operation: (Q. 9.23)
    (a) Each hour of station operation.
    (b) At least once each 24 hours.
    (c) At least once each 12 hours.
    (d) Only during inclement weather and then, hourly.
    (e) Whenever modulation and power output checks are made.

IX-9. If the remote antenna ammeter becomes defective, the station: (Q. 9.05)
    (a) Must be shut down until it is replaced.
    (b) Can be operated, but only under reduced power.
    (c) Can be operated for 10 days without the meter.
    (d) Can be operated for 60 days, by shorting out the meter.
    (e) Can be operated only if the modulation is reduced to 75%.

IX-10. The frequency tolerance of broadcast FM stations is: (Q. 9.07)
    (a) Plus or minus 20 cycles.
    (b) Plus or minus 200 cycles.
    (c) Plus or minus 0.05%.
    (d) Plus or minus 0.005%.
    (e) Plus or minus 2000 cycles.

IX-11. Station logs must be retained for a period of: (Q. 9.15)
    (a) Two years.
    (b) One year.
    (c) Indefinitely, until notified by the FCC.
    (d) 90 days.
    (e) Six months.

IX-12. In the station operating log, entries regarding the technical operation of the station shall be entered, after the initial daily entry, at intervals: (Q. 9.12)
    (a) Of one hour.
    (b) Not to exceed 30 minutes.
    (c) Not to exceed two hours.
    (d) Of 15 minutes.
    (e) Not to exceed 90 minutes.

IX-13. If the modulation monitor becomes defective, the station: (Q. 9.18)
    (a) Must immediately cease operation until such time as the monitor is repaired.

(b) Can be operated, but only if the modulation (estimated) does not exceed 50%.

(c) Must immediately notify the FAA.

(d) May continue to operate for 60 days.

(e) May continue to operate for 10 days.

IX-14. EBS consists of broadcasting stations and interconnecting facilities that have been authorized to operate: (Q. 9.26)

(a) In the event any one of the stations breaks down.

(b) In order to relay messages in the event of aircraft hijackings.

(c) In order to relay "hot-line" messages from Russia and China.

(d) Only during a national emergency.

(e) In order to relay messages from ships in distress.

IX-15. In Fig. 9.03(c), the frequency meter indicates that the station frequency is: (Q. 9.03)

(a) Ten cycles above the designated frequency.

(b) Ten cycles below the designated frequency.

(c) Ten kc above the designated frequency.

(d) Exactly right.

(e) Ten kc below the designated frequency.

IX-16. In the VU meter shown in Fig. 9.03(d), when the modulation is at 100%, the VU reading will be: (Q. 9.03)

(a) −2 VU.

(b) +3 VU.

(c) −20 VU.

(d) 0 VU.

(e) 100 VU.

IX-17. "Broadcast day" is defined as the period between: (Q. 9.01)

(a) Local sunrise and local sunset.

(b) Local sunrise and 3 a.m., local standard time.

(c) 6 a.m. and 12 midnight, local standard time.

(d) Local sunrise and 12 midnight, local standard time.

(e) 6 a.m. and 3 a.m. the following day, local standard time.

IX-18. "Daytime" is defined as the period between: (Q. 9.01)

(a) 6 a.m. and 6 p.m., local standard time.

(b) Local sunrise and local sunset.

(c) 7 a.m. and local sunset.

(d) Local sunrise and 6 p.m., local standard time.

(e) None of the above.

IX-19. If the remote control devices at a station malfunction, resulting in improper control, the operator shall: (Q. 9.05)

(a) Continue remote operation for not more than 60 days.

(b) Continue remote operation, not to exceed 10 days.

(c) Immediately cease remote control operation.

(d) Continue remote operation, but immediately notify the FCC.

(e) Continue remote operation, but enter the details of the problem in the operating log.

IX-20. A Third-Class Broadcast Operator may routinely operate: (Q. 9.08)

(a) AM stations with a power greater than 10 kW.

(b) AM stations using directional antennas only.

(c) FM stations with a power greater than 25 kW.

(d) All types of AM and FM Broadcast stations, regardless of type of antenna used.

(e) AM stations with a power greater than 10 kW and employing directional antennas.

IX-21. The pointer on the modulation meter shown in Fig. 9-A (addendum) indicates that the modulation percentage is: (Ref. Element IX Addendum)

(a) 20%

(b) 75%

(c) 100%

(d) 50%

(e) None of the above.

IX-22. An antenna phase meter is shown in Fig. 9-A (addendum). The phase angle shown is: (Ref. Element IX Addendum)

(a) Either 25 or 155 degrees.

(b) Only 25 degrees.

(c) Only 155 degrees.

(d) 45 degrees.

(e) 75 degrees.

IX-23. A standard broadcast station is authorized to broadcast on the following frequency band: (Q. 9.01)

(a) 88–108 mc.

(b) 500–1500 kc.

(c) 1000–2500 kc.

(d) 535–1605 kc.

(e) 200–500 kc.

IX-24. FM stereophonic broadcasts are accomplished by the use of: (Ref. Element IX Addendum)

(a) One FM channel and one TV channel.

(b) One AM channel and one FM channel.

(c) One FM channel and an AM subcarrier.

(d) Two separate FM channels.

(e) An FM channel and a subcarrier within that channel.

IX-25. The program log of a broadcast station must contain information showing: (Ref. Element IX Addendum)

(a) Antenna current and phase.

(b) Name of each program and time slot.

(c) Time the operator goes on duty.

(d) Remote meter readings.

(e) Name of each operator on duty.

IX-26. The antenna current meter shown in Fig. 9-A (addendum) normally indicates the: (Ref. Element IX Addendum)

(a) RF current at the center of the antenna.

(b) RF power applied to the feed point of the antenna.

(c) RF current applied to the feed point of the antenna.

(d) The dc current used to rotate the antenna.

(e) None of the above.

IX-27. When stationed at a transmitter, a third class operator may: (Ref. Element IX Addendum)

(a) Repair it as needed.

(b) Do all required maintenance.

(c) Make only minor adjustments.

(d) Adjust external controls to make routine changes in power.

(e) Both (c) and (d).

IX-28. The permissible frequency tolerance of standard broadcast (AM) stations is: (Q. 9.07)

(a) Plus and minus 20 cycles.

(b) Plus and minus 200 cycles.

(c) Within 0.005% of the assigned frequency.

(d) Both (a) and (c).

(e) Plus and minus 2000 cycles.

IX-29. The purpose of a "peak flasher" at a broadcast station is to: (Ref. Element IX Addendum)

(a) Illuminate the antenna tower.

(b) Warn of excessive antenna current.

(c) Warn of excessive modulation.

(d) Act as a substitute for the VU meter, if defective.

(e) Both (b) and (c).

IX-30. To determine if a directional antenna system is functioning correctly, an instrument is employed at the station, which is called: (Ref. Element IX Addendum)

(a) A power monitor.

(b) A digital reference meter.

(c) A directional meter.

(d) An antenna monitor.

(e) A compass locator.

IX-31. The reading on the antenna current meter in Fig. 9-A (addendum) is: (Ref. Element IX Addendum)

(a) 1.7 amperes.

(b) 17 amperes.

(c) 1.7 volts.

(d) 11.7 amperes.

(e) 1.17 amperes.

IX-32. In Fig. 9-A (addendum), the plate current meter reads: (Ref. Element IX Addendum)

(a) 270 milliamperes.

(b) 270 amperes.

(c) 25.2 milliamperes.

(d) 27.0 milliamperes.

(e) None of the above.

IX-33. Nighttime is defined as the period between: (Q. 9.01)

(a) Local sunrise and local sunset.

(b) Local sunset and 2 A.M.

(c) 12 midnight Greenwich time and 6 A.M. Greenwich time.

(d) Onset of darkness to the first light of morning.

(e) Local sunset and local sunrise.

IX-34. In Fig. 9-A (addendum) is shown an RF transmission line power meter. The reading on this meter is: (Ref. Element IX Addendum)

(a) 4500 watts.

(b) 4.5 kilowatts.

(c) 4.5 megawatts.

(d) Both (a) and (b).

(e) None of the above.

IX-35. Official station identification shall consist of: (Ref. Element IX Addendum)

(a) Station call letters and the state.

(b) Station call letters, the time, and the city.

(c) Corporation ownership and call letters.

(d) Current sponsor identification and call letters.

(e) Station call letters followed by the community name.

IX-36. Any rebroadcast may occur with the express permission of: (Ref. Element IX Addendum)

(a) The owner of the rebroadcasting station.

(b) The originating station.

(c) The FCC.

(d) Any first class license holder.

(e) The regional FCC manager.

IX-37. Before broadcasting or recording a telephone conversation for later broadcast, the parties involved (except station employees) must: (Ref. Element IX Addendum)

(a) Be informed of the intention to broadcast the conversation.

(b) Obtain the permission of the station manager.

(c) Submit a request in writing to the FCC.

(d) Obtain a security clearance.

(e) Both (a) and (d).

IX-38.   The "normal operating position" of a transmitter must be so located that any deviations from normal indications of instruments: (Ref. Element IX Addendum)

(a) Can be observed in a 360 degree arc.

(b) Can be detected by a warning buzzer.

(c) Can be instantly corrected.

(d) Will not affect transmitter operation.

(e) Both (b) and (c).

IX-39.   Among the normal transmitter indicating instruments are found: (Ref. Element IX Addendum)

(a) Plate voltmeter, plate current meter, and frequency counter.

(b) Antenna current meter, digital clock, and modulation indicator.

(c) Antenna phase indicator, antenna current indicator, and transmission line power indicator.

(d) Antenna phase indicator, FET meter, and plate current meter.

(e) Modulation indicator, frequency counter, and FET meter.

IX-40.   When operators are employed at more than one station, they use a "posting statement" known as: (Ref. Element IX Addendum)

(a) FCC Form 759.

(b) FAA Form 759.

(c) His duplicate license.

(d) Transmitter control point statement.

(e) The posting statement.

APPENDIX I *

EXTRACTS FROM THE RULES AND REGULATIONS OF THE FEDERAL COMMUNICATIONS COMMISSION

PART 1: PRACTICE AND PROCEDURE

R & R 1.85   Suspension of Operator Licenses.... Upon receipt by the Commission of such application for hearing, said order of suspension shall be designated for hearing by the Chief, Safety and Special Radio Services Bureau or the Chief, Field Engineering Bureau, as the case may be, and said order of suspension shall be held in abeyance until the conclusion of the hearing. Upon the conclusion of said hearing, the Commission may affirm, modify, or revoke said order of suspension. If the license is ordered suspended, the operator shall send his operator license to the office of the Commission in Washington, D. C., on or before the effective date of the order, or, if the effective date has passed at the time notice is received, the license shall be sent to the Commission forthwith.

*   *   *   *   *   *

PART 2: FREQUENCY ALLOCATIONS AND TREATY MATTERS: GENERAL RULES AND REGULATIONS

R & R 2.1   Definitions. The following definitions are issued*:

Citizens radio service: A radiocommunication service of fixed, land, and mobile stations intended for personal or business radiocommunications, radio signaling, control of remote objects or devices by means of radio, and other purposes not specifically prohibited.

---

* Appendices I through IV contain all the information referenced by the January 1965 FCC Supplement, both as to answers to questions and as to recommended reference reading. In all elements, questions pertaining to Rules and Regulations and Radio Laws have reference numbers assigned for additional study. These reference numbers pertain to the material in the appendices.

* Only selected definitions are given here.

Domestic fixed public service. A fixed service, the stations of which are open to public correspondence, for radiocommunications originating and terminating solely at points all of which lie within: (a) the State of Alaska, or (b) the State of Hawaii, or (c) the contiguous 48 states and the District of Columbia, or (d) a single possession of the United States. Generally, in cases where service is afforded on frequencies above 72 Mc/s, radiocommunications between the contiguous 48 States (including the District of Columbia) and Canada or Mexico, or radiocommunications between the State of Alaska and Canada, are deemed to be in the domestic fixed public service.

Experimental station. A non-amateur station utilizing radio waves in experiments with a view to the development of science or technique.

Facsimile. A system of telecommunication for the transmission of fixed images, with or without half-tones, with a view to their reproduction in a permanent form.

Industrial radio services. Any service of radiocommunication essential to, operated by, and for the sole use of, those enterprises which for purposes of safety or other necessity require radiocommunication in order to function efficiently, the radio transmitting facilities of which are defined as fixed, land, mobile or radiolocation stations.

Industrial, scientific and medical equipment (ISM equipment). Devices which use radio waves for industrial, scientific, medical, or any other purposes including the transfer of energy by radio and which are neither used nor intended to be used for radiocommunication.

Land transportation radio service. Any private service of radiocommunication essential to the conduct of certain land transportation activities and operated for the use of persons engaged in those activities, the transmitting facilities of which are defined as fixed, land, mobile or radiolocation stations.

Marker beacon. A transmitter in the aeronautical radionavigation service that radiates vertically a distinctive pattern for providing position information to aircraft.

Marker beacon station. An aeronautical radionavigation land station employing a marker beacon.

Mobile station. A station in the mobile service intended to be used while in motion or during halts at unspecified points.

Operational fixed station. A fixed station, not open to public correspondence, operated by and for the sole use of those agencies operating their own radiocommunication facilities in the public safety, industrial, land transportation, marine, or aviation service.

Private aircraft station. An aircraft station on board an aircraft not operated as an air carrier.

Public correspondence. Any telecommunication which the offices and stations must, by reason of their being at the disposal of the public, accept for transmission.

Public safety radio service. Any service of radiocommunication essential either to the discharge of non-Federal governmental functions or the alleviation of an emergency endangering life or property, the radio transmitting facilities of which are defined as fixed, land, mobile, or radiolocation stations.

Radio direction finding station. A radiodetermination station using radio direction finding.

Radio range station. A radionavigation land station in the aeronautical radionavigation service providing radial equisignal zones.

Radiobeacon station. A station in the radionavigation service the emissions of which are intended to enable a mobile station to determine its bearing or direction in relation to the radiobeacon station.

*   *   *   *   *   *

R & R 2.101   Nomenclature of Frequencies.

Band No.	Frequency subdivision	Frequency range
4	VLF (very low frequency)	Below 30 kc/s.
5	LF (low frequency)	30 to 300 kc/s.
6	MF (medium frequency)	300 to 3000 kc/s.
7	HF (high frequency)	3 to 30 Mc/s.
8	VHF (very high frequency)	30 to 300 Mc/s.
9	UHF (ultra high frequency)	300 to 3000 Mc/s.
10	SHF (super high frequency)	3 to 30 Gc/s.
11	EHF (extremely high frequency)	30 to 300 Gc/s.

*   *   *   *   *   *

R & R 2.201   Emission, Modulation, and Transmission Characteristics.
The following system of designating emission, modulation, and transmission shall be employed.

(a) Emissions are designated according to their classification and their necessary bandwidth.

(b) Emissions are classified and symbolized according to the following characteristics.

(1) Type of modulation of main carrier.

(2) Type of transmission.

(3) Supplementary characteristics.

(c) Types of modulation of main carrier:

                                                              Symbol
(1) Amplitude . . . . A
(2) Frequency (or phase) . . . . F
(3) Pulse . . . . P

(d) Types of transmission:

(1) Absence of any modulation intended to carry information 0
(2) Telegraphy without the use of a modulating audio frequency . . 1
(3) Telegraphy by the on-off keying of a modulating audio frequency or audio frequencies, or by the on-off keying of the modulated emission (special case: an unkeyed modulated emission) . . . 2
(4) Telephony (including sound broadcasting) 3
(5) Facsimile (with modulation of main carrier either directly or by a frequency modulated sub-carrier) 4
(6) Television (visual only) 5
(7) Four-frequency diplex telegraphy 6
(8) Multichannel voice-frequency telegraphy 7
(9) Cases not covered by the above 9

(e) Supplementary characteristics:

(1) Double sideband . . . . (None)
(2) Single sideband:
    (i) Reduced carrier . . . . A
    (ii) Full carrier . . . . H
    (iii) Suppressed carrier . . . . J
(3) Two independent sidebands . . . . B
(4) Vestigial sideband C
(5) Pulse:
    (i) Amplitude modulated . . . . D
    (ii) Width (or duration) modulated . . . . E
    (iii) Phase (or position) modulated . . . . F
    (iv) Code modulated . . . . G

(f) The classification of typical emissions is as shown in Table 1 on pages 463 through 465.

(g) Type B emission: As an exception to the above principles, damped waves are symbolized in the Commission's rules and regulations as type B emissions.

(h) Whenever the full designation of an emission is necessary, the symbol for that emission, as given above, shall be preceded by a number indicating in kilocycles per second the necessary bandwidth of the emission. Bandwidths shall generally be expressed to a maximum of three significant figures, the third figure being almost always a nought or a five.

*   *   *   *   *   *

R & R 2.402   Control of Distress Traffic. The control of distress traffic is the responsibility of the mobile station in distress or of the mobile staton, which by the application of the provisions of R & R 2.403, has sent

Table 1. Classification of Typical Emissions

Type of modulation of main carrier	Type of transmission	Supplementary characteristics	Symbol
Amplitude modulation	With no modulation		A0
	Telegraphy without the use of a modulating audio frequency (by on-off keying).		A1
	Telegraphy by the on-off keying of an amplitude modulating audio frequency or audio frequencies, or by the on-off keying of the modulated emission (special case: an unkeyed emission amplitude modulated).		A2
	Telephony	Double sideband	A3
		Single sideband, reduced carrier	A3A
		Single sideband, suppressed carrier	A3J
		Two independent sidebands	A3B
	Facsimile (with modulation of main carrier either directly or by a frequency modulated sub-carrier).		A4
	Facsimile	Single sideband, reduced carrier	A4A
	Television	Vestigial sideband	A5C
	Multichannel voice-frequency telegraphy	Single sideband, reduced carrier	A7A
	Cases not covered by the above, e.g., a combination of telephony and telegraphy.	Two independent sidebands	A9B

TABLE 1. *Classification of Typical Emissions (Cont.)*

Type of modulation of main carrier	Type of transmission	Supplementary characteristics	Symbol
Frequency (or Phase) modulation	Telegraphy by frequency shift keying without the use of a modulating audio frequency: one of two frequencies being emitted at any instant.	. . . .	F1
	Telegraphy by the on-off keying of a frequency modulating audio frequency or by the on-off keying of a frequency modulated emission (special case: an unkeyed emission, frequency modulated).	. . . .	F2
	Telephony	. . . .	F3
	Facsimile by direct frequency modulation of the carrier.	. . . .	F4
	Television	. . . .	F5
	Four-frequency diplex telegraphy	. . . .	F6
	Cases not covered by the above, in which the main carrier is frequency modulated.	. . . .	F9

TABLE 1. *Classification of Typical Emissions (Cont.)*

Type of modulation of main carrier	Type of transmission	Supplementary characteristics	Symbol
Pulse modulation	A pulsed carrier without any modulation intended to carry information (e.g. radar).	. . . .	P0
	Telegraphy by the on-off keying of a pulsed carrier without the use of a modulating audio frequency.	. . . .	P1D
	Telegraphy by the on-off keying of a modulating audio frequency or audio frequencies, or by the on-off keying of a modulated pulsed carrier (special case: an unkeyed modulated pulsed carrier).		
		Audio frequency or audio frequencies modulating the amplitude of the pulses.	P2D
		Audio frequency or audio frequencies modulating the width (or duration) of the pulses.	P2E
		Audio frequency or audio frequencies modulating the phase (or position) of the pulses.	P2F
	Telephony . . .	Amplitude modulated pulses . . .	P3D
		Width (or duration) modulated pulses . .	P3E
		Phase (or position) modulated pulses . .	P3F
		Code modulated pulses (after sampling and quantization).	P3G
	Cases not covered by the above in which the main carrier is pulse modulated.	. . . .	P9

the distress call. These stations may, however, delegate the control of the distress traffic to another station.

R & R 2.403   Retransmission of Distress Message. Any station which becomes aware that a mobile station is in distress may transmit the distress message in the following cases:

(a) When the station in distress is not itself in a position to transmit the message.

(b) In the case of mobile stations, when the master or the person in charge of the ship, aircraft or other vehicles carrying the station which intervenes believes that further help is necessary.

(c) In the case of other stations, when directed to do so by the station in control of distress traffic or when it has reason to believe that a distress call which it has intercepted has not been received by any station in a position to render aid.

R & R 2.404   Resumption of Operation After Distress. No station having been notified to cease operation shall resume operation on frequency or frequencies which may cause interference until notified by the station issuing the original notice that the station involved will not interfere with distress traffic as it is then being routed or until the receipt of a general notice that the need for handling distress traffic no longer exists.

R & R 2.405   Operation During Emergency. The licensee of any station (except amateur, standard broadcast, FM broadcast, noncommercial educational FM broadcast, or television broadcast) may, during a period of emergency in which normal communication facilities are disrupted as a result of hurricane, flood, earthquake, or similar disaster, utilize such station for emergency communication service in communicating in a manner other than that specified in the instrument of authorization: *Provided,*

(a) That as soon as possible after the beginning of such emergency use, notice be sent to the Commission at Washington, D. C., and to the Engineer in Charge of the district in which the station is located, stating the nature of the emergency and the use to which the station is being put, and

(b) That the emergency use of the station shall be discontinued as soon as substantially normal communication facilities are again available, and

(c) That the Commission at Washington, D. C., and the Engineer in Charge shall be notified immediately when such special use of the station is terminated: *Provided, further,*

(d) That in no event shall any station engage in emergency transmission on frequencies other than, or with power in excess of, that specified in the instrument of authorization or as otherwise expressly provided by the Commission, or by law: *And provided further,*

(e) That any such emergency communication undertaken under this section shall terminate upon order of the Commission.

*　　*　　*　　*　　*　　*

R & R 2.551   Program Defined. In order to carry out its responsibilities under the Communications Act and the various treaties and international regulations, it is necessary for the Commission to ascertain that the equipment involved is capable of meeting the technical operating standards set forth in said statutes, treaties and the Commission's rules and regulations. To facilitate such determinations in those services where equipment is generally standardized, to promote the improvement of equipment and to promote the efficient use of the radio spectrum, the Commission has designated 2 specific procedures for securing advance approval of equipment. These procedures are designated as type approval and type acceptance. Ordinarily, type approval contemplates tests conducted by Commission personnel, while type acceptance is based on data concerning the equipment submitted by the manufacturer or the individual prospective licensee. The procedures described in this subpart are intended to apply to equipment in those services which specifically require either type approval or type acceptance. These procedures may also be applied to equipment components, such as radio-frequency power amplifiers, etc., to the extent specified in the rules of the particular service in which such components will be used.

PART 13: COMMERCIAL RADIO OPERATORS

R & R 13.4   Term of Licenses. (a) Except as provided in paragraphs (b) and (c) of this section, commercial operator licenses will normally be issued for a term of five years from the date of issuance.

*　　*　　*　　*　　*　　*

R & R 13.5   Eligibility for New License. (a) Commercial licenses are issued only to citizens and other nationals of the United States except, in the case of aliens who hold Aircraft Pilot Certificates issued by the Civil Aeronautics Administration or the Federal Aviation Agency, the Commission, if it finds that the public interest will be served thereby, may waive the requirement of United States nationality.

*　　*　　*　　*　　*　　*

R & R 13.6   Operator License, Posting of. The original license of each station operator shall be posted at the place where he is on duty, except as otherwise provided in this part or in the rules governing the class of station concerned.

*   *   *   *   *   *

R & R 13.11   Procedure. (a) *General.* Applications shall be governed by applicable rules in force on the date when application is filed (see R & R 13.28). The application in the prescribed form and including all required subsidiary forms and documents, properly completed and signed, and accompanied by the prescribed fee (see R & R 13.14 and 13.15), shall be submitted to the appropriate office as indicated in paragraph (b) of this section. If the application is for renewal of license, it may be filed at any time during the final year of the license term or during a 1-year period of grace after the date of expiration of the license sought to be renewed. During this 1-year period of grace, an expired license is not valid. A renewed license issued upon the basis of an application filed during the grace period will be dated currently and will not be backdated to the date of expiration of the license being renewed. A renewal application shall be accompanied by the license sought to be renewed. If the prescribed service requirements for renewal without examination (see R & R 13.28) are fulfilled, the renewed license may be issued by mail. If the service record on the reverse side of the license does not fully describe or cover the service desired by the applicant to be considered in connection with license renewal (as might occur in the case of service rendered at U.S. Government stations), the renewal application shall be supported by documentary evidence describing in detail the service performed and showing that the applicant actually performed such service in a satisfactory manner. A separate application must be submitted for each license involved, whether it requests renewal, new license, endorsement, duplicate, or replacement.

*   *   *   *   *   *

R & R 13.26   Canceling and Issuing New Licenses. If a holder of a license qualifies for a higher class in the same group, the license held will be canceled upon the issuance of the new license. Similarly, if the holder of a restricted operator permit qualifies for a first- or second-class operator license of the corresponding type, the permit held will be canceled upon issuance of the new license.

*   *   *   *   *   *

R & R 13.61   Operating Authority. The various classes of commercial radio operator licenses issued by the Commission authorize the holders thereof to operate radio stations except amateur, as follows (see also R & R 13.62 (c) for additional operating authority with respect to standard and FM broadcast stations):

*　　*　　*　　*　　*　　*

(e) Radiotelephone first-class operator license. Any station except—

(1) Stations transmitting telegraphy by any type of the Morse Code, or

(2) Ship stations licensed to use telephony and power in excess of 100 watts for communication with Class I-B coast stations.

(3) At a ship radar station licensed in the Ship Service, the holder of this class of license may not supervise or be responsible for the performance of any adjustments or tests during or coincident with the installation, servicing or maintenance of the radar equipment while it is radiating energy unless he has satisfactorily completed a supplementary examination qualifying him for that duty and received a ship radar endorsement on his license certifying to that fact: *Provided*, That nothing in this subparagraph shall be construed to prevent persons holding licenses not so endorsed from making replacements of fuses or of receiving-type tubes. The supplementary examination shall consist of:

(i) Written examination element: 8.

(f) Radiotelephone second-class operator license. Any station except—

(1) Stations transmitting telegraphy by any type of the Morse Code, or

(2) Standard broadcast stations, or

(3) International broadcast stations, or

(4) FM broadcast stations, or

(5) Noncommercial educational FM broadcast stations with transmitter power rating in excess of 1 kilowatt, or

(6) Television broadcast stations licensed for commercial operation, or

(7) Ship stations licensed to use telephony and power in excess of 100 watts for communication with coastal stations.

(8) At a ship radar station licensed in the Ship Service, the holder of this class of license may not supervise or be responsible for the performance of any adjustments or tests during or coincident with the installation, servicing or maintenance of the radar equipment while it is radiating energy unless he has satisfactorily completed a supplementary examination qualifying him for that duty and received a ship radar endorsement on his license certifying to that fact: *Provided*, That nothing in this subparagraph shall be construed to prevent persons holding licenses not so endorsed from making replacements of fuses or of receiving-type tubes. The supplementary examination shall consist of:

(i) Written examination element: 8.

(g) Radiotelephone third-class operator permit. Any station except—

(1) Stations transmitting television, or

(2) Stations transmitting telegraphy by any type of the Morse code, or

(3) Any of the various classes of broadcast stations other than noncommercial educational FM broadcast stations using transmitters with power ratings of 10 watts or less, remote pickup broadcast stations and ST broadcast stations, or

(4) Class I-B coast stations at which the power in the antenna of the unmodulated carrier wave is authorized to exceed 250 watts, or

(5) Class II-B or Class III-B coast stations, other than those in Alaska, at which the power in the antenna of the unmodulated carrier wave is authorized to exceed 250 watts, or

(6) Ship stations or aircraft stations other than those at which the installation is used solely for telephony and at which the power in the antenna of the unmodulated carrier wave is not authorized to exceed 250 watts: *Provided*, That (1) Such operator is prohibited from making any adjustments that may result in improper transmitter operation, and (2) the equipment is so designed that the stability of the frequencies of the transmitter is maintained by the transmitter itself within the limits of tolerance specified by the station license, and none of the operations necessary to be performed during the course of normal rendition of the service of the station may cause off-frequency operation or result in any unauthorized radiation, and (3) any needed adjustments of the transmitter that may affect the proper operation of the station are regularly made by or under the immediate supervision and responsibility of a person holding a first- or second-class commercial radio operator license, either radiotelephone or radiotelegraph as may be appropriate for the class of station involved (as determined by the scope of the authority of the respective licenses as set forth in paragraphs (a), (b), (e), and (f) of this section and R & R 13.62, who shall be responsible for the proper functioning of the station equipment, and (4) in the case of ship radiotelephone or aircraft radiotelephone stations when the power in the antenna of the unmodulated carrier wave is authorized to exceed 100 watts, any needed adjustments of the transmitter that may affect the proper operation of the station are made only by or under the immediate supervision and responsibility of an operator holding a first- or second-class radiotelegraph license, who shall be responsible for the proper functioning of the station equipment.

(h) Restricted radiotelephone operator permit. Any station except—

(1) Stations transmitting television, or

(2) Stations transmitting telegraphy by any type of the Morse Code, or

(3) Any of the various classes of broadcast stations other than remote pickup, broadcast STL, and FM intercity relay stations, or

(4) Ship stations licensed to use telephony for communication with Class I coast stations on frequencies between 4000 kc/s and 30 Mc/s, or

(5) Radio stations provided on board vessels for safety purposes pursuant to statute or treaty, or

(6) Coast stations, other than those in Alaska, while employing a frequency below 30 Mc/s, or

(7) Coast stations at which the power in the antenna of the unmodulated carrier wave is authorized to exceed 250 watts;

(8) At a ship radar station the holder of this class of license may not supervise or be responsible for the performance of any adjustments or tests during or coincident with the installation, servicing or maintenance of the radar equipment while it is radiating energy: *Provided,* That nothing in this subparagraph shall be construed to prevent any person holding such a license from making replacements of fuses or of receiving type tubes:

Provided, That, with respect to any station which the holder of this class of license may operate, such operator is prohibited from making any adjustments that may result in improper transmitter operation, and the equipment is so designed that the stability of the frequencies of the transmitter is maintained by the transmitter itself within the limits of tolerance specified by the station license, and none of the operations necessary to be performed during the course of normal rendition of the service of the station may cause off-frequency operation or result in any unauthorized radiation, and any needed adjustments of the transmitter that may affect the proper operation of the station are regularly made by or under the immediate supervision and responsibility of a person holding a first- or second-class commercial radio operator license, either radiotelephone or radiotelegraph, who shall be responsible for the proper functioning of the station equipment.

*   *   *   *   *   *

R & R 13.63   Operator's Responsibility. The licensed operator responsible for the maintenance of a transmitter may permit other persons to adjust a transmitter in his presence for the purpose of carrying out tests or making adjustments requiring specialized knowledge or skill, provided that he shall not be relieved thereby from responsibility for the proper operation of the equipment.

*   *   *   *   *   *

R & R 13.65   Damage to Apparatus. No licensed radio operator shall willfully damage, or cause or permit to be damaged, any radio apparatus or installation in any licensed radio station.

R & R 13.66   Unnecessary, Unidentified, or Superfluous Communications. No licensed radio operator shall transmit unnecessary, unidentified, or superfluous radio communications or signals.

R & R 13.67   Obscenity, Indecency, Profanity. No licensed radio operator or other person shall transmit communications containing obscene, indecent, or profane words, language, or meaning.

R & R 13.68   False Signals. No licensed radio operator shall transmit false or deceptive signals or communications by radio, or any call létter or signal which has not been assigned by proper authority to the radio station he is operating.

R & R 13.69   Interference. No licensed radio operator shall willfully or maliciously interfere with or cause interference to any radio communication or signal.

R & R 13.70   Fraudulent Licenses. No licensed radio operator or other person shall alter, duplicate, or fraudulently obtain, or assist another to alter, duplicate, or fraudulently obtain an operator license. Nor shall any person use a license issued to another or a license which he knows to have been altered, duplicated, or fraudulently obtained.

R & R 13.71   Issue of Duplicate or Replacement Licenses. (a) An operator whose license or permit has been lost, mutilated, or destroyed shall immediately notify the Commission. If the authorization is of the diploma form, a properly executed application for duplicate should be submitted to the office of issue. If the authorization is of the card form (Restricted Radiotelephone Operator Permit), a properly executed application for replacement should be submitted to the Federal Communications Commission, Gettysburg, Pa., 17325. In either case the application shall embody a statement of the circumstances involved in the loss, mutilation, or destruction of the license or permit. If the authorization has been lost, the applicant must state that reasonable search has been made for it, and, further, that in the event it be found, either the original or the duplicate (or replacement) will be returned for cancellation. If the authorization is of the diploma form, the applicant should also submit documentary evidence of the service that has been obtained under the original authorization, or a statement embodying that information.

(b) The holder of any license or permit whose name is legally changed may make application for a replacement document to indicate the new legal name by submitting a properly executed application accompanied by the license or permit affected. If the authorization is of the diploma form, the application should be submitted to the office where it was issued. If the authorization is of the card form (Restricted Radiotelephone Operator Permit), it should be submitted to the Federal Communications Commission, Gettysburg, Pa., 17325.

R & R 13.72   Exhibiting Signed Copy of Application. When a duplicate or replacement operator license or permit has been requested, or request has been made for renewal upon service or for an endorsement or a verification card, the operator shall exhibit in lieu of the original document a signed copy of the application which has been submitted by him.

*   *   *   *   *   *

R & R 13.74 Posting Requirements for Operators. (a) Performing duties other than, or in addition to, service or maintenance at two or more stations. The holder of any class of radio operator license or permit of the diploma form (as distinguished from the card form) who performs any radio operating duties, as contrasted with but not necessarily exclusive of service or maintenance duties, at two or more stations at which posting of his license or permit is required, shall post at one such station his operator license or permit and shall post at all other such stations a duly issued verified statement (Form 759).

(b) Performing service or maintenance duties at one or more stations. The holder of a radiotelephone or radiotelegraph first- or second-class radio operator license who performs, or supervises, and is responsible for service or maintenance work on any transmitter of any station for which a station license is required, shall post his license at the transmitter involved whenever the transmitter is in actual operation while service or maintenance work is being performed: *Provided,* That in lieu of posting his license, he may have on his person either his license or a verification card (Form 758-F): *And provided further,* That if he performs operating duties in addition to service or maintenance duties he shall, in lieu of complying with the foregoing provisions of this paragraph, comply with the posting requirements applicable to persons performing such operating duties, as set forth in paragraph (a) of this section, and in the rules and regulations applicable to each service.

(c) One or more verified statements (Form 759), as necessary, will be issued to the holder of a restricted radiotelephone operator permit (card form license) who because of an operator license posting requirement at one station would not otherwise be able to comply with a license posting requirement or to carry his permit on his person when so required at another station or stations.

R & R 13.75 Record of Service and Maintenance Duties Performed. In every case where a station log or service and maintenance records are required to be kept and where service or maintenance duties are performed which may affect the proper operation of a station, the responsible operator shall sign and date an entry in the log of the station concerned, or in the station maintenance records if no log is required, giving:

(a) Pertinent details of all service and maintenance work performed by him under his supervision;

(b) His name and address; and

(c) The class, serial number and expiration date of his license: *Provided,* That the responsible operator shall not be subject to requirements in paragraphs (b) and (c) of this section in relation to a station, or stations of one licensee at a single location, at which he is regularly employed as an operator on a full time basis and at which his license is properly posted.

* * * * * *

PART 17: CONSTRUCTION, MARKING, AND LIGHTING OF ANTENNA STRUCTURES

R & R 17.21   Painting and Lighting, When Required. Antenna structures shall be painted and lighted when:

(a) They require special aeronautical study; or

(b) They exceed 170 feet in height above the ground.

(c) The Commission may modify the above requirement for painting and/or lighting of antenna structures, when it is shown by the applicant that the absence of such marking would not impair the safety of air navigation, or that a lesser marking requirement would insure the safety thereof.

* * * * * *

R & R 17.23   Specifications for the Painting of Antenna Structures in Accordance with R & R 17.21. Antenna structures shall be painted throughout their height with alternate bands of aviation surface orange and white, terminating with aviation surface orange bands at both top and bottom. The width of the bands shall be equal and approximately one-seventh the height of the structure, provided however, that the bands shall not be more than 40 feet nor less than 1½ feet in width.

* * * * * *

R & R 17.25   Specifications for the Lighting of Antenna Structures Over 150 Feet Up To and Including 300 Feet in Height. (a) Antenna structures over 150 feet up to and including 300 feet in height above the ground shall be lighted as follows:

(1) There shall be installed at the top of the structure one 300 m/m electric code beacon equipped with two 500- or 620-watt lamps (PS–40, Code Beacon type), both lamps to burn simultaneously, and equipped with aviation red color filters. Where a rod or other construction of not more than 20 feet in height and incapable of supporting this beacon is mounted on top of the structure and it is determined that this additional

construction does not permit unobstructed visibility of the code beacon from aircraft at any angle of approach, there shall be installed two such beacons positioned so as to insure unobstructed visibility of at least one of the beacons from aircraft at any angle of approach. The beacon shall be equipped with a flashing mechanism producing not more than 40 flashes per minute nor less than 12 flashes per minute with a period of darkness equal to one-half of the luminous period.

(2) At the approximate midpoint of the overall height of the tower there shall be installed at least two 100-, 107-, or 116-watt lamps (#100 A21/TS, #107 A21/TS, or #116 A21/TS, respectively) enclosed in aviation red obstruction light globes. Each light shall be mounted so as to insure unobstructed visibility of at least one light at each level from aircraft at any angle of approach.

(3) All lights shall burn continuously or shall be controlled by a light sensitive device adjusted so that the lights will be turned on at a north sky light intensity level of about 35 foot-candles and turned off at a north sky light intensity level of about 58 foot-candles.

*   *   *   *   *   *

R & R 17.27 Specifications for the Lighting of Antenna Structures Over 450 Feet Up To and Including 600 Feet in Height. (a) Antenna structures over 450 feet up to and including 600 feet in height above the ground shall be lighted as follows:

(1) There shall be installed at the top of the structure one 300 m/m electric code beacon equipped with two 500- or 620-watt lamps (PS–40, Code Beacon type), both lamps to burn simultaneously, and equipped with aviation red color filters. Where a rod or other construction of not more than 20 feet in height and incapable of supporting this beacon is mounted on top of the structure and it is determined that this additional construction does not permit unobstructed visibility of the code beacon from aircraft at any angle of approach, there shall be installed two such beacons positioned so as to insure unobstructed visibility of at least one of the beacons from aircraft at any angle of approach. The beacons shall be equipped with a flashing mechanism producing not more than 40 flashes per minute nor less than 12 flashes per minute with a period of darkness equal to one-half of the luminous period.

(2) At approximately one-half of the overall height of the tower, one similar flashing 300 m/m electric code beacon shall be installed in such position within the tower proper that the structural members will not impair the visibility of this beacon from aircraft at any angle of approach. In the event this beacon cannot be installed in a manner to insure unobstructed visibility of it from aircraft at any angle of approach, there shall

be installed two such beacons. Each beacon shall be mounted on the out-side of diagonally opposite corners or opposite sides of the tower at the prescribed height.

(3) On levels at approximately three-fourths and one-fourth of the overall height of the tower, at least one 100-, 107-, or 116-watt lamp (#100 A21/TS, #107 A21/TS, or #116 A21/TS, respectively) enclosed in an aviation red obstruction light globe shall be installed on each out-side corner of the tower at each level.

(4) All lights shall burn continuously or shall be controlled by a light sensitive device adjusted so that the lights will be turned on at a north sky light intensity level of about 35 foot-candles and turned off at a north sky light intensity level of about 58 foot-candles.

*　　*　　*　　*　　*　　*

R & R 17.39　Cleaning and Repainting. All towers shall be cleaned or repainted as often as necessary to maintain good visibility.

R & R 17.40　Time When Lights Shall Be Exhibited. All lighting shall be from sunset to sunrise unless otherwise specified.

R & R 17.41　Spare lamps. A sufficient supply of spare lamps shall be maintained for immediate replacement purposes at all times.

R & R 17.42　Lighting Equipment. The lighting equipment, color of filters, and shade of paint referred to in the specifications are further de-fined in the following government and/or Army-Navy Aeronautical Specifications, Bulletins, and Drawings: (Lamps are referred to by stand-ard numbers). (See Table 2.)

*　　*　　*　　*　　*　　*

R & R 17.44　Maintenance of Lighting Equipment. Replacing or re-pairing of lights, automatic indicators or automatic alarm systems shall be accomplished as soon as practicable.

*　　*　　*　　*　　*　　*

R & R 17.47　Inspection of Tower Lights and Associated Control Equipment. The licensee of any radio station which has an antenna structure requiring illumination pursuant to the provisions of section 303(q) of the Communications Act of 1934, as amended, as outlined elsewhere in this part:

(a) (1) Shall make an observation of the tower lights at least once each 24 hours either visually or by observing an automatic properly

TABLE 2. *Lighting Equipment Specifications*

Outside white	Federal Specifications	TT–P–102.[1]
Aviation surface orange	do	TT–P–59 [1] (Color #12197 of
Aviation surface orange		Federal Standard 595).
enamel	do	TT–E–489 [1] (Color #12197
		of Federal Standard 595).
Code beacon	FAA Specifications	446 (Sec. II–d–Style 4).[3]
Obstruction light globe,		
prismatic	Army-Navy Drawing	
Obstruction light globe,		AN–L–10A.[2]
Fresnel	do	
Single multiple obstruction		or
light fitting assembly	do	
Obstruction light fitting		FAA Specification L–810.[3]
assembly	do	
100-watt lamp		#100 A21/TS.[4]
107-watt lamp		#107 A21/TS (3,000 hours).
116-watt lamp		#116 A21/TS (6,000 hours).
500-watt lamp		#500 PS 40C/45. (1,000
		hours).[4]
620-watt lamp		#620 PS 40 (3,000 hours).

[1] Copies of this specification can be obtained from the Specification Activity, Room 1643, Federal Supply Service Center, General Services Administration, Seventh and D Streets SW., Washington, D.C., 20407. (Outside white, 5 cents; aviation surface orange, paint 5 cents, enamel 10 cents.)

[2] Copies of Army-Navy Specifications or drawings can be obtained by contacting the Commanding General, Air Materiel Command, Wright Field, Dayton, Ohio, 45433, or the Bureau of Navy Weapons, Navy Department, Washington, D.C., 02036. Information concerning Army-Navy Specifications or drawings can also be obtained from the Federal Aviation Agency, Washington, D.C., 20553.

[3] Copies of this specification can be obtained from the Federal Aviation Agency, Washington, D.C., 20553.

[4] It is strongly recommended that the 116-watt, 6,000-hour lamp and the 620-watt, 3,000-hour lamp be used instead of the 100-watt and the 500-watt lamps whenever possible in view of the extended life, lower maintenance cost, and greater safety which they provide.

maintained indicator designed to register any failure of such lights, to insure that all such lights are functioning properly as required; or alternatively,

(2) Shall provide and properly maintain an automatic alarm system designed to detect any failure of such lights and to provide indication of such failure to the licensee.

(b) Shall inspect at intervals not to exceed 3 months all automatic or mechanical control devices, indicators, and alarm systems associated with the tower lighting to insure that such apparatus is functioning properly.

R & R 17.48 Notification of Extinguishment or Improper Functioning of Lights. The licensee of any radio station which has an antenna structure requiring illumination pursuant to the provisions of section 303 (q) of the Communications Act of 1934, as amended, as outlined elsewhere in this part:

(a) Shall report immediately by telephone or telegraph to the nearest Flight Service Station or office of the Federal Aviation Administration any observed or otherwise known extinguishment or improper functioning of a code or rotating beacon light (no matter where located on the tower) or top light not corrected within 30 minutes. Further notification by telephone or telegraph shall be given immediately upon resumption of the required illumination.

(b) An extinguishment or improper functioning of a steady burning side intermediate light or lights, shall be corrected as soon as possible, but notification to the FAA of such extinguishment or improper functioning is not required.

R & R 17.49   Recording of Tower Light Inspections in the Station Record. The licensee of any radio station which has an antenna structure requiring illumination shall make the following entries in the station record of the inspections required by R & R 17.47.

(a) The time the tower lights are turned on and off each day if manually controlled.

(b) The time the daily check of proper operation of the tower lights was made, if automatic alarm system is not provided.

(c) In the event of any observed or otherwise known extinguishment or improper functioning of a tower light:

(1) Nature of such extinguishment or improper functioning.

(2) Date and time the extinguishment or improper functioning was observed, or otherwise noted.

(3) Date, time, and nature of the adjustments, repairs, or replacements made.

(4) Identification of Flight Service Station (Federal Aviation Administration) notified of the extinguishment of improper functioning of any code or rotating beacon light or top light not corrected within 30 minutes, and the date and time such notice was given.

(5) Date and time notice was given to the Flight Service Station (Federal Aviation Administration) that the required illumination was resumed.

(d) Upon completion of the periodic inspection required at least once each 3 months:

(1) The date of the inspection and the condition of all tower lights and associated tower lighting control devices, indicators and alarm systems.

(2) Any adjustments, replacements, or repairs made to insure compliance with the lighting requirements and the date such adjustments, replacements or repairs were made.

PART 73: RADIO BROADCAST SERVICES

R & R 73.1   Standard Broadcast Station. The term "standard broadcast station" means a broadcasting station licensed for the transmission of radiotelephone emissions primarily intended to be received by the general public and operated on a channel in the band 535–1605 kilocycles.

R & R 73.2   Standard Broadcast Band. The term "standard broadcast band" means the band of frequencies extending from 535 to 1605 kilocycles.

R & R 73.3   Standard Broadcast Channel. The term "standard broadcast channel" means the band of frequencies occupied by the carrier and two side bands of a broadcast signal with the carrier frequency at the center. Channels shall be designated by their assigned carrier frequencies. The 107 carrier frequencies assigned to standard broadcast stations shall begin at 540 kilocycles and be in successive steps of 10 kilocycles.

*   *   *   *   *   *

R & R 73.6   Daytime. The term "daytime" means that period of time between local sunrise and local sunset.

R & R 73.7   Nighttime. The term "nighttime" means that period of time between local sunset and local sunrise.

R & R 73.8   Sunrise and Sunset. The terms "sunrise" and "sunset" mean, for each particular location and during any particular month, the time of sunrise and sunset as specified in the instrument of authorization.

R & R 73.9   Broadcast Day. The term "broadcast day" means that period of time between local sunrise and 12 midnight local standard time.

*   *   *   *   *   *

R & R 73.14   Technical Definitions. (a) *Combined Audio Harmonics.* The term "combined audio harmonics" means the arithmetical sum of the amplitudes of all the separate harmonic components. Root sum square harmonic readings may be accepted under conditions prescribed by the Commission.

(b) *Effective Field.* The term "effective field" or "effective field intensity" is the root-mean-square (RMS) value of the inverse distance fields at a distance of 1 mile from the antenna in all directions in the horizontal plane.

(c) *Nominal power.* "Nominal power" is the power of a standard broadcast station, as specified in a system of classification which includes the following values; 50 kW., 25 kW., 10 kW., 5 kW., 1 kW., 0.5 kW., 0.25 kW.

(d) *Operating power.* Depending on the context within which it is employed, the term "operating power" may be synonymous with "nominal power" or "antenna power."

(e) *Maximum rated carrier power.* "Maximum rated carrier power" is the maximum power at which the transmitter can be operated satisfactorily and is determined by the design of the transmitter and the type and number of vacuum tubes used in the last radio stage.

(f) *Plate input power.* "Plate input power" means the product of the direct plate voltage applied to the tubes in the last radio stage and the total direct current flowing to the plates of these tubes, measured without modulation.

(g) *Antenna power.* "Antenna input power" or "antenna power" means the product of the square of the antenna current and the antenna resistance at the point where the current is measured.

(h) *Antenna current.* "Antenna current" means the radio-frequency current in the antenna with no modulation.

(i) *Antenna resistance.* "Antenna resistance" means the total resistance of the transmitting antenna system at the operating frequency and at the point at which the antenna current is measured.

(j) *Modulator stage.* "Modulator stage" means the last amplifier stage of the modulating wave which modulates a radio-frequency stage.

(k) *Modulated stage.* "Modulated stage" means the radio-frequency stage to which the modulator is coupled and in which the continuous wave (carrier wave) is modulated in accordance with the system of modulation and the characteristics of the modulating wave.

(l) *Last radio stage.* "Last radio stage" means the oscillator or radio-frequency-power amplifier stage which supplies power to the antenna.

(m) *Percentage modulation* (amplitude). In a positive direction:

$$M = \frac{MAX - C}{C} \times 100$$

In a negative direction:

$$M = \frac{C - MIN}{C} \times 100$$

$M =$ Modulation level in percent.

$MAX =$ Instantaneous maximum level of the modulated radio frequency envelope.

$MIN =$ Instantaneous minimum level of the modulated radio frequency envelope.

$C =$ (Carrier) level or radio frequency envelope without modulation.

(n) *Maximum percentage of modulation.* "Maximum percentage of modulation" means the greatest percentage of modulation that may be obtained by a transmitter without producing in its output harmonics of the modulating frequency in excess of those permitted by these regulations.

(o) *High level modulation.* "High level modulation" is modulation produced in the plate circuit of the last radio stage of the system.

(p) *Low level modulation.* "Low level modulation" is modulation produced in an earlier stage than the final.

(q) *Plate modulation.* "Plate modulation" is modulation produced by introduction of the modulating wave into the plate circuit of any tube in which the carrier frequency wave is present.

(r) *Grid modulation.* "Grid modulation" is modulation produced by introduction of the modulating wave into any of the grid circuits of any tube in which the carrier frequency wave is present.

(s) *Blanketing.* Blanketing is that form of interference which is caused by the presence of a broadcast signal of one volt per meter (v/m) or greater intensity in the area adjacent to the antenna of the transmitting station. The 1 v/m contour is referred to as the blanket contour and the area within this contour is referred to as the blanket area.

* * * * * *

R & R 73.51   Antenna Input Power; How Determined. (a) Except in those circumstances described in paragraph (d) of this section, the antenna input power shall be determined by the direct method, i.e., as the product of the antenna resistance at the operating frequency (see R & R 73.54) and the square of the unmodulated antenna current at that frequency, measured at the point where the antenna resistance has been determined.

* * * * * *

(d) The antenna input power shall be determined on a temporary basis by the indirect method described in paragraphs (e) and (f) of this section in the following circumstances: (1) In an emergency, where the authorized antenna system has been damaged by causes beyond the control of the licensee or permittee (see R & R 73.45), or (2) pending completion of authorized changes in the antenna system, or (3) if changes occur in the antenna system or its environment which affect or appear likely to affect the value of antenna resistance or (4) if the antenna current meter becomes defective (see R & R 73.58). Prior authorization for the indirect determination of antenna input power is not required. However, an appropriate notation shall be made in the operating log.

R & R 73.52   Antenna Input Power; Maintenance of. (a) The actual antenna input power of each station shall be maintained as near as is practicable to the authorized antenna input power and shall not be less than 90 percent nor greater than 105 percent of the authorized power; except that, if, in an emergency, it becomes technically impossible to operate with the authorized power, the station may be operated with reduced power for a period of 10 days, or less, without further authority from the Commission: *Provided,* That the Commission and the Engineer in Charge of the radio district in which the station is located shall be immediately notified in writing if the station is unable to maintain the minimum operating schedule, specified in R & R 73.71, with authorized power, and shall be subsequently notified upon resumption of operation with authorized power.

(b) In addition to maintaining antenna input power within the above limitations, each station employing a directional antenna shall maintain the relative amplitudes of the antenna currents in the elements of its array within 5 percent of the ratios specified in its license or other instrument of authorization, unless more stringent limits are specified therein.

*   *   *   *   *   *

R & R 73.55   Modulation. The percentage of modulation shall be maintained at as high a level as is consistent with good quality of transmission and good broadcast service. In no case shall it exceed 100 percent on negative peaks of frequent recurrence, or 125 percent on positive peaks at any time. Generally, modulation should not be less than 85 percent on peaks of frequent recurrence, but where such action may be required to avoid objectionable loudness, the degree of modulation may be reduced to whatever level is necessary for this purpose, even though, under such circumstances, the level may be substantially less than that which produces peaks of frequent recurrence at a level of 85 percent.

R & R 73.56   Modulation Monitors. (a) Each station shall have in operation, either at the transmitter or at the place the transmitter is controlled, a modulation monitor of a type approved by the Commission.

NOTE: Approved modulation monitors are included on the Commission's Radio Equipment List. Copies of this list are available for inspection at the Commission's office in Washington, D.C., and at each of its field offices.

(b) In the event that the modulation monitor becomes defective the station may be operated without the monitor pending its repair or replacement for a period not in excess of 60 days without further authority of the Commission: *Provided,* That: (1) Appropriate entries shall be made in the maintenance log of the station showing the date and time the monitor was removed from and restored to service. (2) The Engineer in Charge of the radio district in which the station is located shall be notified both immediately after the monitor is found to be defective and immediately after the repaired or replacement monitor has been installed and is functioning properly. (3) The degree of modulation of the station shall be monitored with a cathode ray oscilloscope or other acceptable means.

(c) If conditions beyond the control of the licensee prevent the restoration of the monitor to service within the above allowed period, informal request in accordance with R & R 1.549 of this chapter may be filed with the Engineer in Charge of the radio district in which the station is operating for such additional time as may be required to complete repairs of the defective instrument.

(d) Each station operated by remote control shall continuously, except when other readings are being taken, monitor percent of modulation or shall be equipped with an automatic device to limit percent of modulation on negative peaks to 100.

*   *   *   *   *   *

R & R 73.58   Indicating Instruments. (a) Each standard broadcast station shall be equipped with indicating instruments which conform with the specifications set forth in R & R 73.39 for measuring the d-c plate circuit current and voltage of the last radio-frequency amplified stage; the radio-frequency base current of each antenna element; and, for stations employing directional antenna systems, the radio-frequency current at the point of common input to the directional antenna. (b) In the event that any one of these indicating instruments becomes defective when no substitute which conforms with the required specifications is available, the station may be operated without the defective instrument pending its repair or replacement for a period not in excess of 60 days without further authority of the Commission: *Provided,* That: (1) Appropriate entries shall be made in the maintenance log of the station showing the date and time the meter was removed from and restored to service. (2) The Engineer in Charge of the radio district in which the station is located shall be notified immediately after the instrument is found to be defective and immediately after the repaired or replacement instrument has been installed and is functioning properly. (3) If the defective instrument is the antenna current meter of a nondirectional station which does not employ a remote antenna ammeter, or if the defective instrument is the common point meter of a station which employs a directional antenna, and does not employ a remote common point meter, the operating power shall be determined by the indirect method in accordance with R & R 73.51 (d), (e), and (f) during the entire time the station is operated without the antenna current meter or common point meter. However, if a remote antenna ammeter or a remote common point meter is employed and the antenna current meter or common point meter becomes defective, the remote meter may be used in determining operating power by the direct method pending the return to service of the regular meter, provided other meters are maintained at same value previously employed. (c) If conditions beyond the control of the licensee prevent the restoration of the meter to service within the above allowed period, informal request in accordance with R & R 1.549 of this chapter may be filed with the Engineer in Charge of the radio district in which the station is located for such additional time as may be required to complete repairs of the defective instrument. (d) Remote antenna ammeters and remote common point meters are not required; therefore, authority to operate without them is not necessary. However, if a remote antenna ammeter or common point meter is employed and becomes defective, the antenna base currents may be read and logged once daily for each mode of operation, pending the return to service of the regular remote meter.

R & R 73.59   Frequency Tolerance. The operating frequency of each station shall be maintained within 20 cycles of the assigned frequency.

*   *   *   *   *   *

R & R 73.67   Remote Control Operation.

*   *   *   *   *   *

(3) A malfunction of any part of the remote control equipment and associated line circuits resulting in improper control or inaccurate meter readings shall be cause for the immediate cessation of operation by remote control.

*   *   *   *   *   *

R & R 73.93   Operator Requirements. (a) One or more operators holding a radio operator license or permit of a grade specified in this section shall be in actual charge of the transmitting system, and shall be on duty either at the transmitter location or at the remote control point. If operation by remote control has not been authorized, the transmitter, required monitors and other required metering equipment shall be readily accessible, clearly visible, and located sufficiently close to the operator at the normal operating position that deviations from normal indications of required instruments can be observed readily. If operation by remote control is authorized, the required controls and instruments shall be readily accessible, clearly visible, and located sufficiently close to the operator at the normal operating position that deviations from normal indications of required instruments can be observed readily.

(b) With the exceptions set forth in paragraph (f) of this section, adjustments of the transmitting system and inspection, maintenance, and required equipment performance measurements and required field strength measurements shall be performed only by a first-class radiotelephone operator.

*   *   *   *   *   *

(4) A partial proof of performance as defined in Note 2 at the end of this section shall be made once each calendar year, with intervals between successive proofs not to exceed fourteen (14) months. The report of such proof measurements shall be prepared and filed as specified in paragraph (b) of R & R 73.47.

(5) Field strength measurements shall be made at the monitoring points specified in the station authorization at least once each 30 days unless more frequent measurements are required by such authorization. The results of these measurements shall be entered in the station maintenance log. The licensee shall have readily available, and in proper working condition, field strength measuring equipment to perform these measurements.

*   *   *   *   *   *

(g) It is the responsibility of the station licensee to insure that each operator is fully instructed in the performance of all the above adjustments, as well as in other required duties, such as reading meters and making log entries. Printed step-by-step instructions for those adjustments which the lesser grade operator is permitted to make, and a tabulation or chart of upper and lower limiting values of parameters required to be observed and logged, shall be posted at the operating position. The emissions of the station shall be terminated immediately whenever the transmitting system is observed operating beyond the posted parameters, or in any other manner inconsistent with the rules or the station authorization, and the above adjustments are ineffective in correcting the condition of improper operation, and a first-class radiotelephone operator is not present.

(h) When lesser grade operators are used, in accordance with paragraphs (d) or (c) of this section, for any period of operation using authorized power in excess of 10 kilowatts, or using a directional radiation pattern, the station licensee shall designate one first-class radiotelephone operator in full-time employment as the chief operator who, together with the licensee, shall be responsible for the technical operation of the station. The station licensee shall notify the Engineer in Charge of the radio district in which the station is located of the name and license number of the designated chief operator. Such notification shall be by letter within three (3) days of such designation. A copy of the notification shall be posted with the chief operator's license.

(1) An operator designated as chief operator for one station may not be so designated concurrently at any other standard broadcast station.

(2) The station licensee shall vest such authority in, and afford such facilities to the chief operator as may be necessary to insure that the chief operator's primary responsibility for the proper technical operation of the station may be discharged efficiently.

(3) At such times as a regularly designated chief operator is unavailable or unable to act as chief operator (e.g., vacations, sickness), the station licensee shall designate another first-class radiotelephone operator as acting chief operator on a temporary basis. Within 3 days of the date such action is taken, the engineer in charge of the radio district in which the station is located shall be notified by the licensee by letter of the name and license number of the acting chief operator, and shall be notified by letter, again within 3 days of the date when the regularly designated chief operator returns to duty.

(4) The designated chief operator may serve as a routine duty transmitter operator at any station only to the extent that it does not interfere with the efficient discharge of his responsibilities as listed below.

(i) The inspection and maintenance of the transmitting system including the antenna system and required monitoring equipment.

(ii) The accuracy and completeness of entries in the maintenance log.

(iii) The supervision and instruction of all other station operators in the performance of their technical duties.

(iv) A review of completed operating logs to determine whether technical operation of the station has been in accordance with the rules and terms of the station authorization. After review, the chief operator shall sign the log and indicate the date of such review. If the review of the operating logs indicates technical operation of the station is in violation of the rules or the terms of the station authorization, he shall promptly initiate corrective action. The review of each day's operating log shall be made within 24 hours, except that, if the chief operator is not on duty during a given 24-hour period, the logs must be reviewed within 2 hours after his next appearance for duty. In any case, the time before review shall not exceed 72 hours.

(i) The operator on duty at the transmitter or remote control point, may, at the discretion of the licensee and the chief operator, if any, be employed for other duties or for the operation of another radio station or stations in accordance with the class of operator's license which he holds and the rules and regulations governing such other stations: *Provided, however,* That such other duties shall *not* interfere with the proper operation of the standard broadcast transmitting system and keeping of required logs.

(j) At all standard broadcast stations, a complete inspection of the transmitting system and required monitoring equipment in use, shall be made by an operator holding a first-class radiotelephone license at least once each day, 5 days each week, with an interval of no less than 12 hours between successive inspections. This inspection shall include such tests, adjustments, and repairs as may be necessary to insure operation in conformance with the provisions of this subpart and the current station authorization.

*   *   *   *   *   *

NOTE 1: The effectiveness of subparagraph (2) of paragraph (e) of this section is suspended pending final action in Docket 18471.

NOTE 2: The partial proof of performance is to consist of at least 10 field strength measurements including the point designated as a monitoring point, taken at a distance of from 2 to 10 miles from the antenna on each radial measured in connection with the latest complete adjustment of the directional antenna system. These measurements shall be analyzed in the manner prescribed in R&R 73.186.

*   *   *   *   *   *

R & R 73.111   General Requirements Relating to Logs. (a) The licensee or permittee of each standard broadcast station shall maintain program, operating, and maintenance logs as set forth in R & R 73.112, 73.113, and 73.114. Each log shall be kept by the station employee or employees (or contract operator) competent to do so, having actual knowledge of the facts required, who in the case of program and operating logs shall sign the appropriate log when starting duty, and again when going off duty.

(b) The logs shall be kept in an orderly and legible manner, in suitable form, and in such detail that the data required for the particular class of station concerned is readily available. Key letters or abbreviations may be used if proper meaning or explanation is contained elsewhere in the log. Each sheet shall be numbered and dated. Time entries shall be made in local time. For the period from the last Sunday in April until the last Sunday in October of each year, the program and operating log entries showing times of sign-on, sign-off, and change in the station's mode of operation shall specifically be indicated as advanced or nonadvanced time.

(c) No log or preprinted log or schedule which becomes a log, or portion thereof, shall be erased, obliterated, or willfully destroyed within the period of retention provided by the provisions of this part. Any necessary correction shall be made only pursuant to R & R 73.112, 73.113, and 73.114, and only by striking out the erroneous portion, or by making a corrective explanation on the log or attachment to it as provided in those sections.

(d) Entries shall be made in the logs as required by R & R 73.112, 73.113, and 73.114. Additional information such as that needed for billing purposes or for the cuing of automatic equipment may be entered on the logs. Such additional information, so entered, shall not be subject to the restrictions and limitations in the Commission's rules on the making of corrections and changes in logs.

R & R 73.112   Program Log. (a) The following entries shall be made in the program log:

(1) *For each program.* (i) An entry identifying the program by name or title.

(ii) An entry of the time each program begins and ends. If programs are broadcast during which separately identifiable program units of a different type or source are presented, and if the licensee wishes to count such units separately, the beginning and ending time for the longer program need be entered only once for the entire program. The program units which the licensee wishes to count separately shall then be entered underneath the entry for a longer program, with the beginning and ending time of each such unit, and with the entry indented or otherwise distinguished so as to make it clear that the program unit referred to was broadcast within the longer program.

(iii) An entry classifying each program as to type.

(iv) An entry classifying each program as to source. (For network programs, also give name or initials of network, e.g., ABC, CBS, NBC, Mutual.)

(v) An entry for each program presenting a political candidate, showing the name and political affiliation of such candidate.

(2) *For commercial matter.* (i) An entry identifying (*a*) the sponsor(s) of the program, (*b*) the person(s) who paid for the announcement, or (*c*) the person(s) who furnished materials or services referred to in R & R 73.119(d). If the title of a sponsored program includes the name of the sponsor, e.g., XYZ News, a separate entry for the sponsor is not required.

(ii) An entry or entries showing the total duration of commercial matter in each hourly time segment (beginning on the hour) or the duration of each commercial message (commercial continuity in sponsored programs, or commercial announcements) in each hour.

(iii) An entry showing that the appropriate announcement(s) (sponsorship, furnishing material or services, etc.) have been made as required by Section 317 of the Communications Act and R & R 73.119. A checkmark (✔) will suffice but shall be made in such a way as to indicate the matter to which it relates.

(3) *For public service announcements.* (i) An entry showing that a

public service announcement (PSA) has been broadcast together with the name of the organization or interest on whose behalf it is made.

(4) *For other announcements.* (i) An entry of the time that each required station identification announcement is made (call letters and licensed location; see R & R 73.117).

(ii) An entry for each announcement presenting a political candidate showing the name and political affiliation of such candidate.

(iii) An entry for each announcement made pursuant to the local notice requirements of R & R 1.580 (pre-grant) and 1.594 (designation for hearing) of this chapter, showing the time it was broadcast.

(iv) An entry showing that a mechanical reproduction announcement has been made in accordance with the provisions of R & R 73.118.

(b) Program log entries may be made either at the time of or prior to broadcast. A station broadcasting the programs of a national network which will supply it with all information as to such programs, commercial matter and other announcements for the composite week need not log such data, but shall record in its log the time when it joined the network, the name of each network program broadcast, the time it leaves the network, and any nonnetwork matter broadcast required to be logged. The information supplied by the network for the composite week which the station will use in its renewal of application shall be retained with the program logs and associated with the log pages to which it relates.

(c) No provision of this section shall be construed as prohibiting the recording or other automatic maintenance of data required for program logs. However, where such automatic logging is used, the licensee must comply with the following requirements:

(1) The licensee, whether employing manual or automatic logging or a combination thereof, must be able accurately to furnish the Commission with all information required to be logged;

(2) Each recording, tape, or other means employed shall be accompanied by a certificate of the operator or other responsible person on duty at the time or other duly authorized agent of the licensee, to the effect that it accurately reflects what was actually broadcast. Any information required to be logged which cannot be incorporated in the automatic process shall be maintained in a separate record which shall be similarly authenticated;

(3) The licensee shall extract any required information from the recording for the days specified by the Commission or its duly authorized representative and submit it in written log form, together with the underlying recording, tape, or other means employed.

(d) Program logs shall be changed or corrected only in the manner prescribed in R & R 73.111(c) and only in accordance with the following:

(1) *Manually kept log.* Where, in any program log, or preprinted program log, or program schedule which upon completion is used as a pro-

gram log, a correction is made before the person keeping the log has signed the log upon going off duty, such correction, no matter by whom made, shall be initialed by the person keeping the log prior to his signing of the log when going off duty, as attesting to the fact that the log as corrected is an accurate representation of what was broadcast. If corrections or additions are made on the log after it has been so signed, explanation must be made on the log or on an attachment to it, dated and signed by either the person who kept the log, the station program director or manager, or an officer of the licensee.

*   *   *   *   *   *

R & R 73.113   Operating Log. (a) The entries specified in subparagraphs (1), (2), (3), (5), and (6) of this paragraph, shall be made in the operating log by the properly licensed operator on duty in actual charge of the transmitting system. The entries required by subparagraph (4) of this paragraph shall be made only by a first-class radiotelephone operator.

(1) An entry of the time the station begins to supply power to the antenna and the time it stops.

(2) An entry of each interruption of the carrier wave, where restoration is not automatic, its cause and duration followed by the signature of the person restoring operation (if licensed operator other than the licensed operator on duty).

(3) An entry, at the beginning of operation and at intervals not exceeding one-half hour, of the following (actual readings observed prior to making any adjustments to the equipment) and, when appropriate, an indication of corrections made to restore parameters to normal operating values:

(i) Operating constants of last radio stage (total plate voltage and plate current).

(ii) Antenna current or common point current (if directional) without modulation, or with modulation if the meter reading is not affected by modulation.

(iii) Frequency monitor reading.

(4) An entry each day of the following where applicable:

(i) Antenna base current(s) without modulation, or with modulation if the meter reading is not affected by modulation, for each mode of operation:

(*a*) Where remote antenna meters or a remote common point meter are normally employed but are defective.

(*b*) Where required by the station license for directional antenna operation.

(ii) Where there is remote control operation of a directional antenna station, readings for each pattern taken at the transmitter (within 2 hours of commencement of operation with each pattern) of:

(*a*) Common point current without modulation, or with modulation if the meter reading is not affected by modulation.

(*b*) Base current(s) without modulation, or with modulation if the meter reading is not affected by modulation.

(*c*) Phase monitor sample loop current(s) without modulation or with modulation if the meter reading is not affected by modulation.

(*d*) Phase indications.

(5) Any other entries required by the instrument of authorization or the provisions of this part. See the additional entries required by R & R 73.51 (e) (2) when power is being determined by the indirect method.

(6) The entries required by R & R 17.49 (a), (b), and (c) of this chapter concerning daily observations of tower lights.

(b) Automatic devices accurately calibrated and with appropriate time, date and circuit functions may be utilized to record the entries in the operating log: *Provided,* That:

(1) They do not affect the operation of circuits or accuracy of indicating instruments of the equipment being recorded;

(2) The recording devices have an accuracy equivalent to the accuracy of the indicating instruments;

(3) The calibration is checked against the original indicators at least once a week and the results noted in the maintenance log;

(4) Provision is made to actuate automatically an aural alarm circuit located near the operator on duty if any of the automatic log readings are not within the tolerances or other requirements specified in the rules or instrument of authorization;

(5) Unless the alarm circuit operates continuously, devices which record each parameter in sequence must read each parameter at least once during each 10-minute period and clearly indicate the parameter being recorded;

(6) The automatic logging equipment is located at the remote control point if the transmitter is remotely controlled, or at the transmitter location if the transmitter is directly controlled;

(7) The automatic logging equipment is located in the near vicinity of the operator on duty and is inspected by him periodically during the broadcast day; and

(8) The indicating equipment conforms with the requirements of R & R 73.39 except that the scales need not exceed 2 inches in length and arbitrary scales may not be used.

(c) In preparing the operating log, original data may be recorded in rough form and later transcribed into the log, but in such a case all portions of the original memoranda shall be preserved as a part of the complete log.

(d) Operating logs shall be changed or corrected only in the manner prescribed in R & R 73.111(c) and only in accordance with the following:

(1) *Manually kept log.* Any necessary corrections in a manually kept operating log shall be made only by the person making the original entry who shall make and initial each correction prior to signing the log when going off duty in accordance with R & R 73.111(a). If corrections or additions are made on the log after it has been so signed, explanation must be made on the log or on an attachment to it, dated and signed by either the operator who kept the log, the station technical supervisor or an officer of the licensee.

(2) *Automatic logging.* No automatically kept operating log shall be altered in any way after entries have been recorded. Any errors or omissions found in an automatically kept operating log shall be noted and explained in a memorandum signed by the operator on duty (who, under the provisions of paragraph (b)(7) of this section, is required to inspect the automatic equipment), or by the station technical supervisor or an officer of the licensee. Such memorandum shall be affixed to the original log in question.

(e) If required by R & R 73.93(h)(4)(iv), each completed operating log shall bear a signed and dated notation by the station's chief operator of the results of the review of that log.

*   *   *   *   *   *

R & R 73.115   Retention of Logs. Logs of standard broadcast stations shall be retained by the licensee or permittee for a period of 2 years: *Provided, however,* That logs involving communications incident to a disaster or which include communications incident to or involved in an investigation by the Commission and concerning which the licensee or permittee has been notified, shall be retained by the licensee or permittee until he is specifically authorized in writing by the Commission to destroy them: *Provided, further,* That logs incident to or involved in any claim or complaint of which the licensee or permittee has notice shall be retained by the licensee or permittee until such claim or complaint has been fully satisfied or until the same has been barred by statute limiting the time for the filing of suits upon such claims.

Note: Application forms for licenses and other authorizations require that certain operating and program data be supplied. It is suggested that these application forms be kept in mind in connection with maintenance of station program and operating records.

R & R 73.116   Availability of Logs and Records. The following shall be available upon request by an authorized representative of the Commission: (a) Program operating and maintenance logs. (b) Equipment performance measurements required by R & R 73.47. (c) Copy of most

recent antenna resistance or common-point impedance measurements submitted to the Commission. (d) Copy of most recent field intensity measurements to establish performance of directional antennas required by
R & R 73.151.

R & R 73.117, see R & R 73.1201 (follows).

R & R 73.1201   Station Identification. (a) *When regularly required.* Broadcast station identification announcements shall be made:
(1) At the beginning and ending of each time of operation, and (2)
hourly, as close to the hour as feasible, at a natural break in program
offerings. Television broadcast stations may make these announcements visually or aurally.

(b) *Content.* (1) Official station identification shall consist of the
station's call letters immediately followed by the name of the community or communities specified in its license as the station's location.

(2) When given specific written authorization to do so, a station
may include in its official station identification the name of an additional community or communities, but the community to which the
station is licensed must be named first.

(3) A licensee shall not in any identification announcements, promotional announcements or any other broadcast matter either lead or
attempt to lead the station's audience to believe that the station has been
authorized to identify officially with cities other than those permitted
to be included in official station identifications under subparagraphs
(1) and (2) of this paragraph.

NOTE: Commission interpretations of this paragraph may be found in a
separate Public Notice issued Oct. 30, 1967, entitled Examples of Application
of Rule Regarding Broadcast of Statements Regarding a Station's Licensed Location. (FCC 67–1132; 10 FCC 2d 407).

(c) *Channel*—(1) *General.* Except as otherwise provided in this
paragraph, in making the identification announcement the call letters
shall be given only on the channel identified thereby.

(2) *Simultaneous AM–FM broadcasts.* If the same licensee operates
an FM broadcast station and a standard broadcast station and simultaneously broadcasts the same programs over the facilities of both such
stations, station identification announcements may be made jointly for
both stations for periods of such simultaneous operation. If the call
letters of the FM station do not clearly reveal that it is an FM station,
the joint announcement shall so identify it.

(d) *Program interruption.* Licensees shall, in general, arrange their
programming so as to permit the broadcast of station identification
announcements at the regular times prescribed in paragraph (a) of this
section without undue disruption of program continuity. Subject to
this requirement, a station identification announcement need not be

presented at the time it is regularly required, if to do so would objectionably break program continuity essential to the value of the program to the audience. However, program continuity is deemed to be broken, and therefore an anouncement is required, if during the 4-minute period in which an announcement is regularly due there is presented any nonprogram matter, such as commercial, public service or promotional announcements. While there may be exceptions, normally program continuity is also deemed to be broken, and an identification announcement is required, if during the 4-minute period there occurs the end of a regular period in a sports event being broadcast (e.g., round, quarter, or half-inning), the end of an act in a dramatic or variety program, the intermission of a live concert, opera, recital, or other musical performance presented live in its entirety (presented simultaneously or by rebroadcast), or the end of any other musical selection.

(e) *Deferred station identification.* (1) If a station omits a regular station identification announcement as permitted under paragraph (d) of this section, it shall broadcast a deferred station identification announcement at the next opportunity when it can be presented without objectionably breaking program continuity essential to the value of the program to the audience. Such opportunity is deemed to occur, at the latest, when any of the material or events mentioned in paragraph (d) of this section is presented or occurs.

(2) If no opportunity for an announcement (as defined in subparagraph (1) of this paragraph) occurs after a regular station identification is omitted, a deferred station identification shall be broadcast promptly at the end of the program unless the next regular station identification is broadcast within 5 minutes after the program ends.

(f) *Equipment performance measurements.* Station identifications falling due during equipment performance measurements may be deferred up to a quarter of an hour.

R & R 73.118   Mechanical Reproductions. (a) No mechanically reproduced program consisting of a speech, news event, news commentator, forum, panel discussion, or special event in which the element of time is of special significance, or any other program in which the element of time is of special significance and presentation of which would create, either intentionally or otherwise, the impression or belief on the part of the listening audience that the event or program being broadcast is in fact occurring simultaneously with the broadcast, shall be broadcast without an appropriate announcement being made either at the beginning or end of such reproduction or at the beginning or end of the program in which such reproduction is used that it is a mechanical reproduction or mechanically reproduced program: *Provided, however,* That each such program of one minute or less need not be announced as such.

*   *   *   *   *   *

R & R 73.119   Sponsored Programs, Announcement of. (a) When a standard broadcast station transmits any matter for which money, services, or other valuable consideration is either directly or indirectly paid or promised to, or charged or received by, such station, the station shall broadcast an announcement that such matter is sponsored, paid for, or furnished, either in whole or in part, and by whom or on whose behalf such consideration was supplied: *Provided, however,* That "service or other valuable consideration" shall not include any service or property furnished without charge or at a nominal charge for use on, or in connection with, a broadcast of any person, product, service, trademark, or brand name beyond an identification which is reasonably related to the use of such service or property on the broadcast.

*   *   *   *   *   *

(e) The announcement required by this section shall fully and fairly disclose the true identity of the person or persons by whom or in whose behalf such payment is made or promised, or from whom or in whose behalf such services or other valuable consideration is received, or by whom the material or services referred to in paragraph (d) of this section are furnished. Where an agent or other person contracts or otherwise makes known to the station, the announcement shall disclose the identity of the person or persons in whose behalf such agent is acting instead of the name of such agent.

*   *   *   *   *   *

R & R 73.252   Frequency Monitor. (a) Each station shall have in operation, either at the transmitter or at the place where the transmitter is controlled, a frequency monitor of a type approved by the Commission which shall be independent of the frequency control of the transmitter.

NOTE: Approved frequency monitors are included on the Commission's "Radio Equipment List, Part B, Aural Broadcast Equipment." Copies of this list are available for inspection at the Commission's office in Washington, D.C., and at each of its field offices.

(b) In the event that the frequency monitor becomes defective the station may be operated without the monitor pending its repair or replacement for a period not in excess of 60 days without further authority of the Commission: *Provided,* That:

(1) Appropriate entries shall be made in the maintenance log of the station showing the date and time the monitor was removed from and restored to service.

(2) The Engineer in Charge of the radio district in which the station is located shall be notified both immediately after the monitor is found to be defective and immediately after the repaired or replacement monitor has been installed and is functioning properly.

(3) The frequency of the station shall be compared with an external frequency source of known accuracy at sufficiently frequent intervals to insure that the frequency is maintained within the tolerance prescribed in R & R 73.269. An entry shall be made in the station log as to the method used and the results thereof.

(c) If conditions beyond the control of the licensee prevent the restoration of the monitor to service within the above allowed period, informal request in accordance with R & R 1.549 of this chapter may be filed with the Engineer in Charge of the radio district in which the station is located for such additional time as may be required to complete repairs of the defective instrument.

*   *   *   *   *   *

R & R 73.269   Frequency Tolerance. The center frequency of each FM broadcast station shall be maintained within 2000 cycles of the assigned center frequency.

*   *   *   *   *   *

R & R 73.310   (a) FM Broadcast Band. The band of frequencies extending from 88 to 108 megahertz, which includes those assigned to noncommercial educational broadcasting.

FM Broadcast Station. A station employing frequency modulation in the FM broadcast band and licensed primarily for the transmission of radiotelephone emissions intended to be received by the general public.

*   *   *   *   *   *

R & R 73.907   Emergency Action Notification. The Emergency Action Notification is the notice to all licensees and regulated services of the Federal Communications Commission, participating non-Government industry entities, and to the general public of the existence of an Emergency Action Condition. The Emergency Action Notification is disseminated only via the Emergency Action Notification System in accordance with the Detailed non-Government Activation and Termination Procedures and Standing Operating Procedures (SOP's) for the Emergency Broadcast System which are promulgated and issued only by the Federal Communications Commission to those non-Government entities concerned.

R & R 73.908   **Emergency Action Condition.** The Emergency Action Condition is a National, State, or Operational (local) Area emergency situation posing a threat to the safety of life or property covering the period of time between the transmission of an Emergency Action Notification and the transmission of the Emergency Action Condition Termination.

R & R 73.909   **Emergency Action Condition Termination.** The Emergency Action Condition Termination is the notice to all licensees and regulated services of the Federal Communications Commission, participating non-Government industry entities, and to the general public of the termination of an Emergency Action Condition. The Emergency Action Condition Termination is disseminated only via the Emergency Action Notification System in accordance with the Detailed non-Government Activation and Termination Procedures and Standing Operating Procedures (SOP's) for the Emergency Broadcast System which are promulgated and issued only by the Federal Communications Commission to those non-Government entities concerned.

*   *   *   *   *   *

R & R 73.912   **Emergency Broadcast System (EBS).** The Emergency Broadcast System (EBS) is composed of facilities and personnel of non-Government broadcast stations and other authorized facilities licensed or regulated by the Federal Communications Commission and participating non-Government industry entities, including approved and authorized integral facilities or systems, arrangements, procedures, and interconnecting facilities, which have been authorized by the Federal Communications Commission to operate on a voluntary organized basis during National, State, or Operational (local) Area situations covering a broad range of emergency contingencies posing a threat to the safety of life or property for the purpose of expeditiously transmitting emergency Presidential Messages, National, State, or Operational (local) Area emergency information, emergency programing, or news to the general public.

R & R 73.913   **Basic Emergency Broadcast System (EBS) Plan.** The Basic Emergency Broadcast System (EBS) Plan contains, among other things, approved basic concepts and designated systems, arrangements, procedures, and interconnecting facilities to provide the requisite guidance to all non-Government participating elements and industry entities in the detailed development, designation and approval of facilities, mutually compatible operational arrangements, procedures, and interconnection arrangements for the expeditious dissemination on a voluntary organized basis of emergency information and instructions at the request of National, State, and Operational (local) Area authorities in addition to emergency Presidential Messages, National

Programming and News during National, State, or Operational (local) Area situations covering a broad range of emergency contingencies posing a threat to the safety of life or property.

*   *   *   *   *   *

R & R 73.917   Primary Station Emergency Broadcast System (EBS) Authorization. A Primary Station Emergency Broadcast System (EBS) Authorization is the authorization issued to one or more broadcast station licensees in an Operational (local) Area assigning such licensees the responsibility for broadcasting a common emergency program for the initial period of, or for the duration of a National-level Emergency Action Condition. Broadcasts by such stations are intended for direct public reception in an Operational (local) Area, as specified in an approved Detailed State Emergency Broadcast System (EBS) Operational Plan.

*   *   *   *   *   *

R & R 73.932   Radio Monitoring Requirement. (a) In order to insure the effectiveness of the Third Method of the Emergency Action Notification System, all broadcast station licensees must install and operate during their hours of broadcast operation, equipment capable of receiving Emergency Action Notifications or Terminations transmitted by other radio broadcast stations. This equipment must be maintained in operative condition, including arrangements for human listening watch or automatic alarm devices, and shall have its termination at each transmitter control point. However, where more than one broadcast transmitter is controlled from a common point by the same operator, only one set of equipment is required at that point.

(b) The Third Method off-the-air monitoring assignment of each standard, FM, and television broadcast station is specified in the Detailed State Emergency Broadcast System (EBS) Operational Plan.

(c) Prior to commencing routine operation or originating any emissions under program test, equipment test, experimental, or other authorizations or for any other purpose, licensees or permittees shall first ascertain whether an Emergency Action Condition exists and, if so, shall operate only in accordance with the Basic Emergency Broadcast System (EBS) Plan and Detailed State Emergency Broadcast System (EBS) Operational Plan.

R & R 73.933   Emergency Broadcast System (EBS) Operation During a National-Level Emergency Action Condition. (a) All broadcast stations are furnished complete instructions on an Emergency Action Checklist to be posted at broadcast operating positions. This Checklist summarizes the procedures to be followed by operating personnel of all broadcast stations subject to this part upon receipt of a

National-Level Emergency Action Notification or Emergency Action Condition Termination. This notification may be received by one or more of the following: Receipt of the Emergency Action Notification via any one of the following is sufficient notice to begin emergency action.

(1) Via the commercial radio and television network facilities;

(2) Via the radio press wires (AP/UPI) ;

(3) Via off-the-air monitoring of the Primary Station for the Operational (local) Area;

(4) Via off-the-air monitoring of the Primary (FM) Relay Station for the Operational (local) Area.

(b) Immediately upon receipt of such notifications, all standard, commercial FM (including all subcarriers), and noncommercial educational FM (including all subcarriers), and television broadcast stations, including all such stations operating under equipment or program test authority, will proceed as follows:

NOTE: It is suggested that appropriate arrangements be made to tape all emergency broadcasts, including the Emergency Action Notification. Appropriate notations should also be made in the station log of all significant events as they transpire. These records should be carefully preserved in the event they are required at some later date.

(1) Immediately monitor the commercial radio and television network facilities (ABC, CBS, IMN, MBS, NBC, UPI Audio, ABC-TV, CBS-TV, NBC-TV) for any further instructions from the Network Control Point.

(2) Immediately check the Radio Press Wire (AP/UPI). Verify authenticity of message with current EBS Authenticator List (Red Envelope).

(3) Immediately monitor the radio receiving equipment tuned to a Primary Station for the Operational (Local) Area and/or to a Primary Relay (FM) Station for the State EBS Network or the Statewide leased common carrier State EBS Network for receipt of any further instructions.

(4) Discontinue normal program and broadcast the following announcement:

We interrupt this program. This is a National Emergency. Important instructions will follow:

(5) Transmit the Emergency Action Notification Attention Signal as set forth in R & R 73.906 as follows:

(i) Cut the transmitter carrier for 5 seconds. (Sound carrier only for TV stations.)

(ii) Return carrier to the air for 5 seconds.

(iii) Cut transmitter carrier for 5 seconds. (Sound carrier only for TV stations.)

(iv) Return carrier to the air.

(v) Broadcast 1000-hertz steady-state tone for 15 seconds.

*   *   *   *   *   *

R & R 73.961   Tests of the Emergency Action Notification System. Tests of the Emergency Action Notification System will be made at regular intervals with appropriate entries in the station operating log, as follows:

(a) Test transmissions of the First Method, National-Level interconnecting facilities of the Emergency Action Notification System will be conducted on a random basis once each week or as prescribed by the White House. The test transmissions will originate on an alternate week basis from one of two specified origination points; thence via a dedicated teletype network to specified control points of the commercial Radio and Television Broadcast Networks and the American Telephone and Telegraph Co. in accordance with the test procedures set forth in the EBS Standing Operating Procedures (EBS SOP–1), copies of which are furnished to the non-Government entities involved.

(b) Test transmissions of the Second Method National-Level interconnecting facilities of the Emergency Action Notification System will be conducted on a random basis once each week or as prescribed by the White House. The test transmissions will originate on an alternate week basis from one of two specified origination points; thence via a dedicated teletype network with a dedicated automatic telephone network for backup confirmation purposes in accordance with the test procedures set forth in the EBS Standing Operating Procedures (EBS SOP–1), copies of which are furnished to the non-Government entities involved.

*   *   *   *   *   *

(d) Test transmissions to standard, FM, and television broadcast stations using the Second Method of the Emergency Action Notification System and utilizing the facilities of the Associated Press (AP) and United Press International (UPI) Radio Wire Teletype Networks will be conducted once each week in accordance with the test procedures set forth in the EBS Standing Operating Procedures (EBS SOP–2), copies of which are furnished to all stations. AP and UPI will separately transmit the Test Message on a random basis once each week at times of their choice. The date and time of receipt of these test transmissions should be entered in the Station Operating Log.

*   *   *   *   *   *

(e) Test transmission of the Third Method of the Emergency Action Notification System will be conducted by standard, FM, and television broadcast stations once each week on a random basis between the hours of 8:30 a.m. and local sunset.

Note: The above descriptions of the tests are summarized because of space limitations. Refer to Vol. III of the FCC Rules and Regulations for the complete text.

PART 74: EXPERIMENTAL, AUXILIARY, AND SPECIAL BROADCAST SERVICES

R & R 74.435   Power Limitations. Remote pickup broadcast stations will be licensed with a power output not in excess of that necessary to render satisfactory service. The license for these stations will specify the maximum authorized power. The operating power shall not be greater than necessary to carry on the service and in no event more than 5 percent above the maximum power specified. Engineering standards have not been established for these stations. The efficiency factor for the last radio stage of transmitters employed will be subject to individual determination but shall be in general agreement with values normally employed for similar equipment operated within the frequency range authorized.

*   *   *   *   *   *

R & R 74.481   Logs. (a) The licensee of a remote pickup broadcast base or mobile station shall maintain an operating log to show when and for what purpose the station is operated. The following basic data shall be recorded.

(1) The date and time of operation.

(2) The purpose of the operation.

(3) The location of the transmitter, if a mobile or portable station.

(4) The station with which it communicates.

(5) Frequency check, if made.

(6) Entries required by R & R 17.49 of this chapter concerning daily observations of tower lights and quarterly inspections of the condition of the tower lights and associated control equipment and an entry when towers are cleaned or repainted as required by R & R 17.50 of this chapter.

(7) Any pertinent remarks concerning the transmissions or equipment deemed desirable or necessary by the operator.

(b) In cases where a series of intermittent transmissions relating to coverage of a single event are made, an entry showing the time of the beginning of the series and time of the conclusion of the series will suffice. A notation such as "intermittent transmissions in connection with coverage of automobile accident at Main and Fern Streets" will explain the purpose of the operation and location of the transmitter. The station with which it communicates could be the base station (call sign) or the associated broadcast station (call sign). Intermittent but unrelated transmissions shall be logged separately. A single time entry may be made for short transmissions of less than one minute duration. The time of beginning and ending shall be logged for longer transmissions. In all cases, the purpose of the transmission shall be shown and the approximate location of the mobile unit. If the mobile unit is halted, the exact location should be known.

(c) In cases where a base station is used for dispatching mobile units, a running log may be kept at the base station, containing entries for both the base station and one or more mobile units. Each entry should be identified by the call sign of the station making the transmission. The operator in the mobile unit shall keep a record of all transmissions by the mobile unit which are not acknowledged by the base station so that these missed transmissions may be inserted at the appropriate place in the log kept at the base station.

(d) In cases where only mobile units are used, the logs shall be kept by the operator in the mobile unit. A rough log may be kept by the operator in the mobile unit and these notes entered in a permanent log at the end of the tour of duty.

(e) An entry shall be made of any frequency check made pursuant to the requirements of R & R 74.462.

(f) If the station instrument of authorization requires painting and the lighting of the antenna structure, the log entries concerning lighting shall be made daily whether or not the transmitter is used.

(g) Station records shall be kept in such manner as to be available for inspection by a duly authorized representative of the Commission upon request. The records shall be retained for a period of 2 years.

*   *   *   *   *   *

R & R 74.501   Classes of Stations. (a) *Aural broadcast STL station.* A fixed station utilizing telephony for the transmission of aural program material between a studio and the transmitter of a broadcasting station other than an international broadcasting station, for simultaneous or delayed broadcast.

(b) *Aural broadcast intercity relay station.* A fixed station utilizing telephony for the transmission of aural program material between broadcasting stations other than international broadcasting stations, for simultaneous or delayed broadcast.

*   *   *   *   *   *

R & R 74.536   Directional Antenna Required. Each aural broadcast STL and intercity relay station is required to employ a directional antenna. Considering one kilowatt of radiated power as a standard for comparative purposes, such antenna shall provide a free space field intensity at one mile of not less than 435 mv/m in the main lobe of radiation toward the receiver and not more than 20 percent of the maximum value in any azimuth 30 degrees or more off the line to the receiver. Where more than one antenna is authorized for use with a single station, the radiation pattern of each shall be in accordance with the foregoing requirement.

*   *   *   *   *   *

R & R 74.561   Frequency Tolerance. The licensee of each aural broadcast STL and intercity relay station shall maintain the operating frequency of the station within plus or minus 0.005 percent of the assigned frequency.

*   *   *   *   *   *

PART 81: STATIONS ON LAND IN THE MARITIME SERVICES

R & R 81.179   Message Charges. (a)(1) No charge shall be made for the service of any public coast station unless effective tariffs applicable to such service are on file with the Commission, pursuant to the requirements of Section 203 of the Communications Act and Part 61 of this chapter.

(2) No charge shall be made for the service of any station subject to this part, other than a public coast station, except as provided by and in accordance with R & R 81.352.

(b) No charge shall be made by any station in the maritime mobile service of the United States for the transmission of distress messages and replies thereto in connection with situations involving the safety of life and property at sea.

(c) No charge shall be made by any station in the maritime mobile service of the United States for the transmission receipt or relay of the information concerning dangers to navigation designated in R & R 83.303 (b) of this chapter, originating on a ship of the United States or of a foreign country.

*   *   *   *   *   *

R & R 81.302 Points of Communication. (a) Subject to the conditions and limitations imposed by the terms of the particular coast station license or by the applicable provisions of this part with respect to the use of particular radio channels, public coast stations using telephony are authorized to communicate:

(1) With any ship station or aircraft station operating in the maritime mobile service for the transmission or reception of safety communication;

(2) With any land station for the purpose of facilitating the transmission or reception of safety communication to or from a ship or aircraft station;

*   *   *   *   *   *

PART 83: STATIONS ON SHIPBOARD IN THE MARITIME SERVICES

R & R 83.6 Operational.

*   *   *   *   *   *

(c) Harmful interference. Any emission, radiation, or induction which endangers the functioning of a radionavigation service or of other safety services, or seriously degrades, obstructs, or repeatedly interrupts a radiocommunication service operating in accordance with regulations in this chapter.

*   *   *   *   *   *

(f) *Calling.* Transmissions from a station solely to secure the attention of another station, or other stations, for a particular purpose.

(g) *Working.* Radiocommunication carried on, for a purpose other than calling, by any station or stations using telegraphy, telephony, or facsimile.

R & R 83.155 Waivers of Operator License.

*   *   *   *   *   *

(b) *For ship radar.* (1) No radio operator license is required for the operation on board ship, during the course of the normal rendition of service, of ship radar stations: *Provided,* That the following conditions are met or provided for by the licensee of the station:

(i) The radar equipment shall employ as its frequency determining element a non-tunable, pulse-type magnetron;

(ii) The radar equipment shall be capable of being operated during the course of normal rendition of service in accordance with the radio law and the rules and regulations of the Commission by means of exclusively external controls, and

(iii) Operation during the course of normal rendition of service pursuant to this subparagraph (1) must be performed exclusively by the master of the radar-equipped ship or by one or more other persons responsible to him and authorized by him to do so.

(2) All adjustments or tests during or coincident with the installation, servicing, or maintenance of the equipment while it is radiating energy must be performed by or under the immediate supervision and responsibility of a person holding a first- or second-class commercial radio operator license, radiotelephone or radiotelegraph, containing a ship-radar endorsement, who shall be responsible for the proper functioning of the equipment in accordance with the radio law and the Commission's rules and regulations and for the avoidance and prevention of harmful interference from improper transmitter external effects: *Provided, however,* That nothing in this subparagraph shall be construed to prevent persons not holding such licenses or not holding such licenses so endorsed from making replacements of fuses or of receiving-type tubes.

(3) Nothing in this subparagraph shall be construed to change or diminish in any respect the responsibility of any ship radar station licensee for having and maintaining control over the station licensed to him, or for the proper functioning and operation of such station in accordance with the terms of the station license.

(c) *For survival craft.* No radio operator license is required for the operation of a survival craft station while it is being used solely for survival purposes.

R & R 83.156 Posting of Operator License. When a licensed operator is required for the operation of a station subject to this part, the original license of each such operator while he is employed or designated as radio operator of the station shall be posted in a conspicuous place at the principal location on board ship at which the station is operated: *Provided,* That in the case of stations of a portable nature, including marine-utility stations, or in the case where the operator holds a restricted radiotelephone operator permit, the operator may in lieu of posting have on his person either his required operator license or a duly issued verification card (FCC Form 758–F) attesting to the existence of that license.

R & R 83.157 Adjustment or Test of Equipment. Notwithstanding any other provisions of this subpart (except R & R 83.155(b)(2) which specifically covers ship radar stations), all adjustments or tests of radio transmitting apparatus in any station subject to this part during or coincident with the installation, servicing, or maintenance of such apparatus which may affect the proper operation of such station, must be performed by or under the immediate supervision and responsibility of a person holding a first- or second-class commercial radio operator license, either radiotelephone or radiotelegraph as may be appropriate for the class of station involved, who shall be responsible for the proper functioning of the station equipment.

*   *   *   *   *   *

R & R 83.184   Maintenance of Station Log. (a) Each station on board ship subject to this part which is required, under the provisions of this part pertaining to the particular class of station, to keep a radio station log, shall in addition, comply with the applicable provisions of paragraphs (b) and (c) of this section; the station licensee and the licensed radio operator (when a licensed radio operator is required) in charge of the station shall be responsible for compliance with this section.

(b) The log shall be kept in an orderly manner, in useable form, and in such detail that the information required for the particular class of station concerned is readily available. Key letters or abbreviations may be used if their proper meaning or explanation is contained elsewhere in the same log.

(c) The station log or any portion thereof shall not be erased, obliterated, or wilfully destroyed within the period of retention required. However, during this period any necessary correction may be made of such but only by the person originating the entry and that person shall strike out the erroneous portion, initial the correction made, and indicate the date of correction.

*   *   *   *   *   *

R & R 83.234   Distress Signals. (a) The international radiotelegraph distress signal consists of the group "three dots, three dashes, three dots" ($\cdots$ $-$ $-$ $-$ $\cdots$), symbolized herein by $\overline{SOS}$, transmitted as a single signal in which the dashes are slightly prolonged so as to be distinguished clearly from the dots.

(b) The international radiotelephone distress signal consists of the word MAYDAY, pronounced as the French expression "m'aider."

(c) These distress signals indicate that a mobile station is threatened by grave and imminent danger and requests immediate assistance.

*　　*　　*　　*　　*　　*

R & R 83.235　Distress Calls. (a) The distress call sent by radio-telegraphy consists of:

(1) The distress signal SOS, sent three times;

(2) The word DE;

(3) The call sign of the mobile station in distress, sent three times.

(b) The distress call sent by radiotelephony consists of:

(1) The distress signal MAYDAY spoken three times;

(2) The words THIS IS;

(3) The call sign (or name, if no call sign assigned) of the mobile station in distress, spoken three times.

(c) The distress call shall have absolute priority over all other transmissions. All stations which hear it shall immediately cease any transmission capable of interfering with the distress traffic and shall continue to listen on the frequency used for the emission of the distress call. This call shall not be addressed to a particular station and acknowledgment of receipt shall not be given before the distress message which follows it is sent.

*　　*　　*　　*　　*　　*

R & R 83.236　Distress Messages. (a) The radiotelegraph distress message consists of:

(1) The distress signal SOS;

(2) The name of the mobile station in distress;

(3) Particulars of its position;

(4) The nature of the distress;

(5) The kind of assistance desired;

(6) Any other information which might facilitate rescue.

(b) The radiotelephone distress message consists of:

(1) The distress signal MAYDAY;

(2) The name of the mobile station in distress;

(3) Particulars of its position;

(4) The nature of the distress;

(5) The kind of assistance desired;

(6) Any other information which might facilitate rescue (for example, the length, color, and type of vessel; number of persons on board, etc.)

(c) As a general rule, a ship shall signal its position in latitude and longitude (Greenwich), using figures for the degrees and minutes, together with one of the words NORTH or SOUTH and one of the words EAST or WEST. In radiotelegraphy, the signal . - . - . - shall be used to separate the degrees from the minutes. When practicable, the true bearing and distance in nautical miles from a known geographical position may be given.

*   *   *   *   *   *

R & R 83.238 Radiotelephone Distress Call and Message Transmission Procedure. (a) The radiotelephone distress procedure shall consist of:

(1) The radiotelephone alarm signal (whenever possible);

(2) The distress call

(3) The distress message

(b) The radiotelephone distress transmissions shall be made slowly and distinctly, each word being clearly pronounced to facilitate transcription.

(c) After the transmission by radiotelephony of its distress message, the mobile station may be requested to transmit suitable signals followed by its call sign or name, to permit direction-finding stations to determine its position. This request may be repeated at frequent intervals if necessary.

(d) The distress message, preceded by the distress call, shall be repeated at intervals until an answer is received. This repetition shall be preceded by the radiotelephone alarm signal whenever possible.

(e) When the mobile station in distress receives no answer to a distress message transmitted on the distress frequency, the message may be repeated on any other available frequency on which attention might be attracted.

R & R 83.239 Acknowledgment of Receipt of Distress Message. (a) Stations of the maritime mobile service which receive a distress message from a mobile station which is, beyond any possible doubt, in their vicinity, shall immediately acknowledge receipt. However, in areas where reliable communication with one or more coast stations are practicable, ship stations may defer this acknowledgment for a short interval so that a coast station may acknowledge receipt.

(b) Stations of the maritime mobile service which receive a distress message from a mobile station which, beyond any possible doubt, is not in their vicinity, shall allow a short interval of time to elapse before acknowledging receipt of the message, in order to permit stations nearer to the mobile station in distress to acknowledge receipt without interference.

R & R 83.240 Form of Acknowledgment. (a) The acknowledgment of receipt of a distress message is transmitted, when radiotelegraphy is used, in the following form:

(1) The call sign of the station sending the distress message, sent three times;

(2) The word DE;

(3) The call sign of the station acknowledging receipt, sent three times;

(4) The group RRR;

(5) The distress signal $\overline{SOS}$.

(b) The acknowledgment of receipt of a distress message is transmitted, when radiotelephony is used, in the following form:

(1) The call sign or other identification of the station sending the distress message, spoken three times;

(2) The words THIS IS;

(3) The call sign or other identification of the station acknowledging receipt, spoken three times;

(4) The word RECEIVED;

(5) The distress signal MAYDAY.

R & R 83.241   Information Furnished by Acknowledging Station. (a) Every mobile station which acknowledges receipt of a distress message shall, on the order of the master or person responsible for the ship, aircraft, or other vehicle carrying such mobile station, transmit as soon as possible the following information in the order shown:

(1) Its name;

(2) Its position, in the form prescribed in R & R 83.236(c);

(3) The speed at which it is proceeding towards, and the approximate time it will take to reach, the mobile station in distress.

(b) Before sending this message, the station shall ensure that it will not interfere with the emissions of other stations better situated to render immediate assistance to the station in distress.

R & R 83.242   Transmission of Distress Message By a Station Not Itself in Distress. (a) A mobile station or a land station which learns that a mobile station is in distress shall transmit a distress message in any of the following cases:

(1) When the station in distress is not itself in a position to transmit the distress message;

(2) When the master or person responsible for the ship, aircraft, or other vehicle not in distress, or the person responsible for the land station, considers that further help is necessary;

(3) When, although not in a position to render assistance, it has heard a distress message which has not been acknowledged. When a mobile station transmits a distress message under these conditions, it shall take all necessary steps to notify the authorities who may be able to render assistance.

(b) The transmission of a distress message under the conditions prescribed in paragraph (a) of this section shall be made on either or both of the international distress frequencies (500 kc/s radiotelegraph; 2182 kc/s radiotelephone) or on any other available frequency on which attention might be attracted.

(c) The transmission of the distress message shall always be preceded by the call indicated below, which shall itself be preceded whenever possible by the radiotelegraph or radiotelephone alarm signal. This call consists of:

(1) When radiotelegraphy is used:

(i) The signal $\overline{DDD}$ $\overline{SOS}$ $\overline{SOS}$ $\overline{SOS}$ $\overline{DDD}$;

(ii) The word DE.

(iii) The call sign of the transmitting station, sent three times;

(2) When radiotelephony is used:

(i) The signal MAYDAY RELAY, spoken three times;

(ii) The words THIS IS;

(iii) The call sign or other identification of the transmitting station, spoken three times.

(d) When the radiotelegraph alarm signal is used, an interval of two minutes shall be allowed, whenever this is considered necessary, before the transmission of the call mentioned in subparagraph (c)(1) of this section.

*   *   *   *   *   *

R & R 83.243. Control of Distress Traffic. (a) Distress traffic consists of all messages relating to the immediate assistance required by the mobile station in distress. In distress traffic, the distress signal shall be sent before the call and at the beginning of the preamble of any radiotelegram.

(b) The control of distress traffic is the responsibility of the mobile station in distress or of the station which, pursuant to R & R 83.242(a), has sent the distress message. These stations may, however, delegate the control of the distress traffic to another station. . . .

*   *   *   *   *   *

R & R 83.247   Urgency Signals. (a) The urgency signal indicates that the calling station has a very urgent message to transmit concerning the safety of a ship, aircraft, or other vehicle, or the safety of a person. The urgency signal shall be sent only on the authority of the master or person responsible for the mobile station.

(b) In radiotelegraphy, the urgency signal consists of three repetitions of the group XXX, sent with the individual letters of each group, and the successive groups clearly separated from each other. It shall be transmitted before the call.

(c) In radiotelephony, the urgency signal consists of the word PAN, spoken three times and transmitted before the call.

(d) The urgency signal shall have priority over all other communications, except distress. All mobile and land stations which hear it shall take care not to interfere with the transmission of the message which follows the urgency signal.

*   *   *   *   *   *

R & R 83.248   Urgency Message. (a) The urgency signal and call, and the message following it, shall be sent on one of the international distress frequencies (500 kc/s radiotelegraph; 2182 kc/s radiotelephone). However, stations which cannot transmit on a distress frequency may use any other available frequency on which attention might be attracted.

(b) Mobile stations which hear the urgency signal shall continue to listen for at least 3 minutes. At the end of this period, if no urgency message has been heard, they may resume their normal service. However, land and mobile stations which are in communication on frequencies other than those used for the transmission of the urgency signal and of the call which follows it may continue their normal work without interruption provided the urgency message is not addressed "to all stations" (CQ).

(c) When the urgency signal has been sent before transmitting a message "to all stations" (CQ) and which calls for action by the stations receiving the message, the station responsible for its transmission shall cancel it as soon as it knows that action is no longer necessary. This message of cancellation shall likewise be addressed "to all stations" (CQ).

*   *   *   *   *   *

R & R 83.249   Safety Signals. (a) The safety signal indicates that the station is about to transmit a message concerning the safety of navigation or giving important meteorological warnings.

(b) In radiotelegraphy, the safety signal consists of three repetitions of the group TTT, sent with the individual letters of each group, and the successive groups clearly separated from each other. It shall be sent before the call.

(c) In radiotelephony, the safety signal consists of the word SECURITY, spoken three times and transmitted before the call.

(d) The safety signal and call shall be sent on one of the international distress frequencies (500 kc/s radiotelegraph; 2182 kc/s radiotelephone). However, stations which cannot transmit on a distress frequency may use any other available frequency on which attention might be attracted.

*   *   *   *   *   *

R & R 83.352   Frequencies For Use in Distress. (a) The frequency 2182 kc/s is the international distress frequency for radiotelephony. It shall be used for this purpose by ship, aircraft, and survival craft stations using frequencies in the authorized bands between 1605 and 4000 kc/s when requesting assistance from the maritime services.

*   *   *   *   *   *

R & R 83.353   Frequencies For Calling. (a) The international general radiotelephone calling frequency for the maritime mobile service is 2182 kc/s. It may be used as a carrier frequency for this purpose by ship stations and aircraft stations operating in the maritime mobile service.

*   *   *   *   *   *

R & R 83.365   Procedure in Testing. (a) Ship stations must use every precaution to insure that, when conducting operational transmitter tests, the emissions of the station will not cause harmful interference. Radiation must be reduced to the lowest practicable value and if feasible shall be entirely suppressed. When radiation is necessary or unavoidable, the testing procedure described below shall be followed:

(1) The licensed radio operator or other person responsible for operation of the transmitting apparatus shall ascertain by careful listening that the test emissions will not be likely to interfere with transmissions in progress; if they are likely to interfere with the working of a coast or aeronautical station in the vicinity of the ship station, the consent of the former station(s) must be obtained before the test emissions occur;...

*   *   *   *   *   *

R & R 83.366   General Radiotelephone Operating Procedure. (a) *Calling coast stations.* (1) Use by ship stations of the frequency 2182 kc/s for calling coast stations, and for replying to calls from coast stations, is authorized; however, whenever practicable such calls and replies shall be made on the appropriate ship–shore working frequency.

(2) Use by ship stations and marine utility stations on board ship of the frequency 156.8 Mc/s for calling coast stations and marine utility stations on shore, and for replying to calls from such stations, is authorized; however, whenever practicable such calls and replies shall be made on the appropriate ship-shore working frequency.

(b) *Calling ship stations.* (1) Except when other operating procedure is used to expedite safety communication, ship stations, before transmitting on the intership working frequencies 2003, 2638, 2738, or 2830 kc/s, shall first establish communication with other ship stations by call and reply on 2182 kc/s: *Provided,* That calls may be initiated on an intership working frequency when it is known that the called vessel maintains a simultaneous watch on such working frequency and on 2182 kc/s.

(2) Except when other operating procedure is used to expedite safety communication, the frequency 156.8 Mc/s shall be used for call and reply by ship stations and marine utility stations on board ship before establishing communication on either of the intership working frequencies 156.3 or 156.4 Mc/s.

(c) *Change to working frequency.* After establishing communication with another station by call and reply on 2182 kc/s or 156.8 Mc/s, stations on board ship shall change to an authorized working frequency for the transmission of messages which, under the provisions of this subpart, cannot be transmitted on the respective calling frequencies.

(d) *Authorized use of 2003, 2638, 2738, and 2830 kc/s.* The intership working frequencies 2003, 2638, 2738, and 2830 kc/s shall be used for transmissions by ship stations in accordance with the provisions of R & R 83.176, 83.177, and 83.358.

(e) *Simplex operation only.* All transmission on 2003, 2638, 2738, and 2830 kc/s by two or more stations, engaged in any one exchange of signals or communications, shall take place on only one of these frequencies, i.e., the stations involved shall transmit and receive on the same frequency: *Provided,* That this requirement is waived in the event of emergency when by reason of interference or limitation of equipment, single-frequency operation cannot be used.

*   *   *   *   *   *

(g) *Limitation on duration of working.* Any one exchange of communications between any two ship stations on 2003, 2638, 2738, or 2830 kc/s, or between a ship station and a limited coast station on 2738 or 2830 kc/s shall not exceed 3 minutes in duration after the two stations have established contact by calling and answering. Subsequent to such exchange of communications, the same two stations shall not again use 2003, 2638, 2738, or 2830 kc/s for communication with each other until 10 minutes have elapsed: *Provided,* That this provision shall in no way limit or delay the transmission of communications concerning the safety of life or property.

(h) *Transmission limitation on 2182 kc/s and 156.8 Mc/s.* Any one exchange of signals by ship stations on 2182 kc/s or 156.8 Mc/s (including calls, replies thereto, and operating signals) shall not exceed 2 minutes: *Provided,* That this time limitation is not applicable to the transmission of distress, alarm, urgency, or safety signals, or to messages preceded by one of these signals.

(i) *Limitation on business and operational communication.* On frequencies above 30 Mc/s, the exchange of all business and operational communication shall be limited to the minimum practicable transmission time. In the conduct of ship-shore communication, other than distress, stations on board ship shall comply with instructions given by the limited coast station or marine utility station on shore with which they are communicating, in all matters relative to operating practices and procedures and to the suspension of transmission in order to minimize interference.

(j) *2182 kc/s silence period in Regions 1 and 3.* Transmission by ship or survival craft stations when in Regions 1 and 3 (except in the territorial waters of Japan and the Philippines) is prohibited on any frequency (including 2182 kc/s) within the band 2170–2194 kc/s during each 2182 kc/s silence period, i.e., for 3 minutes twice each hour beginning at x h. 00 and x h. 30, Greenwich mean time: *Provided,* That this provision is not applicable to the transmission of distress, alarm, urgency, or safety signals, or to messages preceded by one of these signals.

*   *   *   *   *   *

R & R 83.403 Radiodetermination by Cable-Repair Ship. Provided radio transmitting equipment attached to a cable-marker buoy has been adequately described in an application for ship radio station license for a cable repair ship with which the buoy is associated, and provided further that such equipment is authorized in the related ship station license, that equipment may be operated (outside the territorial waters of a foreign country) on such radio channels within the band 285–325 kc/s (285–315 kc/s only in Region 1) as may be expressly authorized in each case by the Commission under authority of the ship station license, with A1 or A2 emission and a maximum plate input power of 30 watts: *Provided,* That interference shall not be caused by such operation to any maritime radionavigation service. The call signals that must be used for a transmitter operating under the provisions of this section shall be the regularly assigned call of the ship station with which the buoy is associated, to be followed by the letters "BT," and the identifying number of the buoy. The buoy transmitter shall be continuously monitored by a licensed radiotelegraph operator on board the associated cable-repair ship. Should a frequency deviation in excess of the authorized frequency tolerance, or interference to the service of any other station, be reported or observed, the radiation of the transmitter shall be suspended until the excessive deviation is eliminated or until the transmitter can be operated without causing interference.

R & R 83.404 Assignable Frequencies Above 2400 Mc/s. (a) The following frequency bands, when designated in the station license, are authorized for use by ship radionavigation stations (including ship radar stations):

2900 to 3100 Mc/s
5460 to 5650 Mc/s
9300 to 9500 Mc/s

The use of the band 5460 to 5650 Mc/s is limited to shipborne radar. Transmitters in ship radionavigation stations (including developmental stations) which are authorized for operation in the 3000 to 3246 Mc/s band as of April 16, 1958, and which operate on frequencies between 3100 and 3246 Mc/s may continue to be authorized for operation on the same vessel provided that any renewal of the authorization shall be subject to the condition that no protection shall be given from any interference caused by emission from United States Government stations operating in the 3100 to 3246 Mc/s band.

(b) The following frequency bands, when designated in the station license, are authorized for use by ship radiolocation stations:

(1) 2450 to 2500 Mc/s, on condition that harmful interference shall not be caused to the fixed and mobile services, and on the condition that no protection shall be given from interference caused by emission from industrial, scientific, or medical equipment;

(2)

$$2900 \text{ to } 3100 \text{ Mc/s}$$
$$5460 \text{ to } 5650 \text{ Mc/s}$$
$$9300 \text{ to } 9500 \text{ Mc/s}$$

The use of frequencies within these bands for radiolocation shall not cause harmful interference to the radionavigation service and to the Government radiolocation service. Each ship radiolocation station authorized to operate in the band 3000 to 3246 Mc/s as of April 16, 1958, and which operates on frequencies between 3100 and 3246 Mc/s may continue to operate in the band 3100 to 3246 Mc/s for the duration of the term of its authorization in effect as of that date. Renewals of such authorizations, however, shall be contingent upon the condition that each such station shall not cause harmful interference to United States Government services.

R & R 83.405   Special Provisions Applicable to Ship-Radar Stations.
(a) A ship-radar station may be operated under an interim ship station license. The use and operation of a radar station on board ship under the authority conferred by an interim ship station license shall be subject to and in accordance with all applicable rules of the Commission.

(b) Each ship-radar station installation, the manufacture of which was completed on or after 1947, shall be furnished with a durable name plate with the manufacturer's name, transmitter model number, and month and year of completion of manufacture permanently inscribed thereon. Such name plate shall be affixed to the indicator housing at the principal radar operating position or to some other component of the radar installation which is readily accessible for inspection.

(c) Each ship-radar station license issued shall be subject to the condition that the station licensee, in relation to the proper operation of the station in accordance with the radio law, and rules and regulations of the

Commission, will be represented on board the radar-equipped vessel by the person who at any given time occupies the position of master.

(d) The following provisions shall apply to ship-radar stations:

(1) The station licensee of each ship-radar station shall provide and require to be kept at the station a permanent installation and maintenance record. Entries in this record shall be made by or under the personal direction of the responsible installation, service, or maintenance operator concerned in each particular instance, but the station licensee shall have joint responsibility with the responsible operator concerned for the faithful and accurate making of such entries as are required by the paragraph.

(2) Each entry in this record shall be personally signed by the responsible operator concerned.

(3) The following entries shall be made in this record:

(i) The date and place of initial installation.

(ii) Any necessary steps taken to remedy any interference found to exist at the time of such installation.

(iii) The nature of any complaint (including interference to radio communication) arising subsequent to initial installation, and the date thereof.

(iv) The reason for the trouble leading to the complaint, including the name of any component or component part which failed or was misadjusted.

(v) Remedial measures taken, and date thereof.

(vi) The name, license number, and date of the ship-radar operator endorsement on the first- or second-class radio operator license of the responsible operator performing or immediately supervising the installation, servicing, or maintenance.

(e) Until the Commission shall otherwise provide, the ship-radar station licensee, by such arrangement as may be necessary with the ship master, operating agency, or ship owner, shall, upon specific request made by the Commission, be responsible for the submission of such reports as are requested by the Commission to show the value and practical performance of the ship-radar station. For assistance in preparing these reports, daily records, when the radar installation is tested or used, should, when practicable, be kept showing at least the following:

(1) Approximate number of hours of use while the ship is in operation;

(2) Number of service failures, and duration, nature, and cause of each failure if known;

(3) Performance under local weather conditions which are unfavorable for marine navigation; and

(4) Unusual incidents, including, among others, cases in which radar may have aided or hindered safe operation of the ship.

(f) In addition to the installation and maintenance record required by paragraphs (d) and (e) of this section, the following documents shall be available for reference on board each radar-equipped vessel whose ship-radar station is licensed by the Commission:

(1) Part 8 of this chapter.

(2) At least one set of instructions from the respective manufacturer relative to the use and operation of the particular type of ship-radar installation.

(g) No provisions of this part shall require any ship-radar station to transmit any signal(s) intended solely for the purpose of identifying that station.

PART 89: PUBLIC SAFETY RADIO SERVICES

R & R 89.51   Station Authorization Required. No radio transmitter shall be operated in the Public Safety Radio Services except under and in accordance with proper station authorization granted by the Federal Communications Commission.

* * * * * *

R & R 89.55 Filing of Applications. (a) To assure that necessary information is supplied in a consistent manner by all persons, standard forms are prescribed for use in connection with the majority of applications and reports submitted for Commission consideration. Standard numbered forms applicable to the Public Safety Radio Services are discussed in R & R 89.59, and may be obtained from the Washington, D.C. 20554, office of the Commission, or from any of its engineering field offices. Concerning matters where no standard form is applicable, the procedure outlined in R & R 89.61 should be followed.

* * * * * *

R & R 89.57   Who May Sign Applications. (a) Except as provided in paragraph (b) of this section, applications, amendments thereto, and related statements of fact required by the Commission shall be personally signed by the applicant, if the applicant is an individual; by one of the partners, if the applicant is a partnership; by an officer, if the applicant is a corporation; or by a member who is an officer, if the applicant is an unincorporated association. Applications, amendments, and related statements of fact filed on behalf of eligible government entities, such as states and territories of the United States and political subdivision thereof, the District of Columbia, and units of local government, including incorporated municipalities, shall be signed by such duly elected or appointed officials as may be competent to do so under the laws of the applicable jurisdiction.

(b) Applications, amendments thereto, and related statements of fact required by the Commission may be signed by the applicant's attorney in case of the applicant's physical disability or of his absence from the United States. The attorney shall in that event separately set forth the reason why the application is not signed by the applicant. In addition, if any matter is stated on the basis of the attorney's belief only (rather than his knowledge), he shall separately set forth his reasons for believing that such statements are true.

(c) Only the original of applications, amendments, or related statements of fact, need be signed; copies may be conformed.

(d) Applications, amendments, and related statements of fact need not be signed under oath. Willful false statements made therein, however, are punishable by fine and imprisonment, U.S. Code, Title 18, section 1001, and by appropriate administrative sanctions, including revocation of station license pursuant to Section 312(a)(1) of the Communications Act of 1934, as amended.

*　　*　　*　　*　　*　　*

R & R 89.103　Frequency Stability. (a) A permittee or licensee in these services shall maintain the carrier frequency of each authorized transmitter within the following percentage of the assigned frequency.

Frequency Range	All Fixed and Base Stations	All Mobile Stations	
		Over 3 W	3 W or Less
MHz	Percent	Percent	Percent
Below 25	0.01	0.01	0.02
25 to 50	.002	.002	.005
50 to 450	[1].0005	.0005	.005
450 to 470	[2] [4].00025	.0005	.0005
470 to 512	.00025	.0005	.0005
806 to 820	.00015	.00025	.00025
851 to 866	.00015	.00025	.00025
950 to 1,427	([2])	([2])	([2])
1,427 to 1,435	[5].03	.03	.03
Above 1,435	([2])	([2])	([2])

[1] Stations authorized for operation on or before Dec. 1, 1961, in the frequency band 73.0–74.6 MHz may operate with a frequency tolerance of 0.005 percent.

[2] Radiolocation equipment using pulse modulation shall meet the following frequency tolerance: The frequency at which maximum emission occurs shall be within the authorized frequency band and shall not be closer than 1.5/T MHz to the upper and lower limits of the authorized frequency band where T is the pulse duration in microseconds. For other radiolocation equipment, tolerances will be specified in the station authorization. See also R & R 89.121.

[3] Effective Nov. 1, 1967. Stations authorized before Nov. 1, 1967, may continue to operate with a frequency tolerance of 0.0005 percent, 0.005 percent for mobile stations with power of 3 watts or less, until Nov. 1, 1971.

[4] Operational fixed stations controlling mobile relay stations, through use of the associated mobile frequency, may operate with a frequency tolerance of 0.0005 percent.

[5] For fixed stations with power above 200 watts, the frequency tolerance is .01 percent if the necessary bandwidth of the emission does not exceed 3 kHz. For fixed station transmitters with a power of 200 watts or less and using time division multiplex, the frequency tolerance may be increased to .05 percent.

(b) For the purpose of determining the frequency tolerance applicable to a particular transmitter in accordance with the foregoing provisions of this section, the power of a transmitter shall be the maximum rated plate power input to its final radio frequency stage, as specified by the manufacturer.

*   *   *   *   *   *

R & R 89.107   Emission Limitations.

*   *   *   *   *   *

(1) For all type A3 emissions, the maximum authorized bandwidth shall be 8 kHz.

(2) For all F3 emission, the maximum authorized bandwidth and maximum authorized frequency deviation shall be as follows:

Frequency Band (MHz)	Authorized Bandwidth (kHz)	Frequency Deviation (kHz)
25 to 50	20	5
50 to 150	[1] 20	[1] 5
150 to 450	20	5
450 to 470	[2] 20	[3] 5
470 to 512	20	5
806 to 821	20	5
851 to 866	20	5

¹ Stations authorized for operation on or before Dec. 1, 1961, in the frequency band 73.0–74.6 MHz may continue to operate with a bandwidth of 40 kHz and a deviation of ± 15 kHz.

² Effective Nov. 1, 1967. Stations authorized before Nov. 1, 1967, may continue to operate with a maximum of 40 kHz bandwidth until Nov. 1, 1971.

³ Effective Nov. 1, 1967, for new stations. Effective June 1, 1968, for stations authorized prior to Nov. 1, 1967, if located less than 100 miles from the center of any urbanized area of 200,000 or more population. Stations authorized prior to Nov. 1, 1967, for operation outside of 100 miles of any urbanized area of 200,000 or more population, may continue to operate with a deviation of 15 kHz until Nov. 1, 1971. Such wide-band systems will be required to reduce deviation at the time of any frequency change or should harmful interference be caused to stations operating on adjacent 25 kHz channels. Urbanized areas are listed in the U.S. Census of Population, 1960, vol. 1, table 23, page 1–50.

(3) For all type A1 emissions, the maximum authorized bandwidth shall be 0.25 kHz.

(c) The mean power of emissions shall be attenuated below the mean output power of the transmitter in accordance with the following schedule:

(1) On any frequency removed from the assigned frequency by more than 50 percent up to and including 100 percent of the authorized bandwidths: At least 25 decibels;

(2) On any frequency removed from the assigned frequency by more than 100 percent up to and including 250 percent of the authorized bandwidth: At least 35 decibels;

(3) On any frequency removed from the assigned frequency by more than 250 percent of the authorized bandwidth: At least 43 plus $10 \log_{10}$ (mean output power in watts) decibels or 80 decibels, whichever is the lesser attenuation.

*   *   *   *   *   *

R & R 89.109   Modulation Requirements. (a) The maximum audio frequency required for satisfactory radiotelephone intelligibility in these services is considered to be 3000 cycles per second.

(b) When amplitude modulation is used for telephony, the modulation percentage shall be sufficient to provide efficient communication and normally shall be maintained above 70 percent on peaks, but shall not exceed 100 percent on negative peaks.

(c) Each transmitter shall be equipped with a device which automatically prevents modulation in excess of that specified in this subpart which may be caused by greater than normal audio level: *Provided, however,* That this requirement shall not be applicable to transmitters authorized to operate as mobile stations with a maximum plate power input to the final radio-frequency stage of 3 watts or less.

*   *   *   *   *   *

R & R 89.113   Transmitter Control Requirements. (a) Each transmitter shall be so installed and protected that it is not accessible or capable of operation by persons other than those duly authorized by the licensee.

(b) A control point is an operating position which meets all of the following conditions:

(1) The position must be under the control and supervision of the licensee;

(2) It is a position at which the monitoring facilities required by this section are installed; and

(3) It is a position at which a person immediately responsible for the operation of the transmitter is stationed.

(c) Each station which is not authorized for unattended operation shall be provided with a control point, the location of which will be specified in the license. Unattended stations may be provided with a control point if authorized by the Commission. In urban areas the location will be specified "same as transmitter" unless the control point is at a street address different from that of the transmitter. In rural areas the location will be specified "same as transmitter" unless the control point is more than 500 feet from the transmitter, in which case the approximate location will be specified in distance and direction from the transmitter in terms of feet and geographical quadrant, respectively. It will be assumed that the location of the control point is the same as the location of the transmitter unless the application includes a request for a different location described in appropriate terms as indicated in this paragraph. Authority must be obtained from the Commission for the installation of additional control points.

(d) A dispatch point is any position from which messages may be transmitted under the supervision of the person at a control point who is responsible for the operation of the transmitter. Dispatch points may be installed without authorization.

(e) At each control point, the following facilities shall be installed:

(1) A carrier operated device which will provide continuous visual indication when the transmitter is radiating; or, in lieu thereof, a pilot lamp or meter which will provide continuous visual indication when the transmitter control circuits have been placed in a condition to produce radiation: *Provided, however,* That the provisions of this subparagraph shall not apply to hand-carried or pack-carried transmitters or to transmitters installed on motorcycles;

(2) Equipment to permit the person responsible for the operation of the transmitter to aurally monitor all transmissions originating at dispatch points under his supervision;

(3) Facilities which will permit the person responsible for the operation of the transmitter either to disconnect the dispatch point circuits from the transmitter or to render the transmitter inoperative from any dispatch point under his supervision; and

(4) Facilities which will permit the person responsible for the operation of the transmitter to turn the transmitter carrier on and off at will.

*   *   *   *   *   *

R & R 89.117   Acceptability of Transmitters for Licensing. (a) From time to time. the Commission will publish a list of equipment entitled "Radio Equipment List, Part C, List of Equipment Acceptable for Licensing." Copies of this list are available for inspection at the Commission's Offices in Washington, D.C., and at each of its field offices. This list will include type approved and type accepted equipment and equipment which was included in this list on May 16, 1955. Such equipment will continue to be included on the list unless it is removed therefrom by Commission action.

(b) Except for transmitters used in developmental stations, transmitters authorized as of January 1, 1965, in police zone and interzone stations, and transmitters in radiolocation stations during the term of any license issued prior to January 1, 1973, each transmitter utilized by a station authorized for operation under this part must be of a type which is included on the Commission's current Radio Equipment List and is designated for use under this part or be of a type which has been type accepted by the Commission for use under this part.

(c) Transmitters to be operated in any of the frequency bands between 952 and 12,700 Mc/s, except the 8400–8500 Mc/s band, authorized under this part shall be type accepted if specified in an application filed after July 20, 1962, except that equipment authorized prior thereto may continue to be used provided such operation does not result in harmful interference to other stations or systems which are conforming to the microwave technical standards in R & R 89.121.

*   *   *   *   *   *

R & R 89.171   Inspection and Maintenance of Tower Marking and Associated Control Equipment. The licensee of any radio station which has an antenna structure required to be painted or illuminated pursuant to the provisions of Section 303(q) of the Communications Act of 1934, as amended, and/or Part 17 of this chapter shall comply with the provisions of this section in the operation and maintenance of such tower marking as follows:

(a) Shall make an observation of the tower lights at least once each 24 hours either visually or by observing an automatic and properly maintained indicator designed to register any failure of such lights, to insure that all such lights are functioning properly as required; or alternatively.

(b) Shall provide and properly maintain an automatic alarm system designed to detect any failure of such lights and to provide indication of such failure to the licensee.

(c) Shall report immediately by telephone or telegraph to the nearest Flight Service Station or office of the Federal Aviation Agency any observed or otherwise known failure of a code or rotating beacon light or top light not corrected within 30 minutes, regardless of the cause of such failure. Further notification by telephone or telegraph shall be given immediately upon resumption of the required illumination.

(d) Shall inspect at intervals not to exceed 3 months all automatic or mechanical control devices, indicators and alarm systems associated with the tower lighting to insure that such apparatus is functioning properly.

(e) Shall exhibit all lighting from sunset to sunrise unless otherwise specified.

(f) Shall maintain a supply of spare purposes at all times.

(g) Shall clean and repaint all towers as often as necessary to maintain good visibility.

* * * * * *

R & R 89.175   Content of Station Records. Each licensee of a station in these services shall maintain records in accordance with the following:

(a) For all stations, the results and dates of the transmitter measurements required by these rules and the name of the person or persons making the measurements.

(b) For all stations, when service or maintenance duties are performed, the responsible operator shall sign and date an entry in the station record giving:

(1) Pertinent details of all duties performed by him or under his supervision;

(2) His name and address, and

(3) The class, serial number, and expiration date of his license, *Provided,* That the information called for by subparagraphs (2) and (3) of this paragraph, so long as it remains the same, need be entered only once in the station record at any station where the responsible operator is regularly employed on a full-time basis and at which his license is properly posted.

(c) [Reserved]

(d) [Reserved]

(e) For stations whose antenna or antenna supporting structure is required to be illuminated, a record in accordance with the following:

(1) The time the tower lights are turned on and off each day if manually controlled.

(2) The time the daily check of proper operation of the tower lights was made, if an automatic alarm system is not provided.

(3) In the event of any observed or otherwise known failure of a tower light:

(i) Nature of such failure.

(ii) Date and time the failure was observed, or otherwise noted.

(iii) Date, time, and nature of the adjustments, repairs, or replacements that were made.

(iv) Identification of the Flight Service Station (FAA) notified of the failure of any code or rotating beacon light or top light not corrected within thirty minutes, and the date and time such notice was given.

(v) Date and time notice was given to the Flight Service Station (FAA) that the required illumination was resumed.

(4) Upon the completion of the periodic inspection required at least once each three months:

(i) The date of the inspection and the condition of all tower lights and associated tower lighting control devices, indicators and alarm systems.

(ii) Any adjustments, replacements, or repairs made to insure compliance with the lighting requirements and the date such adjustments, replacements, or repairs were made.

*   *   *   *   *   *

EXTRACTS OF THE COMMUNICATIONS ACT
OF 1934, AS AMENDED

PURPOSES OF ACT

Sec. 1.   For the purpose of regulating interstate and foreign commerce in communication by wire and radio so as to make available, so far as possible, to all the people of the United States a rapid, efficient, Nation-wide, and world-wide wire and radio communication service with adequate facilities at reasonable charges, for the purpose of the national defense, for the purpose of promoting safety of life and property through the use of wire and radio communication, and for the purpose of securing a more effective execution of this policy by centralizing authority heretofore granted by law to several agencies and by granting additional authority with respect to interstate and foreign commerce in wire and radio communication, there is hereby created a commission to be known as the "Federal Communications Commission," which shall be constituted as hereinafter provided, and which shall execute and enforce the provisions of this Act.

*   *   *   *   *   *

LICENSE FOR RADIO COMMUNICATION OR TRANSMISSION
OF ENERGY

Sec. 301.   It is the purpose of this Act, among other things, to maintain the control of the United States over all the channels of interstate and foreign public transmission; and to provide for the use of such channels, but not the ownership thereof, by persons for limited periods of time, under licenses granted by Federal authority, and no such license shall be construed to create any right, beyond the terms, conditions, and periods of the license. No person shall use or operate any apparatus for the transmission of energy or communications or signals by radio (a) from one place in any Territory or possession of the

United States or in the District of Columbia to another place in the same Territory, possession, or district; or (b) from any State, Territory, or possession of the United States, or from the District of Columbia to any other State, Territory, or possession of the United States; or (c) from any place in any State, Territory, or possession of the United States, or in the District of Columbia, to any place in any foreign country or to any vessel; or (d) within any State when the effects of such use extend beyond the borders of said State, or when interference is caused by such use or operation with the transmission of such energy, communications, or signals from within said State to any place beyond its borders, or from any place beyond its borders to any place within said State, or with the transmission or reception of such energy, communications, or signals from and/or to places beyond the borders of said State; or (e) upon any vessel or aircraft of the United States; or (f) upon any other mobile stations within the jurisdiction of the United States, except under and in accordance with this Act and with a license in that behalf granted under the provisions of this Act.

GENERAL POWERS OF THE COMMISSION

Sec. 303. Except as otherwise provided in this Act, the Commission from time to time, as public convenience, interest, or necessity requires, shall—

*   *   *   *   *   *

(2) No order of suspension of any operator's license shall take effect until fifteen days' notice in writing thereof, stating the cause for the proposed suspension, has been given to the operator licensee who may make written application to the Commission at any time within said fifteen days for a hearing upon such order. The notice to the operator licensee shall not be effective until actually received by him, and from that time he shall have fifteen days in which to mail the said application. In the event that physical conditions prevent mailing of the application at the expiration of the fifteen-day period, the application shall then be mailed as soon as possible thereafter, accompanied by a satisfactory explanation of the delay. Upon receipt by the Commission of such application for hearing, said order of suspension shall be held in abeyance until the conclusion of the hearing which shall be conducted under such rules as the Commission may prescribe. Upon the conclusion of said hearing the Commission may affirm, modify, or revoke said order of suspension.

(n) Have authority to inspect all radio installations associated with stations required to be licensed by any Act or which are subject to the provisions of any Act, treaty, or convention binding on the United States, to ascertain whether in construction, installation, and operation they conform to the requirements of the rules and regulations of the Commission, the provisions of any Act, the terms of any treaty or convention binding on the United States, and the conditions of the license or other instrument of authorization under which they are constructed, installed, or operated.

*   *   *   *   *   *

(r) Make such rules and regulations and prescribe such restrictions and conditions, not inconsistent with law, as may be necessary to carry out the provisions of the Act, or any international radio or wire communications treaty or convention, or regulations annexed thereto, including any treaty or convention insofar as it relates to the use of radio, to which the United States is or may hereafter become a party.

*   *   *   *   *   *

OPERATION OF TRANSMITTING APPARATUS

Sec. 318. The actual operation of all transmitting apparatus in any radio station for which a station license is required by this Act shall be carried on only by a person holding an operator's license issued hereunder, and no person shall operate any such apparatus in such station except under and in accordance with an operator's license issued to him by the Commission: *Provided, however,* That the Commission if it shall find that the public interest, convenience, or necessity will be served thereby may waive or modify the foregoing provisions of this section for the operation of any station except (1) stations for which licensed operators are required by international agreement, (2) stations for which licensed operators are required for safety purposes, (3) stations engaged in broadcasting, and (4) stations operated as common carriers on frequencies below thirty thousand kilocycles: *Provided, further,* That the Commission shall have power to make special regulations governing the granting of licenses for the use of automatic radio devices and for the operation of such devices.

*   *   *   *   *   *

DISTRESS SIGNALS AND COMMUNICATIONS

Sec. 321. (a) The transmitting set in a radio station on shipboard may be adjusted in such a manner as to produce a maximum of radiation, irrespective of the amount of interference which may thus be caused, when such station is sending radio communications or signals of distress and radio communications relating thereto.

(b) All radio stations, including Government stations and stations on board foreign vessels when within the territorial waters of the United States shall give absolute priority to radio communications or signals relating to ships in distress; shall cease all sending on frequencies which will interfere with hearing a radio communication or signal of distress, and, except when engaged in answering or aiding the ship in distress, shall refrain from sending any radio communications or signals until there is assurance that no interference will be caused with the radio communications or signals relating thereto, and shall assist the vessel in distress, so far as possible, by complying with its instructions.

INTERCOMMUNICATION IN MOBILE SERVICE

Sec. 322.   Every land station open to general public service between the coast and vessels or aircraft at sea shall, within the scope of its normal operations, be bound to exchange radio communications or signals with any ship or aircraft station at sea; and each station on shipboard or aircraft at sea shall, within the scope of its normal operations, be bound to exchange radio communications or signals with any other station on shipboard or aircraft at sea or with any land station open to general public service between the coast and vessels or aircraft at sea: *Provided*, That such exchange of radio communication shall be without distinction as to radio systems or instruments adopted by each station.

INTERFERENCE BETWEEN GOVERNMENT AND COMMERCIAL STATIONS

Sec. 323.   (a) At all places where Government and private or commercial radio stations on land operate in such close proximity that interference with the work of Government stations cannot be avoided when they are operating simultaneously, such private or commercial stations as do interfere with the transmission or reception of radio communications or signals by the Government stations concerned shall not use their transmitters during the first fifteen minutes of each hour, local standard time.

*   *   *   *   *   *

USE OF MINIMUM POWER

Sec. 324.   In all circumstances, except in case of radio communications or signals relating to vessels in distress, all radio stations, including those owned and operated by the United States, shall use the minimum amount of power necessary to carry out the communication desired.

FALSE DISTRESS SIGNALS; REBROADCASTING; STUDIOS OF FOREIGN STATIONS

Sec. 325.   (a) No person within the jurisdiction of the United States shall knowingly utter or transmit, or cause to be uttered or transmitted, any false or fraudulent signal of distress, or communication relating thereto, nor shall any broadcasting station rebroadcast the program or any part thereof of another broadcasting station without the express authority of the originating station.

*   *   *   *   *   *

CENSORSHIP; INDECENT LANGUAGE

Sec. 326.   Nothing in the this Act shall be understood or construed to give the Commission the power of censorship over the radio communications or signals transmitted by any radio station, and no regulation or condition shall be promulgated or fixed by the Commission which shall interfere with the right of free speech by means of radio communication.

*   *   *   *   *   *

SHIP RADIO INSTALLATIONS AND OPERATIONS

Sec. 351.   (a) Except as provided in Section 352 hereof it shall be unlawful—

(1) For any ship of the United States, other than a cargo ship of less than five hundred gross tons, to be navigated in the open sea outside of a harbor or port, or for any ship of the United States or any foreign country, other than a cargo ship of less than five hundred gross tons, to leave or attempt to leave any harbor or port of the United States for a voyage in the open sea, unless such ship is equipped with an efficient radio installation in operating condition in charge of and operated by a qualified operator or operators, adequately installed and protected so as to insure proper operation, and so as not to endanger the ship and radio installation, as hereinafter provided, and in the case of a ship of the United States, unless there is on board a valid station license issued in accordance with this Act: *Provided,* That the Commission may defer the application of the provisions of this section for a period not beyond January 1, 1955, with respect to cargo ships of less than sixteen hundred gross tons not subject to the radio requirements of the Safety Convention when it is found impracticable to obtain or install equipment necessary for compliance therewith;

(2) For any ship of the United States of sixteen hundred gross tons, or over, to be navigated outside of a harbor or port, in the open sea, or for any such ship of the United States or any foreign country to leave or attempt to leave any harbor or port of the United States for a voyage in the open sea, unless such ship is equipped with an efficient radio direction finding apparatus (radio compass) properly adjusted in operating condition as hereinafter provided, which apparatus is approved by the

Commission: *Provided,* That the Commission may defer the application of the provisions of this section with respect to radio direction finding apparatus to a ship or ships between one thousand six hundred and five thousand gross tons for a period not beyond November 19, 1954, if it is found impracticable to obtain or install such direction finding apparatus.

(b) A ship which is not subject to the provisions of this part at the time of its departure on a voyage shall not become subject to such provisions on account of any deviation from its intended voyage due to stress of weather or any other cause over which neither the master, the owner, nor the charterer (if any) has control.

*   *   *   *   *   *

UNAUTHORIZED PUBLICATION OF COMMUNICATIONS

Sec. 605. No person receiving or assisting in receiving, or transmitting, or assisting in transmitting, any interstate or foreign communication by wire or radio shall divulge or publish the existence, contents, substance, purport, effect, or meaning thereof, except through authorized channels of transmission or reception, to any person other than the addressee, his agent, or attorney, or to a person employed or authorized to forward such communication to its destination, or to proper accounting or distributing officers of the various communicating centers over which the communication may be passed, or to the master of a ship under whom he is serving, or in response to a subpoena issued by a court of competent jurisdiction, or on demand of other lawful authority; and no person not being authorized by the sender shall intercept any communication and divulge or publish the existence, contents, substance, purport, effect, or meaning of such intercepted communication to any person; and no person not being entitled thereto shall receive or assist in receiving any interstate or foreign communication by wire or radio and use the same or any information therein contained for his own benefit or for the benefit of another not entitled thereto; and no person having received such intercepted communication or having become acquainted with the contents, substance, purport, effect, or meaning of the same or any part thereof, knowing that such information was so obtained, shall divulge or publish the existence, contents, substance, purport, effect, or meaning of the same or any part thereof, or use the same or any information therein contained for his own benefit or for the benefit of another not entitled thereto: *Provided,* That this section shall not apply to the receiving, divulging, publishing, or utilizing the contents of any radio communication broadcast, or transmitted by amateurs or others for the use of the general public, or relating to ships in distress.

*   *   *   *   *   *

EXTRACTS FROM THE INTERNATIONAL TELE-COMMUNICATIONS CONVENTION, ATLANTIC CITY, 1947

ARTICLE 32

§ 1 Members and Associate Members agree to take all possible measures, compatible with the system of telecommunication used, with a view to insuring the secrecy of international correspondence.

* * * * * *

ARTICLE 43

§ 1 Stations performing radio communication in the mobile service shall be bound, within the limits of their normal employment, to exchange radio communications reciprocally without distinction as to the radio system adopted by them.

* * * * * *

ARTICLE 44

§ 1 All stations, whatever their purpose, must be established and operated in such a manner as not to result in harmful interference to the radio services or communications of other Members or Associate Members or of recognized private operating agencies, or of other duly authorized operating agencies which carry on radio service, and which operate in accordance with the provisions of the Radio Regulations.

* * * * * *

ARTICLE 45

§ 1 Radio stations shall be obligated to accept, with absolute priority, distress calls and messages regardless of their origin, to reply in the same manner to such messages, and immediately to take such action in regard thereto as may be required.

*   *   *   *   *   *

ARTICLE 46

Members and Associate Members agree to take the steps required to prevent the transmission or circulation of false or deceptive distress or safety signals and the use, by a station, of call signs which have not been regularly assigned to it.

EXTRACTS FROM THE INTERNATIONAL RADIO REGULATIONS ANNEXED TO THE INTERNATIONAL TELECOMMUNICATIONS CONVENTION, ATLANTIC CITY, 1947

ARTICLE 13

372   § 1   Unnecessary transmissions and transmission of superflous signals and correspondence are forbidden to all stations.

*   *   *   *   *   *

382   § 9   The transmission of signals without identification is forbidden to all stations.

*   *   *   *   *   *

ARTICLE 21

485   The administrations bind themselves to take the necessary measures to prohibit and prevent:
486   (a)   the unauthorized interception of radiocommunications not intended for the general use of the public;
487   (b)   the divulgence of the contents, simple disclosure of the existence, publication or any use whatever without authorization, of information of any nature whatever obtained by the interception of the radiocommunications mentioned in 486.

ARTICLE 22

488   § 1   (1)   No transmitting station may be established or oper-

ated by a private person or by any enterprise without a license issued
by the government of the country to which the station in question is
subject.

*   *   *   *   *   *

ARTICLE 23

493   § 1   (1) The governments or appropriate administrations of
countries where a mobile station calls may require the production of
the license. The operator of the mobile station, or the person responsible for the station, must facilitate this examination. The license must
be kept in such a way that it can be produced without delay. As far
as possible, the license, or a copy certified by the authority which has
issued it, should be permanently exhibited in the station.

*   *   *   *   *   *

ARTICLE 26

565   § 1   The service of a mobile station is placed under the su-
preme authority of the master or of the person responsible for the ship,
aircraft, or other vehicle carrying the mobile station.
566   § 2   The person holding this authority must require the operators to comply with these Regulations.
567   § 3   The master or the person responsible, as well as all persons who may have knowledge of the text or even of the existence of
the radiotelegrams, or of any information whatever obtained by means
of the radiocommunication service, are placed under the obligation of
observing and ensuring the secrecy of correspondence.

*   *   *   *   *   *

ARTICLE 29

610   § 6   (1) Before emitting, every station must listen for a period
long enough to satisfy itself that it will not cause harmful interference
to transmissions in progress within its range; if such interference is
likely, the station awaits the first break in the transmission with which
it might interfere.

*   *   *   *   *   *

679   § 26   Where it is necessary for a mobile station to send signals
for testing or adjustment which are liable to interfere with the working

of a neighboring coast or aeronautical station, the consent of the station must be obtained before such signals are sent.

680 § 27 When it is necessary for a station in the mobile service to make test signals, either for the adjustment of a transmitter before making a call or for the adjustment of a receiver, they must not continue for more than 10 seconds and must be composed of a series of VVV followed by the call sign of the station emitting the test signals.

*   *   *   *   *   *

ARTICLE 37

871 § 5 Aircraft.
Any aircraft in distress must transmit the distress call on the frequency on which the land or mobile stations capable of helping it, keep watch. When the call is addressed to stations of the maritime service, the frequencies to be used shall be the international distress frequency 500 kc/s or other watchkeeping frequencies of these stations.

872 § 6 (1) In radiotelegraphy, the distress signal consists of the group · · · — — — · · · transmitted as a single signal in which the dashes must be emphasized so as to be distinguished clearly from the dots.

873 (2) In radiotelephony, the distress signal consists of the word MAY-DAY pronounced as the French expression "m'aider".

874 § 7 These distress signals indicate that the ship, aircraft, or other vehicle sending the distress signal is threatened by grave and imminent danger and requests immediate assistance.

875 § 8 The distress call and message are sent only on the authority of the master or person responsible for the ship, aircraft or other vehicle carrying the mobile station.

*   *   *   *   *   *

879 § 11 The distress call, when sent by radiotelephony, is generally preceded by the signal · · · — — — · · · produced by a whistle or any other suitable means.

*   *   *   *   *   *

882 § 14 (1) The distress call must be followed as soon as possible by the distress message. This message comprises:
    —the distress call;
    —the name of the ship, aircraft, or vehicle in distress;
    —particulars of its position, the nature of the distress and the kind of assistance desired;
    —any other information which might facilitate the rescue.

883   (2) As a general rule, a ship signals its position in latitude and longitude (Greenwich), using figures for the degrees and minutes, together with one of the words NORTH or SOUTH and one of the words EAST or WEST. The signal · — · — · — is used to separate the degrees from the minutes. When practicable, the true bearing and distance in nautical miles from a known geographical point may be given.

884   (3)   As a general rule, and if time permits, an aircraft shall transmit in its distress message the following information:
   —estimated position and time of the estimate;
   —true heading and indicated air speed;
   —altitude;
   —type of aircraft;
   —nature of distress;
   —intention of person in command (such as forced alighting on the sea or crash landing).

885   (4) As a general rule, an aircraft in flight signals its position:
   —if possible by latitude and longitude (Greenwich), using figures for the degrees and minutes, together with one of the words NORTH and SOUTH and one of the words EAST or WEST; or
   —by the name of the nearest place, and its approximate distance in relation thereto, together with one of the words NORTH, SOUTH, EAST, or WEST, as the case may be, or, when practicable, by words indicating intermediate directions.

886   § 15   After the transmission of its distress message, the mobile station transmits two dashes of approximately 10 seconds' duration each, followed by its call sign, to permit direction-finding stations to determine its position. This transmission will be repeated at frequent intervals in case of necessity.

*   *   *   *   *   *

895   § 19 (1) Stations of the mobile service which receive a distress message from a mobile station which is, beyond any possible doubt, in their vicinity, must immediately acknowledge receipt (see 913, 914 and 915). If the distress call has not been preceded by the alarm signal, these stations may transmit this alarm signal with the permission of the authority responsible for the station taking care not to interfere with the transmission of acknowledgments of receipt sent by other stations.

896   (2) Stations of the mobile service which receive a distress message from a mobile station which, beyond any possible doubt, is not in their vicinity, must allow a short interval of time before acknowledging receipt of the message, in order to permit stations nearer to the mobile station in distress to answer and acknowledge receipt without interference.

*   *   *   *   *   *

900   § 22   The control of distress traffic is the responsibility of the mobile station in distress or of the mobile station which, by the application of the provisions of 892 and 893, has sent the distress call. These stations may, however, delegate the control of the distress traffic to another station.

*   *   *   *   *   *

932   § 34   (1) The urgency signal may be transmitted only on the authority of the master or the person responsible for the ship, aircraft or other vehicle carrying the mobile station.

933   (2) The urgency signal may be transmitted by a land station only with the approval of the responsible authority.

934   § 35   (1) In radiotelegraphy, the urgency signal consists of three repetitions of the group XXX, sent with the letters of each group and the successive groups clearly separated from each other. It is sent before the call.

935   (2) In radiotelephony, the urgency signal consists of three repetitions of the word PAN pronounced as the French word "panne." It is sent before the call.

936   § 36   (1) The urgency signal indicates that the calling station has a very urgent message to transmit concerning the safety of a ship, aircraft or other vehicle or of some person on board or within sight.

937   (2) The urgency signal has priority over all other communications, except distress. All mobile and land stations which hear it must take care not to interfere with the transmission of the message which follows the urgency signal.

938   (3) Where the urgency signal is used by a mobile station, it must, as a general rule, be addressed to a specific station.

*   *   *   *   *   *

940   § 38   (1) Mobile stations which hear the urgency signal must continue to listen for at least three minutes. At the end of this period, if no urgency message has been heard, they may resume their normal service.

941   (2) However, land and mobile stations which are in communication on frequencies other than those used for the transmission of the urgency signal and of the call which follows it may continue their normal work without interruption provided the urgency message is not addressed "to all stations" (CQ).

*   *   *   *   *   *

943 § 40 (1) In radiotelegraphy, the safety signal consists of three repetitions of the group TTT, sent with the letters of each group and the successive groups clearly separated from each other. It is sent before the call.

944 (2) In radiotelephone, the word SÉCURITÉ, pronounced as the French "sécurité," repeated three times, is used for the safety signal.

945 § 41 (1) The safety signal indicates that the station is about to transmit a message concerning the safety of navigation or giving important meterological warnings.

946 (2) The safety signal and the message which follows it are sent on the distress frequency or on one of the frequencies which may be used in case of distress . . .

*   *   *   *   *   *

949 § 43 All stations hearing the safety signal must continue to listen on the frequency on which the safety signal has been transmitted until they are satisfied that the message is of no interest to them. They must, moreover, not make any transmissions likely to interfere with the message.

RADIOTELEGRAMS

ARTICLE 38

Order of Priority of Communications in the Mobile Service

950 The order of priority of communications in the mobile service is as follows:

1. Distress calls, distress messages and distress traffic.

2. Communications preceded by the urgency signal.

3. Communications preceded by the safety signal.

4. Communications relative to radio direction-finding bearings.

5. Radiotelegrams relative to the navigation and safe movement of aircraft.

6. Radiotelegrams relative to the navigation, movements, and needs of ships; weather observation messages destined for an official meteorological service.

7. Government radiotelegrams for which priority right has been claimed.

8. Service radiotelegrams relating to the working of the radiocommunication service or to radiotelegrams previously transmitted.

9. All other communications.

EXTRACTS FROM THE GENEVA, 1959, TREATY

ARTICLE 1

SECTION III. TECHNICAL CHARACTERISTICS

93 *Harmful Interference:* Any emission, radiation or induction which endangers the functioning of a radionavigation service or of other safety services or seriously degrades, obstructs or repeatedly interrupts a radiocommunication service operating in accordance with these Regulations.

*   *   *   *   *   *

ARTICLE 21

INSPECTION OF MOBILE STATIONS

838 § 1 (1) The governments or appropriate administrations of countries which a mobile station visits, may require the production of the license for examination. The operator of the mobile station, or the person responsible for the station, shall facilitate this examination. The license shall be kept in such a way that it can be produced upon request. As far as possible, the license, or a copy certified by the authority which has issued it, should be permanently exhibited in the station.

ANSWERS TO THE FCC-TYPE SAMPLE TESTS,

INCLUDING TEXT REFERENCES

Note: The question number following each answer refers to the question in the body of the text on which the sample-test question is based. In the event that the student has an incorrect answer to a sample-test question, or wishes to refresh his knowledge of the particular subject, he should study the information supplied in connection with the referenced text question.

ELEMENT I

1. (b), Q. 1.13	2. (d), Q. 1.19	3. (c), Q. 1.19
4. (a), Q. 1.15	5. (b), Q. 1.12	6. (d), Q. 1.11
7. (e), Q. 1.05	8. (d), Q. 1.01	9. (c), Q. 1.03
10. (a), Q. 1.14	11. (c), Q. 1.16	12. (d), Q. 1.06
13. (e), Q. 1.07	14. (b), Q. 1.08	15. (b), Q. 1.18
16. (b), Q. 1.17	17. (d), Q. 1.09	18. (c), Q. 1.04
19. (b), Q. 1.12	20. (c), Q. 1.02	

ELEMENT II — CATEGORY "O"—GENERAL

1. (c), Q. 2.07	2. (b), Q. 2.01	3. (c), Q. 2.14
4. (a), Q. 2.06	5. (e), Q. 2.02	6. (c), Q. 2.12
7. (d), Q. 2.05	8. (b), Q. 2.02	9. (c), Q. 2.13
10. (c), Q. 2.04	11. (e), Q. 2.02	12. (a), Q. 2.11
13. (d), Q. 2.09	14. (a), Q. 2.02	15. (c), Q. 2.02
16. (b), Q. 2.03	17. (d), Q. 2.08	18. (c), Q. 2.10
19. (d), Q. 2.02	20. (b), Q. 2.02	

ELEMENT II — CATEGORY "M"—MARITIME

1. (a), Q. 2.05	2. (c), Q. 2.09	3. (e), Q. 2.15
4. (b), Q. 2.13	5. (d), Q. 2.01	6. (d), Q. 2.01
7. (c), Q. 2.02	8. (d), Q. 2.08	9. (b), Q. 2.15
10. (d), Q. 2.12	11. (b), Q. 2.11	12. (a), Q. 2.07
13. (c), Q. 2.02	14. (a), Q. 2.04	15. (b), Q. 2.06
16. (e), Q. 2.06	17. (b), Q. 2.14	18. (a), Q. 2.03
19. (b), Q. 2.04	20. (e), Q. 2.08	

ELEMENT III

1. (b), Q. 3.01	2. (b), Q. 3.04	3. (d), Q. 3.09(B)
4. (a), Q. 3.13	5. (b), Q. 3.27	6. (e), Q. 3.36
7. (b), Q. 3.46(D)	8. (c), Q. 3.52	9. (a), Q. 3.58

10. (c), Q. 3.64	11. (b), Q. 3.65	12. (c), Q. 3.72
13. (d), Q. 3.79	14. (b), Q. 3.79	15. (a), Q. 3.81
16. (c), Q. 3.82	17. (a), Q. 3.84	18. (d), Q. 3.85
19. (c), Q. 3.86	20. (c), Q. 3.86	21. (b), Q. 3.86
22. (d), Q. 3.87	23. (e), Q. 3.98	24. (d), Q. 3.95
25. (c), Q. 3.102	26. (b), Q. 3.100	27. (e), Q. 3.103
28. (a), Q. 3.52	29. (c), Q. 3.110f	30. (d), Q. 3.116
31. (b), Q. 3.86	32. (e), Q. 3.298	33. (b), Q. 3.122
34. (e), Q. 3.124	35. (c), Q. 3.125	36. (a), Q. 3.131
37. (b), Q. 3.137	38. (d), Q. 3.134	39. (c), Q. 3.135
40. (a), Q. 3.136	41. (e), Q. 3.126	42. (b), Q. 3.137
43. (c), Q. 3.139	44. (a), Q. 3.140	45. (e), Q. 3.142
46. (a), Q. 3.144	47. (d), Q. 3.161	48. (a), Q. 3.156
49. (a), Q. 3.162	50. (c), Q. 3.163	51. (b), Q. 3.167
52. (e), Q. 3.169	53. (c), Q. 3.178	54. (b), Q. 3.176
55. (e), Q. 3.177	56. (a), Q. 3.177	57. (c), Q. 3.184
58. (d), Q. 3.188	59. (a), Q. 3.187	60. (c), Q. 3.192J
61. (b), Q. 3.192K	62. (c), Q. 3.192L	63. (b), Q. 3.192M
64. (b), Q. 3.193	65. (a), Q. 3.193	66. (c), Q. 3.203
67. (d), Q. 3.201	68. (c), Q. 3.208	69. (d), Q. 3.210
70. (c), Q. 3.213	71. (c), Q. 3.216	72. (b), Q. 3.218
73. (e), Q. 3.129	74. (a), Q. 3.223	75. (e), Q. 3.225
76. (b), Q. 3.221	77. (c), Q. 3.220	78. (b), Q. 3.222
79. (c), Q. 3.226	80. (a), Q. 3.232	81. (c), Q. 3.232
82. (d), Q. 3.227	83. (b), Q. 3.227	84. (d), Q. 3.228
85. (a), Q. 3.239	86. (e), Q. 3.245	87. (c), Q. 3.244
88. (a), Q. 3.242	89. (b), Q. 3.237	90. (e), Q. 3.235
91. (c), Q. 3.251	92. (d), Q. 3.251	93. (a), Q. 3.249
94. (c), Q. 3.248	95. (a), Q. 3.247	96. (c), Q. 3.255
97. (a), Q. 3.254	98. (d), Q. 3.286	99. (b), Q. 3.279
100. (c), Q. 3.288		

ELEMENT IV

1. (b), Q. 4.06	2. (a), Q. 4.04	3. (b), Q. 4.02
4. (d), Q. 4.07	5. (c), Q. 4.08	6. (d), Q. 4.09
7. (a), Q. 4.13	8. (e), Q. 4.15	9. (b), Q. 4.18
10. (e), Q. 4.20	11. (b), Q. 4.24	12. (a), Q. 4.25
13. (c), Q. 4.31	14. (d), Q. 4.34	15. (c), Q. 4.35
16. (b), Q. 4.36	17. (b), Q. 4.37	18. (e), Q. 4.42
19. (a), Q. 4.44	20. (c), Q. 4.45	21. (d), Q. 4.46
22. (a), Q. 4.48	23. (d), Q. 4.49	24. (a), Q. 4.50
25. (b), Q. 4.53	26. (b), Q. 4.51	27. (b), Q. 4.54
28. (d), Q. 4.56	29. (b), Q. 3.203	30. (e), Q. 4.58
31. (d), Q. 4.60	32. (b), Q. 4.61	33. (e), Q. 4.63
34. (a), Q. 4.64	35. (d), Q. 4.68	36. (a), Q. 4.71

37. (b), Q. 4.73   38. (c), Q. 4.74   39. (b), Q. 4.76
40. (c), Q. 4.77   41. (d), Q. 4.80   42. (a), Q. 4.83
43. (b), Q. 4.83   44. (d), Q. 4.85   45. (b), Q. 4.86
46. (c), Q. 4.89   47. (a), Q. 4.93   48. (d), Q. 4.114
49. (c), Q. 4.123   50. (a), Q. 4.135

ELEMENT VIII

1. (b), Q. 8.07   2. (e), Q. 8.10   3. (c), Q. 8.12
4. (a), Q. 8.01   5. (d), Q. 8.02   6. (c), Q. 8.34
7. (d), Q. 8.38   8. (a), Q. 8.39   9. (c), Q. 8.39
10. (b), Q. 8.48   11. (a), Q. 8.62   12. (d), Q. 8.70
13. (a), Q. 8.70   14. (c), Q. 8.69   15. (d), Q. 8.64
16. (b), Q. 8.58   17. (c), Q. 8.59   18. (a), Q. 8.55
19. (d), Q. 8.50   20. (c), Q. 8.41   21. (a), Q. 8.39
22. (d), Q. 8.48   23. (b), Q. 8.42   24. (a), Q. 8.39
25. (c), Q. 8.37   26. (d), Q. 8.34   27. (a), Q. 8.39
                                   Q. 8.35
28. (b), Q. 8.43   29. (d), Q. 8.28   30. (c), Q. 8.23
                                                             Q. 8.24
31. (e), Q. 8.08   32. (b), Q. 8.42   33. (c), Q. 8.67
34. (b), Q. 8.66   35. (a), Q. 8.62   36. (b), Q. 8.39
37. (a), Q. 8.62   38. (b), Q. 8.39   39. (e), Q. 8.62
40. (c), Q. 8.48   41. (b), Q. 8.42   42. (b), Q. 8.39
43. (d), Q. 8.67   44. (a), Q. 8.20   45. (e), Q. 8.39
46. (d), Q. 8.62   47. (c), Q. 8.39   48. (b), Q. 8.39
49. (a), Q. 8.39   50. (a), Q. 8.63

ELEMENT IX

1. (d), Q. 9.13   2. (a), Q. 9.09   3. (c), Q. 9.01
4. (b), Q. 9.02   5. (a), Q. 9.06   6. (c), Q. 9.25
7. (b), Q. 9.29   8. (b), Q. 9.23   9. (d), Q. 9.05
10. (e), Q. 9.07   11. (a), Q. 9.15   12. (b), Q. 9.12
13. (d), Q. 9.18   14. (d), Q. 9.26   15. (a), Q. 9.03
16. (d), Q. 9.03   17. (d), Q. 9.01   18. (b), Q. 9.01
19. (c), Q. 9.05   20. (d), Q. 9.08   21. (b), *
22. (a), *   23. (d), Q. 9.01   24. (e), *
25. (b), *   26. (c), *   27. (c), *
28. (a), Q. 9.07   29. (c), *   30. (d), *
31. (a), *   32. (a), *   33. (e), Q. 9.01
34. (d), *   35. (e), *   36. (b), *
37. (a), *   38. (a), *   39. (c), *
40. (a), *

NOTE: An asterisk (*) indicates reference is to the Element IX Addendum.

Index

The index has been prepared to facilitate the use of this book for studying for a particular class of license as well as for reference and review. **Question numbers** rather than page numbers are cited for each entry. It is believed that this will make for more convenient usage.

Special headings and entries are incorporated into the index. These are **Definitions, Diagrams, Rules and Regulations (FCC),** and **Troubleshooting.** The reader will find these entries particularly useful for reference.

651

657